Theory of X-Ray and Thermal-Neutron Scattering by Real Crystals

Theory of X-Ray and Thermal-Neutron Scattering by Real Crystals

Mikhail A. Krivoglaz

Director, Institute of Metal Physics
Academy of Sciences of the Ukrainian SSR, Kiev

Translated from Russian

Translation Edited and with a Foreword by
Simon C. Moss

Department of Metallurgy
Massachusetts Institute of Technology
Cambridge, Massachusetts

PLENUM PRESS • NEW YORK • 1969

Mikhail Aleksandrovich Krivoglaz, born in Kiev in 1929, was graduated from Kiev University in 1950, defended his candidate's dissertation in 1954, and his doctoral dissertation in 1962. Professor Krivoglaz is director of the Institute of Metal Physics of the Academy of Sciences of the Ukrainian SSR and a professor at Kiev University. He has published three books and more than 100 scientific papers in various fields of solid state physics, including the theory of semiconductors, the theory of light absorption and scattering by crystals, the theory of diffusion, the theory of solid solutions, the theory of the scattering of x rays and neutrons by crystals, the theory of the Mössbauer effect, and the theory of the damping of vibrations in crystals.

Library of Congress Catalog Card Number 68-26771

The original Russian text, published by Nauka Press in Moscow in 1967, has been extensively revised by the author for the present edition.

Михаил Александрович Кривоглаз

Теория рассеяния рентгеновских лучей
и тепловых нейтронов реальными кристаллами

TEORIYA RASSEYANIYA RENTGENOVSKIKH LUCHEI

I TEPLOVYKH NEITRONOV REAL'NYMI KRISTALLAMI

A Division of Plenum Publishing Corporation
227 West 17 Street, New York, N. Y. 10011

Printed in the United States of America

Foreword

Since about 1956 Professor M. A. Krivoglaz has been extremely prolific in the fields covered by this book, and it seems to me most appropriate and topical that his numerous contributions and those of several of his Soviet co-workers and associates have been brought together here. In short, I am delighted that Plenum Press has undertaken the translation of his book. It will serve an important pedagogical function and be an invaluable text for researchers in x-ray and neutron scattering. It is not, of course, confined solely to the development of ideas peculiar to the Russian school, as a glance at the bibliography immediately shows.

The book reflects a truly catholic range of interests. Professor Krivoglaz is certainly current; but what is apparent from this treatise, and what many of us whose training is in scattering theory and diffraction will find, is that we are often not so current in our approaches to several of the problems treated here. This is perhaps less true of the approximately fifteen percent of the book devoted to inelastic neutron scattering from ideal and nonideal crystals: the treatment of anharmonic effects, of local mode scattering, and so forth. This is mainly because, with the development of high-flux reactors with intense thermal-neutron sources, the subject has been extensively researched in the West and has thereby received a great deal of theoretical attention. Taking the book as a whole, however, it is obviously a personal statement of Professor Krivoglaz' scientific preferences and deals only with subjects to which he has made substantial contributions. Indeed, there are not many solid-state theorists who have in such a short time made contributions to such seemingly disparate areas as, for instance, critical unmixing in binary alloys of atoms with an appreciable size difference and Green's function calculations of phonon correlation functions in solid solutions.

Metallurgists and metal physicists will, I think, be most interested in Part I of this book. Many of us have for some time been reading Professor Krivoglaz' papers on scattering from solid solutions and have noted the relevance of his calculations. In my own case, I was made patently aware of this relevance in some work I was doing on martensite in which I tacitly assumed that the static atomic displacements could be represented, in their effect on the x-ray pattern, in a manner identical to the Debye–Waller weakening of the normal Bragg reflections. I presented this work at the Seventh Congress of the IUC in Moscow, where I met M. A. Krivoglaz and discussed the problem with him. He suggested that I might look at a publication or two of his on the subject in which the appropriate formulae describing my results were developed. It was a very gentle, tentative suggestion that perhaps I had not been as rigorous as I should have been. He was, of course, more than right, and when I finally did absorb his papers, I had to throw away all my calculations and begin again.

The scope of Part I is quite ambitious, covering a vast variety of phenomenology, most of which is brought together through the application of fluctuation theory. The number of disciplines that are brought to bear on these phenomena is also extensive, including, in one case or another, more than a nodding familiarity with the basic scattering theory and formalism, classical thermodynamics, perturbation theory and the theory of solid solutions, elasticity theory — both macroscopic (continuum) and microscopic (lattice dynamics) — as well as an appreciation of Fourier transform methods and reciprocal lattice concepts, tensor notation, and so forth. The introductory sections are helpful and explicit, and while the book is certainly not an introductory text, it is an excellent one, and the material is coherently, albeit rapidly, developed.

Part II treats inelastic effects, and after an interesting development of the equations governing the thermal diffuse scattering of x rays, the book is devoted exclusively to the inelastic scattering of neutrons. The x-ray treatment differs somewhat from similar treatments elsewhere and is interesting in some of the finer points which Professor Krivoglaz chooses to emphasize. For example, he notes that thermal scattering can be considered as a quasi-elastic Bragg scattering off the separate normal modes — that each mode is a fluctuation in the lattice with its characteristic wavelength producing its own Bragg peak at the appropriate position in reciprocal space. This is equivalent to the more familiar statement that normal mode scattering produces a continuous set of side-bands about each Bragg peak whose intensity falls off as the square of the wavelength.

The neutron-scattering calculations also carry the Krivoglaz stamp, because again he is, as the title of the book suggests, interested in real crystals. He therefore is tempted to tread, as it were, where many angels would not and to consider the effects of local order and static inhomogeneities on the phonon spectrum and resultant scattering from solid solutions.

It would seem altogether appropriate, in these brief comments, to include only a few of the many points developed by Professor Krivoglaz which to me were particularly interesting. His microscopic treatment of static displacements in alloy solutions is especially powerful, yielding scattering equations that permit the calculation of the complete diffuse scattering function for an alloy containing both local order and the attendant fluctuations in atomic displacements. The discussion of critical unmixing in alloys is also excellent. Here he demonstrates that, if static displacements accompany composition fluctuations, there will be a suppression of the thermodynamic critical point to a lower temperature, because of the usually anisotropic elastic energy contribution to the compositional free energy and its derivatives. This means that the infinite fluctuations will be suppressed, and that in real alloys one should hardly ever expect to see critical scattering at the chemical spinodal of the phase diagram. This is rather reminiscent of some of the conclusions of J. W. Cahn, but it is developed along different lines — starting with fluctuation theory and including the microscopic realm.

It is very interesting to read Professor Krivoglaz' discussion of severely distorted crystals (with very high dislocation densities, for example), because he demonstrates how the sharp Bragg peaks become attenuated and are finally <u>replaced</u> by the intense asymmetric diffuse scattering. While the Bragg peaks appear at positions given by the average lattice, the diffuse scattering has maxima corresponding to a lattice distorted by image forces only and not by localized displacements. As a result of this, if the Bragg and diffuse maxima are treated as a "quasi-line," the corresponding lattice constant will differ from the dilatometer value. This is an unusual result. Again, in a similar connection, Professor Krivoglaz treats the displacement effects associated with coherency strains that accompany Guinier–Preston zone formation in alloys and develops equations, incorporating anisotropic elastic effects, for the scattering in the vicinity of reflections other than (000), the usual low-angle portion.

Such an enumeration could continue for several pages, but perhaps it might suffice here to say that, given the careful reading it requires, Professor Krivoglaz' book is bound to receive the critical acclaim it so richly deserves. It will, I am sure, take its place with the great texts on diffraction, such as R. W. James', and the forthcoming book of B. E. Warren, as standard reading for metallurgists and physicists interested in scattering theory. Plenum Press is also to be congratulated both on its expert translation and on the speed with which this important book has been brought to press.

S. C. Moss

Cambridge
August, 1968

Preface to the American Edition

I was very pleased to learn that this book was being translated into English. This will enable American readers to become acquainted with a new approach to the theory of x-ray scattering in solid solutions and crystals containing defects; in this approach the theory is treated as a branch of theoretical physics rather than crystallography.

Since the Russian manuscript was completed, a number of new experimental and theoretical results on scattering in real crystals have become available. Some of these are included in the present edition as minor insertions, principally in Sections 2, 3, 22, and 39. I am very grateful to Plenum Publishing Corporation for enabling me to introduce these results into the American edition.

M. A. Krivoglaz

Kiev
November, 1967

Preface to the Russian Edition

The scattering of x rays was originally considered with respect to ideal crystals, in which every atom lay precisely in a particular lattice site. The intensity distribution of the scattered radiation given by this theory leads to the appearance of sharp lines (or spots) on the x-ray diffraction picture; by studying the positions and intensities of these the crystal structure may be solved. In real crystals, however, owing to thermal vibrations, defects, impurities, and disorder in the arrangement of various types of atoms, the atoms are displaced from the nodes of the ideal lattice, and may even lie in "foreign" lattice points. The disruption of the ideal structure of the crystal leads to a substantial change in the intensity distribution of the scattered radiation; the x-ray diffraction lines broaden or their intensity is reduced and diffuse scattering appears. The study of these x-ray diffraction effects constitutes one of the best methods of studying defects and other departures from ideal crystal structure, enabling us to determine the distortions in the crystal, the type of defects, the distribution of defects over the crystal, and so on.

This kind of investigation is of particular interest at the present time, since it has now become clear that various kinds of departure from ideal crystal structure affect many important properties of solids to no less a degree than the characteristics of ideal crystals. For this reason the majority of laboratories studying the physical properties of crystals by the x-ray diffraction method devote special attention to those effects associated with the disruption of the ideal crystal lattice. The theory of such x-ray diffraction effects occupies the first part of this book.

Departures from ideal crystal structure may arise in a state of thermodynamic equilibrium or may be caused by nonequilibrium defects. The departure from the ideal structure of equilibrium crystals arising at finite temperatures (concentration inhomogeneities, disorder in the arrangement of various kinds of atom, vacancies, interstitial atoms, and other defects) may be considered as fluctuations of the corresponding internal parameters. Such a description of the inhomogeneities of a crystal is extremely useful for calculating the intensity of diffuse x-ray scattering at static inhomogeneities of the crystal, which may conveniently be regarded as scattering at fluctuation waves, for example, at fluctuation waves of the composition or order parameters and the waves of static atomic displacements engendered by these.

The method of fluctuation waves is probably simpler and more physically significant than the ordinary method in which we consider scattering at individual defects; it also enables us to study a whole series of diffuse-scattering effects on a single unified principle. Thus we may quite simply consider the anomalously large scattering near phase transformations of the second kind and critical points, study the part played by static distortions in nonideal solutions, the role of long-range forces, effects associated with the fluctuations of short-range ordering parameters, and so on. In view of this we shall consider diffuse scattering at inhomogeneities in crystals existing in a state of thermodynamic equilibrium by means of the method of fluctuation waves. In the first three chapters we shall set out the theory of fluctuation waves and the associated waves of static displacements, which are largely reminiscent of the waves of the thermal vibrations of atoms; then in Chapter V we shall consider the scattering of x rays at these waves.

X-ray diffraction effects in crystals not existing in a state of thermodynamic equilibrium, especially in plastically deformed crystals, are often described phenomenologically by relating them to distortions of the first, second, and third kinds. This approach is clearly to a certain extent formal. At the present time we are able to give a more detailed description of a nonideal crystal on the basis of various kinds of defects; we can thus set up a more detailed theory of x-ray scattering by bearing in mind the fact that the scattering is related to such defects. In the absence of thermodynamic equilibrium, departures from ideal structure may include both point defects (such as vacancies or interstitial atoms) and extended (line) defects (dislocations, stacking faults, and so on). Defects of different kinds lead to qualitatively differing changes in the intensity distribution of the scattered radiation, sometimes broadening the x-ray lines and sometimes not doing so.

Clearly a theory of x-ray scattering by defects must first of all give a general analysis of x-ray diffraction effects created by various kinds of defects and establish criteria relating the characteristics of the defects to the qualitative picture of intensity distribution, thus providing a specific classification of defects. A general analysis of this kind for defects of arbitrary types is given in Chapter IV. The method employed for calculating the intensity of the scattered radiation is valid not only in the case of weakly distorted crystals, in which the static displacements of the atoms are fairly small (as usually occurs in solid solutions) but also in the case of defects produced by large distortions.

Scattering by severely distorted crystals (containing particles of a new phase, linear dislocations, or dislocation loops) is considered by this method in Chapter VII. In Chapter VI we consider diffuse scattering, line broadening, and the weakening of x-ray diffraction lines by thermal and static displacements of the atoms. All the theory set out in the following pages will be conducted on the basis of the kinematic theory of scattering. Some interesting dynamic effects appearing in crystals with a high degree of perfection require special methods of study and will not be discussed here.

In addition to the x-ray diffraction study of real crystals, useful information may also be obtained by neutron diffraction. From the point of view of studying static inhomogeneities, there are no differences in principle between the use of thermal neutrons and x rays. The elastic nuclear scattering of neutrons is in essence described by the same formulas as the scattering of x rays at static departures from ideal crystal structure, so that the results set out in the first part of the book are also applicable to the same extent in the case of the nuclear scattering of neutrons. The use of neutrons instead of x rays thus only involves advantages (and disadvantages) of a methodical character.

Some major advantages arise, however, when studying the inelastic scattering of neutrons and also magnetic scattering; these are associated with the low energy of the thermal neutrons and the existence of a magnetic moment. A study of the relatively easily resolved peaks of single-phonon (or single-magnon) scattering in the spectrum of inelastically scattered neutrons probably gives the best contemporary method of determining vibration spectra (and spin waves). It has recently become clear that the study of finer characteristics of the inelastic neutron-scattering spectrum (the widths of the peaks and the variation in their positions with temperature) yields valuable information not only of the spectrum of elementary excitations but also of their relaxation characteristics, the inhomogeneities of real crystals, the mechanism of diffusion, and other aspects of the dynamics of the motion of atoms and spins in the crystal. These questions will be considered in the second part of the book, special attention being devoted to the single-phonon scattering of neutrons in ideal and real crystals and to the possibilities of a neutron-diffraction study of crystal dynamics. We shall also consider the inelastic scattering of x rays at thermal vibrations of the lattice.

The main discussions will be devoted to the theory of x-ray and neutron scattering. Only in individual cases shall we consider the corresponding experimental results.

M. A. Krivoglaz

Contents

PART II. INELASTIC SCATTERING OF X RAYS AND THERMAL NEUTRONS IN CRYSTALS

PART I

ELASTIC SCATTERING OF X RAYS AND NEUTRONS AT STATIC INHOMOGENEITIES IN REAL CRYSTALS

Chapter I

Fluctuations of Composition and Order Parameters in Undistorted Solid Solutions

§1. Order in Solid Solutions and Fluctuations

As the temperature tends to absolute zero, the state of thermodynamic equilibrium in a solid solution is represented by complete order in the arrangement of the atoms at the points of the crystal lattice. This is a consequence of Nernst's theorem, since any macroscopic state corresponding to incomplete order may be set up by taking a large number of configurations of atoms of different types at the lattice points. The number W of distinguishable rearrangements of the atoms establishing such configurations and corresponding to given macroscopic values of the order parameters is very large, and the configuration part of the entropy $S = k_B \ln W$ (k_B is Boltzmann's constant) for such a state would differ from zero, which would contradict Nernst's theorem as $T \rightarrow 0$. It follows in particular from this that, at low enough temperatures, a solution of nonstoichiometric composition cannot exist in a state of thermodynamic equilibrium but has to decompose; as $T \rightarrow 0$ the decomposition products must be completely ordered solutions of stoichiometric compositions or pure elements.

Naturally this discussion only relates to a state of equilibrium, and owing to the low velocity of diffusion processes at low temperatures it may well be that solutions with nonequilibrium order parameters will persist for a long time.

As temperature rises, some of the atoms move to "foreign" positions and the solution ceases to be completely ordered. The appearance of this kind of disorder leads to a sharp rise in the number of distinguishable rearrangements of the atoms, and at finite temperatures reduces the configuration entropy terms in the free energy ($k_BT \ln W$), so that the incompletely ordered state of the solution will be a thermodynamically equilibrium state. The breakdown of order in the arrangement of the atoms at lattice points constitutes the most important type of nonideal solid solution; it will be considered in more detail later (Chapters I to III). The departure from periodicity (which leads in particular to the appearance of new features in the characteristics of x-ray scattering as compared with the case of scattering at an ideal crystal) is due primarily to the very fact that the lattice points of a sublattice of a given type are occupied by atoms of different types (leading to a difference in the atomic scattering factors). In addition to this, the difference in the atomic radii of the components in an incompletely ordered solution leads to the displacement of atoms from the lattice points, i.e., to static distortions.

Right at the beginning of this chapter we shall discuss the very simple case of solutions in which the atomic radii are almost the same and the distortions may be neglected; then in Chapters II and III we shall consider the effects of such distortions. In order to avoid complication with unnecessary detail, we shall hereafter confine attention to the case of binary solutions.

Let us first consider the parameters characterizing the state of order in the solution. We shall number the nodes in the unit cell by means of an index $\gamma (\gamma = 1, 2, \ldots, \nu)$, and the unit cells themselves by the index $s (s = 1, 2, \ldots, N)$, where ν is the number of nodes in the cell and N is the number of cells in the crystal. Clearly the distribution of atoms A and B over the lattice points (nodes) of a binary solution A–B may be unambiguously characterized by assigning a set $N\nu$ of variables $c_{s\gamma}$, each of which takes two values:

$$c_{s\gamma} = \begin{cases} 1 \text{ if an A atom lies at the point } s\gamma, \\ 0 \text{ if a B atom lies at the point } s\gamma. \end{cases} \tag{1.1}$$

In disordered solutions having one atom in the unit cell ($\nu = 1$), we may omit the index γ and characterize the state of the solution by assigning the numbers $c_s = 1, 0$.

It is clear, however, that in order to find any experimentally determinable properties of a crystal of macroscopic dimensions we shall certainly not have to give all the numbers $c_{s\gamma}$; we shall in fact only have to know the average values (over the whole crystal or over a statistical aggregate) of certain combinations of these quantities, which determine the internal parameters characterizing the order in the solution. Such internal parameters are given primarily by the average values of the numbers $c_{s\gamma}$ themselves

$$c_\gamma = \bar{c}_{s\gamma}, \tag{1.2}$$

which are equal to the probabilities that sublattice points γ are occupied by A atoms; these quantities unambiguously define the long-range order in the solution. The probability of points γ being occupied by B atoms is correspondingly $1-c_\gamma$.

In a disordered solution the quantities c_γ are simply equal to the concentrations c of the A atoms in solution. In an ordered solution, however, the c_γ define the concentrations of these atoms at the points γ, which are, generally speaking, different for lattice points of different types. In a solution having ν' types of equivalent points, instead of using the quantities c_γ, we may clearly characterize the long-range order by giving the average concentration c and ν' thermodynamic internal parameters (long-range-order parameters). Thus if the ordered structure is characterized by two types of nonequivalent points and the unit cell contains ν_1 points of the first type (legitimately belonging to the A atoms) and ν_2 of the second type (legitimately belonging to the B atoms), where $\nu_1 + \nu_2 = \nu$,

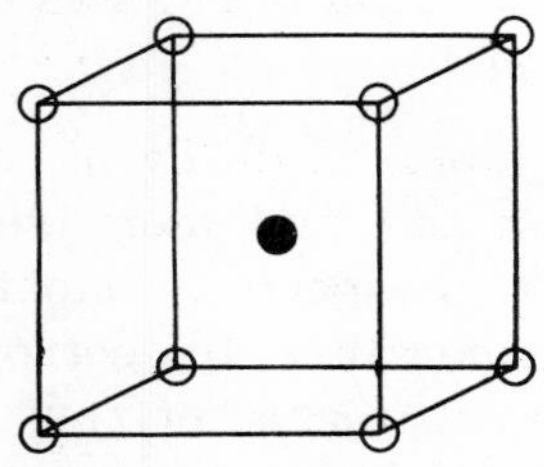

Fig. 1. Arrangement of lattice points in the unit cell of an alloy of the β-brass type.

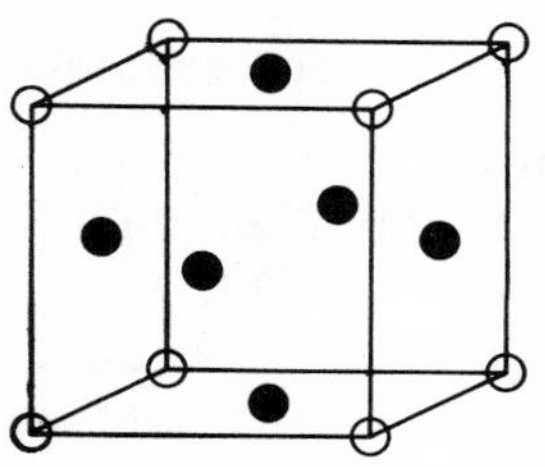

Fig. 2. Arrangement of lattice points in the unit cell of an alloy of the $AuCu_3$ type.

we find that in such a solution (of stoichiometric composition $A_{\nu_1}B_{\nu_2}$) the probabilities c_1 and c_2 may be expressed in terms of the concentration c and degree of long-range order η by means of the expressions

$$c_1 = c + \frac{\nu_2}{\nu}\eta, \qquad c_2 = c - \frac{\nu_1}{\nu}\eta. \tag{1.3}$$

Here the parameter of long-range order η is taken in such a way as to make $\eta = 1$ in a completely ordered solution of stoichiometric composition ($c_1 = 1$, $c_2 = 0$). In a disordered solution ($c_1 = c_2 = c$) we have $\eta = 0$.

One of the simplest ordered structures having nodes of two types is the β-brass type of lattice (Fig. 1). In this lattice the nodes of the first type lie at the centers of the cubic cells of the body-centered cubic lattice (black circles in the figure) and nodes of the second type at the corners (light circles in the figure). The unit cell contains two such nodes, and the number of nodes of the first and second types is the same ($\nu_1 = \nu_2 = 1$). Another very widespread ordered structure is that of the $AuCu_3$ type, in which the nodes of the first type are situated at the corners of the cubic cells of a face-centered cubic lattice and those of the second type in the faces (Fig. 2). The unit cell contains four nodes, one being a node of the first type and the three other equivalent nodes being of the second type ($\nu_1 = 1$, $\nu_2 = 3$). By way of example of an ordered structure with three types of nodes we may take Fe_3Al, in which the nodes of the first type occupy the corners of the cubic cells of a body-centered cubic lattice and those of the second and third types lie in the centers of the cells and form a lattice of the NaCl type. Examples of other ordered structures and an indication of the structures of specific solutions may be found in reviews on ordering in alloys (see, for example, [19–21]).

An ordered structure arises if atoms of different types interact more strongly than atoms of the same type (otherwise the solution decomposes). This energy factor is especially important at low temperatures. On raising the temperature, the entropy contribution to the free energy starts playing a greater part, as a result of which the degree of order in the solution as a rule falls off monotonically. On reaching the ordering temperature there is a phase transformation from the ordered to the disordered state and the degree of long-range order vanishes. However, the difference in the interaction energies of the different atoms means that, even in the disordered solution, for which long-range order no longer exists, a given atom is mainly surrounded by atoms of another (or sometimes the same) sort, i.e., the distribution of atoms over the lattice points is not random but has a short-range order or correlation as regards the occupation of the crystal-lattice points of the solution by atoms of different types.

The extent of this short-range order in a disordered solution is characterized by the difference in the a posteriori probabilities that a particular point (point 1) will be occupied by an atom of a given type on condition that the occupation of the other point (point 2) is already fixed, and the a priori probabilities relating to the occupation of point 1 (these probabilities are equal to the concentrations).* Whereas long-range order is determined by the average values of the numbers $c_{s\gamma}$, correlation is determined by the means of their products.

The parameters characterizing correlation in a solution may be introduced in different ways (differing in respect of certain numerical factors). For our own purposes it is convenient to introduce the correlation parameters $\varepsilon(\boldsymbol{\rho})$, which define the correlation for the occupation of a pair of points separated by lattice vector $\boldsymbol{\rho}$ in the lattice of a disordered solution by atoms of type A, simply as the difference between the actual probability $p_{AA}(\boldsymbol{\rho})$ that this pair of points will be occupied by A atoms in the solution in question and the probability that it will be occupied in accordance with a random distribution of atoms over the lattice points. Remembering that the product $c_s c_{s'}$ will only differ from zero if atoms of type A lie at the points s and s', we may write $p_{AA}(\boldsymbol{\rho})$ as the average value of this product $\overline{c_s c_{s'}}^{\boldsymbol{\rho}}$, where the averaging is carried out over pairs of points separated by the vector $\boldsymbol{\rho}$. For a random distribution of atoms, the probabilities that points s and s' will be occupied by A atoms are independent of each other and equal to c,

*In the literature the term "short-range" order is often only applied to the case of disordered solutions in which pairs of atoms of different types are principally formed. We shall use this term to mean the predominant formation of pairs of either similar or dissimilar atoms.

so that $\overline{c_s c_{s'}}^{\rho} = c^2$. Hence in the disordered solution

$$\varepsilon(\rho) = p_{AA}(\rho) - c^2 = \overline{c_s c_{s'}}^{\rho} - c^2$$

or

$$\varepsilon(\rho) = \overline{(c_s - c)(c_{s'} - c)}^{\rho}. \tag{1.4}$$

In ordered solutions, we may consider either correlation between the manner of occupation of lattice points of a given type γ and γ', which is characterized by parameters $\varepsilon_{\gamma\gamma'}(\rho)$ depending on ρ, γ, and γ', or correlation between the manner of occupation of all the points of the solution, which is characterized by parameters $\varepsilon(\rho)$ depending only on ρ. Generalizing formula (1.4), in an ordered solution these parameters may be defined as follows

$$\varepsilon_{\gamma\gamma'}(\rho) = \overline{(c_{s\gamma} - c_\gamma)(c_{s'\gamma'} - c_{\gamma'})}^{\rho\gamma\gamma'}, \quad \varepsilon(\rho) = \overline{(c_{s\gamma} - c_\gamma)(c_{s'\gamma'} - c_{\gamma'})}^{\rho}. \tag{1.5}$$

Here

$$\rho = \mathbf{R}_{s\gamma} - \mathbf{R}_{s'\gamma'},$$

where $\mathbf{R}_{s\gamma}$ is the radius vector of the point $s\gamma$, and in the formula for $\varepsilon_{\gamma\gamma'}(\rho)$ the averaging is only carried out over pairs of points $s\gamma$ and $s'\gamma'$ of the given sublattices γ and γ' separated by the vector ρ, while in the formula for $\varepsilon(\rho)$ the averaging is carried out over pairs of such points belonging to any sublattices of the solution.

In describing correlation in a solution, attention is usually confined to giving parameters of the $\varepsilon_{\gamma\gamma'}(\rho)$ type. It is easy to see, however, that these parameters do not give the short-range order in the solution completely. Thus, for example, in a disordered solution, the short-range order may be homogeneous over the whole crystal or the solution may consist of small regions with high short-range order, distributed among regions with low order; in both cases the parameters $\varepsilon(\rho)$ may be the same. In order to distinguish these cases we must assign parameters which characterize correlation between the manner of occupation of not only pairs but also large numbers of lattice points, for example, the parameters

$$\varepsilon(\rho_1, \rho_2) = \overline{(c_s - c)(c_{s'} - c)(c_{s''} - c)}^{\rho_1\rho_2},$$

$$\varepsilon(\rho_1, \rho_2, \rho_3) = \overline{(c_s - c)(c_{s'} - c)(c_{s''} - c)(c_{s'''} - c)}^{\rho_1\rho_2\rho_3}, \tag{1.6}$$

where

$$\rho_1 = \mathbf{R}_{s'} - \mathbf{R}_s, \quad \rho_2 = \mathbf{R}_{s''} - \mathbf{R}_s, \quad \rho_3 = \mathbf{R}_{s'''} - \mathbf{R}_s$$

and the averaging is carried out for constant values of these vectors.

Order in the arrangement of the atoms is closely connected with fluctuations in solutions. Thus, if the short-range order in a disordered solution corresponds to the predominant formation of pairs of similar atoms, there will be small regions in the solution with high concentrations of A or B atoms (as compared with the average concentrations), i.e., fluctuations of composition develop. The preferential formation of pairs of similar atoms may be associated with fluctuations of long-range order.

In order to establish a quantitative relation between fluctuations and correlation parameters, it is convenient to pass over into Fourier representation. For example, instead of the quantities $c_{s\gamma}$ characterizing the distribution of the atoms over the lattice points, we may introduce their Fourier components:

$$c_{s\gamma} - c = \sum_{\mathbf{k}} c_{\mathbf{k}\gamma} e^{-i\mathbf{k}\mathbf{R}_{s\gamma}}, \quad c_{\mathbf{k}\gamma} = \frac{1}{N} \sum_{s=1}^{N} (c_{s\gamma} - c_\gamma) e^{i\mathbf{k}\mathbf{R}_{s\gamma}}. \tag{1.7}$$

Since the replacement of $\mathbf{k}$ by $\mathbf{k} + 2\pi\mathbf{K}_n$, where $\mathbf{K}_n$ is an arbitrary vector of the reciprocal lattice of the ordered solution, leaves $\exp(-i\mathbf{k}\mathbf{R}_{s\gamma})$, unchanged, we may suppose that the summation over $\mathbf{k}$ in (1.7) is carried out over all vectors $\mathbf{k}/2\pi$ which lie in the first unit cell of the reciprocal lattice and satisfy the cyclical conditions. It is clear that $c^*_{\mathbf{k}\gamma} = c_{-\mathbf{k}\gamma}$ and that $c_{\mathbf{k}\gamma} = 0$ for $\mathbf{k} = 0$. The sum $\sum_s (c_{s\gamma} - c)$, taken over the set of cells s in a small region of the solution determines the fluctuation change in the concentration of A atoms at the points γ in this region. Hence (as may be seen from equation 1.7) for small $\mathbf{k}$ the quantities $c_{\mathbf{k}\gamma}$ determine the amplitude of the long-wave fluctuation waves of concentration at the points γ. In the general case of arbitrary $\mathbf{k}$ also, we may consider $c_{\mathbf{k}\gamma}$ as Fourier components of the fluctuations in the concentration of A atoms at the points γ.

Let us determine the average values $\overline{c_{\mathbf{k}\gamma} c^*_{\mathbf{k}\gamma'}}$ of the squares or products of the quantities $c_{\mathbf{k}\gamma}$, corresponding to a given $\mathbf{k}$.

It follows from (1.7) that for $\gamma = \gamma'$

$$\overline{c_{\mathbf{k}\gamma} c^*_{\mathbf{k}\gamma}} = \frac{1}{N^2} \Big[\sum_s \overline{(c_{s\gamma} - c_\gamma)^2} + \sum_{s \neq s'} \overline{(c_{s\gamma} - c_\gamma)(c_{s'\gamma} - c_\gamma)}\, e^{i\mathbf{k}(\mathbf{R}_{s\gamma} - \mathbf{R}_{s'\gamma})} \Big]. \quad (1.8)$$

Since $c_{s\gamma}$ only takes the values 0 and 1

$$c^2_{s\gamma} = c_{s\gamma} \text{ and } \overline{c^2_{s\gamma}} = c_\gamma.$$

Hence

$$\overline{(c_{s\gamma} - c_\gamma)^2} = c_\gamma (1 - c_\gamma). \quad (1.8a)$$

Taking (1.5) into account as well, we rewrite expression (1.8) in the form

$$\overline{|c_{\mathbf{k}\gamma}|^2} = \frac{1}{N} \Big[c_\gamma (1 - c_\gamma) + \sum_{\boldsymbol{\rho} \neq 0} \varepsilon_{\gamma\gamma}(\boldsymbol{\rho})\, e^{i\mathbf{k}\boldsymbol{\rho}} \Big]. \quad (1.9)$$

In an analogous way for $\gamma \neq \gamma'$

$$\overline{c_{\mathbf{k}\gamma} c_{\mathbf{k}\gamma'}} = \frac{1}{N} \sum_{\boldsymbol{\rho} \neq 0} \varepsilon_{\gamma\gamma'}(\boldsymbol{\rho})\, e^{i\mathbf{k}\boldsymbol{\rho}}. \quad (1.10)$$

Thus the mean squares of the Fourier components of the concentrations at points of different types (determining the Fourier components of the composition and the long-range-order parameters) are simply related to the Fourier components of the correlation parameters $\varepsilon_{\gamma\gamma'}(\boldsymbol{\rho})$.

In formula (1.7) the expansion of $c_{s\gamma} - c_\gamma$ into Fourier series is carried out separately for each sublattice. In addition to the corresponding Fourier components $c_{\mathbf{k}\gamma}$ we may also introduce the components $c_{\mathbf{k}}$, which are given in the form of a sum over all the lattice points and not only those of a specific sublattice:

$$c_{\mathbf{k}} = \frac{1}{N\nu} \sum_{s=1}^{N} \sum_{\gamma=1}^{\nu} (c_{s\gamma} - c_\gamma)\, e^{i\mathbf{k}\mathbf{R}_{s\gamma}} = \frac{1}{\nu} \sum_{\gamma=1}^{\nu} c_{\mathbf{k}\gamma}. \quad (1.11)$$

Remembering formula (1.5) for $\varepsilon(\boldsymbol{\rho})$ and formula (1.8a), we find that the mean squares of the Fourier components $\overline{|c_{\mathbf{k}}|^2}$ are expressed in terms of the Fourier components of the correlation parameters $\varepsilon(\boldsymbol{\rho})$:

$$\overline{|c_{\mathbf{k}}|^2} = \frac{1}{N\nu}\left[\frac{1}{\nu}\sum_{\gamma=1}^{\nu} c_\gamma(1-c_\gamma) + \sum_{\rho\neq 0}\varepsilon(\boldsymbol{\rho})\cos\mathbf{k}\boldsymbol{\rho}\right]. \tag{1.12}$$

Here we have considered that $\varepsilon(-\boldsymbol{\rho}) = \varepsilon(\boldsymbol{\rho})$. In particular, for disordered solutions with one lattice point in the unit cell ($\nu = 1$, $c_{\mathbf{k}1} = c_{\mathbf{k}}$)

$$\overline{|c_{\mathbf{k}}|^2} = \frac{1}{N}\left[c(1-c) + \sum_{\rho\neq 0}\varepsilon(\boldsymbol{\rho})\cos\mathbf{k}\boldsymbol{\rho}\right]. \tag{1.13}$$

If correlation in the arrangement of atoms in the lattice points is absent ($\varepsilon(\boldsymbol{\rho}) = 0$), i.e., the solution is ideal, we have

$$\overline{|c_{\mathbf{k}}|^2} = \frac{1}{N}c(1-c) \tag{1.14}$$

and $\overline{|c_{\mathbf{k}}|^2}$ are independent of the wave vector $\mathbf{k}$. In the general case of a nonideal solution, however, $\overline{|c_{\mathbf{k}}|^2}$ may depend considerably on $\mathbf{k}$.

We note that in this general case there is a simple integral relation for the quantities $\overline{|c_{\mathbf{k}}|^2}$. In fact, if we carry out a summation of expression (1.12) or (1.13) over all $\mathbf{k}$ for which $\mathbf{k}/2\pi$ lies in some unit cell of the disordered solution, then, remembering that $\sum_{\mathbf{k}}\cos\mathbf{k}\boldsymbol{\rho} = 0$ for $\boldsymbol{\rho} \neq 0$ and $\sum_{\mathbf{k}} 1 = N\nu$, we immediately obtain

$$\sum_{\mathbf{k}}\overline{|c_{\mathbf{k}}|^2} = \frac{1}{\nu}\sum_{\gamma=1}^{\nu} c_\gamma(1-c_\gamma) = c(1-c), \tag{1.15}$$

where the second equation is written for disordered solutions. Thus the mean values of $\overline{|c_{\mathbf{k}}|^2}$ over a cell in reciprocal-lattice space are simply determined by the long-range-order parameters and the concentration of the solution.

We see from the foregoing results that correlation and fluctuations in the concentration and long-range-order parameters are in fact directly related to each other. Knowing the whole set of correlation parameters in the solution, we may find the mean squares and products of the different Fourier components of the fluctuations. On the other hand, if we know $\overline{c_{\mathbf{k}\gamma}c^*_{\mathbf{k}\gamma'}}$ for all the wave vectors $\mathbf{k}/2\pi$ lying in a unit cell of reciprocal-lattice space, a Fourier transformation of expressions (1.9) and (1.10) will enable us to find $\varepsilon_{\gamma\gamma'}(\boldsymbol{\rho})$ for various $\boldsymbol{\rho}$. Hence it is sufficient simply to calculate one set of quantities, either $\varepsilon_{\gamma\gamma'}(\boldsymbol{\rho})$ or $\overline{c_{\mathbf{k}\gamma}c^*_{\mathbf{k}\gamma'}}$.

In future we shall principally consider solutions existing in a state of thermodynamic equilibrium. The correlation parameters of these solutions may be determined in principle by the methods of statistical physics, on the basis of a Boltzmann probability distribution of the various configurations of the atoms in the solution. In practice, however, even in a highly simplified model, the calculation of the whole set of correlation parameters for the different coordination spheres is quite complicated. It is considerably more convenient to calculate the mean squares and products of the Fourier components of the concentrations directly. This approach will be consistently used here; it is especially convenient in connection with x-ray scattering since, as we shall see later, the intensity of the diffuse scattering of monochromatic radiation by a single crystal is determined (apart from a proportionality factor) by the average value $\overline{|c_{\mathbf{k}}|^2}$, corresponding to a specific wave vector $\mathbf{k}$.

§2. Macroscopic Theory of Fluctuation Waves of Concentration and Long-Range-Order Parameters

The probabilities of fluctuations in any small volume element or the probabilities of fluctuation waves in the crystal may be calculated by means of either the macroscopic or the microscopic theory.

In the macroscopic theory we consider fluctuations in elements of volume small compared with that of the whole crystal, but large compared with atomic volumes. For such elements of volume we may neglect surface effects and consider that within them the specific thermodynamic functions are no different from the corresponding functions in massive samples. The probabilities of the fluctuations are calculated (without using any specific model) by means of the thermodynamic theory of fluctuations, and are expressed in terms of derivatives of the thermodynamic potential, which in a number of cases may be determined from independent experimental data.

Obvious advantages of the macroscopic theory of fluctuations arise from the fact that it is not based on any simplified model of the crystal and that it is extremely general yet simple. On the other hand, the results of this theory are only applicable to elements of volume considerably larger than that of the atoms. Hence in considering fluctuation waves it is essential that the wavelength should greatly exceed the interatomic distance if the macroscopic theory is to remain valid.

Nevertheless, in a number of problems, especially those concerned with x-ray scattering, not only do we have to consider smooth fluctuations* but also fluctuations varying rapidly in space (at distances of the order of the lattice constant d), corresponding to fluctuation wave lengths approximately equal to d. The probabilities of such fluctuation waves may only be calculated on the microscopic theory, which is based on a specific model. This model must necessarily be so simplified that it will naturally reduce the accuracy of the results obtained. At the same time, the use of a specific model not only makes it possible to consider short-wave fluctuations, but also in principle enables us to calculate and study the temperature and concentration dependence of the thermodynamic characteristics, which determine the probabilities of the fluctuations in the macroscopic theory (and which cannot in all cases be determined from independent experimental data).

Thus either the macroscopic or the microscopic approach may be appropriate, according to the nature of the problem. In view of this we shall now consider both variations of the theory.

In this paragraph we shall set out the macroscopic theory of fluctuation waves, first considering fluctuations of concentration and then fluctuations of long-range order. We shall only here consider cases in which the long-range forces associated with the distortions of crystals, Coulomb interactions, and so forth may be neglected, and in which the interatomic interaction falls off rapidly with distance. The effect of long-range forces on the probabilities of the fluctuation waves will be considered separately in Chapter III.

*Smooth fluctuations, corresponding to long fluctuation waves, not only determine the scattering of long-wave radiation, for example, light, but also determine the diffuse scattering of x rays (with a wavelength of the order of the interatomic distance) at small scattering angles, or when the diffraction vector (divided by 2π) falls in the neighborhood of a reciprocal-lattice point (see Chapter V). It is just in these cases that diffuse scattering has a number of interesting features, which are considered below.

2.1. Fluctuations of Concentration. Let us first consider fluctuations of concentration in a small element of volume V' of a solid solution A–B. Such fluctuations lead to a change in the number of A and B atoms for a constant total number of atoms N' in this element. The remaining part of the crystal (volume V ≫ V') is considered as an external medium, which may exchange atoms with the isolated volume V'.

It is well known that in the thermodynamic theory of fluctuations (according to Boltzmann's principle) the probability w of a certain fluctuation taking place is

$$w \sim \exp\left(-\frac{R}{k_B T}\right). \tag{2.1}$$

Here R denotes the minimum work necessary for setting up the given fluctuation. The fluctuation corresponds to a nonequilibrium state of the system, and the transformation into this state may be effected in many ways; for different means of creating the fluctuation in the physical quantities under consideration, the external forces creating this fluctuation produce different amounts of work.

The minimum work R determining the probability of a fluctuation in accordance with (2.1) corresponds to the process of changing the physical quantities from their equilibrium to their fluctuation values, which is carried out reversibly by the external source of work. It is an important point that the system is here in the most complete state of equilibrium corresponding to these changed values of the fluctuating parameters under consideration. For example, in considering fluctuations of concentration, the minimum work is calculated for equilibrium values of the internal parameters corresponding to the changed concentration.

If the temperature and volume (or the temperature and pressure) remain constant when a fluctuation develops in a single-component substance, the minimum work is equal to the difference between the free energies (or the thermodynamic potentials) of the states respectively corresponding to the fluctuation and equilibrium values of the physical quantities.* In solid solutions, the minimum

*The meaning of the free energy of a nonequilibrium fluctuation state is described in detail by Leontovich (see [172a], §31).

work necessary for the creation of a fluctuational change in concentration (for the case under consideration, in which the fluctuations do not produce any distortion in the crystal) may be written in the form (see [1], §117)

$$R = \delta\Phi' - \mu_A \delta N_A - \mu_B \delta N_B = V'\delta\varphi - N'(\mu_A - \mu_B)\,\delta c. \qquad (2.2)$$

Here

$$\delta\Phi' = \Phi'(c + \delta c) - \Phi'(c)$$

is the change in the thermodynamic potential of the isolated element of volume on changing the concentration by δc; μ_A and μ_B are the chemical potentials of the A and B atoms; φ is the thermodynamic potential of unit volume.

From the definition of the chemical potentials

$$\mu_A = \left(\frac{\partial\Phi}{\partial N_A}\right)_{PTN_B}, \qquad \mu_B = \left(\frac{\partial\Phi}{\partial N_B}\right)_{PTN_A}$$

(Φ relates to the whole crystal) we have the obvious identity

$$\mu_A - \mu_B = \frac{1}{N^0}\left(\frac{\partial\Phi}{\partial c}\right)_{PTN} = v_0 \frac{d\varphi}{dc}, \qquad (2.3)$$

where $N^0 = N\nu$ is the number of atoms in the whole crystal, $\nu_0 = V/N^0$ is the atomic volume, and the derivative $d\varphi/dc$ is calculated for constant P and T. Expanding $\delta\varphi$ with respect to δc, remembering (2.3), and confining attention to the square terms of the expansion, we find that the minimum work

$$R = \frac{1}{2} V' \frac{d^2\varphi}{dc^2} (\delta c)^2 \qquad (2.4)$$

is proportional to $(\delta c)^2$, i.e., the distribution (2.1) of the probabilities of the concentration fluctuations is Gaussian. It thus follows that the mean square fluctuation of the concentration in the volume element V' is determined by the second derivative of the thermodynamic potential with respect to concentration:

$$\overline{(\delta c)^2} = \frac{k_B T}{V'} \frac{1}{\dfrac{d^2\varphi}{dc^2}}. \qquad (2.5)$$

In order to determine the probability of fluctuation waves, we must consider the fluctuational change in concentration distributed over the whole crystal and not in the isolated volume element. In the macroscopic approximation, the fluctuations in concentration at different points of the solution are characterized by specifying a continuous function $\delta c(\mathbf{r})$. The minimum work necessary for creating a fluctuation distribution $\delta c(\mathbf{r})$ is now determined by the integral of expression (2.2) over the whole volume of the crystal V. In the case considered below, the fluctuations reduce to a redistribution of the concentration between different parts of the crystal ($\int \delta c(\mathbf{r})\, dV = 0$), and the minimum work has the form

$$R = \int \delta\varphi \, dV. \tag{2.6}$$

In view of the fact that the concentration distribution is inhomogeneous, in the expansion of $\delta\varphi$ we must consider not only the terms containing the actual function $\delta c(\mathbf{r})$ to various powers but also terms containing its derivatives with respect to the coordinates. Here terms with first derivatives $\partial c/\partial x_i$ ($i = 1, 2, 3$) and with products of the type $\delta c(\mathbf{r})(\partial c/\partial x_i) = 1/2\,(\partial \delta c^2(\mathbf{r})/\partial x_i)$ vanish on integrating over the whole crystal (for simplicity we shall use cyclic boundary conditions). Terms with third and higher derivatives may be neglected in the case of the smooth (long-wave) fluctuations considered. Hence of the terms containing derivatives we need only retain those of the $(\partial c/\partial x_i)(\partial c/\partial x_j)$ type [and $\delta c(\mathbf{r})(\partial^2 c/\partial x_i^2)$ terms, which reduce to these after integration by parts]. The expansion of $\delta\varphi$ will thus have the form

$$\delta\varphi = \frac{1}{2}\frac{d^2\varphi}{dc^2}(\delta c)^2 + \frac{1}{2}\beta_{ij}\frac{\partial c}{\partial x_i}\frac{\partial c}{\partial x_j}, \tag{2.7}$$

where β_{ij} is a symmetric tensor of the second order, and i and j enumerate the Cartesian coordinates.*

An estimate carried out in the next section (§ 3) shows that β_{ij} are of the order $k_B T_0/r_0$, where T_0 is the ordering (or decomposition) temperature of the solution and r_0 is the interatomic distance. In cubic crystals, clearly, the tensor β_{ij} degenerates into a

*Here and subsequently summation is carried out from 1 to 3 over twice-repeated indices i and j.

scalar ($\beta_{ij} = \beta\delta_{ij}$) and the second term in (2.7) takes the simpler form $1/2\,\beta\,(\nabla c)^2$.

The continuous concentration distribution $\delta c\,(\mathbf{r})$ given within the volume of the crystal V may be expanded into a Fourier series

$$\delta c\,(\mathbf{r}) = \sum_{\mathbf{k}} c_{\mathbf{k}} e^{-i\mathbf{k}\mathbf{r}}, \qquad c_{\mathbf{k}} = c^*_{-\mathbf{k}} = \frac{1}{V} \int \delta c\,(\mathbf{r})\, e^{i\mathbf{k}\mathbf{r}}\, dV. \tag{2.8}$$

Comparing (2.8) and (1.11), it is easy to see that for small k, for which we may replace the sum over $s\gamma$ by an integral in (1.11), expressions (1.11) and (2.8) for $c_{\mathbf{k}}$ coincide. If the distribution $\delta c\,(\mathbf{r})$ corresponds to any specific fluctuation wave, i.e., if

$$\delta c\,(\mathbf{r}) = c_{\mathbf{k}} \exp(-i\mathbf{k}\mathbf{r}) + c_{-\mathbf{k}} \exp(i\mathbf{k}\mathbf{r}),$$

then we see from (2.7) and (2.6) that the minimum work $R_{\mathbf{k}}$ necessary for the creation of this fluctuation will equal

$$R_{\mathbf{k}} = V \left(\frac{d^2\varphi}{dc^2} + \beta_{ij} k_i k_j \right) c_{\mathbf{k}} c^*_{\mathbf{k}}. \tag{2.9}$$

If we write the complex quantities $c_{\mathbf{k}}$ in the form

$$c_{\mathbf{k}} = c'_{\mathbf{k}} + i c''_{\mathbf{k}},$$

then we see from (2.1) and (2.9) that the probabilities of the fluctuation waves depend on the real and imaginary part of their amplitudes in accordance with a Gaussian law. It follows at once from this that the mean square of the **k**-th Fourier component of the concentration fluctuation equals

$$\overline{|c_{\mathbf{k}}|^2} = \frac{k_B T}{V} \frac{1}{\frac{d^2\varphi}{dc^2} + \beta_{ij} k_i k_j}. \tag{2.10}$$

This type of expression for $\overline{|c_{\mathbf{k}}|^2}$ was obtained by Einstein [2] when considering the critical scattering of light in solutions.

Except for regions in the phase diagrams close to critical points (considered in detail later), for $kr_0 \ll 1$ the second term in the denominator of (2.10)

$$\beta_{ij}k_ik_j \sim k_B T_0 v_0^{-1} (kr_0)^2$$

is much smaller than the first. Hence in the case of long waves the second term may usually be neglected and the mean-square fluctuations are completely determined by the thermodynamic quantity $d^2\varphi/dc^2$. We see from (2.3) that this quantity may be found from experimental thermodynamic data relating to the concentration dependence of the chemical potentials. Since the derivatives $\partial\mu_A/\partial c$ and $\partial\mu_B/\partial c$ are connected by the Gibbs-Duhem relation, it is only essential to know one of these. The second term in the denominator of (2.10) becomes important even for small k near the critical points. It is clear that formula (2.10), which was derived by means of the macroscopic consideration of fluctuations, is only valid for the case of long waves, when the criterion

$$kr_0 \ll 1 \tag{2.11}$$

is satisfied and we may neglect the higher derivatives in expansion (2.7).

It is clear that expression (2.10), defining the fluctuations in terms of thermodynamic characteristics, and expression (1.12), defining them in terms of the correlation parameters, should be equivalent. Equating these expressions in the limiting case of $k \to 0$, we obtain an interesting general relationship:

$$\frac{1}{\nu}\sum_{\gamma=1}^{\nu} c_\gamma(1-c_\gamma) + \sum_{\rho\neq 0} \varepsilon(\rho) = \frac{k_B T}{v_0}\left(\frac{d^2\varphi}{dc^2}\right)^{-1}. \tag{2.12}$$

This relation connects the purely thermodynamic quantity $d^2\varphi/dc^2$ on the one hand and the parameters $\varepsilon(\varrho)$, characterizing the correlation in the arrangement of neighboring atoms (i.e., the microscopic characteristics of the solution) on the other.

2.2 Fluctuation Waves of the Long-Range-Order Parameters in Single-Component Crystals. In the very simplest case, long-range order in single-component crystals (consisting of "molecules" of only one type) is simply characterized by a single internal parameter, the degree of long-range-order η. Fluctuations of long-range order in this case were considered by Landau [3] when studying the scattering of x rays near phase transformations of the second kind. In a state of thermodynamic equilibrium, the degree of long-range order in the crystal takes an average value of η determined by the equilibrium condition $\partial\varphi/\partial\eta = 0$. Fluctuations lead to deviations from this value; in the macroscopic approximation these may be considered as a smooth function of the coordinates $\delta\eta(\mathbf{r})$.

The minimum work necessary for the development of such a distribution of fluctuations, as in the case of concentration fluctuations, is clearly given by formula (2.6), where now

$$\delta\varphi = \frac{1}{2}\varphi_{\eta\eta}(\delta\eta)^2 + \frac{1}{2}\alpha_{ij}\frac{\partial\eta}{\partial x_i}\frac{\partial\eta}{\partial x_j}. \tag{2.13}$$

Here we have introduced the notation $\varphi_{\eta\eta} = \partial^2\varphi/\partial\eta^2$. Since this expression differs from (2.7) only in respect of the replacement of c by η, in determining the probabilities of the fluctuation waves in the degree of long-range order

$$\delta\eta(\mathbf{r}) = \eta_{\mathbf{k}}\exp(-i\mathbf{kr}) + \eta_{-\mathbf{k}}\exp(i\mathbf{kr})$$

we may repeat the earlier discussion relating to fluctuations of concentration. As a result we find that the average value of the square of the k-th Fourier component of the fluctuation in the long-range-order parameter is determined by the formula

$$\overline{|\eta_{\mathbf{k}}|^2} = \frac{k_B T}{V}\frac{1}{\varphi_{\eta\eta} + \alpha_{ij}k_i k_j}. \tag{2.14}$$

For small enough k, even in this case $\overline{|\eta_{\mathbf{k}}|^2}$ is determined by the thermodynamic quantity $\varphi_{\eta\eta}$.

Landau's results may easily be extended to the more general case in which the long-range order in the single-component crystal is characterized by specifying not one but several parameters of long-range order, $\eta_\mu (\mu = 1, 2, \ldots, r)$. The change in the thermodynamic potential $\delta\varphi$ when fluctuations of long-range order $\delta\eta_\mu$ arise reduces in this case to a positive definite quadratic form of all the variables $\delta\eta_\mu$:

$$\delta\varphi = \frac{1}{2}\sum_{\mu,\mu'=1}^{r}\left[\varphi_{\mu\mu'}\delta\eta_\mu\delta\eta_{\mu'} + \alpha_{\mu\mu' ij}\frac{\partial\eta_\mu}{\partial x_i}\frac{\partial\eta_{\mu'}}{\partial x_j}\right], \tag{2.15}$$

where $\varphi_{\mu\mu'} \equiv \partial^2\varphi/\partial\eta_\mu\partial\eta_{\mu'}$ and $\alpha_{\mu\mu' ij}$ (for given μ and μ') is a second-rank tensor.

If the changes in the order parameters $\delta\eta_\mu$ correspond to fluctuation waves with a specific wave vector **k**, i.e., if

$$\delta\eta_\mu = \eta_{\mu\mathbf{k}} \exp(-i\mathbf{kr}) + \text{c.c.},$$

it follows from (2.1), (2.6), and (2.15) that the probabilities of the amplitudes of these waves $\eta_{\mu\mathbf{k}}$ are determined by a Gaussian distribution:

$$w \sim \exp\left[-\frac{V}{k_B T} \sum_{\mu,\mu'=1}^{r} \varphi_{\mathbf{k}\mu\mu'} (\eta'_{\mu\mathbf{k}}\eta'_{\mu'\mathbf{k}} + \eta''_{\mu\mathbf{k}}\eta''_{\mu'\mathbf{k}})\right], \tag{2.16}$$

where

$$\eta_{\mu\mathbf{k}} = \eta'_{\mu\mathbf{k}} + i\eta''_{\mu\mathbf{k}}, \qquad \varphi_{\mathbf{k}\mu\mu'} = \varphi_{\mu\mu'} + \alpha_{\mu\mu' ij} k_i k_j. \tag{2.17}$$

It is an important point that the derivatives $\varphi_{\mu\mu'}$ with $\mu \neq \mu'$ may differ from zero, i.e., the fluctuations $\eta_{\mu\mathbf{k}}$ of different order parameters are, generally speaking, not statistically independent, and the probability distribution (2.16) does not decompose into the product of the distributions corresponding to different μ. The determination of the average values $\overline{\eta'_{\mu\mathbf{k}}\eta'_{\mu'\mathbf{k}}}$ (or $\overline{\eta''_{\mu\mathbf{k}}\eta''_{\mu'\mathbf{k}}}$) in this general case reduces (see, for example, [1], §113) to the inversion of a matrix of the r-th order made up of the coefficients of the $\eta'_{\mu\mathbf{k}}\eta'_{\mu'\mathbf{k}}$. The mean values of the squares and products of the k-th Fourier components of the fluctuations will be determined by the formulas

$$\frac{1}{2}\overline{(\eta_{\mu\mathbf{k}}\eta^*_{\mu'\mathbf{k}} + \eta^*_{\mu\mathbf{k}}\eta_{\mu'\mathbf{k}})} = \frac{k_B T}{V}\varphi^{-1}_{\mathbf{k}\mu\mu'}, \tag{2.18}$$

where $\varphi^{-1}_{\mathbf{k}\mu\mu'}$ are the matrix elements of the matrix reciprocal to the matrix $\varphi_{\mathbf{k}\mu\mu'}$. In the limiting case $k \to 0$ $\varphi^{-1}_{\mathbf{k}\mu\mu'}$ coincides with the matrix $\varphi^{-1}_{\mu\mu'}$ reciprocal to the matrix composed of the second derivatives of $\varphi_{\mu\mu'}$.*

*In crystals of certain classes of symmetry (in which the atoms are not necessarily centers of inversion), the expansion in powers of the derivatives $\partial\eta_\mu/\partial x_i$ may contain not only quadratic but also linear terms [1, 4]. Such terms will come into the expansion of $\delta\varphi$ in the form of the combinations

$$\frac{1}{2}\delta_{\mu\mu' i}\left(\delta\eta_\mu \frac{\partial\eta_{\mu'}}{\partial x_i} - \delta\eta_{\mu'}\frac{\partial\eta_\mu}{\partial x_i}\right)$$

In the general case, the second derivatives of $\varphi_{\mu\mu'}$ with respect to the order parameters, in contrast to the derivative $d^2\varphi/dc^2$, cannot be expressed in terms of quantities which can be determined from independent experimental data; they must therefore be found theoretically. However, in two interesting cases in which the long-range order in the crystal may be unambiguously characterized by specifying the spontaneous polarization (in ferroelectrics) or magnetization (in ferromagnetics), the parameters of long-range order being taken as the components of the polarization vector P_i (or magnetization vector M_i), the derivatives of $\varphi_{\mu\mu'}$ may be related to the components of the tensor of dielectric susceptibility $\varkappa_{ij}$ (or magnetic susceptibility χ_{ij}), which are determined from independent experiments.

In considering fluctuations of polarization, generally speaking, long-range dipole–dipole forces (which alter the formulas for the fluctuations) are important. However, if there is a sufficiently high concentration of charges (conduction electrons or ions), these forces are screened and have no long-range character. We shall here consider that such screening does in fact take place, putting off the discussion of long-range effects until Chapter III. It is then quite easy to obtain a relation between the second derivatives $\partial^2\varphi/\partial P_i \partial P_j$ and $\varkappa_{ij}$ [5]: For this purpose we remember that, in the presence of an external electric field $\mathbf{E}$, the thermodynamic poten-

---

(symmetrical combinations of the type

$$\delta\eta_{\mu}\frac{\partial\eta_{\mu'}}{\partial x_i}+\delta\eta_{\mu'}\frac{\partial\eta_{\mu}}{\partial x_i}=\frac{\partial}{\partial x_i}(\delta\eta_{\mu}\,\delta\eta_{\mu'})$$

vanish on integrating over the whole crystal). Hence additional terms will appear in the index of the exponent of probability distribution (2.16), namely

$$2V(k_BT)^{-1}\sum_{\substack{\mu,\mu'=1\\(\mu<\mu')}}^{r}\delta_{\mu\mu' i}k_i\,(\eta'_{\mu\mathbf{k}}\eta''_{\mu'\mathbf{k}}-\eta''_{\mu\mathbf{k}}\eta'_{\mu'\mathbf{k}}).$$

In this case the determination of the average $\overline{\eta'_{\mu\mathbf{k}}\eta'_{\mu'\mathbf{k}}}$ and $\overline{\eta''_{\mu\mathbf{k}}\eta''_{\mu'\mathbf{k}}}$ reduces to the inversion of a matrix of the 2r-th order (not the r-th order as earlier), and, in contrast to the case in which terms linear in the derivatives were absent, the average $\overline{\eta_{\mu\mathbf{k}}\eta''_{\mu'\mathbf{k}}}$ will differ from zero (and will be proportional to k). We would simply note that (as is quite obvious) in the limit $k \to 0$, when $\varphi^{-1}_{\mathbf{k}\mu\mu'}$ coincides with $\varphi^{-1}_{\mu\mu'}$, formula (2.18) remains valid as before.

tial of a unit of volume φ may be written in the form

$$\varphi = \varphi(\mathbf{P}) - \mathbf{PE}, \tag{2.19}$$

where $\varphi(\mathbf{P})$ is independent of $\mathbf{E}$. From the equilibrium condition $\partial\varphi/\partial\mathbf{P} = 0$ it follows that the equilibrium value of the field corresponding to a given $\mathbf{P}$ equals

$$E_i = \frac{\partial\varphi(\mathbf{P})}{\partial P_i}.$$

Differentiating this equation with respect to P_j and remembering the definition of the tensor of dielectric susceptibility

$$\varkappa_{ij} = \frac{\partial P_i}{\partial E_j},$$

we obtain a relation between $\partial^2\varphi/\partial P_i \partial P_j$ and $\varkappa_{ij}$:

$$\varphi_{ij} \equiv \frac{\partial^2\varphi}{\partial P_i\, \partial P_j} = \varkappa_{ij}^{-1}, \tag{2.20}$$

where $\varkappa_{ij}^{-1}$ are the components of the tensor inverse to the tensor χ_{ij}. Substituting this relation in (2.18) we find that for $k \to 0$ the mean values of the squares and products of the Fourier components of the fluctuations of polarization equal

$$\frac{1}{2}\overline{(P_{\mathbf{k}i}P_{\mathbf{k}j}^* + P_{\mathbf{k}i}^*P_{\mathbf{k}j})} = \frac{k_{\mathrm{B}}T}{V}\varkappa_{ij}, \tag{2.21}$$

i.e., they are in fact expressed in terms of quantities determinable from independent experimental data.* Analogous formulas (neglecting long-range forces) are also valid for the fluctuations of magnetization on replacing $\varkappa_{ij}$ by the magnetic-susceptibility tensor χ_{ij}.

2.3. Fluctuation Waves of the Parameters of Long-Range Order and Concentration in Solid Solutions. A characteristic feature of fluctuations in solid solutions is the fact that these involve the development of both fluctua-

*Since the high-frequency electron polarization is not called for in the case of fluctuations, the use of the quantum theory of fluctuations instead of the classical theory here treated leads to a change in the meaning of the quantities $\varkappa_{ij}$ in (2.21). These quantities are equal to the difference between the static dielectric susceptibility $\varkappa_{ij}$ and the high-frequency susceptibility $\varkappa_{\infty ij}$ (this is considered in more detail in §10).

tions of the long-range-order parameters and fluctuations of concentration. The fluctuations in order and composition are, generally speaking, not statistically independent, and in order to determine their probabilities we must simultaneously consider the deviations of composition and order from their equilibrium values. As a result of this, there is a change in the formulas for the fluctuations of the order parameters, and some new characteristics appear (as compared with the single-component crystals considered in [6]).

Let the long-range order in the solution be defined by a single parameter and the wave-like fluctuations of composition and order in the macroscopic approximation be characterized by the smooth functions

$$\delta c(\mathbf{r}) = c_{\mathbf{k}} \exp(-i\mathbf{kr}) + \text{c.c.}, \quad \delta\eta(\mathbf{r}) = \eta_{\mathbf{k}} \exp(-i\mathbf{kr}) + \text{c.c.},$$

Then the minimum work necessary for reversibly creating these fluctuation waves in a cubic crystal will be determined by a formula constituting a simple generalization of formula (2.9):

$$R_{\mathbf{k}} = V[(\varphi_{\eta\eta} + \alpha k^2) |\eta_{\mathbf{k}}|^2 + (\varphi_{cc} + \beta' k^2) |c_{\mathbf{k}}|^2 + 2(\varphi_{c\eta} + \gamma k^2)(\eta_{\mathbf{k}} c_{\mathbf{k}}^* + \eta_{\mathbf{k}}^* c_{\mathbf{k}})], \tag{2.22}$$

where

$$\varphi_{cc} = \frac{\partial^2 \varphi}{\partial c^2}, \qquad \varphi_{c\eta} = \frac{\partial^2 \varphi}{\partial c\, \partial \eta}.$$

Substituting (2.22) into (2.1) and inverting the second-order matrix of the coefficients in $R_{\mathbf{k}}$, we easily find expressions for the mean squares of the Fourier components:

$$\overline{|\eta_{\mathbf{k}}|^2} = \frac{k_B T}{V} \frac{\varphi_{cc} + \beta' k^2}{\varphi_{\eta\eta}\varphi_{cc} - \varphi_{c\eta}^2 + (\alpha\varphi_{cc} + \beta'\varphi_{\eta\eta} - 2\gamma\varphi_{c\eta}) k^2}, \tag{2.23}$$

$$\overline{|c_{\mathbf{k}}|^2} = \frac{k_B T}{V} \frac{\varphi_{\eta\eta} + \alpha k^2}{\varphi_{\eta\eta}\varphi_{cc} - \varphi_{c\eta}^2 + (\alpha\varphi_{cc} + \beta'\varphi_{\eta\eta} - 2\gamma\varphi_{c\eta}) k^2}. \tag{2.24}$$

In the case of noncubic crystals we must clearly replace αk^2 terms by $\alpha_{ij} k_i k_j$ in these formulas.

The partial derivatives $\partial/\partial c$ in φ_{cc} and $\varphi_{c\eta}$, from the very definition of these quantities, are taken for a constant (equilibrium) value of η. In contrast to these, the derivative $d^2\varphi/dc^2$ is given (in accordance with the principles of the thermodynamic theory of fluctuations) by the increase in the thermodynamic potential associated with a change in concentration, accompanied by a change in the order parameters. Hence the derivatives d/dc must be calculated for values of η corresponding to the changed (fluctuation) values of composition (and the same temperature). From the condition of equilibrium

$$\frac{\partial\varphi}{\partial\eta} \equiv \varphi_\eta = 0,$$

and hence it is readily seen that

$$\varphi_{cc} - \frac{\varphi_{c\eta}^2}{\varphi_{\eta\eta}} = \frac{d^2\varphi}{dc^2}.^*$$

It thus follows that expressions (2.24) and (2.10) for $\overline{|c_k|^2}$ are equivalent in cubic crystals. This result, of course, would be expected, since formula (2.10) is clearly general and determines concentration fluctuations both in ordered and disordered solutions.

In disordered solutions, for which $\eta \equiv 0$ for any concentration, i.e., $d\eta/dc = 0$, the derivative $\varphi_{c\eta} = -\varphi_{\eta\eta}(d\eta/dc)$ also equals zero (also $d^2\varphi/dc^2 = \varphi_{cc}$). Hence for small k fluctuations in the concentration and long-range-order parameters in disordered solutions† are statistically independent and the formula for $\overline{|\eta_k|^2}$ in solid solutions has the same form as in the case of single-component crystals. In ordered solutions, however, $\varphi_{c\eta}$ differs from zero (except for certain concentrations), so that expressions (2.23) and (2.14) for $\overline{|\eta_k|^2}$ in solid solutions differ from the case of single-component crystals.

*Remembering that the condition $\varphi_\eta = 0$ is satisfied for any concentration, we find that

$$\frac{d\varphi_\eta}{dc} = \varphi_{c\eta} + \varphi_{\eta\eta}\frac{d\eta}{dc} = 0, \text{ i.e., } \frac{d\eta}{dc} = -\frac{\varphi_{c\eta}}{\varphi_{\eta\eta}}.$$

Putting this expression into the formula for $d^2\varphi/dc^2$ (considering that $\varphi_\eta = 0$)

$$\frac{d^2\varphi}{dc^2} = \varphi_{cc} + 2\varphi_{c\eta}\frac{d\eta}{dc} + \varphi_{\eta\eta}\left(\frac{d\eta}{dc}\right)^2,$$

we immediately obtain the relation given.

†Although the average value of the degree of long-range order in disordered solutions equals zero, fluctuational deviations from this zero value may occur in either the positive or negative direction, thus differing from zero.

If the long-range order in the solid solution is characterized by $r-1$ parameters η_{μ}, the fluctuations of these parameters and the concentration are also not statistically independent, and must be considered simultaneously. It is clear that the mean squares and products of the Fourier components may in this case be determined from formula (2.18) if we replace η_r in this formula by c.

The formulas presented enable us to determine the fluctuations if we know the way in which the thermodynamic potentials vary with c and η. In a number of cases, as we have already seen, these relationships may be obtained from independent experimental data. In order to calculate these and determine the temperature and concentration dependence of the fluctuations in explicit form, we may also use various theoretical (thermodynamic or statistical) expressions for φ. It is clearly more reliable to use the thermodynamic expressions for φ, since these are obtained without using any specific statistical model of the solution and are valid in all parts of the phase diagram.

In the case of weak solutions, for which the concentration of one of the components of the binary solution is low ($c \ll 1$), by neglecting the terms quadratic in c the expression for φ may be written in the form (see, for example, [1], §88):

$$\varphi = \varphi_B + \frac{N}{V} k_B T c \ln c + c g(P, T), \tag{2.25}$$

where φ_B is the thermodynamic potential of unit volume of the pure component B and g(P, T) is independent of c. For sufficiently small c, the derivative of the thermodynamic potential (2.25) $\varphi_{cc} = N k_B T / Vc$ for any $\mathbf{k}/2\pi$ (in the first cell of the reciprocal lattice) is much greater than the second term in the denominator of (2.10). Hence in weak solutions

$$\overline{|c_{\mathbf{k}}|^2} = \frac{c}{N}. \tag{2.26}$$

For fairly high temperatures, much higher than the ordering (or decomposition) temperature, correlation becomes insignificant and the solution may be regarded as ideal. In this case the expression for φ also has a simple form

$$\varphi = \varphi^0 + \frac{N}{V} k_B T [c \ln c + (1-c) \ln (1-c)], \tag{2.27}$$

where φ^0 depends linearly on concentration. Since in approximately ideal solutions we may neglect the dependence of φ on the gradient of c and put $\beta = 0$, it follows from (2.10) and (2.27) that in ideal solutions for any **k**

$$\overline{|c_{\mathbf{k}}|^2} = \frac{1}{N} c(1-c). \tag{2.28}$$

This result agrees with formula (1.14) obtained on the basis of the other type of considerations (probability).

A thermodynamic expression for φ may also be obtained for almost completely ordered solutions. This is the state of solutions with compositions close to stoichiometric at low temperatures (compared with the ordering temperature). The concentrations of the atoms at "foreign" sites in such solutions may be regarded as small parameters, which makes it possible to carry out a thermodynamical calculation of φ. In particular, if the stoichiometric composition corresponds to $c = 1/2$, then for $c \approx 1/2$ the thermodynamic potential [7] equals

$$\varphi = \varphi' + N\chi_1(1-c_1) + N\chi_2 c_2 + Nk_B T\,[c_1 \ln c_1 +$$

$$+ c_2 \ln c_2 + (1-c_1)\ln(1-c_1) + (1-c_2)\ln(1-c_2)], \tag{2.29}$$

where φ', χ_1, and χ_2 depend only on T and P and are independent of c and η.

Putting (2.29) into (2.23) and (2.24), remembering that in the denominators of these formulas the terms independent of **k** increase more rapidly than terms quadratic in k, and considering (1.3) (for $\nu_1 = \nu_2 = \nu/2$), we find that in almost completely ordered solutions

$$\overline{|c_{\mathbf{k}}|^2} = \frac{1}{4}\overline{|\eta_{\mathbf{k}}|^2} = \frac{1}{2N}\left[c(1-c) - \frac{1}{4}\eta^2\right]. \tag{2.30}$$

In solutions of stoichiometric composition in particular ($c = 1/2$)

$$\overline{|c_{\mathbf{k}}|^2} = \frac{1}{4}\overline{|\eta_{\mathbf{k}}|^2} = \frac{1}{8N}(1-\eta^2) \approx \frac{1}{4N}(1-\eta), \tag{2.31}$$

i.e., the mean squares of the Fourier components of the fluctuations are proportional to $1-\eta$. Since in these solutions η tends toward unity exponentially with falling temperature [1, 7] in accordance with the law

$$1-\eta=2\exp\left(-\frac{\chi_1+\chi_2}{2k_BT}\right), \tag{2.32}$$

$\overline{|c_k|^2}$ and $\overline{|\eta_k|^2}$ also fall off exponentially.

Expression (2.30) for $\overline{|c_k|^2}$ coincides with expression (1.12) (for $\nu=2$) if we put $\varepsilon(\rho)=0$ in the latter. Thus in a solution correlation becomes less important not only at high but also at low temperatures near the state of complete order.

2.4 Fluctuations near Critical Points on the Decomposition Curves and Points Representing a Phase Transformation of the Second Kind. Near critical points on the decomposition curves and points representing phase transformations of the second kind, fluctuations of concentration or long-range-order parameters become anomalously large. This leads to a number of interesting physical effects, in particular to a sharp rise in the scattering cross section of the waves on approaching such points in the phase diagram.

Anomalously large fluctuations arise near lines of phase equilibrium in the phase diagram in those cases in which the difference between the phases becomes small. Thus, for example, near the critical point on the decomposition curve of a system in which the phase diagram has the form of Fig. 3 and the phases in equilibrium differ little as regards composition, concentration fluctuations increase sharply. This follows from the formulas derived in the preceding section if we consider that at the critical

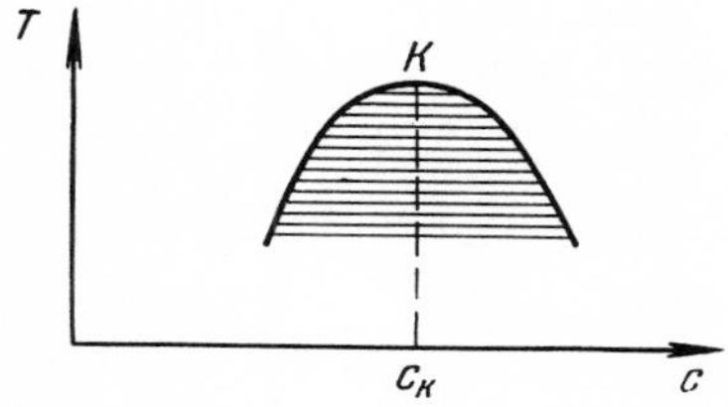

Fig. 3. Phase diagram in the neighborhood of a critical point on the decomposition curve.

point the condition

$$\frac{d^2\varphi}{dc^2} = 0 \tag{2.33}$$

is satisfied.

It follows from (2.33) and (2.5) that the mean square of the concentration fluctuations in some element of volume V' passes to infinity at the actual critical point. This result, however, is not quite precise, as it involves the neglect of surface effects when calculating the minimum amount of work R from formula (2.4). Although, in the absence of long-range forces, the surface energy may usually be neglected for fairly large V', nevertheless, on approaching the critical point, at which, as we see from (2.4) and (2.33) the volume term in R tends to zero, surface effects also have to be taken into account. On considering these effects, the minimum work R, and hence the probability distribution (2.1), depend on the fluctuational variation of concentration not only in the given volume elements but also in elements neighboring this, i.e., the spatial correlation of fluctuations at considerable distances becomes important.

In the microscopic approximation, the contribution of such surface effects to R for a slight fluctuational change in concentration is described by the second term in (2.7), which contains derivatives with respect to the coordinates and does not tend to zero on approaching the critical point. The calculation of concentration fluctuations in an isolated element of volume, allowing for gradient terms in R, is clearly quite complicated, and the result depends not only on the shape but also the volume of the isolated element. However, even in this case the calculation of the fluctuations in the Fourier components causes no difficulty and leads to formula (2.10) for $\overline{|c_{\mathbf{k}}|^2}$. The importance of spatial correlation of the fluctuations near the critical point was first emphasized by Ornstein and Zernicke [8] (see also [1, 9, 10]).

It follows from (2.10) and (2.33) that on approaching the critical point the mean squares of the Fourier components of the fluctuations of concentration $\overline{|c_{\mathbf{k}}|^2}$ do in fact rise sharply for small k, although $\overline{|c_{\mathbf{k}}|^2}$ does not pass to infinity for any finite k (for very small $k \sim 1/\Lambda$, where Λ is the size of the whole crystal, clearly, surface effects will come into $\overline{|c_{\mathbf{k}}|^2}$ and formula (2.10) will no longer be applicable). Whereas a long way from the critical point (in the case of small k, for which condition (2.11) is satisfied) we may neglect the second term in (2.10), near the critical point this term may be substantial even for $kr_0 \ll 1$. It should be noted at once, however, that the law of variation of β_{ij} on approaching the critical point has not yet been very reliably established (see later). The analytical properties of R_k as a function of $\mathbf{k}$ near the critical point are also not clear, nor is it obvious over what region we may confine consideration to simplify the first terms of the expansion in $\mathbf{k}$.

At the point representing a phase transformation of the second kind, the long-range-order parameter passes to zero continuously on disordering. Near the line formed by these points on the phase diagram, just as in the neighborhood of the critical point on the decomposition curve, anomalously large fluctuations develop, except that they are now of the long-range-order parameters instead of the concentration. This follows from formulas (2.14) and (2.23) if we consider that at the temperature of a phase transformation of the second kind T_0 the second derivatives $\varphi_{\eta\eta}$ and $\varphi_{c\eta}$ vanish (while φ_{cc} remains finite):

$$\varphi_{\eta\eta}=0, \quad \varphi_{c\eta}=0 \quad \text{at} \quad T=T_0. \tag{2.34}$$

Near temperature T_0 these derivatives are small, so that for fairly small k the mean squares of the Fourier components of the order parameter $\overline{|\eta_k|^2}$ become anomalously large. As in the neighborhood of the critical point on the decomposition curve, the spatial correlation of the fluctuations at considerable distance becomes substantial; this is taken into account by the last terms in the denominators of formulas (2.14) or (2.23).

The very fact of the vanishing of the derivatives $\varphi_{\eta\eta}$ and $\varphi_{c\eta}$ at a phase-transformation point of the second kind follows from quite general considerations regarding the thermodynamic potential $\varphi(\eta, T)$, considered as a function of η and T. It is sufficient to consider, for example, that at the transformation point for $\eta = 0$ the derivatives $\varphi_{\eta\eta}$ and $\varphi_{c\eta}$ do not pass to infinity and that they are continuous functions of temperature.* However, in order to study

*Actually for $T > T_0$ the derivative $\varphi_{\eta\eta}(0, T)$ should be positive in order to ensure that the equation $\varphi_\eta(\eta, T) = 0$ (equilibrium condition) should not have nonzero roots and that the equilibrium value of η should be zero. For $T < T_0$ and fairly small $T_0 - T$, on the other hand, we must have $\varphi_{\eta\eta}(0, T) < 0$, so that the equilibrium value of η, being the

the temperature dependence of $\varphi_{\eta\eta}$ and $\varphi_{c\eta}$, and hence $\overline{|\eta_k|^2}$, near the temperature T_0, we must employ some thermodynamic or statistical theory of phase transformations of the second kind. The results are obtained in very simple form if we use the thermodynamic theory of phase transformations of the second kind [11, 1]. In this theory the thermodynamic potential near the transformation point is written in the form of an expansion

$$\varphi=\varphi_0+\frac{1}{2}a(T-T_0)\eta^2+\frac{1}{4}A_4\eta^4, \qquad (2.35)$$

where φ_0, a, and A_4 are constants (for given composition and pressure) and the higher terms of the expansion may be neglected. Allowing for the equilibrium condition

$$\varphi_\eta \equiv a(T-T_0)\eta+A_4\eta^3=0,$$

we obtain the following expressions for $\varphi_{\eta\eta}$ and $\varphi_{c\eta}$ from (2.35):

$$\text{for } T>T_0 \qquad \varphi_{\eta\eta}=a(T-T_0), \quad \varphi_{c\eta}\equiv 0;$$

$$\text{for } T<T_0 \qquad \varphi_{\eta\eta}=2a(T_0-T), \quad \varphi_{c\eta}=a^2\left(\frac{dT_0}{dc}\right)^2\eta^2=\frac{a^3(T_0-T)}{A_4}\left(\frac{dT_0}{dc}\right)^2 \qquad (2.36)$$

Thus in this theory $\varphi_{\eta\eta}$ and $\varphi_{c\eta}$ do in fact vanish at $T = T_0$. The second derivative $\varphi_{cc} = \partial^2\varphi/\partial c^2$ approximately equals $\varphi^0_{cc} = \partial^2\varphi_0/\partial c^2$ near the transformation point and differs from zero.

Putting expressions (2.36) into (2.23), we find that near the phase-transformation point (where we may neglect $\beta'\varphi_{\eta\eta}k^2$ and $2\gamma\varphi_{c\eta}k^2$ in the denominator of (2.23) the square of the Fourier component of the long-range-order parameter in solid solutions of cubic symmetry above the transformation temperature equals

$$\overline{|\eta_k|^2}=\frac{k_BT}{V}\frac{1}{a(T-T_0)+\alpha k^2} \qquad (T>T_0), \qquad (2.37)$$

---

solution of the equation $\varphi_\eta(\eta, T) = 0$, should be fairly small, and for $T \to T_0$ should tend continuously to zero in accordance with the definition of a phase transformation of the second kind. It follows from this and from the continuity condition that $\varphi_{\eta\eta} = 0$ for $T = T_0$. Since $\varphi_{c\eta} \equiv 0$ identically in the disordered phase, as mentioned earlier, it also follows from the condition of continuity that $\varphi_{c\eta} = 0$ for $T = T_0$.

and below the transformation temperature

$$\overline{|\eta_k|^2}=\frac{k_BT}{V}\frac{1}{2aM(T_0-T)+\alpha k^2} \qquad (T\leqslant T_0); \tag{2.38}$$

$$M=1-\frac{\varphi_{c\eta}^2}{\varphi_{\eta\eta}\varphi_{cc}^0}=1-\frac{a^2}{2A_4\varphi_{cc}^0}\left(\frac{dT_0}{dc}\right)^2. \tag{2.39}$$

It follows from (2.14) and (2.36) that in single-component crystals $\overline{|\eta_k|^2}$ is given by the same formulas, in which now M = 1. It follows from these formulas, which were derived by Landau [3] for the case of single-component crystals, that $\overline{|\eta_k|^2}$ takes a maximum value (the larger, the smaller k) at $T = T_0$, and then falls linearly on either raising or lowering the temperature.

The Fourier components of the fluctuations in concentration, as may be seen from (2.24) and (2.35), do not become anomalously large near an ordinary phase-transformation point of the second kind. However, anomalously large concentration fluctuations, together with anomalously large fluctuations in the degree of long-range order, arise in the ordered phase near a critical point at which the curve AK of phase transformations of the second kind passes into the decomposition curve KB. The form of the phase diagram in this region is shown in Fig. 4, where the region I corresponds to the disordered solution, region II to the ordered substance, and III represents the two-phase region. Landau [11] showed that at such a critical point the condition M = 0 was satisfied at $T = T_k$, $c = c_k$. Near the critical point (according to thermodynamic theory), M may be expanded in series in powers of $T-T_k$ and $c-c_k$ (according to [11], $c-c_k$ is proportional to $T_0(c)-T_k$) and limited to linear terms

$$M=g_1(T_0-T)+g_2(T_0-T_k),$$

where g_1 and g_2 are of the order of $1/T_k$. Putting this expression and expressions (2.36) into (2.24) and (2.38), we find that in the ordered region near the critical point

$$\overline{|\eta_k|^2}=\frac{k_BT}{V}\frac{1}{2a[g_1(T_0-T)+g_2(T_0-T_k)](T_0-T)+\alpha k^2} \qquad (T<T_0), \tag{2.40}$$

$$\overline{|c_k|^2}=\frac{k_BT}{V}\frac{2a(T_0-T)+\alpha k^2}{2a\varphi_{cc}^0[g_1(T_0-T)+g_2(T_0-T_k)](T_0-T)+\alpha\varphi_{cc}^0k^2}. \tag{2.41}$$

In the disordered region $\varphi_{c\eta}\equiv 0$, $M\equiv 1$ and as before we have formula (2.37) for $\overline{|\eta_k|^2}$, and $\overline{|c_k|^2}=k_BTV^{-1}(\varphi_{cc}^0)^{-1}$.

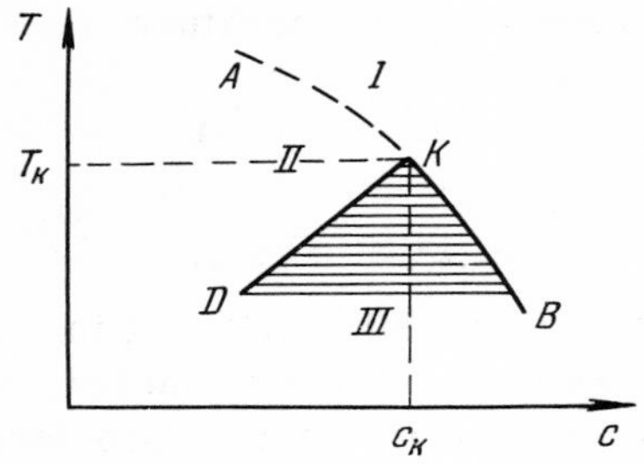

Fig. 4. Phase diagram near the critical point on the curve of phase transformations of the second kind in solid solutions.

Thus near the critical point, on moving away from the temperature T_0, $\overline{|\eta_k|^2}$ falls much more slowly in the ordered region than in the disordered. We see from (2.41) that for fairly small k the Fourier components of the fluctuations in the degree of long-range order and those of the fluctuations in concentration become anomalously large near the critical point for $T < T_0$. In the disordered region, and also at the temperature T_0 and slightly below this, no such anomalies should take place.

If the long-range order in the crystal is characterized by not one but several order parameters η_μ, then at a phase-transformation point of the second kind a number of second derivatives vanish simultaneously, including

$$\varphi_{\mu\mu'} = \frac{\partial^2\varphi}{\partial\eta_\mu\partial\eta_{\mu'}}$$

with $\mu = 1, \ldots, r'$, $\mu' = 1, \ldots, r$ and $\mu = 1, \ldots, r$, $\mu' = 1, \ldots, r'$,

where r' of the order parameters correspond to the irreducible representation of the symmetry group of the more symmetric phase (associated with the transformation into the less symmetric phase) and r is the total number of parameters η_μ. Hence on approaching the phase-transformation point the corresponding matrix elements of the reciprocal matrix $\varphi^{-1}_{\mu\mu'}$ tend to infinity, and, as may be seen from (2.18) the mean squares and products of the Fourier components of the r' long-range-order parameters in question become anomalously large (both in single-component crystals and in solid solutions). Near a point of transformation into the ferroelectric state in particular, certain components of the tensor $\varkappa_{ij}$ increase sharply, and, as may be seen from (2.21), fluctuations in polarization rise anomalously.

As already mentioned, near critical points or phase transformations of the second kind, the spatial correlation of fluctuations at large distances becomes considerable. In order to determine the law governing the fall in the macroscopic correlation parameter $\xi(\mathbf{r})$ between fluctuations $\delta\eta$ at large distances r in explicit form, we may use the fact that the Fourier components of $\xi(\mathbf{r})$ are connected with $\overline{|\eta_{\mathbf{k}}|^2}$ by the same relation as that linking the Fourier components of the correlation parameters $\varepsilon(\rho)$ with $\overline{|c_{\mathbf{k}}|^2}$, i.e., a relation of the (1.13) type. Putting expression (2.37) instead of $\overline{|\eta_{\mathbf{k}}|^2}$ and inverting this relationship, we find that above the temperature T_0 near the transformation point

$$\xi(\mathbf{r}) = \frac{k_B T}{4\pi \alpha r} \exp\left(-r\sqrt{\frac{a}{\alpha}(T-T_0)}\right). \qquad (2.42)$$

Whereas correlation usually vanishes at distances of atomic order, on approaching the transformation point the "correlation radius" $\sqrt{(\alpha/a)}\,(T-T_0)^{-1/2}$ tends to infinity, and at the actual transformation point the exponential factor vanishes and $\xi(\mathbf{r})$ falls off much more slowly (on a power law).

The thermodynamic theory of phase transformations of the second kind correctly describes the fact that the derivative $\varphi_{\eta\eta}$ vanishes, and also offers the possibility of carrying out a very basic analysis revealing the fundamental connection which exists between phase transformations and the symmetry of crystals [1]. However, the explicit form of the temperature dependence of $\varphi_{\eta\eta}$ (and of the other thermodynamic quantities) near the transformation point is in this theory obtained from an expansion of the thermodynamic potential in powers of η (2.35), which (as has by now become clear) is not sufficiently well founded. In order to establish the character of the singularities of the thermodynamic quantities at the transformation temperature and determine their temperature dependence near a phase transformation of the second kind (and also in order to solve the analogous problem for the neighborhood of the critical point on the decomposition curve), we must use a specific statistical model, fairly accurately describing the interatomic interaction in the crystal, and within the framework of this model calculate the thermodynamic potential in the neighborhood of the transformation point.

In the theory of solid solutions, a model of this kind widely used is that based on the nearest-neighbor approximation with pair interaction (equivalent to the Ising model in the theory of ferromagnetism), as described below in §3. This approximation should give a correct qualitative description of the singularities associated with phase transformations, although naturally it cannot claim a detailed quantitative description of specific systems. Despite the fact that the model is greatly simplified, the problem of calculating the thermodynamic potential in the region of a transformation is extremely complicated, and at the present time can only be solved exactly for the two-dimensional case [12]. It follows in particular from this exact solution that in two-dimensional lattices $\varphi_{\eta\eta}$ at $T > T_0$ is proportional not to $T-T_0$, as in the thermodynamic theory, but to $(T-T_0)^{7/4}$.

In the three-dimensional case, although as yet it has proved impossible to solve the problem exactly, high-temperature expansions in powers of $\tanh(w/4k_BT)$ (w is the ordering energy, see §3) or low-temperature expansions in powers of $\exp(-w/2k_BT)$, containing a large number of terms with known coefficients, have been obtained for various thermodynamic quantities. Analysis of the relation between these coefficients and their (serial) number (for large numbers) in the case of constant-sign series enables us to establish the nature of the singularity in the corresponding thermodynamic quantities at the transformation point [13].

We may study the behavior of a function $f(z)$ given in the form of a series still more accurately by the Padé approximant method,* also used for the analysis of alternating-sign series. This method is especially convenient if (for example, in the case of a logarith-

*In the method of the Padé approximant, the function $f(z) = P(z)/Q(z)$ is approximated by the ratio of two polynomials $P(z)$ and $Q(z)$ of degrees N and M (the [N, M] Padet approximant) and the coefficients of the polynomials are determined by equating the coefficients of the same powers of z (from z^0 to z^{N+M}) in the expansion $f(z)Q(z)$ and in the polynomial of the N-th degree $P(z)$.

mic derivative of the function $\varphi_{\eta\eta}$) we expect that the function has a simple pole [14]. An analysis carried out in this way showed [13, 14] that in the three-dimensional case also, for $T > T_0$, $\varphi_{\eta\eta}$ was not proportional to $T-T_0$ in the first degree but to $(T-T_0)^{5/4}$, i.e.

$$\varphi_{\eta\eta}=\zeta\frac{k_B T_0}{v}\left|\frac{T-T_0}{T_0}\right|^{\gamma};\ \gamma=\frac{5}{4}, \tag{2.43}$$

where ζ is a dimensionless constant (ζ = 1.886, 2.014, and 2.051, respectively, for simple, body-centered, and face-centered lattices), the error in determining the value of the power being no greater than 0.001.*

In the nearest-neighbor approximation of the model of pair interaction, the derivative $d^2\varphi/dc^2$ has the same temperature dependence near the critical point on the decomposition curve (see Fig. 3) in a solution of critical composition.† The formula for $d^2\varphi/dc^2$ in this case is obtained from (2.43) if we replace T_0 by the critical temperature T_k.

The temperature dependence quoted is the same for different three-dimensional structures, i.e., it does not depend on the coordination number. Although on making a qualitative change in the statistical model this temperature dependence changes (in the Heisenberg model of ferromagnetism the power index in (2.43) rises to 4/3 [17]), we may nevertheless consider that formula (2.43) describes the temperature dependence of $\varphi_{\eta\eta}$ or $d^2\varphi/dc^2$ during the ordering or decomposition of solid solutions (to which the nearest-neighbor approximation is applicable) fairly accurately.

*The same type of analysis led to the conclusion that, in the three-dimensional case, the equilibrium value of the degree of long-range order near the transformation point was not proportional to $(T_0-T)^{1/2}$, as in the thermodynamic theory, but that $\eta \sim (T_0-T)^{5/16}$ [14] (with an error of under ±0.01 in the exponent; in the two-dimensional case, according to the exact theory $\eta \sim (T_0-T)^{1/8}$ [15]). We may consider it as established [13, 16] that the specific heat in this model (both above and below the transformation point) will tend to infinity as $T \to T_0$ on a power law $(T-T_0)^{-\alpha}$ with a small exponent ($\alpha \leq 0.2$ for $T > T_0$ and $\alpha \lessapprox 0.1$ for $T < T_0$), or else on a logarithmic law.

†In the model considered, the expressions for the thermodynamic functions of an ordered system above the ordering temperature, a solution of critical composition above the critical decomposition temperature, a gas of critical concentration above the critical temperature of the gas/liquid transformation, and a ferromagnetic in the absence of a field coincide.

Since the thermodynamic quantities have singularities at a phase-transformation point of the second kind, it is not only ill-based to expand them in powers of η but also to expand them in powers of the wave vector **k**. The question arises, in particular, as to whether, in accordance with the general principles of the Ornstein and Zernicke theory, we may consider that the coefficient α in the denominators of (2.14) or (2.37) and (2.38) tends to a finite, nonzero limit as $T \to T_0$, and also as to whether the expansion of $\varphi_{\eta\eta}(\mathbf{k}) = \varphi_{\eta\eta} + \alpha \mathbf{k}^2$ is regular near the transformation point. In order to elucidate the possibility of expanding in powers of **k**, we may either directly consider the dependence of $\overline{|\eta_{\mathbf{k}}|^2}$ on **k**, or study the behavior of the correlation function $\xi(\mathbf{r})$ at large distances (the validity of expression (2.42) clearly remains doubtful).

In the two-dimensional case the exact theory [12] leads to a formula for $\xi(\mathbf{r})$ differing from formula (2.42) of the thermodynamic theory. It is found that the coefficient of r in the exponential term should be proportional to $T-T_0$ and not $\sqrt{T-T_0}$, as in (2.42), and at the transformation point $\xi(\mathbf{r})$ is proportional to $1/r^{1/4}$, and not ln r, as in the thermodynamic theory (in the two-dimensional case).

An interesting attempt to study the $\xi(\mathbf{r})$ relationship near a transformation point in the three-dimensional pair-interaction model was undertaken by Fisher [18]. It was considered that for $r \gg r_0$ and $T > T_0$ the correlation function could be put in the form

$$\xi(\mathbf{r}) = \text{const}\,\frac{1}{r^{D-2+\psi}}\exp\left(-h(T-T_0)^{\sigma} r\right) Q\left(h(T-T_0)^{\sigma} r\right), \quad (2.44)$$

where D is the number of dimensions of the crystal, h is a constant, and Q(x) is an unknown function, having, however, the properties that

$$\text{for } x \to 0 \qquad Q(x) \to 1,$$

$$\text{for } x \to \infty \qquad Q(x) \sim x^{\frac{1}{2}(D-3)+\psi}.$$

This formula represents the generalized formulas of Ornstein and Zernicke (2.42). In writing down the formula it is considered that, apart from the transformation point, at fairly large r $[h(T-T_0)^{\sigma} r \gg 1]$ the pre-exponential factor should vary in proportion to $r^{-1/2(D-1)}$, as in the Ornstein-Zernicke theory, but for small r

$[h(T-T_0)^{\sigma} r \ll 1]$ and at the actual transformation point the law of variation is in general different $(\sim r^{-(D-2+\psi)})$. Also taken into consideration is a possible difference in the temperature dependence of the index of the exponential ($\sigma \neq 1/2$). On approaching the transformation point the region of small r widens [as $(T-T_0)^{-\sigma}$] and at the actual transformation point itself $\xi(\mathbf{r}) \sim r^{-(D-2+\psi)}$.

Since the Fourier transformation of the function $\xi(\mathbf{r})$ determines $\overline{|\eta_{\mathbf{k}}|^2}$, the expression given for $\xi(\mathbf{r})$ enables us to find the dependence of $\overline{|\eta_{\mathbf{k}}|^2}$ on $\mathbf{k}$. For small k, for which $k \ll h(T-T_0)^{\sigma}$, the Fourier component is determined by the behavior of $\xi(\mathbf{r})$ at large r, and in cubic crystals this relationship may be put in the form

$$\overline{|\eta_{\mathbf{k}}|^2} = \frac{1}{N}\,\frac{1}{\zeta\left(\frac{T-T_0}{T_0}\right)^{\sigma(2-\psi)} + \zeta_2\left(\frac{T-T_0}{T_0}\right)^{-\sigma\psi} k^2} \approx$$

$$\approx \frac{\text{const}}{\left[\left(\frac{T-T_0}{T_0}\right)^{2\sigma} + \frac{2\zeta_2 k^2}{\zeta(2-\psi)}\right]^{1-\frac{\psi}{2}}} \quad (k \ll h(T-T_0)^{\sigma}). \qquad (2.45)$$

Hence ζ_2 has the order of r_0^2 and the numerical factor in front of $[(T-T_0)/T_0]^{\sigma(2-\psi)}$ is taken in such a way that, as $k \to 0$, the resultant expression for $\overline{|\eta_{\mathbf{k}}|^2}$ agrees with expression (2.14), in which $\varphi_{\eta\eta}$ is determined by formula (2.43). In order to secure this agreement it is also necessary that the indices σ and ψ should not be independent but be related to the γ in (2.43) by the equation

$$\gamma = \sigma(2-\psi).$$

In the two-dimensional case, as already remarked, at the critical point

$$\xi(\mathbf{r}) \sim 1/r^{1/4}, \text{ i.e., } \psi = 1/4.$$

Since in this case $\gamma = 7/4$, it follows from the relation given that $\sigma = 1$ in agreement with the exact result of Onsager [12].

In the three-dimensional case, an estimate of ψ and σ was made by analyzing the high-temperature expansions for the second moment of the correlation function $\xi(\mathbf{r})$ [18, 425]. It was found that

$$\psi = 0.056 \pm 0.008, \quad \sigma = \gamma(2-\psi)^{-1} = 0.6430 \pm 0.0025, \qquad (2.46)$$

i.e., ψ is small and close to 1/18, while σ is close to 9/14.

Bearing in mind the fact that, in accordance with (2.43)

$$\sigma(2-\psi)=\gamma={}^{5}/_{4},$$

we may write expression (2.45) for $\overline{|\eta_{\mathbf{k}}|^2}$ in the form

$$\overline{|\eta_{\mathbf{k}}|^2}=\frac{1}{N}\,\frac{1}{\zeta\left(\frac{T-T_0}{T_0}\right)^{5/4}+\zeta_2\left(\frac{T-T_0}{T_0}\right)^{-\frac{5\psi}{4(2-\psi)}}k^2}$$

$$\left(k\ll h\,(T-T_0)^{\frac{5}{4(2-\psi)}}\right). \tag{2.47}$$

Since, according to (2.46), $\psi > 0$, it follows from (2.47) that as $T \to T_0$ the coefficient α in (2.14) tends to infinity and the radius of convergence of the expansion of $R_{\mathbf{k}}$ (or $\varphi^{-1}_{\eta\eta\mathbf{k}}$) in powers of $\mathbf{k}$, tends to zero. For large k, when $k \gg h(T-T_0)^{\sigma}$, the Fourier component is determined by the behavior of $\xi(\mathbf{r})$ at small r, and it follows from (2.44) that

$$\overline{|\eta_{\mathbf{k}}|^2}=\frac{\text{const}}{k^{2-\psi}}\qquad\left(h\,(T-T_0)^{\frac{5}{4(2-\psi)}}\ll k\ll\frac{2\pi}{d}\right), \tag{2.48}$$

i.e., near the transformation point $\overline{|\eta_{\mathbf{k}}|^2}$ falls with increasing k, not as $1/k^2$, but rather more slowly, as $1/k^{2-\psi}$.

In an analogous way, near the critical point on the decomposition curve the square of the Fourier component of the concentration in a solution of critical composition is determined for small k by the formula

$$\overline{|c_{\mathbf{k}}|^2}=\frac{1}{N}\,\frac{1}{\zeta\left(\frac{T-T_k}{T_k}\right)^{5/4}+\zeta_2\left(\frac{T-T_k}{T_k}\right)^{-\frac{5\psi}{4(2-\psi)}}k^2}$$

$$\left(k\ll h\,(T-T_k)^{\frac{5}{4(2-\psi)}}\right), \tag{2.49}$$

and for large k by formula (2.48) (with T_0 replaced by T_k).

It should be noted that, although the singularities of the temperature dependence of $\varphi_{\eta\eta}$ in the Ising model, i.e., the first terms in the denominators of (2.47) and (2.49), have apparently been determined quite reliably by studying the high-temperature expansions, the analysis of the singularities of the dependence of $R_{\mathbf{k}}$ on $\mathbf{k}$ and T near the transformation point [(2.48) and the second terms in (2.47) and (2.49)] is based on the assumption (2.44) relating to the form of the correlation function, and is less accurate. It must be emphasized that the temperature dependences given are derived for the case in which the interatomic forces are short ranged, and they may change considerably in the case of long-range forces, for example, of the elastic or dipole–dipole type (see Chapter III). In particular, for a large radius of interatomic interaction, the results of the thermodynamic theory of phase transformations and formulas (2.37) to (2.42) are applicable over a wide temperature range near the transformation point (but not too near T_0). According to [424], for forces of finite radius, R_0, this temperature range is bounded by the conditions $T_0(r_0/R_0)^6 \ll |T-T_0| \ll T_0$, and a relationship of the (2.43) type holds only very close to the temperature T_0, for $|T-T_0| \ll T_0(r_0/R_0)^6$. The thermodynamic theory may also be applied over a wide range in uniaxial ferroelectrics [424], where the dipole–dipole interaction is substantial.

The expressions (2.45) to (2.49) given for $\overline{|\eta_{\mathbf{k}}|^2}$ and $\overline{|c_{\mathbf{k}}|^2}$ are only applicable for very small and relatively large k. A more general formula was proposed in [425]; this was to some extent of an interpolation nature, embracing the whole range of k values. Nevertheless, considering that the k are small in comparison with $1/r_0$ (the macroscopic approximation is valid), the corresponding expressions for $\overline{|\eta_{\mathbf{k}}|^2}$ and $\overline{|c_{\mathbf{k}}|^2}$ at temperatures respectively close to T_0 and T_k may be put in the form

$$\overline{|\eta_k|^2} = \frac{1}{N\zeta}\left(\frac{T-T_0}{T_0}\right)^{-\gamma} \frac{\left[1+\varphi''(ak)^2\left(\frac{T-T_0}{T_0}\right)^{+2\sigma}\right]^{\psi/2}}{1+\varphi'(ak)^2\left(\frac{T-T_0}{T_0}\right)^{-2\sigma}} \qquad (T > T_0,\ T \approx T_0) \tag{2.50}$$

$$\overline{|c_k|^2} = \frac{1}{N\zeta}\left(\frac{T-T_k}{T_k}\right)^{-\gamma} \frac{\left[1+\varphi''(ak)^2\left(\frac{T-T_k}{T_k}\right)^{-2\sigma}\right]^{\psi/2}}{1+\varphi'(ak)^2\left(\frac{T-T_k}{T_k}\right)^{-2\sigma}} \qquad (T > T_k,\ T \approx T_k,\ c = c_k) \tag{2.51}$$

Here a is the lattice parameter, while the constants φ' and φ'' are respectively $\phi' = 0.23$, $\phi'' = 1.6\cdot10^{-3}$; $\phi' = 0.20$, $\phi'' = 1.1\cdot10^{-3}$; $\phi' =$

0.19, $\phi'' = 0.80 \cdot 10^{-3}$ for simple, body-centered, and face-centered cubic lattices.

Formulas (2.45) and (2.47) to (2.49) are obtained from (2.50) and (2.51) in the limiting cases of small and large k. It follows in particular from (2.50) that the maximum on the curve of the temperature dependence of $\overline{|\eta_{\mathbf{k}}|^2}$ for a given k lies not at temperature T_0 but at a slightly higher temperature T_m, the difference $T_m - T_0$ falling as $k \to 0$ (in proportion to k^2).

The results given show that, although the thermodynamic theory of phase transformations of the second kind correctly predicts an anomalous rise in fluctuations of long-range order near the transformation point, it does not give a correct description of the way in which this rise varies with temperature. Hence we shall not subsequently use the results of this theory very much; instead we shall determine $\overline{|\eta_k|^2}$ and $\overline{|c_k|^2}$ from general formulas of the (2.23) and (2.10) type, using the reliably established fact that the derivatives $\varphi_{\eta\eta}$ and $\varphi_{c\eta}$ vanish at a transformation of the second kind, and that the derivative $d^2\varphi/dc^2$ does so at the critical point on the decomposition curve, together with the relations linking these derivatives with independent experimental data. However, in cases in which we have to determine the temperature dependence of $\overline{|\eta_k|^2}$ or $\overline{|c_k|^2}$ in the limiting case of small k, we shall use formulas (2.45) and (2.47)-(2.51).

We also note that expressions (2.40) and (2.41) for $\overline{|\eta_k|^2}$ and $\overline{|c_k|^2}$ near the critical point on the curves of phase transformations of the second kind in solid solutions also correctly describe the anomalous rise of concentration fluctuations in the ordered phase, but not the corresponding temperature dependences. Hence in future we shall simply consider (on the basis of quite general considerations), that on approaching the critical point in the ordered phase $d^2\varphi/dc^2 \equiv \varphi_{cc} - (\varphi^2_{c\eta}/\varphi_{\eta\eta})$ vanishes, while in the disordered phase $d^2\varphi/dc^2 = \varphi_{cc}$ remains finite:

$$\frac{d^2\varphi}{dc^2} \equiv \varphi_{cc} - \frac{\varphi^2_{c\eta}}{\varphi_{\eta\eta}} = \begin{cases} 0 & \text{for } c = c_k,\ T = T_k - 0, \\ \varphi_{cc} \neq 0 & \text{for } c = c_k,\ T = T_k + 0. \end{cases} \qquad (2.52)$$

Hence (2.10) immediately predicts an anomalous fluctuation in concentration in the ordered (but not the disordered) phase near the critical point. Since both factors in the expression $\varphi_{cc}\varphi_{\eta\eta} - \varphi^2_{c\eta} = \varphi_{\eta\eta}(d^2\varphi/dc^2)$ vanish near the critical point in the ordered phase, we see from (2.23) that in this case there should also be a considerably slower fall in $\overline{|\eta_k|^2}$ as the temperature falls below T_0 than in the case of the ordinary phase transformation of the second kind.

§3. Microscopic Theory of Fluctuation Waves of Concentration and Long-Range-Order Parameters in Solid Solutions

The above macroscopic consideration of fluctuation waves was not based on any specific model, and we were thus able to express the mean squares of the fluctuations in terms of the thermodynamic characteristics. These results, however, are only applicable for small k (long waves). In considering x-ray scattering, short-wave fluctuations corresponding to large k values are also important. The study of such fluctuations cannot be carried out on the macroscopic theory but must be based on a specific model of the solution. The use of such a model enables us to relate the probabilities of the fluctuations (and hence also the intensity of diffuse scattering) to the constants of interatomic interaction in the solution, and in principle offers the possibility of explaining the singularities of the thermodynamic characteristics entering into the formulas of the macroscopic theory.

At the present time we are not in possession of any very accurate calculations of the forces of interatomic interaction in crystals, especially in metallic solutions. For this reason it is usual, in the static theory of solutions, to use a severely simplified model of pair interaction (see, for example, [19-21]). In this model, it is considered that the energy of the solution may be put in the form of a sum of the interaction energies of individual pairs of atoms

$$E = \frac{1}{2} \sum_{s\gamma s'\gamma'} c_{s\gamma} c_{s'\gamma'} w_{\boldsymbol{\rho}}, \quad w_{\boldsymbol{\rho}}\big|_{\boldsymbol{\rho}=0} = 0. \tag{3.1}$$

Here the energy is defined to an accuracy limited by smallish terms of the zeroth and first degree in $c_{s\gamma}$ [given by formula (1.1)]. The ordering energies $w_{\boldsymbol{\rho}}$ for a pair of points $s\gamma$ and $s'\gamma'$ separated by a vector $\boldsymbol{\rho}$ is given by the difference

$$w_{\boldsymbol{\rho}} = 2v_{\boldsymbol{\rho}}^{AB} - v_{\boldsymbol{\rho}}^{AA} - v_{\boldsymbol{\rho}}^{BB},$$

where, for example, v_{ρ}^{AB} is the interaction energy of a pair of A and B atoms lying at points $s\gamma$ and $s'\gamma'$ with the sign reversed. By hypothesis w_{ρ} does not depend on the composition and order in the solution. In (3.1) we have considered the interaction of not only neighboring but also more distant atoms.

It should be remembered that, in addition to the energy of direct interaction between pairs of atoms, the expression for the energy should also contain "collective" terms associated with the energy of the conductivity electrons and the vibrations of the atoms in the solution. However, these terms may also be written in the form of (3.1) if we may confine ourselves to the second approximation of the theory of perturbations (in which the deviation of the solution from the ideal "average" crystal is a small perturbation) [22]. Hence the pair model may in essence be considered semi-phenomenologically as a general model, allowing for not only direct pair interaction but also interactions transmitted by various kinds of quasiparticles. However, in considering the higher terms in the theory of perturbations, and also in considering the influence of neighboring atoms on the interaction energy of a given pair in the expression for the energy of the solution, terms containing derivatives of three, four, and larger numbers of quantities $c_{s\gamma}$ arise. The approximation employed involves neglecting such terms, and it is only applicable to a certain class of solutions, in which it leads to no serious error. We note that the method set out below for calculating fluctuations may easily be generalized to the case of more complicated models of solutions.

A calculation of the fluctuation waves in the pair-interaction model was carried out in [23] on the basis of the microscopic theory. The method used is based on the artificial splitting of the lattice of the solution in question into a large number of sublattices. Let us consider, for example, solutions in which, in the disordered state, the unit cell contains one atom. The lattice of such a solution may be divided into ν' geometrically similar and similarly situated sublattices (containing lattice points of a definite type) in such a way that each atom only interacts (in the approximation taken) with neighboring atoms of other sublattices and not with atoms in its own sublattice.

This division into a larger number of sublattices is essentially carried out so that, in calculating the change in the thermodynamic potential (associated with the development of fluctuations) we may neglect terms depending on the manner in which different points of a single sublattice are occupied. If the change in the thermodynamic potential (minimum work) reduced simply to a change of energy, then in order to satisfy this condition it would be sufficient to carry out the division into sublattices in such a way that direct force interacting should not occur between the atoms belonging to a single sublattice. However, in view of the correlation existing between the intermediate atoms, each atom is surrounded by a cloud of atoms of another sort, or by a partly ordered cloud. This gives rise to a special kind of indirect "thermodynamic interaction" through such clouds, which leads to a term in the thermodynamic potential depending on the concentrations at the points considered.

By selecting a large enough ν', we may arrange the system so that neither direct force nor "thermodynamic" interaction should occur between the atoms of one particular sublattice, even in the presence of interaction between atoms lying at considerable distances from each other. Clearly it may still be possible for certain different lattices to contain points of the same type. In lattices with several (ν) atoms in the unit cell, the number ν' should be a multiple of ν; the number of sublattices may be considerably greater than the number of atoms in this cell.

As in §1, we shall number the sublattices by means of the index γ, but now γ runs through ν' values corresponding to the points of a large cell, and not the unit cell as in §1. The Fourier component of the concentration fluctuations in the solution $c_{\mathbf{k}}$ may clearly be expressed in terms of the Fourier component of the fluctuations in individual sublattices $c_{\mathbf{k}\gamma}$ by means of a formula analogous to formula (1.11):

$$c_{\mathbf{k}}=\frac{1}{\nu'}\sum_{\gamma=1}^{\nu'} c_{\mathbf{k}\gamma}, \quad c_{\mathbf{k}\gamma}=\frac{1}{N^0}\sum_{s=1}^{N^0}(c_{s\gamma}-c_{\gamma})\,e^{i\mathbf{k}\mathbf{R}_{s\gamma}}, \tag{3.2}$$

where N^0 is the number of lattice points in the sublattice.

A calculation of the mean squares and products of the Fourier components $\overline{c_{\mathbf{k}\gamma}c^*_{\mathbf{k}\gamma'}}$, and of $\overline{|c_{\mathbf{k}}|^2}$ is given in Appendix I. We see from the formulas (I.7) and (I.8) of the Appendix that $\overline{|c_{\mathbf{k}}|^2}$ is determined by matrix (I.6) of the $\alpha_{\gamma\gamma'}$, i.e., by the derivatives of the thermodynamic potential with respect to the concentrations in the sublattices. If the sum A of the matrix elements of each row in the matrix $\|\alpha_{\gamma\gamma'}\|$ does not depend on the number of the row, then it follows from (I.9) and (I.10) that the expression for $\overline{|c_{\mathbf{k}}|^2}$ takes the simple form

$$\overline{|c_{\mathbf{k}}|^2} = \frac{1}{N_0} \frac{1}{\sum\limits_{\boldsymbol{\rho}} x(\boldsymbol{\rho}) \cos \mathbf{k}\boldsymbol{\rho}}, \tag{3.3}$$

where

$$N_0 = N\nu = N^0\nu',$$

$$x(0) = \frac{1}{N^0 k_B T} \frac{\partial^2 \Phi}{\partial c_1^2}, \quad x(\boldsymbol{\rho}) = \frac{1}{N^0 k_B T z'} \frac{\partial^2 \Phi}{\partial c_1 \, \partial c_{\boldsymbol{\rho}}} \qquad (\boldsymbol{\rho} \neq 0) \tag{3.4}$$

and $c_{\boldsymbol{\rho}}$ is the concentration at the points of the sublattice γ displaced through a vector $\boldsymbol{\rho}$ relative to the first sublattice. After calculating the derivatives in (3.4), we must replace c_γ by the actual values of the concentrations at the points of the type considered, corresponding to the equilibrium long-range-order parameters. For example, in disordered solutions, instead of c_γ we must put the concentration c.

Formula (3.3) is considerably simpler than expression (I.8) for $\overline{|c_{\mathbf{k}}|^2}$ and enables us to study fluctuations in many cases, especially in the case of disordered Bravais solutions, in which the interaction between atoms in different configuration spheres is considerable. The above-mentioned division of the crystal into sublattices may be carried out in this case by selecting a polyhedron in the crystal containing a fair number of unit cells, so that we may neglect the interaction between the atom lying in the middle of the polyhedron and atoms lying outside the latter, and also so that the last term in (I.2) may vanish. Then, if each of the ν' points in the polyhedron may be considered as belonging to its own sublattice, a given atom will not interact with atoms of its own sublattice and will interact most strongly with one atom of each other sublattice, i.e., for calculating $\overline{|c_{\mathbf{k}}|^2}$ we may use the method set out in Appendix I.

Since the number of lattice points z' of any sublattice neighboring one of the lattice points of another sublattice equals unity, the sum (I.6) over π will have only one term. In the disordered solution the derivatives $\partial^2\Phi/\partial c_\gamma \partial c_{\gamma'}$ depend only on the vector $\boldsymbol{\rho}$ joining the nearest neighboring points γ and γ', and do not depend on the numbers of these sublattices. Furthermore, in a crystal lattice of the type considered, all the points are equivalent, and systems of vectors drawn from a given point to all other points are identical, whichever original point is taken. Hence all the diagonal matrix elements $\alpha_{\gamma\gamma}$ are the same, and the same nondiagonal elements enter into the various rows of the $\|\alpha_{\gamma\gamma'}\|$ matrix, although they are arranged in different orders. Thus the sum of the matrix elements in each row is independent of the serial number of the row, so that in the case of disordered solutions we may use formula (3.3) for calculating $\overline{|c_{\mathbf{k}}|^2}$.

In order to use formula (3.3), we must know the thermodynamic potential of the solution as a function of the variables c_γ. It is important to remember that in the three-dimensional case considered here the exact solution for Φ is unknown, and only approximate expressions, valid for various temperatures and compositions of the solution, may be used. In the case of disordered solutions, such approximate expressions exist for the high-temperature region and any compositions in which the ratios $w_\rho/k_B T$ may be treated as small parameters, and also for small concentrations and any temperatures, in which case the small parameter is the concentration c.

For fairly high temperatures (compared with the ordering or decomposition temperature of the solution), we may neglect correlation when calculating the thermodynamic potential. Defining the energy as the average value of expression (3.1), without considering correlation, and employing the usual expression given by the zero approximation in the theory of perturbations for the entropy (see, for example, [20]), we may then write Φ as a function of c_γ in the form

$$\Phi = \Phi' + \frac{N^0}{2} \sum_{\gamma,\gamma'=1}^{\nu'} c_\gamma c_{\gamma'} w_\rho + N^0 k_B T \sum_{\gamma=1}^{\nu'} [c_\gamma \ln c_\gamma + (1 - c_\gamma)\ln(1 - c_\gamma)], \tag{3.5}$$

where Φ' is a linear function of c_γ and the vector $\boldsymbol{\rho}$ connects neighboring points in the sublattices γ and γ'. It follows from (3.4) and (3.5) that, at high temperatures in disordered solutions, the quantities $\chi(\boldsymbol{\rho})$ in (3.3) are equal to

$$x(0) = \frac{1}{c(1-c)}; \qquad x(\boldsymbol{\rho}) = \frac{w_\rho}{k_B T} \text{ for } \boldsymbol{\rho} \neq 0. \tag{3.6}$$

Formulas (3.3) and (3.6) express $\overline{|c_{\mathbf{k}}|^2}$ in terms of the ordering energy of the solution w_{ρ}. Formula (3.6) is only valid at high temperatures, when for all $\boldsymbol{\rho}$ the criteria $|w_{\rho}| \ll k_B T$ are satisfied. We note that, although we have here used the expression for Φ derived without considering correlation, the method employed enables us to allow for correlation automatically in the expression for $\overline{|c_{\mathbf{k}}|^2}$ (to an accuracy governed by terms of higher order in $w_{\rho}/k_B T$).

In the case of a fairly small concentration of one of the components ($c \ll 1$), in the single-phase region of the phase diagram, the solution should be in a disordered state at any temperature. The thermodynamic potential in the pair-interaction model then has the form [7]:

$$\Phi = \Phi' + \frac{N^0}{2} k_B T \sum_{\gamma, \gamma'=1}^{\nu'} c_\gamma c_{\gamma'} \left(1 - e^{-\frac{w_\rho}{k_B T}}\right) + \\ + k_B T N^0 \sum_{\gamma=1}^{\nu'} [c_\gamma \ln c_\gamma + (1 - c_\gamma) \ln (1 - c_\gamma)]. \qquad (3.7)$$

It thus follows that in this case

$$x(0) = \frac{1}{c(1-c)}, \; x(\rho) = 1 - \exp\left(-\frac{w_\rho}{k_B T}\right) \text{ for } \rho \neq 0. \qquad (3.8)$$

If the ordering energies w_ρ are set equal to zero, it then follows from (3.6) and (3.8) that $\chi(\boldsymbol{\rho}) = 0$ for $\boldsymbol{\rho} \neq 0$, and expression (3.3) coincides with formula (1.14) for $\overline{|c_{\mathbf{k}}|^2}$ in an ideal solution. This result is natural, since for $w_\rho = 0$ there is no correlation in the solution and the latter becomes ideal. In a real solution, in which $w_\rho \neq 0$, $x(\rho)$ differ from zero, and the departure of the solution from the ideal state, leading to correlation, is taken into account by the terms with $\boldsymbol{\rho} \neq 0$ in (3.3). The result of the presence of these terms is that $\overline{|c_{\mathbf{k}}|^2}$ depends on $\mathbf{k}$ and is not constant, as in the ideal solution. We see from (3.3), (3.6), and (3.8) that, both on raising the temperature and on reducing the concentration, the role of correlation in the solution diminishes, and the expression for $\overline{|c_{\mathbf{k}}|^2}$ transforms into expression (1.14).

In order to obtain expressions for $\chi(\boldsymbol{\rho})$ more accurate than those of formula (3.6) (i.e., expressions taking account of the higher terms in the expansion in powers of $w_\rho/k_B T$), we must consider correlation in the solution when determining the thermodynamic potential, replacing the zero-approximation formula (3.5) by a more rigorous theory. Such improved expressions for Φ are only obtained, however, in the nearest-neighbor approximation, in which it is assumed that the w_ρ only differ from zero for lattice points in the first coordination sphere ($w_\rho \equiv w$). In this case, for crystals with simple and body-centered cubic lattices, we may use, for example, the expansion of Φ in powers of w/k_BT obtained by Chang [24], using the Kirkwood method [25] (see also [20], §17). If such lattices are divided into two sublattices with the same number of points, in the nearest-neighbor approximation, direct force interaction between the points of a single sublattice will be absent. It may easily be shown that indirect interaction, resulting from correlation through intermediate points, will only contribute to the derivatives $\partial^2\Phi/\partial c_\gamma^\delta \partial c_\gamma^{\delta'}$ for $\delta \neq \delta'$ by virtue of high-order terms, starting from terms $\sim w(w/k_BT)^3$, in the expansion for Φ. If we neglect such higher terms in the expansion (this is legitimate for fairly high temperatures), the last term in (I.2) will equal zero, and in order to calculate $\overline{|c_\mathbf{k}|^2}$ we may use the method set out in Appendix I. Determining $\overline{|c_\mathbf{k}|^2}$ from formulas (3.3) and (3.4) by means of the expression for Φ in the form of an expansion in powers of w/k_BT, it is not difficult to show that in the nearest-neighbor approximation

$$\overline{|c_\mathbf{k}|^2} = \frac{1}{N} \frac{1}{x^0 + x' \sum_{\pi=1}^{z} \cos \mathbf{k}\boldsymbol{\rho}_\pi}, \tag{3.9}$$

where $\boldsymbol{\rho}_\pi$ are radius vectors drawn to the points of the first coordination sphere

$$x^0 = \frac{1}{N^0 k_B T} \frac{\partial^2 \Phi}{\partial c_1^2} = \frac{1}{f} + zf\left(\frac{w}{k_BT}\right)^2 - zf(1-4f)\left(\frac{w}{k_BT}\right)^3, \tag{3.10}$$

$$x' = \frac{1}{zN^0 k_B T} \frac{\partial^2 \Phi}{\partial c_1 \partial c_2} = \frac{w}{k_BT} - \frac{1}{2}(1-4f)\left(\frac{w}{k_BT}\right)^2 + \frac{1}{6}(1-6f)^2\left(\frac{w}{k_BT}\right)^3, \tag{3.11}$$

$f = c(1-c)$; the coordination number $z = 6$ for a simple and $z = 8$ for a body-centered cubic lattice. It should be noted that, on considering terms $\sim (w/k_BT)^4$, the denominator of (3.9) also acquires terms containing $\mathbf{k}\boldsymbol{\rho}$ with vectors $\boldsymbol{\rho}$ drawn to the points of the second coordination sphere.* It may be shown that in the nearest-neighbor approximation formulas (3.9) to (3.11) are also applicable to disordered solutions with face-centered cubic lattices, if attention is confined to terms of the order of $(w/k_BT)^2$. We see from (3.9) that, in the nearest-neighbor approximation and at high temperatures (but not in general), $\overline{|c_\mathbf{k}|^2}$ depends on **k** in a simpler manner.

On approaching the critical point on the decomposition curve (in the model considered the critical concentration $c_k = 1/2$) expression (3.9) becomes anomalously large for small k. In an analogous way, for $\mathbf{k} = \mathbf{K}_m$, where $\mathbf{K}_m \boldsymbol{\rho}_\pi = \pi(2n_m + 1)$ (n_m are whole numbers), in solutions with body-centered cubic lattices, $\overline{|c_\mathbf{k}|^2}$ rises anomalously near phase-transformation points of the second kind. Approximate statistical theories based on the Kirkwood approximation [25] or on the quasichemical approximation [26] lead to the same temperature dependence of the anomalous rise in $\overline{|c_\mathbf{k}|^2}$ as the thermodynamic theory of phase transformations of the second kind. This result, however, does not constitute a basis for the thermodynamic theory, since in its derivation we only considered the first terms in the expansion of Φ in powers of w/k_BT, which is not legitimate near the singular point $T = T_0$. More detailed analysis of the series leads (as shown in §2) to a different temperature dependence near T_0 or T_k. The results given here are only valid a long way from a phase-transformation point of the second kind or the critical point on the decomposition curve.

Let us now consider ordered solutions. In this case the sums of the matrix elements belonging to different rows in the matrix (I.6) are generally speaking not the same, so that in order to calculate $\overline{|c_\mathbf{k}|^2}$ we must use not formula (3.3) but the more general formulas (I.8) and (I.6) of Appendix I. However, the simple formula (3.3) is applicable in the case of solutions of stoichiometric composition AB, in which points of the first type are surrounded

*If the expression for $\overline{|c_\mathbf{k}|^2}$ in the nearest-neighbor approximation had the form (3.9) for any temperatures, i.e., were inversely proportional to a linear function of the sum $\sum_{\pi=1}^{z} \cos \mathbf{k}\boldsymbol{\rho}_\pi$ over nearest neighbors, then by using the integral relation (1.15) linking x' and x^0, we could express $\overline{|c_\mathbf{k}|^2}$ for any **k** in terms of a single function of temperature, e.g., the derivative φ_{cc} determining $\overline{|c_\mathbf{k}|^2}$ for $\mathbf{k} \to 0$. This cannot be done at low temperatures, for which the terms containing $\boldsymbol{\rho}$ vectors drawn to the points of the second and subsequent coordination spheres become important.

by points of the second and first types in the same way as points of the second type are by points of the first and second types. Such structures apply to crystals of the NaCl type, β-brass, AuCu, and so on. The crystal lattices of the structures in question may be divided into ν' sublattices, as was done earlier for disordered solutions. Here $\nu'/2$ sublattices ($\gamma = 1, \ldots, \nu'/2$) consist of points of the first type and the same number ($\gamma = \nu'/2 + 1, \ldots, \nu'$) of points of the second type. In the case of solutions of stoichiometric composition AB, the derivatives $\partial^2\Phi/\partial c_\gamma^2$ for different γ (corresponding to points of both the first and second types) are identical in the statistical model of the solution taken, and for the structures considered the sum of the matrix elements belonging to any row of the matrix (I.6) is independent of the serial number. Hence in this case, as in the case of disordered solutions, we may in fact determine $\overline{|c_{\mathbf{k}}|^2}$ from formula (3.3).

A fairly accurate expression for the thermodynamic potential of an ordered solution may be obtained in the case of almost complete order. For almost completely ordered solutions of stoichiometric composition, this expression [7] has the form

$$\Phi = \Phi' + k_B T N^0 \sum_{\gamma=1}^{\nu'} [c_\gamma \ln c_\gamma + (1 - c_\gamma)\ln(1 - c_\gamma)] +$$

$$+ \frac{1}{2} k_B T N^0 \left\{ \sum_{\gamma,\gamma'=1}^{\nu'/2} (1 - c_\gamma)(1 - c_{\gamma'}) \left[1 - \exp\left(-\frac{w_\rho}{k_B T}\right)\right] + \right.$$

$$+ \sum_{\gamma,\gamma'=\frac{\nu'}{2}+1}^{\nu'} c_\gamma c_{\gamma'} \left[1 - \exp\left(-\frac{w_\rho}{k_B T}\right)\right] -$$

$$\left. - 2 \sum_{\gamma=1}^{\nu'/2} \sum_{\gamma'=\frac{\nu'}{2}+1}^{\nu'} (1 - c_\gamma) c_{\gamma'} \left[\exp\frac{w_\rho}{k_B T} - 1\right]\right\}. \tag{3.12}$$

Putting (3.12) into (3.4) and remembering that $c_1 = {}^1\!/_2(1 + \eta)$, we find expressions for the quantities $\chi(\rho)$ in (3.3):

$$x(0) = \frac{4}{1 - \eta^2}, \tag{3.13}$$

$$x(\rho) = 1 - \exp\left(-\frac{w_\rho}{k_B T}\right), \tag{3.14}$$

if the vector $\boldsymbol{\rho}$ connects points of the same type ($\boldsymbol{\rho} \neq 0$), and

$$x(\boldsymbol{\rho}) = \exp\frac{w_{\boldsymbol{\rho}}}{k_B T} - 1, \tag{3.15}$$

if the vector $\boldsymbol{\rho}$ connects points of the first and second types.

In the case of almost completely ordered solutions AB, in which each point is surrounded by points of another type only (crystals of the NaCl or β-brass type), we find from equations (3.3), (3.4), (3.13), and (3.15) that, in the nearest-neighbor approximation

$$\overline{|c_{\mathbf{k}}|^2} = \frac{1}{4N_0}\,\frac{1-\eta^2}{1+\frac{1}{4}(1-\eta^2)\left[\exp\frac{w}{k_B T}-1\right]\sum\limits_{\pi=1}^{z}\cos \mathbf{k}\boldsymbol{\rho}_{\pi}}. \tag{3.16}$$

Since as $T \to 0$ the quantity η tends exponentially to unity, in accordance with the law $1-\eta \approx 2\exp[-(z/2)(w/k_BT)]$ [7], the second term in the denominator of (3.16), describing the effect of correlation, falls off as $\exp[-((z-2)/2)(w/k_BT)]$, i.e., the role of correlation becomes slight at fairly low temperatures, in the same way as at high temperatures.

On neglecting the second term in the denominator of (3.16), expression (3.16) for $\overline{|c_{\mathbf{k}}|^2}$ coincides with expression (2.31), which was obtained on the macroscopic theory of fluctuations for almost completely ordered solutions ($N_0 = 2N$); $\overline{|c_{\mathbf{k}}|^2}$ ceases to depend on $\mathbf{k}$. With falling temperature, in the nearest-neighbor approximation, the equilibrium value of $\overline{|c_{\mathbf{k}}|^2}$ diminishes as $\exp[-(z/2)(w/k_BT)]$, and in the completely-ordered solution clearly $\overline{|c_{\mathbf{k}}|^2} = 0$.

Fluctuations of concentration in the more general case of ordered solutions of nonstoichiometric composition and also ordered solutions of other structures are considered in [23].

In the above-considered semiphenomenological model of pair interaction the ordering energies $w_{\boldsymbol{\rho}}$ are parameters of the theory. In order to discover the physical significance of these parameters, determine the dependence of the $w_{\boldsymbol{\rho}}$ on the distance $\boldsymbol{\rho}$, and estimate their value, we must consider the different contributions made to the interaction energy by the atoms (ions) of the solution. In particular, in metallic solid solutions, a considerable contribution is made to the energy of the solution by the conduction electrons. Although (as mentioned earlier on p. 41) in the second approximation of perturbation theory, the energy of the electrons may be represented in the same form (3.1) as the energy of the direct pair interaction of ions, the effective pair interaction associated with the electrons should have characteristic features ($w_{\boldsymbol{\rho}}$ should fall off relatively slowly with distance, on a power law) of the same nature as the Kohn singularities in the vibration spectrum of metals [383], largely depending on the shape of the Fermi surface. In view of this it seemed particularly interesting to study the contribution of the electron energy to $w_{\boldsymbol{\rho}}$ and to the probability of the fluctuation waves of concentration [426].

If the potential energies of the interaction between a conduction electron and the A and B ions $V_A(\mathbf{r}-\mathbf{R}_s)$ and $V_B(\mathbf{r}-\mathbf{R}_s)$ are similar, then the energy of a system of electrons E_e in the field of the ions may be determined by means of perturbation theory, regarding V_A-V_B as a small parameter. In the zero and first approximation, E_e does not depend on the distribution of the A and B atoms over the lattice points (on the numbers c_s), i.e., it does not influence the fluctuations. The contribution of $E_e^{(2)}$ to the electron energy of the disordered alloy, however, as calculated to second order, may, according to [426] be written in a form corresponding to the general formula (3.1)

$$E_e^{(2)}=\frac{1}{2}\sum_{\mathbf{k}} w_{\mathbf{k}}^e\,|c_{\mathbf{k}}|^2,\qquad w_{\mathbf{k}}^e=-\,|V_{\mathbf{k}}|^2\frac{p(\mathbf{k})}{\varepsilon(\mathbf{k})}+\frac{1}{N}\sum_{\mathbf{k}}|V_{\mathbf{k}}|^2\frac{p(\mathbf{k})}{\varepsilon(\mathbf{k})} \tag{3.17}$$

or

$$E_e^{(2)}=\frac{1}{2}\sum_{s,s'} w_{\rho}(c_s-c)(c_{s'}-c),\qquad w_{\boldsymbol{\rho}}^e=\frac{1}{N^2}\sum_{\mathbf{k}} w_{\mathbf{k}}^e e^{i\mathbf{k}\boldsymbol{\rho}}. \tag{3.18}$$

Here

$$V_{\mathbf{k}}=\frac{1}{v}\int[V_A(\mathbf{r})-V_B(\mathbf{r})]\,e^{i\mathbf{k}\mathbf{r}}\,d\mathbf{r},$$

$$p(\mathbf{k})=\sum_{nn'\varkappa\mathbf{K}} p_{nn'}^2(\varkappa,\varkappa+\mathbf{k}+\mathbf{K})\frac{n(E_{n\varkappa})-n(E_{n'\varkappa+\mathbf{k}+\mathbf{K}})}{E_{n'\varkappa+\mathbf{k}+\mathbf{K}}-E_{n\varkappa}}\,. \tag{3.19}$$

$E_{n\boldsymbol{\varkappa}}$ is the energy of the electron with wave vector $\boldsymbol{\varkappa}$ in the n-th energy band, and $n(E_{n\boldsymbol{\varkappa}})$ are the Fermi occupation numbers, $\mathbf{k}$ is the reciprocal-lattice vector, $p_{nn'}(\boldsymbol{\varkappa}_1\boldsymbol{\varkappa}+\mathbf{k}+\mathbf{K})$ is the matrix element of the function $\exp(-i\mathbf{kr})$ formed on the basis of single-particle wave functions corresponding to the states $\varkappa n$ and $\varkappa + \mathbf{k} + \mathbf{K}n'$ (for quasi-free electrons $P_{nn'}(\varkappa_1\varkappa + \mathbf{k} + K) = \delta_{\varkappa_1\varkappa} + \mathbf{kK}$).

The quantity $\varepsilon(\mathbf{k}) \equiv \varepsilon(\mathbf{k}_1 0)$ in formula (3.17) denotes the dielectric constant of the electron gas for zero frequency, and accounts for the interaction of the conductivity electrons with each other and the effects of screening (see, for example, [427]). In the usually employed random phase approximation, the dielectric constant is related to $P(\mathbf{k})$ by means of the simple equation

$$\varepsilon(\mathbf{k}) = 1 + \frac{4\pi e^2}{k^2} P(\mathbf{k}). \tag{3.20}$$

It is an important point that, according to (3.19), the sharp termination of the Fermi distribution function for an $E_{n\varkappa}$ equal to the Fermi energy leads to singularities in the quantities $P(\mathbf{k})$ and $\varepsilon(\mathbf{k})$ for certain values of $\mathbf{k}$. As a result of this, according to (3.17), singularities arise in the Fourier component of the ordering energy and hence also the quantity $|c_{\mathbf{k}}|^2$.

Thus, for example, in the case of a quadratic dispersion law, for which $E_{\mathbf{k}} = \hbar^2 k^2/2m$, and the dependence of $p_{nn'}(\varkappa_1\varkappa + \mathbf{k} + \mathbf{K})$ on n, n', $\varkappa$, and $\mathbf{k} + \mathbf{K}$ may be neglected, $P(\mathbf{k})$ is given by the formula

$$p(\mathbf{k}) = \frac{mk_0 p^2}{4\pi^2\hbar^2}\left(1 + \frac{4k_0^2 - k^2}{4k_0 k} \ln \left|\frac{2k_0 + k}{2k_0 - k}\right|\right), \tag{3.21}$$

where k_0 is the radius of the Fermi sphere. As $k \to 2k_0$ the derivative of this function with respect to k (and hence also the derivative $w_{\mathbf{k}}^{e}$) has a logarithmic ("Kohn" [383]) singularity.

In the general case of a Fermi surface of arbitrary shape, a singularity of the function $P(\mathbf{k})$ arises if the vector $\mathbf{k} + \mathbf{K}$ ($\mathbf{K}$ is some vector of the reciprocal lattice) joins two points $\varkappa_1$ and $\varkappa_2$ of the Fermi surface in which the normals to the surface are antiparallel. Explicit expressions for the singularities $P(\mathbf{k})$ in this general case are given in [428, 429, 426].

The singularity of the function $P(\mathbf{k})$ becomes more sharply expressed if the sections of the Fermi surface close to the points $\varkappa_1$ and $\varkappa_2$ are nearly cylindrical or plane [384, 429]. For a cylindrical section of length $\mathcal{L}$ containing a singularity, the term $P'(\mathbf{k})$ in $P(\mathbf{k})$ equals

$$P'(\mathbf{k}) = -\frac{\sqrt{2}}{4\pi^2} \frac{\mathcal{L}\,\overline{p^2}}{|v_{z2} - v_{z1}|\,|a_{xx}|} \sqrt{k_z'} \text{ for } k_z' > 0$$

$$P'(\mathbf{k}) = 0 \text{ for } k_z' < 0 . \tag{3.22}$$

Here $\mathbf{k}' = \mathbf{k} - (\varkappa_2 - \varkappa_1 - \mathbf{K})$ characterizes the deviation of the vector $\mathbf{k}$ from the value at which $P(\mathbf{k})$ has a singularity; $\overline{p^2}$ is the average value of $p^2_{nn'}(\varkappa_1\varkappa + \mathbf{k} + \mathbf{K})$ on the cylindrical section, v_{z1} and v_{z2} are the projections of the electron velocity $\mathbf{v} = (1/\hbar)\,\nabla_{\varkappa} E_{n\varkappa}$ at the points $\varkappa_1$ and $\varkappa_2$ on the z axis parallel to the normal to the Fermi surface at these points, and $a_{xx} = \hbar^2(m^{-1}_{xx2}/v_{z2} - m^{-1}_{xx1}/v_{z1})$ (m_{xx} is the effective mass, and the x axis is perpendicular to the axis of the cylinder).

For a plane section with area S

$$P'(\mathbf{k}) = -\frac{1}{8\pi^3}\,\overline{p^2}\,\frac{S}{|v_{z2} - v_{z1}|} \ln |Ck_z'|, \tag{3.23}$$

where the constant C has the order of $\zeta_e |v_z|^{-1}$ (ζ_e is the Fermi energy). In the latter case the function $P'(\mathbf{k})$ itself and not its derivative has a logarithmic singularity.*

We see from (3.17) that the singularities of the functions $P(\mathbf{k})$ and $\varepsilon(\mathbf{k})$ considered lead to analogous singularities of the electron part of the Fourier component of ordering energy $w^e_{\mathbf{k}}$. It follows from formulas (3.3) and (3.6) that at high temperatures $\overline{|c_{\mathbf{k}}|^2}$ is expressed directly in terms of this Fourier component:

$$\overline{|c_{\mathbf{k}}|^2} = \frac{1}{N} c(1 - c) \left[1 + \frac{c(1 - c)}{k_B TN} (w^e_{\mathbf{k}} + w^0_{\mathbf{k}})\right]^{-1} . \tag{3.24}$$

*It should be noted that this kind of singularity of the function $P(\mathbf{k})$ in alloys will only occur on the second approximation of perturbation theory. In calculating to higher approximations, it must be remembered that the scattering of electrons at static inhomogeneities in alloys (and at thermal vibrations) should lead to a finite lifetime and to indeterminacy of the energy $\sim\Gamma_e$ (Γ_e is the damping of the electron). Hence the $P(\mathbf{k})$ singularities considered should become "blurred" (diffuse) in a range of k values of the order of Γ_e/ζ_e (compare [430]). If the free path of the electron is large, then $\Gamma_e/\zeta_e \ll 1$ and the singularities of $P(\mathbf{k})$ should nevertheless appear quite sharply in experimental measurements.

Here $w_{\mathbf{k}}^{0}$ is the Fourier component of the part of the ordering energy not associated with the conductivity electrons; it accounts for the direct interaction of the ionic shells, the energy associated with the vibrations of the atoms, the energy of spin waves, and so on.

Hence the quantity $\overline{|c_{\mathbf{k}}|^2}$, considered as a function of $\mathbf{k}$, should also have a singularity for values of $\mathbf{k}$ connecting two points of the Fermi surface for which the normals to the surface are antiparallel. Depending on whether the sections of surface near these points have finite radii of curvature or resemble cylindrical or plane sections, the singularity will either correspond to a logarithmic divergence of the derivative of $\overline{|c_{\mathbf{k}}|^2}$ with respect to $\mathbf{k}$, a radical singularity of $\overline{|c_{\mathbf{k}}|^2}$, or a logarithmic singularity of this quantity. These singularities of $\overline{|c_{\mathbf{k}}|^2}$ will lead to singularities of the x-ray scattering-intensity distribution (see §17).

It follows from the general theory of the Fourier transformation that singularities of the functions $\mathbf{k}-w_{\mathbf{k}}^{e}$ should lead to a relatively slow fall-off in the Fourier coefficients $w_{\boldsymbol{\rho}}^{e}$ [see (3.18)] with increasing $\boldsymbol{\rho}$, i.e., to a slow fall-off in the "electron part" of the ordering energy $w_{\boldsymbol{\rho}}$ with the distance $\boldsymbol{\rho}$ between the pairs of ions considered. If the singularity is associated with the ellipsoidal parts of the Fermi surface and, in accordance with (3.21), the derivative of $w_{\mathbf{k}}^{e}$ has a logarithmic singularity, then $w_{\boldsymbol{\rho}}^{e}$ will fall off at large $\boldsymbol{\rho}$ in accordance with the law

$$w_{\rho}^{e} \sim 1/\rho^3. \tag{3.25}$$

If, however, the singularity is associated with the cylindrical or plane sections, then the fall-off will be still slower and will be determined respectively by the relations

$$w_{\rho}^{e} \sim 1/\rho^2 \quad \text{or} \quad w_{\rho}^{e} \sim 1/\rho. \tag{3.26}$$

Here the coefficients of $1/\boldsymbol{\rho}^n$ in (3.25) and (3.26) contain factors oscillating with $\boldsymbol{\rho}$. Since, as may be seen on comparing (1.13) and (3.3) - (3.6), the correlation parameters $\varepsilon(\boldsymbol{\rho})$ at high temperatures are simply related to the energies $w_{\boldsymbol{\rho}}$: $\varepsilon(\boldsymbol{\rho}) = -c^2(1-c)^2(w_{\boldsymbol{\rho}}/k_BT)$, the correlation parameters at large $\boldsymbol{\rho}$ should also fall off on a power law such as (3.25) or (3.26).

Characteristic singularities of the functions $P(\mathbf{k})$, and hence also of $w^e_{\mathbf{k}}$, should occur if the Fermi surface has small ellipsoidal hollows or fine grooves [426]. It is clear from symmetry considerations that some such hollows or grooves must always occur. According to (3.19), singularities should arise in this case over a range of $\mathbf{k}$ values for which $\mathbf{k} + \mathbf{K}$ is close to the vectors connecting two different hollows or grooves. Here the singularity corresponds to a "trough" in the function $P(\mathbf{k})$ and to a rise in $w^e_{\mathbf{k}}$ in the region in question, with a width of the order of the dimensions of the hollow or groove; in the same region we should find two "Kohn" singularities of $P(\mathbf{k})$ of the type discussed earlier. Correspondingly, in accordance with (3.17) and (3.24), "troughs" in the ranges of $\mathbf{k}$ values indicated should also appear in the relationship between $|c_{\mathbf{k}}|^2$ and $\mathbf{k}$.

In addition to the singularities of pair interaction, allowing for the energy of the conduction electrons leads (in the higher approximations of perturbation theory) to the appearance of triple (and higher) interactions of the ions in metallic solutions. The influence of triple interaction on correlation in the solution and on the fluctuation waves of concentration was considered in [426].

§ 4. Fluctuations of Short-Range-Order Parameters in Solid Solutions

The fluctuations of concentration and long-range-order parameters considered above lead to the development of inhomogeneities in various crystal properties, for example, the refractive index of light, and produce a number of physical effects, for example, the scattering of light or other waves. However, inhomogeneities in disordered solutions may be associated not only with fluctuations of concentration but also with fluctuations of the internal parameters characterizing the short-range order or correlation in the solution, i.e., the correlation parameters $\varepsilon(\boldsymbol{\rho})$ defined by formula (1.4). As a result of such fluctuations, the numbers of pairs of similar atoms lying at a specific distance $\boldsymbol{\rho}$ in different (identical) volume elements will be different, even for a specified concentration, and this should lead to additional inhomogeneities.

The actual fact that fluctuations of internal parameters exist does not influence expressions of the (2.5) and (2.10) type for fluctuations of concentration (obtained on the thermodynamic theory of fluctuations) if the derivatives $d^2\varphi/dc^2$ are calculated (as is always done) with due allowance for the fact that, as the concentration varies the equilibrium values of the internal parameters do likewise. Simultaneous consideration of the statistically independent fluctuations of concentration and internal parameters leads to the same formulas for $\overline{(\delta c)^2}$ and $\overline{|c_\kappa|^2}$ if we allow for the relation between the total and partial derivatives of the thermodynamic potential as we saw in §2.3 in relation to fluctuations of composition and long-range order. However, the additional inhomogeneities of the crystal, which appear on taking account of the fluctuations in the correlation parameters, will clearly affect those properties of the crystal which depend on correlation, and may lead, for example, to additional scattering of light (or other waves), which is usually not taken into consideration.

In addition to this, the values of the coefficient linking the quantity representing the inhomogeneities (for example, the refractive index) with the fluctuation in concentration c are usually taken as being equal to the equilibrium change in this quantity corresponding to unit change in c. However, for this equilibrium change in concentration, the $\varepsilon(\boldsymbol{\rho})$ also change in a specific manner, whereas for a fluctuation-type change in c the parameters $\varepsilon(\boldsymbol{\rho})$ may remain unaltered (or change by amounts having no relation to the equilibrium change). Hence the coefficients of δc in the expansion for the quantity representing the inhomogeneity in terms of fluctuations of concentration and correlation parameters are more correctly defined by reference to the unchanged values of $\varepsilon(\boldsymbol{\rho})$; they may in fact differ considerably from the equilibrium coefficients. Thus it becomes essential to study effects associated with fluctuations in the correlation parameters [27].

When considering scattering at fluctuations of density in single-component liquids, we should also strictly speaking, consider the existence of fluctuations of correlation parameters in an analogous way, these now characterizing the probabilities of relative distance between pairs of atoms. Allowing for the fluctuation of such correlation parameters in liquids is clearly a much more complex problem than in the case of solid solutions, for which in a number of cases the calculations may be carried to completion.

For simplicity, let us confine ourselves to discussing fluctuations of the correlation parameters in disordered solutions having one atom per unit cell. Here, as in the case of concentration, we may consider either fluctuations in $\varepsilon(\rho)$ over small volume elements* or fluctuations of the Fourier components of the correlation parameters $\varepsilon_{\mathbf{k}}(\rho)$ over the whole crystal. According to formula (1.4), the **k**-th Fourier component of the fluctuations of $\varepsilon(\rho)$ in a disordered solution is determined by the formula

$$\varepsilon_{\mathbf{k}}(\rho) = \frac{1}{N} \sum_{s}^{(\rho)} (c_s - c)(c_{s'} - c)\, e^{i\mathbf{k}\mathbf{R}_s}, \tag{4.1}$$

where in summing over s the number s' runs through values directly related to s by the expression $\mathbf{R}_{s'} = \mathbf{R}_s - \rho$, and $\rho \neq 0$ (for $\rho = 0$ and $k \neq 0$ the value of $\varepsilon_{\mathbf{k}}(\rho)$ reduces to $c_{\mathbf{k}}$).

The Fourier components of the concentration and correlation parameters, as indicated by (1.7) and (4.1), are determined by the same quantities c_s, and hence they should be related in some way. In fact, by putting expansion (1.7) for $c_s - c$ in (4.1), we express $\varepsilon_{\mathbf{k}}(\rho)$ in terms of $c_{\mathbf{k}}$:

$$\varepsilon_{\mathbf{k}}(\rho) = \sum_{\mathbf{k}'} c_{\mathbf{k}'} c_{\mathbf{k}-\mathbf{k}'}\, e^{i\mathbf{k}'\rho}. \tag{4.2}$$

Thus the set of Fourier components of $\varepsilon_{\mathbf{k}}(\rho)$ for different ρ is unambiguously related to the set of products $c_{\mathbf{k}'} c_{\mathbf{k}-\mathbf{k}'}$ for different **k**'. Relation (4.2) also shows that the **k**-th Fourier component of the square of the concentration fluctuations $[\delta c(\mathbf{r})]^2$ is directly expressed in terms of the **k**-th Fourier components of the correlation parameters $\varepsilon_{\mathbf{k}}(\rho)$ for different ρ.†

The calculation of the mean squares and products of the Fourier components of the parameters of correlation and concen-

*With this form of the problem, the averaging in (1.4) is carried out not over the statistical set but over all pairs of atoms separated by the vector ρ in the volume element V' for a given distribution of atoms at the lattice points. Because different distributions of atoms may occur with specific probabilities, fluctuations arise in the averages so calculated.

†It should be noted that $\overline{|\varepsilon_{\mathbf{k}}(\rho)|^2}$ is not expressed as a sum of the products of the mean squares $\overline{|c_{\mathbf{k}'}|^2}\ \overline{|c_{\mathbf{k}-\mathbf{k}'}|^2}$, as may be shown from the form of formula (4.2). In fact, although the means of the four factors $\overline{c_{\mathbf{k}'} c_{\mathbf{k}-\mathbf{k}'} c^*_{\mathbf{k}''} c^*_{\mathbf{k}-\mathbf{k}''}}$ have the order of $1/N^3$, whereas the products of the mean squares are $\sim 1/N^2$, the number of such groups of four is $\sim N^2$, and they give a contribution of the same order to $\overline{|\varepsilon_{\mathbf{k}}(\rho)|^2}$, as terms of the type $\overline{|c_{\mathbf{k}'}|^2}\ \overline{|c_{\mathbf{k}-\mathbf{k}'}|^2}$.

tration

$$\overline{\varepsilon_{\mathbf{k}}(\rho)\,\varepsilon_{\mathbf{k}}^{*}(\rho')} \text{ and } \overline{\varepsilon_{\mathbf{k}}(\rho)\,c_{\mathbf{k}}^{*}}$$

may easily be carried out in the case of ideal solutions, in which the atoms are distributed at random over the lattice points and the mean values of the correlation parameters are equal to zero. The fact that the mean values of $\varepsilon(\boldsymbol{\rho})$ are equal to zero does not of course mean that there are no fluctuations of these, since even in the absence of a preferential attraction or repulsion of similar atoms it simply follows from the laws of chance and the random distribution of atoms over various elements of volume that the numbers of pairs of similar atoms at a distance of $\boldsymbol{\rho}$ from each other will be either more or less than the average values, and this will lead to fluctuations in $\varepsilon(\boldsymbol{\rho})$. Remembering that for ideal solutions

$$\overline{c_s^2} = \overline{c_s} = c \text{ and } \overline{c_s c_{s'}} = c^2 \text{ for } s \neq s',$$

we obtain from (4.1) and (1.7) (for $\boldsymbol{\rho} \neq 0$):

$$\overline{|\varepsilon_{\mathbf{k}}(\rho)|^2} = \frac{1}{N} c^2 (1-c)^2, \quad \overline{\varepsilon_{\mathbf{k}}(\rho)\,\varepsilon_{\mathbf{k}}^{*}(-\rho)} = \frac{1}{N} c^2 (1-c)^2 e^{i\mathbf{k}\rho},$$
$$\overline{c_{\mathbf{k}}\varepsilon_{\mathbf{k}}^{*}(\rho)} = 0, \quad \overline{\varepsilon_{\mathbf{k}}(\rho)\,\varepsilon_{\mathbf{k}}^{*}(\rho')} = 0 \quad \text{for } \rho' \neq \pm\rho. \tag{4.3}$$

It follows from this that, in ideal solutions, fluctuations in concentration and correlation parameters are statistically independent and that for small concentrations the relative role of fluctuations in the correlation parameters becomes negligible as compared with fluctuations in concentration [see formula (1.14)].

By squaring and averaging expression (4.1), it is quite easy to see that in nonideal solutions the $\overline{|\varepsilon_{\mathbf{k}}(\rho)|^2}$ are expressed in terms of the correlation parameters $\varepsilon(\boldsymbol{\rho}_1, \boldsymbol{\rho}_2)$, $\varepsilon(\rho_1, \rho_2, \boldsymbol{\rho}_3)$ of a large number of points, determined by formula (1.6). For small k it would be possible, using the macroscopic theory of fluctuations, to express $\overline{|\varepsilon_{\mathbf{k}}(\rho)|^2}$ also in terms of the derivatives of the thermodynamic potential with respect to ε. However, since the determination of these derivatives is laborious, we shall not give the corresponding formulas.

The fluctuations of the correlation parameters may also be considered by means of a simplified statistical model of a solution, the pair-interaction model. Thus, for example, in the nearest-neighbor approximation, we easily see that the mean number N_{AA} of pairs of neighboring A atoms and the fluctuation of this number are simply expressed in terms of the derivatives of the thermodynamic potential Φ with respect to the ordering energy for nearest neighbors w:

$$N_{AA}=\frac{\partial\frac{\Phi}{k_BT}}{\partial\frac{w}{k_BT}},\qquad \overline{(N_{AA}-\overline{N}_{AA})^2}=\frac{\partial^2\frac{\Phi}{k_BT}}{\partial\left(\frac{w}{k_BT}\right)^2}. \tag{4.4}$$

Since

$$N_{AA}=\frac{1}{2}Nzc^2+\frac{1}{2}N\sum_{\rho}{}'\,\varepsilon(\rho),$$

where the summation extends over all the nearest points, we may use (4.4) to find the fluctuations of $\varepsilon(\boldsymbol{\rho})$ in any volume element containing N = N' atoms. Using the expression for Φ in the form of an expansion in powers of w/k_BT with accuracy limited to terms of order $\sim(w/k_BT)^4$, as obtained on the Kirkwood approximation (see, for example, [20], §17), it is not hard to show that, for solutions with simple or body-centered cubic lattices, in the case of nearest neighbors

$$\overline{[\varepsilon(\rho)-\overline{\varepsilon}]^2}=\overline{[\varepsilon(\rho)-\overline{\varepsilon}]\,[\varepsilon(-\rho)-\overline{\varepsilon}]}=\frac{1}{N}c^2(1-c)^2\left[1-(1-2c)^2\frac{w}{k_BT}\right]. \tag{4.5}$$

To a higher approximation in w/k_BT, the products of other fluctuational deviations of the correlation parameters also differ from zero. In the same way, allowing for the nonideal nature of the solution in the approximation under consideration leads to the appearance of an additional factor $[1-(1-2c)^2(w/k_BT)]$ in formulas (4.3) for $\overline{|\varepsilon_k(\rho)|^2}$ and $\overline{\varepsilon_k(\rho)\,\varepsilon_k^*(-\rho)}$ at small k. We note that, according to (4.4), the fluctuations in the correlation parameters for nearest neighbors should tend to infinity on approaching the critical point, like the specific heat, but much more slowly than the fluctuations of concentration.

In concluding this chapter, we must mention another case in which relatively large fluctuations may develop in the parameters of long- and short-range order and also concentration (in solid solutions). Such large fluctuations may arise near the points corresponding to phase transformations of the second kind if the surface energy between the two phases is very small.

It is well known that at the transformation point the specific thermodynamic potentials of the two phases become identical; near the transformation point (as noted by Frenkel' [28, 29]), there is therefore a sharp fall in the minimum work required for the fluctuational development of particles of the new phase inside the matrix. The probability of such hetero-phase fluctuations near the transformation point is only limited by the interphase surface energy and becomes substantial even for particles of relatively large dimensions in the case of low values of the surface tension. On the other hand, it is clear that the development of such new-phase particles, differing structurally from the matrix, may also be considered as large fluctuations in long- and short-range order. If, however, new-phase particles in solid solutions have a composition differing from that of the matrix, then large fluctuations of concentration also arise. In the majority of cases the interphase surface energy tends to be large enough to prevent the intensive development of hetero-phase fluctuations.

We should note that there is a qualitative difference in the character of the fluctuations near points corresponding to transformations of the second and first kinds. Whereas, near a phase transformation point of the second kind, fluctuations in the degree of long-range order $\delta\eta$ may arise over the whole volume, their probability falling off monotonically with increasing $\delta\eta$, for a phase transformation of the first kind the hetero-phase fluctuations developing correspond, according to [28, 29], to a finite (i.e., not proportional to $1/\sqrt{N'}$) change in $\delta\eta$, but only in quite sharply limited parts of the crystal. Naturally in this case an especially large part must be played by the fluctuations in the correlation parameters accompanying such local fluctuations in the concentration and parameters of long-range order.

Chapter II

Fluctuation Waves of Static Displacements in Nonideal Crystals

§5. Macroscopic Theory of Waves of Static Displacements

As a result of fluctuations in concentration and order parameters, inhomogeneities bearing a more or less random character arise in the crystal. If the lattice parameters depend sharply on composition (or order), then from the macroscopic point of view the inhomogeneities of composition will lead to concentration stresses, inhomogeneous strains associated with these, and static displacements of the atoms in the crystal. These stresses are to some extent analogous to thermal stresses arising as a result of some chance distribution of temperature in the crystal. On the microscopic scale, if there is any difference in the atomic radii of the components of the solution,* each impurity atom produces static displacements of the surrounding atoms. As a result of the superposition of the fields of the displacements created by different atoms, a complex (especially at high concentrations) distribution of static displacements develops in the solution.

*The concept of "atomic radius" for the atoms of any kind in the solution is really not very strictly defined. We shall use this imprecise but picturesque term to denote characteristic distances, which are identical for the atoms of a solution not containing static stresses, but depend on a number of causes associated with static stresses and lead to a concentration dependence of the lattice constant.

It is clear that the determination of the stresses and static displacements as functions of the coordinates of the atoms in the crystal in the above-mentioned case of a complex and not completely symmetrical fluctuation distribution of stress sources constitutes an extremely difficult problem. The problem is greatly simplified, however, if we use the method of fluctuation waves and transform from the displacements of the atoms to their Fourier components [30]. The amplitudes of the waves of static distortions are linear functions of the amplitudes of the above-mentioned fluctuation waves of concentration, long-range order, and correlation (with the same $\mathbf{k}$), the corresponding coefficients of proportionality being determined by solving some very simple equations.

This method leads to simplifications very reminiscent of those achieved by transforming to normal coordinates in the problem of the vibrations of a crystal. The method is especially convenient in considering diffuse x-ray scattering at distortions, when the effect is associated with only one fluctuation wave, but may also be convenient in solving other problems of a distorted crystal, for example, in determining the static strains around an impurity atom.

In the case of long-wave fluctuation waves we may carry out a macroscopic calculation of the static-displacement waves, based on the use of equations taken from elastic theory and not on any specific model of the crystal. The amplitudes of the displacement waves are expressed in terms of crystal characteristics which may easily be determined experimentally. This kind of macroscopic treatment will be considered in the present section. In the case of short waves, the macroscopic approach becomes inapplicable, and we have to pass on to the microscopic consideration based on the Born theory of crystals (see §6).

In contrast to the case of undistorted crystals considered in the previous chapter, in solutions with different atomic radii of the components the atoms will not experience thermal vibrations relative to the lattice points (with radii vectors $\mathbf{R}_{s\gamma}$), but will vibrate relative to displaced positions determined by the vectors $\mathbf{R}_{s\gamma} + \delta\mathbf{R}_{s\gamma}$. This displacement of the equilibrium position $\delta\mathbf{R}_{s\gamma}$ for atom No. γ of the s-th cell may naturally be regarded as a static displacement. Instead of the quantities $\delta\mathbf{R}_{s\gamma}$ we may introduce their Fourier components, as was done in the case of the quantities

$c_{s\gamma}$ in formula (1.7):

$$\delta\mathbf{R}_{s\gamma} = i\sum_{\mathbf{k}} \mathbf{R}_{\mathbf{k}\gamma} e^{-i\mathbf{k}\mathbf{R}_{s\gamma}}, \quad \mathbf{R}_{\mathbf{k}\gamma} = -\frac{i}{N}\sum_{s} \delta\mathbf{R}_{s\gamma} e^{i\mathbf{k}\mathbf{R}_{s\gamma}}. \qquad (5.1)$$

Here $\mathbf{R}^*_{\mathbf{k}\gamma} = -\mathbf{R}_{-\mathbf{k}\gamma}$ and the factor $i = \sqrt{-1}$ is introduced in order to simplify subsequent formulas.

Let us consider static-displacement waves for small k, first taking the simplest case of disordered solutions with one atom per unit cell ($\nu = 1$) [30]. Here we may omit the index γ on $c_{\mathbf{k}\gamma}$ and $\mathbf{R}_{\mathbf{k}\gamma}$ in (1.7) and (5.1). If the static displacements are only produced by fluctuations of concentration, the displacements of the atoms may be put in the form of a superposition of displacements corresponding to individual fluctuation waves:

$$\delta\mathbf{R}_s = i\sum_{\mathbf{k}} \mathbf{A}_{\mathbf{k}} c_{\mathbf{k}} e^{-i\mathbf{k}\mathbf{R}_s}, \quad \mathbf{R}_{\mathbf{k}} = \mathbf{A}_{\mathbf{k}} c_{\mathbf{k}}, \quad \mathbf{A}_{-\mathbf{k}} = -\mathbf{A}_{\mathbf{k}}. \qquad (5.2)$$

Strictly speaking, in the expansion of $\delta\mathbf{R}_s$ we should also consider terms quadratic in $c_{\mathbf{k}}$ and terms of higher order. Instead of this, in another presentation of the problem [(see (4.2)], we might allow for fluctuations of the correlation parameters together with the concentration fluctuations on the right-hand side of the sum in (5.2). This more detailed kind of consideration will be undertaken later in § 8. However, if the lattice parameters depend linearly on concentration c, i.e., if Vegard's law is satisfied, and if the elastic modulus depends only slightly on c, we may neglect the quadratic $c_{\mathbf{k}}$ terms in $\mathbf{R}_{\mathbf{k}}$ and use formula (5.2). In this case (5.2) becomes valid for small concentrations of one of the components also. Exact criteria for the applicability of this approximation will be given in § 8.

Formula (5.2) links the amplitude of the waves representing the static displacements of the atoms and the fluctuation waves of concentration. In considering static displacements, the concentration waves may be regarded as given (for example, the mean squares $\overline{|c_{\mathbf{k}}|^2}$ are determined from the formulas of the previous chapter), so that the problem of calculating the Fourier components of $\mathbf{R}_{\mathbf{k}}$ (or $\overline{|\mathbf{R}_{\mathbf{k}}|^2}$) reduces to a determination of the coefficients $\mathbf{A}_{\mathbf{k}}$ in (5.2).

In order to find these quantities $\mathbf{A}_{\mathbf{k}}$ in (5.2) and so determine the amplitudes of the waves of static displacements, we may use the equilibrium conditions for the displacements of the atoms. In the macroscopic approximation the fluctuational change in the concentration is characterized by a continuous distribution of $\delta c(\mathbf{r})$, and the displacements of the atoms by the strain tensor u_{ij} and the displacement vector $\delta\mathbf{R}(\mathbf{r}) = \delta\mathbf{R}_s$. An inhomogeneous change in concentration leads, in the same way as a change of temperature (cf. [31], Part II, Chapter I), to the appearance of terms linear with respect to u_{ij} in the expression for the density of the free energy of the solution F^0, considered as a function of u_{ij}. For an elastic anisotropic continuum, this expression may be written in the form

$$F^0 = F_0^0 + \frac{1}{2}\lambda_{ijlm}u_{ij}u_{lm} - \lambda_{ijlm}L_{lm}u_{ij}\delta c, \tag{5.3}$$

where F_0^0 does not depend on δc and u_{ij} and λ_{ijlm} are the components of the tensor of elastic moduli, summation being made over twice-repeated indices from 1 to 3. The derivatives of this expression determine the stress tensor

$$\sigma_{ij} = \frac{\partial F^0}{\partial u_{ij}} = \lambda_{ijlm}u_{lm} - \lambda_{ijlm}L_{lm}\delta c. \tag{5.4}$$

Here the second term takes account of the concentration stresses. The tensor components L_{lm} in (5.3) and (5.4) are connected with quantities characterizing the relation between the size and shape of the cell and the composition of the solution. In order to discover this relationship, let us consider an unstressed crystal ($\sigma_{ij} = 0$) in which the concentration is changed by an amount δc constant throughout the crystal. Equating (5.4) to zero, we find that

$$L_{lm} = \frac{\delta u_{lm}}{\delta c}, \tag{5.5}$$

where $\delta\mu_{lm}$ is the change in the strain tensor corresponding to the change of concentration δc. It is clear that L_{lm} may be determined from formula (5.5) if we know the concentration dependence of the size and shape of the unit cell.

For a wave-like change in concentration

$$\delta c(\mathbf{r}) = c_{\mathbf{k}} \exp(-i\mathbf{kr}),$$

corresponding to the $\mathbf{k}$-th fluctuation wave, the displacements and strains also vary in a wave-like manner in accordance with (5.2):

$$u_{lm}=\frac{1}{2}\left[\frac{\partial(\delta R_l)}{\partial x_m}+\frac{\partial(\delta R_m)}{\partial x_l}\right]=\frac{1}{2}k\,(n_m A_{\mathbf{k}l}+n_l A_{\mathbf{k}m})\,c_{\mathbf{k}}\exp(-i\mathbf{kr}), \tag{5.6}$$

where n_l are the components of the unit vector $\mathbf{n}=\mathbf{k}/k$ parallel to the wave vector $\mathbf{k}$. We see from (5.4) and (5.6) that $\sigma_{ij}\sim\exp(-i\mathbf{kr})$.

Remembering that in a state of equilibrium the density of the forces $\partial\sigma_{ij}/\partial x_j$ equals zero, let us write down the equilibrium condition for the $\mathbf{k}$-th fluctuation wave:

$$\sigma_{ij}n_j=0 \qquad (i=1,\ 2,\ 3). \tag{5.7}$$

Putting expression (5.4) instead of σ_{ij} in these equations and using for δc and u_{ij} the expressions corresponding to the $\mathbf{k}$-th fluctuation wave, we obtain a system of three inhomogeneous linear equations for determining the $A_{\mathbf{k}i}$:

$$k\lambda_{ijlm}n_j n_l A_{\mathbf{k}m}=\lambda_{ijlm}n_j L_{lm} \qquad (i=1,\ 2,\ 3). \tag{5.8}$$

If we know the elastic moduli and the concentration dependence of the shape and size of the cell, then equation (5.8) enables us immediately to calculate the proportionality factors $\mathbf{A}_{\mathbf{k}}$ between the amplitudes of the static-displacement and concentration waves. We see from (5.8) that for long waves the coefficient $\mathbf{A}_{\mathbf{k}}$ is inversely proportional to k, i.e.,

$$\mathbf{A}_{\mathbf{k}}=\frac{a_{\mathbf{k}}\mathbf{e}_{\mathbf{k}}}{k}, \tag{5.9}$$

where $\mathbf{e}_{\mathbf{k}}$ is a unit vector and for small k $a_{\mathbf{k}}$ depends only on the direction (but not the magnitude) of the vector $\mathbf{k}$. The rise in the amplitude of the displacement wave $\mathbf{A}_{\mathbf{k}}$ for small k is due to the fact that the change of concentration δc in some region produces a deformation u_{ij} of this region proportional to δc. Since δR_i is an integral of u_{ij}, an increase in the dimensions of the region in which δc is almost identical (i.e., an increase in the wavelength) leads to a proportional rise in δR_i.

Equations (5.8) are simplified in the case of crystals of the hexagonal, rhombic, tetragonal, and cubic systems, in which, as may be seen from considerations of symmetry, the tensor L_{lm} relates to the principal axes if the coordinate axes are taken along the crystallographic directions. Thus the tensor components equal

$$L_{lm}=\frac{1}{d_l}\frac{\partial d_l}{\partial c}\delta_{lm}, \tag{5.10}$$

where d_l is the length of the section which unites any two lattice points and is directed parallel to the l axis. In different particular cases equation (5.8) may be written more conveniently by using the Voigt notation for the components of the elastic-modulus tensor:

$$\lambda_{ijlm}\equiv c_{pr} \qquad (p, r=1, 2, \ldots, 6).$$

More specific forms of equations (5.8) for crystals of various symmetries (obtained in [32]) are given in Appendix II. Thus, for example, in cubic crystals the system of equations for determining the $A_{\mathbf{k}i}$ has the form of (II.6). The solution of this system may be written in the form

$$A_{\mathbf{k}x}=\frac{1}{3}\frac{c_{11}+2c_{12}}{kD}(1+\xi n_y^2)(1+\xi n_z^2)\frac{1}{v}\frac{\partial v}{\partial c}n_x, \tag{5.11}$$

where v is the atomic volume

$$D=c_{11}+\xi(c_{11}+c_{12})(n_x^2n_y^2+n_x^2n_z^2+n_y^2n_z^2)+\xi^2(c_{11}+2c_{12}+c_{44})n_x^2n_y^2n_z^2,$$

$$\xi=\frac{(c_{11}-c_{12}-2c_{44})}{c_{44}}. \tag{5.12}$$

The parameter ξ characterizes the elastic anisotropy of the cubic crystal.

The expressions for $A_{\mathbf{k}y}$ and $A_{\mathbf{k}z}$ are obtained from (5.11) by cyclic substitution.

For directions of high symmetry of the type [100], [110], [111], or $\mathbf{A_k} \parallel \mathbf{n}$, i.e., the displacements in the fluctuation wave are parallel to $\mathbf{k}$ (the wave is "longitudinal"). Here the corresponding values of $a_{\mathbf{k}}$ equal

$$\begin{aligned}(a_{\mathbf{k}})_{[100]}&=\frac{1}{3}\cdot\frac{c_{11}+2c_{12}}{c_{11}}\frac{1}{v}\frac{\partial v}{\partial c},\\ (a_{\mathbf{k}})_{[110]}&=\frac{2}{3}\cdot\frac{c_{11}+2c_{12}}{c_{11}+c_{12}+2c_{44}}\frac{1}{v}\frac{\partial v}{\partial c},\\ (a_{\mathbf{k}})_{[111]}&=\frac{c_{11}+2c_{12}}{c_{11}+2c_{12}+4c_{44}}\frac{1}{v}\frac{\partial v}{\partial c}.\end{aligned} \tag{5.13}$$

In elastically anisotropic crystals $\mathbf{A}_\mathbf{k} \parallel \mathbf{k}$ for directions of high symmetry, but in general $\mathbf{A}_\mathbf{k}$ and $\mathbf{k}$ are not parallel. However, in an isotropic continuum, where

$$\xi = 0 \quad \text{and} \quad \frac{c_{11} + 2c_{12}}{c_{11}} = \frac{1+\sigma}{1-\sigma}$$

(σ is Poisson's ratio), the displacements in the wave are always parallel to $\mathbf{k}$, and $\mathbf{A}_\mathbf{k}$ equal

$$\mathbf{A}_\mathbf{k} = \frac{1+\sigma}{3(1-\sigma)} \frac{1}{v} \frac{\partial v}{\partial c} \frac{\mathbf{k}}{k^2}, \quad a_\mathbf{k} = a^0 = \frac{1+\sigma}{3(1-\sigma)} \frac{1}{v} \frac{\partial v}{\partial c}, \quad \mathbf{e}_\mathbf{k} = \mathbf{n}, \tag{5.14}$$

i.e., $a_\mathbf{k} = a^0$ depends neither on the magnitude nor the direction of $\mathbf{k}$.

Let us now consider ordered solutions. In this case the Fourier components of $\mathbf{R}_{\mathbf{k}\gamma}$ in expansion (5.1) are linear functions of all the quantities $c_{\mathbf{k}\gamma}$, corresponding to the given $\mathbf{k}$:

$$\mathbf{R}_{\mathbf{k}\gamma} = \sum_{\gamma'=1}^{\nu} \mathbf{A}_{\mathbf{k}\gamma\gamma'} c_{\mathbf{k}\gamma'}. \tag{5.15}$$

Let us confine ourselves to the case of crystals in which the lattice points are in positions of high symmetry, so that on changing the composition and order the relative position of the points in the unit cell remains unaltered. For long-wave fluctuations in these crystals we may neglect the displacement of the sublattices from one another and consider that the cell moves as a whole. Thus all the $\mathbf{R}_{\mathbf{k}\gamma}$ corresponding to the different sublattices γ will be the same, i.e., $\mathbf{A}_{\mathbf{k}\gamma\gamma'} = \mathbf{A}_{\mathbf{k}\gamma'}$ will not depend on γ. The relation between the deformations (strains) u_{lm} corresponding to the $\mathbf{k}$-th fluctuation wave in the sublattice γ' and $c_{\mathbf{k}\gamma'}$ is the same as in formula (5.6), save that the index γ' is added to $\mathbf{A}_\mathbf{k}$ and $c_\mathbf{k}$. Hence we may obtain equations for determining $\mathbf{A}_{\mathbf{k}\gamma'}$ in exactly the same way as (5.8) were obtained for determining $\mathbf{A}_\mathbf{k}$. These equations have the form

$$k\lambda_{ijlm} n_j n_l A_{\mathbf{k}\gamma' m} = \lambda_{ijlm} n_j L_{\gamma' lm} \qquad (i = 1,\ 2,\ 3). \tag{5.16}$$

Here $L_{\gamma' lm}$ is determined by formulas (5.5) and (5.10), in which we must replace c by $c_{\gamma'}$. It is clear that the tensor $L_{\gamma' lm}$ may be determined if we know the dependence of the size and shape of the cell on the composition and long-range-order parameters.

It is known from experimental data that in many solutions the derivatives of the lattice constants with respect to the order parameters are much smaller than their derivatives with respect to the concentration. If after the disordering of the solution the lattice points become equivalent, then in such solutions the quantities $L_{\gamma lm}$ for different γ may be considered as approximately equal and expressed in terms of concentration derivatives:

$$L_{\gamma lm} = \frac{\delta u_{lm}}{\delta c_{\gamma}} \approx \frac{1}{\nu} \frac{\delta u_{lm}}{\delta c} . \qquad (5.17)$$

It should be noted that the dependence of the cell dimensions on η_{μ} is (generally speaking) characterized by the same small parameters as their dependence on the correlation parameters $\varepsilon(\boldsymbol{\rho})$, so that it would be inconsistent to calculate the dependence on $\varepsilon(\boldsymbol{\rho})$.

The results presented may be applied not only to substitution-type solutions but also to those of the interstitial type, if we consider the interstices as one of the sublattices in which interstitial atoms and vacancies are sited. In these solutions, the concentration of impurity atoms is usually small, and for different applications it is only necessary to know the displacements of the atoms from the lattice points (and not the interstitial atoms). If impurity atoms are introduced into the interstices of a single-component crystal and lie in positions of one type only (the interstices form only one sublattice), then the quantities $\mathbf{A_k}$ constitute coefficients of proportionality between the amplitude of the wave of static displacements of the atoms at the lattice points $\mathbf{R_k}$ and the amplitude of the wave of concentration of the interstitial atoms $c_{\mathbf{k}}$. The equations for determining $\mathbf{A_k}$ in the macroscopic approximation then have the same form as in the case of substitution-type solutions, i.e., they are determined by formula (5.8). An example of such interstitial solutions with impurity atoms in positions of one type is provided by solutions with face-centered cubic lattices, in which the interstitial atoms lie in octahedral pores (in the centers of the cubic cells and in the middle of their edges).

Interstitial atoms may, however, occupy positions of several types rather than one. Thus the tensors $L_{\gamma' lm}$ for positions of different types γ' will be different, and the quantities $\mathbf{A}_{\mathbf{k}\gamma'}$, characterizing the displacements of the lattice points associated with fluctuations $c_{\mathbf{k}\gamma'}$ in positions of type γ' will be determined, not by

(5.8), but by the more general equations (5.16). It is an important point that the symmetry of the tensors $L_{\gamma' l m}$ in this case will depend not only on the symmetry of the solution but also on the symmetry of the positions γ'.

Thus, for example, in interstitial solutions with a body-centered cubic lattice, the octahedral pores (centers of the faces and middle points of the edges in the cubic cells) are surrounded by two neighboring points at a distance of d/2 (d is the length of the cell edge) and four at a distance of $(\sqrt{2}/2)d$; there are interstices of three types (x, y, and z) which differ in the direction of the axis joining two neighboring points. Such pores possess not cubic but tetragonal symmetry, and the components of the corresponding tensors L^x_{ij}, L^y_{ij}, and L^z_{ij} do not coincide.

The quantities A_k are not hard to determine in the case in which the interstitial atoms lie only in interstices of one type, for example, type z. A structure of this kind occurs for some interstitial solutions, for example, martensite, in which there is a special ordering process of the interstitial atoms in the interstices [33]. The quantities

$$L^z_{11} = L^z_{22} = \frac{1}{d_1}\frac{\partial d_1}{\partial c} \text{ and } L^z_{33} = \frac{1}{d_3}\frac{\partial d_3}{\partial c}$$

in this case, generally speaking, are very different [34], and it is essential to use the equations for tetragonal and not cubic crystals. However, for small concentrations of the impurity atoms we may neglect their influence on the elastic moduli and consider that these are the same as in a cubic crystal not containing impurities. The A^z_k for the interstitial atoms in positions of type z will be determined by formulas of the type (II.6) and (II.7). The solution of these equations is given in [35]. If the concentrations of the interstitial atoms in positions x, y, and z are the same, then the crystal has cubic symmetry. Nevertheless, the quantities A^x_k, A^y_k, A^z_k are determined even in this case by formulas of the (II.6) and (II.7) type, which allow for the essential tetragonality of the interstices and the noncubic symmetry of the displacements around the defects. Another example of energetically equivalent interstices of several types with noncubic symmetry in a cubic interstitial solution is given by the tetrahedral pores in crystals with face-centered cubic lattices.

§6. Microscopic Theory of Waves of Static Displacements

For small wavelengths of the fluctuations (in the approximation under consideration), relation (5.2) between the Fourier components of the static displacements and the concentration is valid as before. However, in this case the macroscopic approximation becomes inapplicable, and in order to determine the coefficients of proportionality $\mathbf{A}_k$ we must use the equilibrium conditions, not of the continuous theory of elasticity, but of the microscopic theory of crystals, allowing for their atomic structure. In this sense there is a complete analogy with the theory of vibrations, in which, on passing from long to short waves of thermal displacements, the equations of motion of the elastic continuum are replaced by the equations of motions of the atoms in the crystal.

It is natural to undertake a microscopic consideration of the static displacements by means of the model employed in the Born theory of thermal vibrations. As before, we first consider disordered solutions with one atom per unit cell.

In the microscopic theory, the free energy of the solution must be considered not as a function of the deformations but as a function of the static displacements $\delta\mathbf{R}_s$ (i.e., displacements in the equilibrium positions of the thermal vibrations of the atoms). With this presentation of the problem, the averaging over the thermal vibrations and other internal degrees of freedom (required for determining the sum of the states and the free energy) is carried out for specified displacements $\delta\mathbf{R}_s$. In the approximation considered, for which the relation between the $\delta\mathbf{R}_s$ and c_k is regarded as linear, the expression for the free energy, a function of $\delta\mathbf{R}_s$ may be presented in the form

$$F = F_0 - \sum_{s,\, s'=1}^{N} W_{ss'i}\,(c_{s'} - c)\,\delta R_{si} + \frac{1}{2}\sum_{s,\, s'=1}^{N} V_{ss'ij}\,\delta R_{si}\,\delta R_{s'j}. \qquad (6.1)$$

Here the coefficients $W_{ss'i}$ and $V_{ss'ij}$ generally speaking depend not only on the relative position of the atoms s and s' but also on the temperature. In expression (6.1) the term cubic in $\delta\mathbf{R}_s$ (and terms of higher degree) are rejected. This approximation is clearly legitimate if the static displacements are small compared with the interatomic distance. It is also supposed in (6.1) that the coefficients W and V do not depend on the distribution of the atoms in the solution (on c_s), and no account is taken of terms of the $\delta R_{si} c_{s'} c_{s''}$ and $\delta R_{si} \delta R_{s'i'} c_{s''}$ type, which are only important for considerable deviations from Vegard's law and a substantial concentration dependence of the elastic moduli. The role of these terms will be discussed in § 8. We note that $\mathbf{W}_{ss'}$ in (6.1) determines the force acting on the atom s from the direction of the impurity atom lying at the point s'.

Differentiating (6.1) with respect to $\delta \mathbf{R}_s$, we obtain an expression for the average force acting on the atom s:

$$f_{si} = -\frac{\partial F}{\partial \delta R_{si}} = \sum_{s'=1}^{N} W_{ss'i}(c_{s'} - c) - \sum_{s'=1}^{N} V_{ss'ij} \delta R_{s'j}. \qquad (6.2)$$

It is clear that in the state of equilibrium $f_{si} = 0$. On replacing $c_{s'} - c$ and $\delta R_{s'j}$ in this equation by their values [see (1.7) and (5.2)] corresponding to the **k**-th fluctuation wave, as in the derivation of equations (5.8), we obtain a simple system of three linear algebraic equations for determining the $A_{\mathbf{k}i}$:

$$Q_{\mathbf{k}ij} A_{\mathbf{k}j} = P_{\mathbf{k}i} \qquad (i = 1, 2, 3), \qquad (6.3)$$

$$\begin{aligned} Q_{\mathbf{k}ij} &= \sum_{s'=1}^{N} V_{ss'ij} \exp\left[i\mathbf{k}(\mathbf{R}_s - \mathbf{R}_{s'})\right], \\ P_{\mathbf{k}i} &= -i \sum_{s'=1}^{N} W_{ss'i} \exp\left[i\mathbf{k}(\mathbf{R}_s - \mathbf{R}_{s'})\right]. \end{aligned} \qquad (6.4)$$

These equations enable us to determine the coefficients $\mathbf{A}_\mathbf{k}$ in the case of short waves [30]. In order to use them, however, we have to know the interatomic-interaction constants $V_{ss'}$ and $W_{ss'}$. In principle, these quantities may be calculated theoretically, if we use a specific model of the solution, in which we know the law governing the variation in the forces of interatomic interaction with distance. However, at the present time a calculation of this kind can only be carried out for a small number of cases in nonmetallic solutions.

The force constants $V_{ss'}$ also enter into the equations of motion for the thermal vibrations and determine their frequencies.

Hence if we know the frequencies of the vibrations for various **k** from experimental data (e.g., neutron diffraction) we can determine $V_{ss'}$ and regard the coefficients $Q_{\mathbf{k}ij}$ in (6.3) as known. The constants $W_{ss'}$, however, still remain unknown.

On the other hand, we may use the fact that the forces of interatomic interaction usually fall off rapidly with distance. This makes it possible to use a simple model for calculating $\mathbf{A_k}$, in which it is assumed that only certain constants $V_{ss'}$ and $W_{ss'}$ are nonzero for the interaction of neighboring atoms, the number of independent quantities $V_{ss'ij}$ being taken as equal to the number of independent elastic moduli c_{pr}; the number of constants $W_{ss'i}$ is taken as equal to the number of independent components of the tensor L_{ij} (5.5). Then the nonzero constants $V_{ss'}$ and $W_{ss'}$ are expressed in terms of macroscopic quantities determined from simple experiments, c_{pr} and L_{ij} (for example, by passing to the limit of long waves). In this approximation $Q_{\mathbf{k}}$, $P_{\mathbf{k}}$, and also the coefficients $\mathbf{A_k}$, for all **k** are expressed simply in terms of the macroscopic characteristics of the solution. The resultant formulas for $\mathbf{A_k}$ will thus be exact for small k, and for large k will give a certain more or less accurate extrapolation. In cubic crystals, with this model, three force constants $V_{ss'}$ (according to the number of the three elastic moduli c_{11}, c_{12}, c_{44}) and one constant $W_{ss'}$ (determined by the derivative $\partial v/\partial c$) should differ from zero.

For example, in solutions of the substitution type with face-centered cubic lattices, we may use the Born and Begbie approximation [36], in which we allow for interaction between nearest-neighbor atoms only, but also allow for the fact that the forces are not central. In this model the coefficients $Q_{\mathbf{k}ij}$ and $P_{\mathbf{k}i}$ in equations (6.3) are determined [32] by the formulas:

$$Q_{\mathbf{k}11} = dc_{11}\left[2 - \cos\frac{kdn_x}{2}\left(\cos\frac{kdn_y}{2} + \cos\frac{kdn_z}{2}\right)\right] + d\,(2c_{44} - c_{11})\left(1 - \cos\frac{kdn_y}{2}\cos\frac{kdn_z}{2}\right), \qquad (6.5)$$

$$Q_{\mathbf{k}12} = Q_{\mathbf{k}21} = d\,(c_{12} + c_{44})\sin\frac{kdn_x}{2}\sin\frac{kdn_y}{2},$$

$$(6.6)$$

$$P_{\mathbf{k}1} = \frac{kd^2}{12}(c_{11} + 2c_{12})\sin\frac{kdn_x}{2}\left(\cos\frac{kdn_y}{2} + \cos\frac{kdn_z}{2}\right)\frac{1}{v}\frac{\partial v}{\partial c}.$$

The other coefficients $Q_{\mathbf{k}ij}$ and $P_{\mathbf{k}i}$ are obtained from (6.5) and (6.6) by cyclic permutation of the indices x, y, z.

It follows in particular from (6.3), (6.5), and (6.6) that, for directions of high symmetry of the [100], [110], and [111] type, just as in the case of long waves, the displacements are parallel to the wave vector, i.e., $\mathbf{A_k} \| \mathbf{n}$. Thus the expressions for $\mathbf{A_k}$ are obtained directly from (6.3), (6.5), and (6.6) and have a simple form. For example, for the [100] direction

$$\mathbf{A_k} = \frac{1}{2} d\,(c_{11} + 2c_{12})\, c_{11}^{-1} \frac{1}{v} \frac{\partial v}{\partial c} \cot \frac{kd}{4}\,\mathbf{n}.$$

Formulas (6.3), (6.5), and (6.6) make it possible to determine the coefficients $\mathbf{A_k}$ for any $\mathbf{k}$ if we know the elastic moduli and concentration dependence of the lattice parameter. Analogous expressions for $Q_{\mathbf{k}ij}$ and $P_{\mathbf{k}i}$ are obtained for substitution-type solutions with body-centered cubic lattices [37] and hcp lattices [431] and for interstitial solutions with face-centered and body-centered lattices [35].

In actual fact, of course, the interaction is not limited to the first coordination sphere. In addition to this, in metals the conductivity electrons may play a decisive part in the interaction. Hence formulas of the (6.5) and (6.6) type may give considerable errors at large k. Calculation of the vibration frequencies of metals on the basis of an analogous model, however, usually gives erros no greater than 10 to 20%, as comparison with experiment shows [38]. We may well suppose that in calculating $\mathbf{A_k}$ also the error will have the same order. The extent of the error becomes even smaller on using these values of $\mathbf{A_k}$ for calculating integral (with respect to $\mathbf{k}$) characteristics of solutions.

Equations (6.3) and (6.4) for determining $\mathbf{A_k}$ are easy to generalize to the case of ordered solutions. The free energy in this case will be determined by an expression obviously constituting a generalization of (6.1):

$$F = F_0 - \sum_{s\gamma s'\gamma'} W_{s\gamma s'\gamma' i}\,(c_{s'\gamma'} - c_{\gamma'})\,\delta R_{s\gamma i} + \frac{1}{2} \sum_{s\gamma s'\gamma'} V_{s\gamma s'\gamma' ij}\,\delta R_{s\gamma i}\,\delta R_{s'\gamma' j}. \quad (6.7)$$

Substituting into the equilibrium conditions

$$\frac{\partial F}{\partial \delta R_{s\gamma i}} = 0$$

expressions (1.7) and (5.1) for $c_{s\gamma}-c_\gamma$ and $\delta\mathbf{R}_{s\gamma}$, multiplying the resultant equations by exp ($i\mathbf{k}\mathbf{R}_{s\gamma}$), summing over s, and expressing $\mathbf{R}_{\mathbf{k}\gamma}$ in terms of $c_{\mathbf{k}\gamma'}$ by formula (5.15), we obtain a system of 3ν equations for determining the quantities $\mathbf{A}_{\mathbf{k}\gamma'\gamma''}$ for a given γ'' ($\gamma'' = 1, 2, \ldots, \nu$):

$$\sum_{s'\gamma'} V_{s\gamma s'\gamma' ij} \exp\left[i\mathbf{k}\left(\mathbf{R}_{s\gamma}-\mathbf{R}_{s'\gamma'}\right)\right] A_{\mathbf{k}\gamma'\gamma''j} = -i \sum_{s'} W_{s\gamma s'\gamma'' i} \exp\left[i\mathbf{k}\left(\mathbf{R}_{s\gamma}-\mathbf{R}_{s'\gamma''}\right)\right]$$

$$(i=1, 2, 3;\ \gamma=1, 2, \ldots, \nu). \tag{6.8}$$

As in the case of disordered solutions, equations (6.8) enable us to determine the quantities $\mathbf{A}_{\mathbf{k}}$, if we know the constants of interatomic interaction V and W.

The solution of equations (6.3) for disordered solutions may be put in explicit form by referring the third-order matrix of $Q_{\mathbf{k}ij}$ to the principal axes and expressing it in terms of the vibration frequencies [39]. For this purpose we take into account the equations of motion for the vibrations of an ideal crystal with force constants $V_{ss'}$ and atoms of mass M:

$$Q_{\mathbf{k}ij} e_{\mathbf{k}nj} = M\omega_{\mathbf{k}n}^2 e_{\mathbf{k}ni}, \tag{6.9}$$

where n is the number of the branch of the vibrations (n = 1, 2, 3), $\omega_{\mathbf{k}n}$, and $\mathbf{e}_{\mathbf{k}n}$ are the frequency and polarization vector of the vibration $\mathbf{k}n$. Expanding $\mathbf{A}_{\mathbf{k}}$ in terms of the three vectors $\mathbf{e}_{\mathbf{k}n}$, remembering that these vectors are orthogonal, and allowing for (6.9), we immediately obtain the solution of equations (6.3) in the form

$$\mathbf{A}_{\mathbf{k}} = \sum_{n=1}^{3} \frac{(\mathbf{P}_{\mathbf{k}}\mathbf{e}_{\mathbf{k}n})}{M\omega_{\mathbf{k}n}^2} \mathbf{e}_{\mathbf{k}n}. \tag{6.10}$$

This form may be convenient if we know both the frequencies and the polarization vectors of the normal vibrations (for example, from experiment). There is then no need to know the force constants $V_{ss'}$, although as before we must know the $W_{ss'}$. If instead of the frequencies and polarization vectors the force constants $V_{ss'}$ are known, then $\mathbf{A}_{\mathbf{k}}$ may more suitably be determined directly from equations (6.3), since these are simpler than the equations determining $\omega_{\mathbf{k}n}$ and $\mathbf{e}_{\mathbf{k}n}$.

§7. Static Displacements around Point Defects in Crystals

By means of the formulas for $\mathbf{A_k}$, obtained in the two preceding sections, we may determine the Fourier components of static displacements for a given distribution of the atoms of different sorts at the lattice points. Carrying out an inverse Fourier transformation, we may then find the static displacements themselves. Thus we may calculate, for example, the displacements around an isolated impurity atom or other point defect, allowing for the elastic anisotropy and the atomic structure of the crystal. Here the method of calculation based on expanding the displacements into Fourier series [40-42] is more convenient (at least in elastically anisotropic crystals) than the frequently used method based on the solution of, strictly speaking, an infinite system of difference equations.

Suppose that in a crystal with a lattice of the Bravais type there is only one impurity atom, lying at the origin of coordinates. Thus there is only one nonzero number $c_{s\gamma} \equiv c_s = 1$ for $\mathbf{R}_s = 0$, and, as may be seen from (1.7) or (1.11), all the Fourier components $c_\mathbf{k}$ are the same: $c_\mathbf{k} = 1/N$. Putting these values of $c_\mathbf{k}$ into (5.2), we find that the static displacements around the impurity atoms may be written in the form of an integral with respect to **k**:

$$\delta\mathbf{R}_s(\mathbf{r}) = \frac{1}{N}\sum_{\mathbf{k}} \mathbf{A_k}\sin\mathbf{kr} = \frac{v}{8\pi^3}\int d\mathbf{k}\,\mathbf{A_k}\sin\mathbf{kr}, \qquad \mathbf{r} = \mathbf{R}_s, \tag{7.1}$$

where the integration is carried out with respect to values of $\mathbf{k}/2\pi$ lying in the reciprocal-lattice cell.

Expression (7.1) makes it possible to study displacements at large distances from the defect exactly, without using any simplified model. Actually, for large r, the principal part in the integral (7.1) is played by the region of small k, where $\mathbf{A_k}$ is determined from the exact formulas of the macroscopic theory given in §5. As r increases, however, there are rapid oscillations of the factor sin **kr**, and the principal contribution to integral (7.1) comes from the range of integration corresponding to directions of **k** almost perpendicular to the vector **r** (and also to small k). Remembering that $\mathbf{A_k} \sim 1/k$, and carrying out the integration in (7.1) for $r \to \infty$, it is not hard to see that the static displacements for large r will fall off in inverse proportion to the square of the distance from the defect:

$$\delta \mathbf{R}_s(r) = \frac{C(\mathbf{m})}{r^2}\,\mathbf{e}(\mathbf{m}), \qquad \mathbf{m} = \frac{\mathbf{r}}{r} \tag{7.2}$$

[$\mathbf{e}(\mathbf{m})$ is the unit vector], where $C(\mathbf{m})\mathbf{e}(\mathbf{m})$ depends, generally speaking, on the direction of the unit vector $\mathbf{m}$ ($\mathbf{m} \parallel \mathbf{r}$), and may be put in the form of an integral with respect to angle [42]:

$$C(\mathbf{m})\,\mathbf{e}(\mathbf{m}) = \frac{v}{4\pi} \lim_{\substack{k\to 0\\ \mathbf{n}\perp\mathbf{r}}} \frac{1}{2\pi} \int_0^{2\pi} \frac{\partial(k\mathbf{A}_{\mathbf{k}})}{\partial n_{\parallel}}\, d\varphi. \tag{7.3}$$

Here $\partial(k\mathbf{A}_{\mathbf{k}})/\partial n_{\parallel}$ denotes the limiting value of the ratio of a change in the vector $k\mathbf{A}_{\mathbf{k}}$ to the corresponding change $dn_{\parallel}$ in the unit vector $\mathbf{n} = \mathbf{k}/k$ in a direction parallel to $\mathbf{r}$, and the integration over φ is carried out with respect to directions $\mathbf{n}$ perpendicular to $\mathbf{r}$. The formulas for displacements at large distances from the defect may also (in principle) be obtained by means of the expression for the Green's function associated with the equations of the theory of elasticity for an elastically anisotropic medium, derived in [43] (see also [44]).

By means of the macroscopic expressions for $\mathbf{A}_{\mathbf{k}}$, given in §5, formulas (7.2) and (7.3) enable us to carry out a numerical integration and thus determine the values of the displacements at large distances in different directions, if only we know the elastic moduli and the variations in the parameters of the crystal associated with the introduction of impurity atoms. The expressions for $C(\mathbf{m})$ have been obtained in explicit form for cubic crystals [42]. In the particular case of elastically isotropic crystals, it follows from (7.2), (7.3), and (5.14) that the displacements are purely radial:

$$\delta \mathbf{R}_s(\mathbf{r}) = C\frac{\mathbf{r}}{r^3}, \qquad C = \frac{1+\sigma}{12\pi(1-\sigma)}\frac{\partial v}{\partial c}. \tag{7.4}$$

In this case the expression for the displacements may also easily be obtained from the equations of elasticity theory for an isotropic continuum (see, for example [45]).

In weakly anisotropic cubic crystals, for which the anisotropy parameter ξ defined by formula (5.12) is small ($\xi \ll 1$), the integration in (7.3) may be carried out analytically. Thus according to [42]:

$$\delta R_{sx}(\mathbf{r}) = \frac{c_{11}+2c_{12}}{12\pi c_{11}}\left[1+\frac{1}{8}\frac{c_{11}+c_{12}}{c_{11}}\xi(1-9m_x^2+15m_x^4-15m_y^2m_z^2)+\right.$$
$$\left.+\frac{1}{2}\frac{c_{12}}{c_{11}}\xi(1-3m_x^2)\right]m_x\frac{\partial v}{\partial c}\frac{1}{r^2}. \qquad (7.5)$$

The existence of elastic anisotropy (even for small ξ) leads to some new results. Whereas, in an elastically isotropic medium, according to (7.4), $\operatorname{div}\delta\mathbf{R}_S(\mathbf{r}) = 0$ for $\mathbf{r} \neq 0$, we see from (7.5) that on allowing for elastic anisotropy there is a finite change in volume at $r \neq 0$, proportional to $1/r^3$. As a result of this a potential energy of the elastic interaction of the impurity atoms appears, falling off as $1/r^3$ at large distances, proportional to $(\partial v/\partial c)^2$, and depending strongly on angles [45].

The integration in (7.3) may also be carried out analytically in the case of arbitrary anisotropy for directions of the [100] type in cubic crystals. In this case

$$C(\mathbf{m}) = \frac{c_{11}+2c_{12}}{12(c_{11}+c_{12})}\left[\frac{c_{11}+c_{12}(1+\xi)}{\sqrt{c_{11}^2+\frac{1}{4}c_{11}(c_{11}+c_{12})\xi}}+\xi\right]\frac{\partial v}{\partial c},$$

$$\mathbf{e}(\mathbf{m}) = \mathbf{m} \qquad (\mathbf{m}\parallel[100]). \qquad (7.6)$$

It is interesting to note that, according to (7.6), allowing for even a weak anisotropy may greatly change the value of the displacements. Thus, for example, in the case of weakly anisotropic crystals of aluminum, we find by using the values given in Table 1 (p. 83) for the elastic moduli and putting $\sigma = 0.34$ that allowing for elastic anisotropy reduces the values of the displacements in the [100] direction by a factor of 1.34 as compared with the case of an isotropic continuum [formula (7.4)]. In the case of more anisotropic crystals (for example, copper), even the sign of the displacements in this direction may change. Elastic anisotropy may influence the displacements around point defects in hexagonal crystals just as sharply [431].

It is clear that, when determining the displacements at large distances from the defect (distances considerably exceeding the lattice constant and the defect dimensions, so that the continuum approximation is valid), neither the atomic structure of the crystal nor the detailed characteristics of the defects are important. In cubic crystals it is only necessary that the forces on the atoms of the crystal from the direction of the defect should have cubic symmetry. Hence the results here presented are applicable to the calculation of displacements not only around impurity atoms but also around other point defects (for example, vacancies) and in fact any more complex defects at all (for example, particles of a new phase) having cubic symmetry.

In order to determine the displacements of the atoms at short distances from a defect by means of formula (7.1), we must know the $\mathbf{A}_k$ values not only for small but also for large k. In view of the lack of data regarding the forces of interatomic interaction in solutions, the values of $\mathbf{A}_k$ for large k can only be found approximately by means of some simplified model. It is possible in particular to use formulas of the (6.5) and (6.6) type for the coefficients Q_{kij} and P_{ki} in equations (6.3), obtained in the approximation of nearest neighbors. These formulas enable us to express the $\mathbf{A}_k$ for all $\mathbf{k}$ (and hence also $\delta\mathbf{R}_S(\mathbf{r})$ for small r) approximately in terms of the elastic moduli and the derivative $\partial v/\partial c$. Such formulas for the displacements were obtained in [42] by means of an approximate analytical calculation of integral (7.1) (using the Houston method) for solutions of the interstitial and substitution type with face-centered cubic lattices, having arbitrary elastic moduli.

The displacements around impurity atoms may also be determined by direct numerical (not analytical) integration of formula (7.1). In this way the displacements of iron atoms around an impurity carbon atom introduced into the body-centered lattice of α-Fe (or martensite) [35, 432, 433], the displacements around a vacancy and an interstitial atom in argon [40], and the displacements around a potassium impurity atom in a NaCl crystal [47] have been calculated. The static displacements have also been calculated by other methods, and by means of these a number of specific problems have been solved (see, for example, [48-50], which contain references to other papers).

For the calculation of static displacements it is extremely convenient to use Lifshits' [51] Green's functions for the lattice. These functions were used for determining displacements around impurity atoms in crystals by Maradudin and Flinn [44]. By definition the Green's function $G_{ss'ij}$ equals the i-th component of the static displacement of the s-th atom acted upon by unit external force applied to the atom s' and directed along the axis j. According to [51] the Green's function is completely determined by the frequencies $\omega_{\mathbf{k}n}$ and the polarization vectors $\mathbf{e}_{\mathbf{k}n}$ of the ideal crystal not containing impurity atoms, and in the case of a monatomic crystal may be presented in the form of a sum over all the normal vibrations:

$$G_{ss'ij} \equiv G_{ij}(\mathbf{R}_s - \mathbf{R}_{s'}) = \frac{1}{N} \sum_{\mathbf{k}} \sum_{n=1}^{3} \frac{e_{\mathbf{k}ni} e_{\mathbf{k}nj}}{\omega_{\mathbf{k}n}^2} \exp[i\mathbf{k}(\mathbf{R}_s - \mathbf{R}_{s'})]. \tag{7.7}$$

Knowing $\omega_{\mathbf{k}n}$ and $\mathbf{e}_{\mathbf{k}n}$, we may calculate the tensor $G_{ss'}$ for various $\mathbf{R}_s - \mathbf{R}_{s'}$ by numerical integration. For the simple model of crystals with a face-centered cubic lattice, a calculation of this kind was carried out in [44].

If the impurity atom introduced into the point s" does not lead to a change in the force constants $V_{ss'}$, then there is no difficulty in expressing the displacements created by the impurity in terms of functions $G_{ss'ij}$. In actual fact, remembering that according to (6.2) the forces acting from the direction of the impurity atom on a crystal atom s' are equal to $\mathbf{W}_{ss'}$, and considering the definition of the Green's functions, we immediately find that the displacement of the s-th atom created by the defect lying at the point s" equals

$$\delta R_{si} = \sum_{s'} G_{ss'ij} W_{s's''j}. \tag{7.8}$$

In order to determine the displacements from this formula, we must know the force constants $W_{ss'}$.

The use of Green's functions makes it possible, when calculating displacements, to consider not only the effects of the forces $W_{ss'}$ acting on the atoms from the direction of the defect, but also the change in the force constants $V_{ss'}$ near the defect. An allowance may be made for this effect for a low concentration of the impurity by taking account of terms of the

$$\frac{1}{2} V'_{ss's''ij}\, \delta R_{si}\, \delta R_{s'j}\, c_{s''},$$

type in expression (6.1) for the free energy, where $V'_{ss's''}$ is the change in the force constant for the points s, s' on introducing an impurity atom into the point s". In accordance with this we must add a term

$$-\sum_{s_1=1}^{N} V'_{ss_1s''il}\, \delta R_{s_1l}\, c_{s''}$$

to expression (6.2) for the force f_{si} acting on the s-th atom of the defect-containing crystal. Considering this formally added force as an external force (although in actual fact it depends on the displacements δR_{s_1}) acting together with $W_{ss''i}$ on the atoms of the crystal from the defect lying at s", and remembering the definition of the Green's functions, we may write the formula for the displacements around the impurity atom at the point s" in the form

$$\delta R_{si} = \sum_{s'} G_{ss'ij} W_{s's''j} - \sum_{s's_1} G_{ss'ij} V'_{s's_1s''jl} \delta R_{s_1l}. \tag{7.9}$$

This equation for the determination of $\delta \mathbf{R}_s$ was solved in [44] by the iteration method on the assumption that the $V'_{ss'}$ were small. If these quantities are not very small, then it is more convenient to determine $\delta \mathbf{R}_s$ by another method, considering that the constants $V'_{s's_1s''}$ usually only differ from zero for a small number of pairs of atoms near the defect of s". If we consider equation (7.9) for p points s at which $V'_{s'ss''}$ differs from zero, then we obtain a closed system of 3p linear inhomogeneous equations, by solving which we may find the static displacements for these p points. Putting the resultant values in (7.9), we may determine the displacements of all the other atoms. In particular, at large distances from the defect, the displacements are determined by the formulas of the macroscopic theory presented earlier.

The waves of static distortions were considered in § 5 and § 6 without allowing for the boundary conditions relating to the stresses at the boundaries of the crystal. Hence the results derived above are only valid for wavelengths considerably shorter than the crystal dimensions Λ, and cease to be valid for $k\Lambda \sim 1$. It is clear that the disruption of the $\mathbf{A}_\mathbf{k} \sim 1/k$ relationship for such small k values affects only a very small part of the range of integration in (7.1), and cannot change the results obtained above for the displacements around a defect, provided that the distance from the defect is small compared with the dimensions of the crystal. However, for $r \sim \Lambda$ it is precisely this region which becomes important in the integral (7.1), i.e., surface effects begin to exert an influence.

It is an important fact that, as shown by Eshelby [52], the surface effects are by no means negligible, but influence the change in volume of a crystal very considerably when a defect is introduced into it. In fact the displacements determined by formula (7.2), calculated without considering the boundary conditions for an "infinite" crystal, lead to deformations and stresses at the boundary of the crystal proportional to $1/\Lambda^3$. Actually there should be no stresses at all at the boundary if the latter may be regarded as free. Hence the stresses in question, corresponding to the displacements of (7.2), must be compensated by equal and opposite stresses, associated with "mirror-image forces." These image stresses, proportional to $1/\Lambda^3$, must produce deformations of the order

$$\frac{C(\mathbf{m})}{\Lambda^3} \sim \frac{\frac{\partial v}{\partial c}}{\Lambda^3}$$

over the whole volume of the crystal and lead to a total change of volume of the order of

$$\Lambda^3 \frac{\partial v}{\partial c} \Big/ \Lambda^3 \sim \frac{\partial v}{\partial c},$$

i.e., of the same order as the displacements (7.2). However, in contrast to the latter, these deformations are small ($\sim 1/\Lambda^3$) and vary very smoothly (they only change over distances comparable with the dimensions of the crystal Λ). If there is a large number of defects cN uniformly distributed in the crystal, then, neglecting unimportant fluctuational corrections $\sim \delta/\Lambda$ (δ is the mean distance between neighboring defects), the mirror-image forces lead to a uniform expansion or compression of a cubic crystal, which in the approximation of an isotropic continuum [45] equals

$$u_{ii} = \operatorname{div} \delta \mathbf{R}_s(\mathbf{r}) = \varkappa c, \qquad \varkappa = \frac{2}{3} \frac{1-2\sigma}{1-\sigma} \frac{1}{v} \frac{\partial v}{\partial c}. \tag{7.10}$$

The sum of the change in volume $c\varkappa V$ corresponding to (7.10) and the change in volume associated with the displacements of (7.4) around cN defects, the latter being equal to

$$4\pi r^2 \frac{1+\sigma}{12\pi(1-\sigma)} \frac{\partial v}{\partial c} \frac{\mathbf{r}}{r^3} \mathrm{m} cN = \frac{1+\sigma}{3(1-\sigma)} \frac{1}{v} \frac{\partial v}{\partial c} cV,$$

amounts to

$$\frac{1}{v}\frac{\partial v}{\partial c}cV$$

as it should.

On allowing for the elastic anisotropy of the cubic crystal, the quantity $\varkappa$ in (7.10) equals

$$\varkappa=\frac{1}{v}\frac{\partial v}{\partial c}-\int C(\mathbf{m})\,d\Omega,$$

where C ($\mathbf{m}$) is determined by formula (7.3), and the integration is carried out over the angles (over the directions of the vector $\mathbf{m}$).

The smooth deformations (7.10) must be added to the superposition of the rapidly varying deformations (7.2) created by different defects.

A knowledge of the quantities $\mathbf{A}_{\mathbf{k}}$ makes it possible to determine not only the displacements around individual impurity atoms, but also the mean squares of the static displacements of the atoms in the solution $\overline{(\delta R_S)^2}$. It follows from (5.2), in fact, that

$$\overline{(\delta\mathbf{R}_s)^2}=\sum_{\mathbf{k}}\overline{|c_{\mathbf{k}}|^2}\,\mathbf{A}_{\mathbf{k}}^2=\frac{vN}{8\pi^3}\int d\mathbf{k}\,\overline{|c_{\mathbf{k}}|^2}\,\mathbf{A}_{\mathbf{k}}^2. \tag{7.11}$$

In particular, in ideal solutions, for which $\overline{|c_{\mathbf{k}}|^2}=c(1-c)/N$,

$$\overline{(\delta\mathbf{R}_s)^2}=\frac{v}{8\pi^3}c(1-c)\int\mathbf{A}_{\mathbf{k}}^2\,d\mathbf{k}=\frac{3}{4\pi^2}c(1-c)\,d^2M^0, \tag{7.12}$$

i.e., the determination of $\overline{(\delta R_S)^2}$ reduces to the calculation of the integral of $\mathbf{A}_{\mathbf{k}}^2$.

If in calculating $\mathbf{A}_{\mathbf{k}}$ we use the approximation in which $Q_{\mathbf{k}ij}$ and $P_{\mathbf{k}i}$ are determined by formulas of the (6.5) and (6.6) type, and carry out an approximate integration of (7.12) by means of Houston's approximation, then the dimensionless constant

$$M^0\left(\frac{1}{v}\frac{\partial v}{\partial c}\right)^{-2}$$

Table 1

Metal	Elastic moduli in 10^{11} dyn/cm^2			$M^0 / \left(\frac{1}{v}\frac{\partial v}{\partial c}\right)^2$	
	c_{11}	c_{12}	c_{44}	In substitution-type solutions	In interstitial solutions
Ag	12.40	9.34	4.61	0.311	0.669
Al	10.82	6.13	2.85	0.293	0.680
Au	19.2	16.3	4.20	0.419	0.920
Cu	16.84	12.14	7.54	0.277	0.580
Ni	24.65	14.73	12.47	0.224	0.466
Pb	4.66	3.92	1.44	0.366	0.797

in solutions with a face-centered cubic lattice may be expressed as a function of the ratios of the moduli c_{12}/c_{11} and c_{44}/c_{11} [42]. Table 1 shows the values of M^0 calculated by this formula for substitution- and interstitial-type solutions with elastic moduli corresponding to various metals with this lattice.

In nonideal, disordered solutions, as indicated by (7.11) and (1.13), the mean-square displacements depend linearly on the correlation parameters $\varepsilon(\boldsymbol{\rho})$. The estimate made in [42] shows that the establishment of short-range order in a solution may greatly change (e.g., by a factor of two) the value of $\overline{(\delta\mathbf{R}_S)^2}$; as a rule $\overline{(\delta\mathbf{R}_S)^2}$ falls in ordering solutions and rises in decomposing solutions.

The establishment of long-range order in the solution may affect the mean-square displacements still more sharply. For example, if we may neglect correlation in the solution and the dependence of the atomic volume v on order, then in an ordered solution we have the following formula for $\overline{(\delta\mathbf{R}_S)^2}$ instead of (7.2):

$$\overline{(\delta\mathbf{R}_s)^2} = \frac{3}{4\pi^2}\frac{1}{\nu}\sum_{\gamma=1}^{\nu} c_\gamma(1-c_\gamma)\,d^2M^0. \tag{7.13}$$

In particular, in solutions of stoichiometric composition AB $\overline{(\delta\mathbf{R}_S)^2} \sim (1-\eta^2)$. In a completely ordered solution, for which c_γ equal 0 or 1, $\overline{(\delta\mathbf{R}_S)^2}$ clearly vanishes.

§8. Effect of Fluctuations in Correlation Parameters on Static Displacements in Solutions

In §§ 5 and 6 the waves of static displacements in solutions were only associated with fluctuation waves of concentration and long-range-order parameters, and it was correspondingly supposed that $R_{k\gamma}$ was a linear function of $c_{k\gamma'}$. In actual fact the expansion of $R_{k\gamma}$ may also contain higher powers of $c_{k\gamma'}$. In other words, according to (4.2) static displacements may also be produced by fluctuations in the correlation parameters. Neglect of this effect corresponded to writing the free energy in the form of expressions (5.3) or (6.1), which are valid in solutions for which the lattice parameters depend linearly on the concentration, and the concentration dependence of the elastic moduli may be neglected.

In order to study the influence of fluctuations in the correlation parameters on the static displacements in solutions, and thus formulate criteria for the applicability of the treatment given in §§ 5 and 6, we must use a more perfect model of the solution, considering possible deviations from the Vegard rule and also the dependence of the elastic moduli on composition. We shall carry out this investigation, by way of example, for disordered solutions with one atom per unit cell [27].

It is not difficult to generalize expression (6.1) for the free energy (considered in the microscopic theory as a function of the static displacements) by taking account of the dependence of the force constants $W_{ss'}$ and $V_{ss'}$ on the types of atoms α, α' (α, α' = A, B) lying at the points s and s':

$$F = F_0 - \sum_{s,\, s'} W^{\alpha\alpha'}_{ss'i} \delta R_{si} + \frac{1}{2} \sum_{s,\, s'} V^{\alpha\alpha'}_{ss'ij} \delta R_{si} \delta R_{s'j}. \tag{8.1}$$

Here the quantities W and V depend, generally speaking, on the composition of the solution, the correlation parameters, and the temperature. Equation (8.1) allows for the fact that the force acting on the s-th atom from the atom s' depends on the displacement of the latter and on the nature of both atoms. No account is taken, however, of the fact that this force may also depend on the nature of all the rest of the neighboring atoms. It may be shown that allowing for the latter dependence will not change any qualitative conclusions (and will only produce slight quantitative changes).

The model described by expression (8.1) for the free energy enables us to consider deviations from the Vegard rule and study the influence of fluctuations in the correlation parameters on the static distortions.

The quantities $W^{\alpha\alpha'}_{ss'i}$ take three values, $W^{AA}_{ss'i}$, $W^{AB}_{ss'i}$, and $W^{BB}_{ss'i}$. It is not hard to see that, on considering (1.1), these may be expressed in terms of the numbers c_s ($c_s = 1, 0$) by means of the identity

$$W^{\alpha\alpha'}_{ss'i} = W^{0}_{ss'i} + W_{ss'i}(c_s + c_{s'} - 2c) + W'_{ss'i}(c_s - c)(c_{s'} - c), \qquad (8.2)$$

where

$$\begin{aligned} W'_{ss'i} &= W^{AA}_{ss'i} + W^{BB}_{ss'i} - 2W^{AB}_{ss'i}, \\ W_{ss'i} &= W^{AB}_{ss'i} - W^{BB}_{ss'i} + cW'_{ss'i}, \\ W^{0}_{ss'i} &= W^{BB}_{ss'i} + 2cW_{ss'i} - c^2 W'_{ss'i}. \end{aligned} \qquad (8.3)$$

We may write the quantities $V^{\alpha\alpha'}_{ss'ij}$ for $s' \neq s$ in an analogous way (the quantities $V^{\alpha\alpha'}_{ssij}$ are determined from the condition $\sum_{s'} V^{\alpha\alpha'}_{ss'ij} = 0$).

The equilibrium conditions determining the static displacements of the atoms in the solution reduce to the vanishing of the derivatives with respect to δR_{si} from the expression (8.1) for the free energy of the solution. Expressing $W^{\alpha\alpha'}_{ss'}$ and $V^{\alpha\alpha'}_{ss'}$ in terms of c_s, these conditions may be written in the form of a system of equations

$$\sum_{s'} [V_{ss'ij} + V'_{ss'ij}(c_s + c_{s'} - 2c) + V''_{ss'ij}(c_s - c)(c_{s'} - c)](\delta R_{s'j} - \delta R_{sj}) =$$

$$= \sum_{s'} [W_{ss'i}(c_s + c_{s'} - 2c) + W'_{ss'i}(c_s - c)(c_{s'} - c)]. \qquad (8.4)$$

We have not written the sum $\sum_{s'} W^{0}_{ss'i}$, on the right-hand side of equation (8.4), since this vanishes because $W^{\alpha\alpha'}_{ss'i} = -W^{\alpha'\alpha}_{s'si} = -W^{\alpha\alpha'}_{s'si}$.

In future we shall consider that $V'_{ss'}$ and $V''_{ss'}$ are much smaller than the corresponding quantities $V_{ss'}$ and shall solve the system of equations (8.4) by the method of successive approximations. This approximation is valid if the difference in the elastic moduli of solutions of different compositions are much smaller than the moduli themselves. In the zero approximation we put $V'_{ss'} = V''_{ss'} = 0$. The resultant system of equations may easily be solved by means of a Fourier transformation, in the same way as the analogous system of equations in §6. However, in contrast to the earlier system, the right-hand side of equations (8.4) involves not only the differences $c_{s'} - c$, characterizing the fluctuations in concentration, but also the quantities $(c_s - c)(c_{s'} - c)$, the deviations of which from the mean value of $\varepsilon(\boldsymbol{\rho})$ ($\boldsymbol{\rho} = \mathbf{R}_s - \mathbf{R}_{s'}$) determines the fluctuations in the correlation parameters. Multiplying equations (8.4) by $\exp(i\mathbf{k}\mathbf{R}_s)$, adding the results, and taking account of formulas (5.1), (1.11), and (4.1) for the Fourier expansions of $\delta\mathbf{R}_s$, $c_s - c$ and $(c_s - c)(c_{s'} - c)$, we obtain a system of three linear equations expressing the Fourier components of the static displacements $\mathbf{R}_\mathbf{k}$ in terms of the Fourier components of the concentration $c_\mathbf{k}$ and the correlation parameters $\varepsilon_\mathbf{k}(\rho)$:

$$Q_{\mathbf{k}ij} R_{\mathbf{k}j} = P_{\mathbf{k}i} c_\mathbf{k} + \sum_{\rho} P'_i(\rho)\, \varepsilon_\mathbf{k}(\rho). \tag{8.5}$$

Here $Q_{\mathbf{k}ij}$ and $P_{\mathbf{k}i}$ are determined by formulas (6.4) and $P'_i(\boldsymbol{\rho}) \equiv -iW'_{ss'i}$.

We see from (8.5) that the Fourier components of the static displacements are now linear functions of not only the Fourier components of the concentration but also the Fourier components of the correlation parameters $\varepsilon_\mathbf{k}(\rho)$.

The solution of the system (8.5) may clearly be put in the form

$$\mathbf{R}_\mathbf{k} = \mathbf{A}_\mathbf{k} c_\mathbf{k} + \sum_{\rho \neq 0} \mathbf{A}_\mathbf{k}(\rho)\, \varepsilon_\mathbf{k}(\rho), \tag{8.6}$$

where as in §6 the $A_{\mathbf{k}i}$, are determined from equations (6.3), and $A_{\mathbf{k}i}(\rho)$ are solutions of the equations

$$Q_{\mathbf{k}ij} A_{\mathbf{k}j}(\rho) = P'_i(\rho) \qquad (i = 1, 2, 3). \tag{8.7}$$

In order to determine $\mathbf{R}_\mathbf{k}$ in the first approximation relative to $V'_{ss'}$ and $V''_{ss'}$, we must first find the displacements $\delta\mathbf{R}_s^0$ in the zero approximation from formulas (5.1) and (8.6), put these values into the terms of equations (8.4) containing $V'_{ss'}$ and $V''_{ss'}$, and consider the resultant expressions as extra terms on the right-hand sides of these equations. After this the system of equations for $\delta\mathbf{R}_s$ may be solved, as in the zero approximation, by means of a Fourier transformation, and an expression for $\mathbf{R}_k$ may be obtained in the first approximation. As a result of this the coefficients P_{ki} and $P'_i(\boldsymbol{\rho})$ in (8.5) will be changed.

For example, in the case of a small concentration, in accordance with (7.9), the constants $W_{ss'i}$ in the expressions for P_{ki} must be replaced, on considering the change V' in the force constants (which is in general not small), by $W_{ss'i} - V'_{ss_1s'ij}\delta R_{s_1j}$, where $\delta\mathbf{R}_s$ are determined by equations (7.9). In addition to this, on the right-hand side of equations (8.5) for $\mathbf{R}_k$, the terms proportional to c_k and $\varepsilon_k(\rho)$, are supplemented by terms proportional to the Fourier components $\varepsilon_k(\rho_1, \rho_2)$ and $\varepsilon_k(\rho_1, \rho_2, \rho_3)$ of the fluctuations in the correlation parameter (1.6) corresponding to three and four atom groups instead of pairs. Allowance for the fluctuations of these complex correlation functions has no effect on the qualitative results and only leads to slight quantitative corrections if the elastic moduli depend weakly on composition ($V'_{ss'}$ and $V''_{ss'}$ are small), and especially if the concentration is not large (in this case $\overline{|\varepsilon_k(\rho_1, \rho_2)|^2} \sim c^3$). Hence we shall confine ourselves to considering fluctuations in only the binary correlation parameters. As regards the coefficient $W_{ss'}$ and $W'_{ss'}$ in P_{ki} and $P'_i(\boldsymbol{\rho})$, we shall consider that these are changed in a corresponding manner.

For small k, the calculation of the Fourier components $\mathbf{R}_k$ of the static displacements created by long-wave fluctuation waves of concentration and correlation parameters may be carried out by means of the macroscopic theory of elasticity, considering the free energy as a function of the components of the strain tensor and smooth fluctuational variations in c and $\varepsilon(\boldsymbol{\rho})$. This calculation is carried out in the same way as in §5; it is only necessary to remember that the concentration stresses are created not only by fluctuations of concentration but also by fluctuations of the correlation parameters.

Repeating the discussion of §5 it is thus not hard to deduce that, on the macroscopic approximation, the components of the vector $\mathbf{R}_k$ are determined by the equations

$$k\lambda_{ijlm}n_jn_lR_{km} = \lambda_{ijlm}n_j\left[\left(\frac{\delta u_{lm}}{\delta c}\right)_{\varepsilon}c_k + \sum_{\rho\neq 0}\frac{\delta u_{lm}}{\delta\varepsilon(\rho)}\varepsilon_k(\rho)\right] \quad (i = 1, 2, 3). \tag{8.8}$$

Now the lattice parameters of the solution depend both on composition and on the correlation parameters, so that R_k depends both on c_k, and $\varepsilon_k(\rho)$. The coefficients of c_k and $\varepsilon_k(\rho)$ are here determined respectively by the deformations

$$\left(\frac{\partial u_{lm}}{\partial c}\right)_{\varepsilon} \delta c \text{ and } \frac{\partial u_{lm}}{\partial \varepsilon(\rho)} \delta\varepsilon(\rho),$$

arising as a result of a homogeneous change in concentration with unvarying correlation parameters or a homogeneous change in the correlation parameters $\varepsilon(\boldsymbol{\rho})$.

We see by comparing (8.6) and (8.8) that equation (8.8) enables us to determine the coefficients A_k and $A_k(\rho)$ from experimental data relating to the dependence of the cell size and shape on the composition and correlation parameters. However, whereas $(\delta u_{lm}/\delta c)_{\varepsilon}$ may in principle be obtained, for example, from experiments in which solutions of different compositions, after passing through various forms of heat treatment, have the same correlation parameters, ordinary experiments relating to the effect of annealing (which gives rise to the short-range order) on the lattice constant only give the sum of the quantities $\delta u_{lm}/\delta\varepsilon(\boldsymbol{\rho})$ with respect to $\boldsymbol{\rho}$. In order to determine these tensors, corresponding to the individual $\boldsymbol{\rho}$, for example, in cubic crystals, we must carry out some special experiments in which external forces disrupt the cubic symmetry. In particular, we may use the results of experiments on the change in the lattice constant associated with the development of short-range order in the presence of elastic stresses or a magnetic field (in a ferromagnetic).

In order to estimate the influence of fluctuations in the correlation parameters on the static displacements it is convenient to use the nearest-neighbor approximation. In this approximation, for cubic crystals, only some of the components $W'_{ss'i}$ are different from zero (and equal in absolute magnitude) for nearest-neighbor pairs of atoms. For example, in a face-centered cubic lattice, for the pair of points (000) and (110), $W'_x = W'_y = W'$; for points (000) and ($1\bar{1}0$) $W'_x = -W'_y = W'$. For an arbitrary pair of nearest neighbors separated by a vector $\boldsymbol{\rho}$, W'_i may be written in the form

$$W'_i = b_i W',$$

where $(d/2)b_i$ are the components in the expansion of $\boldsymbol{\rho}$ with respect to vectors $\mathbf{e}_i$ directed along the cubic axes:

$$\boldsymbol{\rho} = \frac{d}{2} \sum_{i=1}^{3} b_i \mathbf{e}_i. \tag{8.9}$$

The single parameter W' may be expressed in terms of the derivative of the lattice constant d with respect to the correlation parameter, if we compare equations (8.7) of the microscopic theory with the corresponding equations for $A_k(\rho)$ of the macroscopic theory obtained from (8.8). It is not hard to prove [27] that

$$W' = \frac{1}{24} d^2 (c_{11} + 2c_{12}) \frac{1}{v} \frac{\partial v}{\partial \varepsilon},$$

where the derivative $\partial v/\partial \varepsilon$ is defined by the change in the atomic volume v for an identical change in the correlation parameters for all pairs of neighboring atoms [and not one pair, as in the derivative $\partial v/\partial \varepsilon(\boldsymbol{\rho})$], and may be determined in the ordinary way from experiments giving the relation between annealing conditions and the lattice parameter. Then for crystals with a face-centered cubic lattice, and on the approximation of nearest neighbors, equations (8.7) take the form

$$Q_{kij} A_{kj}(\boldsymbol{\rho}) = -i \frac{d^2}{24} (c_{11} + 2c_{12}) \frac{1}{v} \frac{\partial v}{\partial \varepsilon} b_i, \tag{8.10}$$

where Q_{kij} are determined by formula (6.5). The quantities A_k as before are determined by formulas (6.3), (6.5), and (6.6), in which, however, the derivative $\partial v/\partial c$ must now be taken for constant correlation parameters. For small k, i.e., when the macroscopic discussion is applicable, the coefficients Q_{kij} are determined by expressions (II.6), multiplied by $k^2 v$. In the nearest-neighbor approximation, the quantities $A_k(\rho)$ differ from zero only for vectors $\boldsymbol{\rho}$ drawn to the points of the first coordination sphere. For the remaining $\boldsymbol{\rho}$ the quantities $P_i(\rho)$ and $A_k(\rho)$ equal zero.

The relative role of the effects associated with the fluctuations in the correlation parameters may be estimated by determining the mean squares and products of the components of the vector R_k and comparing the contributions of the fluctuations in concentration and correlation parameters respectively. An estimate of this kind may most simply be made in ideal solutions, for which the squares of the Fourier components of the fluctuations in concentration and correlation parameters are determined by simple formulas (1.14) and (4.3), and according to (4.3) these fluctuations are statistically independent. Denoting the Fourier components of the displacements associated with the fluctuations in concentration and correlation parameters by $\mathbf{R}_{\mathbf{k}}^{(1)}$ and $\mathbf{R}_{\mathbf{k}}^{(2)}$, we may write in accordance with (8.6), (1.14), and (4.3)

$$\overline{R_{\mathbf{k}i}^{(1)}R_{\mathbf{k}j}^{(1)*}} = \frac{1}{N}c(1-c)A_{\mathbf{k}i}A_{\mathbf{k}j}, \quad \overline{R_{\mathbf{k}i}^{(2)}R_{\mathbf{k}j}^{(2)*}} = \frac{1}{N}c^2(1-c)^2\frac{1}{k^2}f_{ij},$$

$$\frac{1}{k^2}f_{ij} = \sum_{\boldsymbol{\rho}}{}' A_{\mathbf{k}i}(\boldsymbol{\rho})A_{\mathbf{k}j}(\boldsymbol{\rho})(1-\cos\mathbf{k}\boldsymbol{\rho}), \tag{8.11}$$

where, in the nearest-neighbor approximation, the summation over $\boldsymbol{\rho}$ is carried out only for the points of the first coordination sphere. The quantities $A_{\mathbf{k}i}(\boldsymbol{\rho})$ are determined from equations (8.10). For small k $Q_{\mathbf{k}ij} \sim k^2$ and $A_{\mathbf{k}i}(\boldsymbol{\rho}) \sim 1/k^2$, i.e., $f_{ij} \equiv f_{ij}(\mathbf{n})$ are functions of the direction of the vector $\mathbf{k} = k\mathbf{n}$ only.

In the general case of elastically anisotropic crystals, the expressions for f_{ij} are very cumbersome even for small k (these expressions are given in explicit form in [27]). Hence we shall here only give the formulas for $f_{ij}(\mathbf{n})$ in elastically isotropic crystals with a face-centered cubic lattice ($\xi = 0$):

$$f_{xx}(\mathbf{n}) = \frac{1}{72}\left(\frac{1+\sigma}{1-\sigma}\right)^2\left(\frac{1}{v}\frac{\partial v}{\partial \varepsilon}\right)^2\{1+n_x^2+2\nu'(1-n_x^2)+$$
$$+\nu'^2[(1-n_x^2)^3+n_x^4(1-n_x^2)+2n_x^2n_y^2n_z^2]\},$$

$$f_{xy}(\mathbf{n}) = \frac{1}{72}\left(\frac{1+\sigma}{1-\sigma}\right)^2\left(\frac{1}{v}\frac{\partial v}{\partial \varepsilon}\right)^2 n_xn_y[2-\nu'(1+n_z^2)-\nu'^2(1-n_z^2+2n_z^4-2n_x^2n_y^2)],$$

$$\nu' = \frac{1}{1-2\sigma}. \tag{8.12}$$

Let us compare, for example, the mean squares of the static displacements $\mathbf{R}_{\mathbf{k}}^{(1)}$ and $\mathbf{R}_{\mathbf{k}}^{(2)}$, associated with the fluctuations of concentration and correlation parameters in the case of long fluctuation waves with wave vector $\mathbf{k}$ directed along the [100] axis (here the $\mathbf{R}_{\mathbf{k}}$ are also parallel to this axis). Defining $f_{xx}(\mathbf{n})$ by formula (8.12) and $A_{\mathbf{k}x}$ by formula (5.14), we find that the ratio $\overline{|\mathbf{R}_{\mathbf{k}}^{(2)}|^2} : \overline{|\mathbf{R}_{\mathbf{k}}^{(1)}|^2}$

is much smaller than unity if the following inequality is satisfied:

$$\left(\frac{\partial v}{\partial c}\right)_{\varepsilon}^{2} \gg \frac{1}{8}(1+\nu'^{2})\, c\,(1-c)\left(\frac{\partial v}{\partial \varepsilon}\right)^{2}. \tag{8.13}$$

Data relating to the derivative $\partial v/\partial \varepsilon$, i.e., the variation in the volume of the crystal in the course of the annealing process responsible for the establishment of short-range order, only exist for a few solutions. Hence it is more convenient to transform the criterion (8.13), replacing the $\partial v/\partial \varepsilon$ by quantities more easily determined by experiment. For this purpose we may, for example, note that, on neglecting the dependence of the quantities $W'_{ss'i}$ on composition for small $(1/v)(\partial v/\partial c)$, we may easily use formulas (8.1) and (8.3) to express W' in terms of the second derivative $\partial^2 v/\partial c^2$, and then relate the first derivative of v with respect to the correlation parameter ε to the second derivative with respect to concentration:

$$2\frac{\partial v}{\partial \varepsilon} \approx \frac{\partial^2 v}{\partial c^2}.$$

Another (and more precise) estimate gives for $\partial v/\partial \varepsilon$ the value

$$\frac{\partial v}{\partial \varepsilon} \approx \frac{\delta v}{\delta \varepsilon},$$

where δv is the change in the atomic volume on passing from the completely ordered solution to a disordered solution with a random distribution of atoms, and the change in the short-range-order parameter $\delta \varepsilon$ associated with this transformation is equal to 1/16 for solutions of the $AuCu_3$ type. If we accept these estimates, then criterion (8.13) may be rewritten in the form

$$\left(\frac{\partial v}{\partial c}\right)^{2} \gg c\,(1-c)\left(\frac{\partial^2 v}{\partial c^2}\right)^{2} \text{ or } \left(\frac{\partial v}{\partial c}\right)^{2} \gg c\,(1-c)\left(\frac{\delta v}{\delta \varepsilon}\right)^{2}, \tag{8.14}$$

in which we have considered that $(1+\nu'^2)/32 \lesssim 1$.

It follows from the results given in this paragraph that the approximation of §§5 and 6, in which the influence of fluctuations in the correlation parameters on the static displacements was not taken into account, is accurate if the quantities $W'_{ss'}$, $V'_{ss'}$, and $V''_{ss'}$ are equal to zero, i.e., if the Vegard rule is satisfied and the elastic moduli are independent of concentration. However, although such conditions are in fact not satisfied exactly, as follows from (8.14), the use of this approximation only involves small errors if the lattice constant varies only slightly with the correlation parameters, or (less exactly) if the concentration dependence of the lattice parameters differs little from a linear relationship (and the elastic moduli do not depend too much on the composition). It should be noted that the relative role of the effects associated with fluctuations in the correlation parameters may be greater in nonideal than in ideal solutions.

Chapter III

Effect of Long-Range Forces on Fluctuations in Crystals

§9. Effect of Elastic Interaction on the Fluctuation of Concentration and Order Parameters in Crystals

In Chapter I we set out the thermodynamic theory of fluctuations in concentration and order parameters on the assumption that the forces of interatomic interaction fell off rapidly with distance. Thus, for example, the mean square of the fluctuations of concentration in any volume element V' is determined by the ordinary formula of the thermodynamic theory of fluctuations (2.5), and the mean square of the Fourier component of concentration by formula (2.10). The results of the theory set out in Chapter I must be modified, however, if the forces of interaction are of the long-range type.

Formula (2.5) was derived for the case in which the volume V' was quite large, so that in determining the change in the thermodynamic potential $\delta\Phi'$ of this volume surface effects could be neglected and the volume in question could be regarded as a subsystem weakly interacting with the rest of the solution. This principle is only valid, however, if the forces of interatomic interaction are of the short-range type. In the case of long-range forces $\delta\Phi'$ will depend on the change of concentration not only in the volume V' but also in other parts of the crystal, i.e., $\delta\Phi'$ will be a functional function of $\delta c(\mathbf{r})$ given over the whole solution. In order to determine $\overline{(\delta c)^2}$ we must now carry out a more complex averaging (with respect to the various distributions of $\delta c(\mathbf{r})$ over the whole crystal, and not just in the volume V') than that used in the derivation of (2.5), and the latter will cease to be valid. There will also be a change in the expression for $\overline{|c_k|^2}$, since, even for long fluctuation waves, interaction at distances considerably greater than the wavelength, which was not considered in the derivation of formula (2.10), will become important. For anisotropic long-range forces, this will lead, in particular, to a dependence of $\overline{|c_k|^2}$ on $\mathbf{k}/k$ for small k, i.e., to the interesting effect of the nonanalytical behavior of $\overline{|c_k|^2}$ as $k \to 0$ (but $k > V^{-1/3}$).

The influence of long-range forces becomes important if the contribution to $\delta\Phi'$ due to the change in concentration outside the isolated volume V' is proportional to V' and not to the area of the surface. It is easy to see that this contribution will be proportional to the area of the surface of the isolated volume if the interaction energy falls on an exponential law, or on a power law $\sim r^{-n}$ with $n \geq 4$, and that it will be proportional to the volume V' for $n = 3$.

Forces of interaction in crystals falling off in accordance with a $1/r^3$ law (or more slowly) are extremely widespread. In particular, as indicated in §7, the energy of elastic interaction in elastically anisotropic crystals diminishes in accordance with a $1/r^3$ law at large r. Long-range elastic interaction between atoms in solution (i.e., interaction which remains finite over distances reasonably small compared with the dimensions of the crystal) also arises as a result of the mirror-image forces (see §7) in elastically isotropic crystals [45]. Another example of energy falling in accordance with a $1/r^3$ law is the case of the energy of dipole–dipole interaction between fluctuations of polarization or magnetization. The interaction of charged impurity ions or other defects falls off still more slowly with distance, obeying a Coulomb law.

If long-range forces make a considerable contribution to $\delta\Phi'$, then in order to calculate the fluctuations we must replace formulas of the (2.5) and (2.10) type by generalized formulas taking due account of these forces. Such generalized formulas, taking account of Coulomb interaction between charged defects, were derived in [54, 55] (for certain particular cases, the influence of elastic energy on fluctuations of composition was discussed in [56]).

Let us first consider the modifications to the formulas in the theory of fluctuations arising from the most widespread type of long-range forces: elastic interaction. Such interactions are closely connected with the static distortions (discussed in Chapter II) arising around atoms in solution if the atomic radii of the components differ, i.e., they take place to a greater or lesser extent in all practical cases. Later in §§ 10 and 11 we shall also consider effects associated with dipole–dipole and Coulomb forces.

Let us first of all discuss the influence of long-range elastic forces on the fluctuation waves of concentration in solid solutions. The energy of elastic interaction of the atoms in the volume V' with those outside V' could be determined by direct summation of the interaction energies of individual pairs of atoms. Instead of this, however, it is more convenient not to consider all the individual atoms outside the volume V', but to describe their combined action by specifying the stresses which they create inside the volume V'. Since effects associated with long-range action should appear most sharply for long waves, let us confine ourselves to the case of long-wave fluctuations, for which the wavelength is much greater than the interatomic distance r_0 and much smaller than the crystal dimensions Λ, i.e.,

$$kr_0 \ll 1 \text{ and } k\Lambda \gg 1.$$

In this case we may use the macroscopic approximation, in which the fluctuational change in concentration is characterized by a smooth function $\delta c(\mathbf{r})$, and the distortions of the crystal are characterized by specifying the strain tensors u_{ij} and the stress tensor σ_{ij}. We shall consider that the distortions are due only to fluctuations of concentration and that deformations created by parameters of order and correlation may be neglected. The value of the deformation created by the fluctuations in concentration is characterized by the tensor L_{ij} (5.5) [or (5.10)].

In the absence of stresses, the minimum work R necessary for reversibly creating concentration fluctuations δc in a part of the crystal with a constant total number N' of A and B atoms is determined by expression (2.4). In essence this expression already allows for the elastic energy associated with the homogeneous deformation $L_{ij}\delta c$ due to the change of concentration in the volume element V' considered (i.e., that associated with the elastic interaction of the atoms in volume V' with each other). Here, however, no allowance is made for the elastic energy due to changes in concentration outside V'. Such a change in concentration outside the volume leads to a certain additional strain $u_{ij} - L_{ij}\delta c$ inside V', added to the strain $L_{ij}\delta c$ resulting from the fluctuation δc inside the volume (and to the appearance of stresses). On adding the elastic free energy corresponding to this strain to the expression for R, we obtain the following formula for the work required to create an arbitrary, inhomogeneous, smooth distribution of concentration

$$R = \frac{1}{2} \int \left[\frac{d^2\varphi}{dc^2} (\delta c)^2 + \lambda_{ijlm} (u_{ij} - L_{ij}\delta c)(u_{lm} - L_{lm}\delta c) \right] dV. \qquad (9.1)$$

If the concentration distribution corresponds to the **k**-th fluctuation wave, then the expressions for δc and u_{ij} may be written in the form

$$\delta c = c_{\mathbf{k}} e^{-i\mathbf{kr}} + \text{c.c.}, \quad u_{ij} = \frac{1}{2} (n_i A_{\mathbf{k}j} + n_j A_{\mathbf{k}i})\, k c_{\mathbf{k}} e^{-i\mathbf{kr}} + \text{c.c.}, \qquad (9.2)$$

where the proportionality factor between the waves of static displacements and concentration, $\mathbf{A}_{\mathbf{k}}$, is given by equations (5.8).

Putting (9.2) into (9.1), we find that in the limit of small k the work $R_{\mathbf{k}}$ required for the development of the **k**-th fluctuation wave equals

$$R_{\mathbf{k}} = V \left[\frac{d^2\varphi}{dc^2} + \lambda_{ijlm} (k n_i A_{\mathbf{k}j} - L_{ij})(k n_l A_{\mathbf{k}m} - L_{lm}) \right] \overline{|c_{\mathbf{k}}|^2}. \qquad (9.3)$$

This formula differs from formula (2.9) (which related to the limiting case of k → 0) in respect of the last term, which allows for the elastic energy.

Putting (9.3) into (2.1) and remembering that the resultant probability distribution of the fluctuations of $c_{\mathbf{k}}$ is Gaussian, we obtain the following expression for the mean square of the **k**-th Fourier component of the fluctuations of concentration:

$$\overline{|c_{\mathbf{k}}|^2} = \frac{k_B T}{V \varphi_{cc}(\mathbf{k})}; \qquad \varphi_{cc}(\mathbf{k}) = \frac{d^2\varphi}{dc^2} + \varphi_{cc}^{y};$$

$$\varphi_{cc}^{y} = \lambda_{ijlm} (k n_i A_{\mathbf{k}j} - L_{ij})(k n_l A_{\mathbf{k}m} - L_{lm}) = \lambda_{ijlm} L_{ij} (L_{lm} - k n_l A_{\mathbf{k}m}). \qquad (9.4)$$

The second term in the formula for $\varphi_{cc}(\mathbf{k})$ allows for the long-range elastic forces and leads to a deviation of formula (9.4) from the ordinary formula (2.10), which was derived for the case of undistorted solid solutions. It is an important point that φ_{cc}^{y} and hence $\overline{|c_{\mathbf{k}}|^2}$, also depends on $\mathbf{n}$ for small k (that is, on the orientation of the vector $\mathbf{k}$ relative to the crystallographic axes), i.e., in an infinite crystal $\overline{|c_{\mathbf{k}}|^2}$ is a nonanalytic function of $\mathbf{k}$.

It should be noted, however, that for $k \sim 1/\Lambda$ formula (9.4) ceases to be applicable (so do the results of §5). For rather larger values of k, as in (2.10), we must also take account of the $\beta_{ij}(\mathbf{k})k_ik_j$ terms in the expression for $\varphi_{cc}(\mathbf{k})$. In contrast to the case of short-range forces considered in §2, when the quantity β was constant for cubic crystals, on taking account of elastic interaction, $\beta(\mathbf{k})$ depends on $\mathbf{n}$ even in the cubic case. This result is not hard to obtain if we consider fluctuation waves for small k and take account of the elastic energy by means of the formulas in §6.

In cubic crystals in particular, by using formula (5.11) for A_{ki} and (5.10) for L_{ij}, we may rewrite expression (9.4) for φ_{cc}^{y} in more explicit form:

$$\varphi_{cc}^{y}=\frac{1}{3}K\left(\frac{1}{v}\frac{\partial v}{\partial c}\right)^2\left\{3-\frac{c_{11}+2c_{12}}{D}\times\right.$$
$$\left.\times\left[1+2\xi\left(n_x^2n_y^2+n_x^2n_z^2+n_y^2n_z^2\right)+3\xi^2n_x^2n_y^2n_z^2\right]\right\}, \tag{9.5}$$

where $K = \frac{1}{3}(c_{11} + 2c_{12})$ is the bulk modulus. Thus even in cubic crystals $\varphi_{cc}(\mathbf{k})$ and $\overline{|c_{\mathbf{k}}|^2}$ depend on the direction of the vector $\mathbf{k}$. In hexagonal crystals, by taking account of (9.4), (5.10), (II.2), and (II.3), we may easily find expressions for the φ_{cc}^{y} corresponding to $\mathbf{k}$ vectors directed parallel or perpendicular to the hexagonal axis Z:

$$\varphi_{cc}^{y}=2\,\frac{c_{11}c_{33}-2c_{13}^2}{c_{33}}\left(\frac{1}{d_\perp}\frac{\partial d_\perp}{\partial c}\right)^2 \quad (\mathbf{k}\parallel Z), \tag{9.6a}$$

$$\varphi_{cc}^{y}=(c_{11}-c_{12})\left(\frac{1}{d_\perp}\frac{\partial d_\perp}{\partial c}\right)^2+\frac{2c_{11}-c_{12}}{c_{11}}c_{13}\frac{1}{d_\perp}\frac{\partial d_\perp}{\partial c}\frac{1}{d_\parallel}\frac{\partial d_\parallel}{\partial c}+$$
$$+\frac{c_{11}c_{33}-c_{13}^2}{c_{11}}\left(\frac{1}{d_\parallel}\frac{\partial d_\parallel}{\partial c}\right)^2 \quad (\mathbf{k}\perp Z). \tag{9.6b}$$

In elastically isotropic crystals it follows from (9.4) and (5.14) that

$$\varphi^{y}_{cc} = \frac{2}{3}\frac{1-2\sigma}{1-\sigma}K\left(\frac{1}{v}\frac{\partial v}{\partial c}\right)^2. \qquad (9.7)$$

In this case $\varphi_{cc}(\mathbf{k})$ and $\overline{|c_{\mathbf{k}}|^2}$ do not depend on the direction of the vector **k**. However, as in the case of elastically anisotropic crystals, $\varphi_{cc}(\mathbf{k}) \neq d^2\varphi/dc^2$, and allowance for elastic interaction changes the form of the formulas for $\overline{|c_{\mathbf{k}}|^2}$.

The fact that on allowing for elastic energy the value of $\overline{|c_{\mathbf{k}}|^2}$ is not determined simply by the value of $d^2\varphi/dc^2$, as in the case of short-range forces, may readily be interpreted by using the approximation of the elastically isotropic continuum. In this approximation, as mentioned in §7, the long-range elastic interaction of impurity atoms, proportional to $1/r^3$, vanishes. Hence for a fluctuational redistribution of concentration in an elastically isotropic solution the long-range elastic energy remains constant, and in the absence of other forms of interaction the fluctuations will be the same as in the ideal solution.

On introducing an impurity atom into the crystal there is a change in the elastic energy due to the mirror-image forces mentioned in §7; this energy does not change on varying the position of the impurity atom through distances considerably smaller than the dimensions of the crystal. This elastic energy, which is almost independent of the position of the impurity atoms (and hence has no effect on the fluctuations), makes a contribution to φ which, according to [45], equals

$$\frac{1}{3}K\frac{1-2\sigma}{1-\sigma}\left(\frac{1}{v}\frac{\partial v}{\partial c}\right)^2 c(1-c)V$$

so that the solution becomes nonideal. However, the corresponding term in $d^2\varphi/dc^2$ falls in accordance with expression (9.7) for φ^{y}_{cc}; this agrees with the earlier-discussed fact that, if a redistribution of concentration takes place over a distance much smaller than Λ, the elastic energy remains unaltered, and in the absence of other interactions the solution behaves in respect of fluctuations as ideal (although the presence of elastic interaction leads to a concentration dependence of the energy of the solution and to the decomposition of the latter, which reduces the elastic energy).

In order to estimate the relative role of the term φ_{cc}^{y} associated with the elastic energy, let us put, for example $c_{11} = 2.5$, $c_{12} = 1.5$, and $c_{44} = 1.2\cdot10^{12}$ dyn/cm^2 (we have taken the values of the elastic moduli for nickel). Then for $(1/v)\,\partial v/\partial c = 0.1$ we have $\varphi_{cc}^{y} = 5\cdot10^{9}$ erg/cm^3 for **k** parallel to the [100] axis, and $\varphi_{cc}^{y} = 8\cdot10^{9}$ erg/cm^3 for **k** parallel to the [111] axis. For comparison we note that in ideal solutions at 700°K, $v = 10^{-23}$ cm^3 and $c = 1/2$, corresponding to (2.12) $d^2\varphi/dc^2 = 4\cdot10^{10}$ erg/cm^3. In some cases the relative role of φ_{cc}^{y} may be considerably greater, since $(1/v)\,\partial v/\partial c$ in certain substitution-type solutions reaches a value of 0.4, and in interstitial solutions $(1/v)\,\partial v/\partial c \sim 1$. On the other hand, for low concentrations (when $d^2\varphi/dc^2 \sim 1/c$) and in ordered solutions with a large degree of short-range order, $d^2\varphi/dc^2$ is much greater than in the estimate given, and the relative role of φ_{cc}^{y} diminishes [especially in solutions with small $(1/v)\,\partial v/\partial c$].

The effects caused by long-range elastic forces becomes especially important in the region of the critical point on the decomposition curve. Since, at the critical point, $d^2\varphi/dc^2 = 0$, in the absence of elastic strain, and in undistorted solutions (as discussed in more detail earlier, see §2.4), the probabilities of long-wave fluctuations ($kr_0 \ll 1$) in this region become anomalously large. However, in distorted solutions, on allowing for long-range elastic forces, $\varphi_{cc}^{y} \neq 0$, and, as indicated by (9.4), $\varphi_{cc}(\mathbf{k})$ does not vanish at the critical point, so that, for $\Lambda^{-1} \ll k \ll r_0^{-1}$, the fluctuations remain finite at the critical point, although they may certainly undergo a considerable rise in the case of a low elastic energy (small L_{ij}). In the presence of distortions, only those fluctuations for which the wavelengths are comparable with the dimensions of the crystals ($k \sim \Lambda^{-1}$), and for which φ_{cc}^{y} falls and vanishes at $k = 0$, rise anomalously at the critical point.

In the pair-interaction model, as indicated by (3.1) and (1.7), the mean thermodynamic energy of a disordered solution $\overline{E}$ is expressed in a simple manner in terms of $\overline{|c_{\mathbf{k}}|^2}$:

$$\overline{E} = \sum_{\mathbf{k}} \overline{|c_{\mathbf{k}}|^2}\, w_{\mathbf{k}}, \text{ where } w_{\mathbf{k}} = \sum_{\boldsymbol{\rho}} w_{\boldsymbol{\rho}} \cos \mathbf{k}\boldsymbol{\rho}.$$

We see from this formula that the tending of $\overline{|c_{\mathbf{k}}|^2}$ to infinity for certain values of **k** may lead to a singularity in the energy (and hence the thermodynamic potential) of the solution; the law by which $\overline{|c_k|^2}$ (as a function of **k** and temperature) tends to infinity determines the character of this singularity. Hence the fact that (as a result of elastic interaction) the region corresponding to the sharp rise in $\overline{|c_k|^2}$ near the critical point is limited to small $k \sim \Lambda^{-1}$ may probably be ascribed to the change in the character of the singularities of the thermodynamic quantities (and in the form of the decomposition curve) in the critical region, as compared with the case in which long-range forces are absent and $\overline{|c_k|^2}$ rises sharply not only for $k \sim \Lambda^{-1}$ but for all $k \ll r_0$.

In an analogous way, we may expect changes in the character of the singularities associated with phase transformations of the second kind, as compared with the results discussed in §2.4 (which were obtained on the nearest-neighbor approximation), if the long-range elastic or dipole–dipole forces seriously influence the fluctuations in the degree of long-range order near the transformation point, as occurs in certain piezoelectric and ferroelectric crystals (see below). In other words, we may say that the long-range forces affect the law governing the fall in the spatial correlation of fluctuations with distance, which is closely connected with the character of the singularities near phase-transformation points of the second kind and critical points (see §2.4).

Although elastic interaction prevents the anomalous rise in fluctuations with $\Lambda^{-1} \ll k \ll r_0^{-1}$ near the critical point, such an anomalous rise may occur at lower temperatures in supercooled solutions, when the homogeneous undecomposed solution is in a nonequilibrium state. If the crystal contains hardly any defects and the rate of formation and growth of the new-phase nuclei is sufficiently low, the solution may find itself in an undecomposed state for a considerable time, sufficient for the establishment of a quasiequilibrium distribution of fluctuations (with moderately sized k), corresponding to the temperature in question. Thus $\overline{|c_k|^2}$ is determined as before by formula (9.4), in which, however, $(d^2\varphi/dc^2) < 0$ below the decomposition temperature.

As temperature falls, so will $\varphi_{cc}(\mathbf{k})$, while $\overline{|c_k|^2}$ will rise, until at some temperature $T_0'(c)$ the quantity $\varphi_{cc}(\mathbf{k})$ vanishes for specific directions $\mathbf{n}_{min} = \mathbf{k}_{min}/k_{min}$ of the vector $\mathbf{n}$. In this case the $\overline{|c_k|^2}$ for such directions of $\mathbf{n}$ will become anomalously large (on allowing for terms $\sim k^2$ in $\varphi_{cc}(\mathbf{k})$ the value of $\overline{|c_k|^2}$ will not pass to infinity). For other directions of **n** in elastically anisotropic crystals, $\varphi_{cc}(\mathbf{k})$ will not vanish at $T = T_0'(c)$ and $k \to 0$, i.e., near this temperature there should be a sharp dependence of $\overline{|c_k|^2}$ on **n**. At temperatures below $T_0'(c)$, the long-wave fluctuational inhomogeneities of composition increase in time without limit, as a result of which the solution decomposes by the spinodal mechanism [57, 58]. It is clear that in respect of nonequilibrium solutions this discussion can only have a qualitative character.

It should be remembered that, in the above consideration of fluctuations, it was assumed that defects were absent. Nevertheless crystals always contain both nonequilibrium defects (dislocations, grain boundaries, mosaic boundaries, or the boundaries of antiphase domains in ordered crystals, and so on) and equilibrium defects (for example, vacancies). In addition to vacancies, other defects, the formation of which does not require the expenditure of any energy, may arise in solid solutions, especially those comprising components with greatly differing atomic radii; such defects include, for example, those containing n + 1 atoms of "small radius" in n points of the "average" lattice. The formation of these defects is hindered by entropy (probability) rather than energy limitations as in the case of vacancies, so that their concentration falls off at high temperatures. It is clear that the development and movement of this kind of defect leads to fluctuations in the total number N' of A and B atoms in a given number of points of the "average" lattice. The fluctuations in the concentration and number of atoms are not statistically independent, and allowance for the fluctuations in N' may well partly remove the concentration-induced elastic stresses and change the formula for $\overline{|c_k|^2}$. If, however, the concentrations of these defects and also of the nonequilibrium defects are not large, the effects associated with them may be neglected, especially for the case of not very long wavelengths of the fluctuation waves.

The results obtained for concentration fluctuations may easily be carried over to the case of fluctuations in various internal parameters. Thus, for example, if the long-range order in a single-component crystal is characterized by a single parameter η, then the formulas describing the fluctuational waves of long-range order may be obtained from the corresponding formulas for the concentration waves if we simply replace c by η. Thus, in accordance with (9.4), on allowing for elastic interaction, instead of being given by (2.14), $\overline{|\eta_{\mathbf{k}}|^2}$ is given (for small k) by the expression

$$\overline{|\eta_{\mathbf{k}}|^2} = \frac{k_B T}{V\varphi_{\eta\eta}(\mathbf{k})}, \qquad \varphi_{\eta\eta}(\mathbf{k}) = \varphi_{\eta\eta} + \lambda_{ijlm} L_{ij}^{\eta} (L_{lm}^{\eta} - k n_l A_{\mathbf{k}m}^{\eta}), \tag{9.8}$$

where $L_{ij}^{\eta} = \delta u_{ij}/\delta\eta$ characterize the strains arising in the crystal for a homogeneous change in η, and $A_{\mathbf{k}m}^{\eta}$ is determined by equations (5.8), in which L_{ij} is replaced by L_{ij}^{η}.

If the crystal has a center of symmetry, then the lattice parameters are even functions of η and in disordered crystals (η = 0) $L_{ij}^{\eta} = 0$, i.e., the elastic interacting forces, in accordance with (9.8), do not influence the long-wave fluctuations of long-range order. For small η in this case $L_{ij}^{\eta} \sim \eta$, so that when the ordered crystal approaches a phase transformation point of the second kind both the first and the second elastic-energy) terms in expression (9.8) for $\varphi_{\eta\eta}(\mathbf{k})$ tend to zero, and for small k $\overline{|\eta_{\mathbf{k}}|^2}$ becomes anomalously large.

However, if the crystal has no center of symmetry, then in the disordered phase we find that in a number of cases (for example, if in the nonferroelectric phase the crystal is a piezoelectric), a change in long-range order $\delta\eta$ produces a proportional change in deformation (the lattice parameters depend linearly on η) and $L_{ij}^{\eta} \neq 0$. In these cases the elastic forces have a considerable influence on the long-wave fluctuations of η, both in the ordered and in the disordered phase. Near a phase transformation point of the second kind $\overline{|\eta_{\mathbf{k}}|^2}$ remains finite for small k (although in the case of small L_{ij}^{η} it may rise considerably) except for the region of very small k $\sim \Lambda^{-1}$.

It should be noted that the lattice parameters usually depend on the degree of order much less than on the concentration (L_{ij}^{η} is much smaller than L_{ij}), i.e., the elastic interaction usually has less effect on the fluctuations of long-range order than on the fluctuations of concentration.

If the long-range order in single-component crystals is characterized by not one but several parameters η_{μ} (μ = 1, 2, ..., r), then the calculation of the minimum work necessary for the creation of fluctuations $\delta\eta_{\mu}$ may be carried out in the same way as above. Transforming to the Fourier components it is not difficult to see that, allowing for the elastic energy, the mean squares and products of the Fourier components for small k are determined by the following formula, replacing formula (2.18), which was derived without allowing for long-range forces:

$$\frac{1}{2}\overline{(\eta_{\mu\mathbf{k}}\eta^*_{\mu'\mathbf{k}}+\eta^*_{\mu\mathbf{k}}\eta_{\mu'\mathbf{k}})}=\frac{k_BT}{V}\varphi^{-1}_{\mu\mu'}(\mathbf{k}), \tag{9.9}$$

$$\varphi_{\mu\mu'}(\mathbf{k})=\frac{\partial^2\varphi}{\partial\eta_\mu\,\partial\eta_{\mu'}}+\varphi^y_{\mu\mu'},$$

$$\varphi^y_{\mu\mu'}=\lambda_{ijlm}L^{\mu}_{ij}(L^{\mu'}_{lm}-kn_lA^{\mu'}_{km}).$$

Here $L^{\mu}_{ij}=\delta u_{ij}/\delta\eta_\mu$, and A^{μ}_{km} is determined by formula (5.8), in which L_{ij} are replaced by L^{μ}_{ij}.

In accordance with the above derivation, (9.9) contains the elastic moduli defined for unvarying values of η_μ. These may be found, for example, by means of high-frequency measurements.

Formula (9.9) may also be used for determining the mean squares and products of the Fourier components of the concentration and order parameters in ordered solutions if by η_μ ($\mu = 1, 2, \ldots, r-1$) we understand the parameters of long-range order and by $\eta_r \equiv c$ the concentration.

§10. Effect of Dipole – Dipole Interaction on Fluctuations of Polarization

As in the case of elastic interaction, dipole–dipole interaction, which obeys a $1/r^3$ law, may lead to a change in the form of the formulas for the probabilities of fluctuations. Electric dipole–dipole forces greatly influence fluctuations of polarization in dielectric crystals, and magnetic forces influence fluctuations in magnetization. Let us consider the effects due to these forces, using fluctuations in polarization as an example. We shall consider long-wave fluctuations, for which the effects of long-range action appear most sharply. Hence the state of polarization in the crystal may be characterized by a macroscopic parameter, the polarization vector $\mathbf{P}(\mathbf{r})$.

In the presence of long-range dipole–dipole forces, the work necessary for creating fluctuations of polarization in an isolated volume V' depends not only on the state of the crystal in this volume but also on the values of the polarization in the rest of the crystal. As in the case of elastic forces, the interaction energy of the dipoles in the volume V' with the dipoles outside this volume may conveniently be determined not by direct summation but by considering the action of the dipoles outside V', as given by the electric field **E** which they create inside V'. For a nonequilibrium state of the crystal, the thermodynamic potential of unit volume φ, considered as a function of the internal parameter **P** and the external parameter (the electric-field strength **E**) is determined by formula (2.19). We also take due account of relation (2.20) between the second derivatives φ with respect to **P** and the dielectric susceptibility tensor $\varkappa_{ij}$, as well as the condition $\mathbf{E} = \partial\varphi/\partial\mathbf{P}$ for the equilibrium value of the field. Then the minimum work necessary for the creation of a space-varying distribution of polarization $\delta\mathbf{P}$ and the variation in electric field $\delta\mathbf{E}$ produced by this polarization may be written in the form

$$R = \frac{1}{2}\int (\varkappa_{ij}^{-1}\delta P_i \delta P_j - \delta P_i \delta E_i)\, dV. \tag{10.1}$$

The change in electric field $\delta\mathbf{E}$ associated with the development of a static fluctuational variation in polarization $\delta\mathbf{P}$ is determined by the electrostatic equations

$$\operatorname{div}\delta\mathbf{E} = -4\pi \operatorname{div}\delta\mathbf{P}, \qquad \operatorname{rot}\delta\mathbf{E} = 0$$

(for a dielectric crystal in the absence of free charges). It follows from the latter equation that for the **k**-th fluctuation wave the amplitude of the field $\mathbf{E_k}$ is directed parallel to **k** ($[\mathbf{kE_k}] = 0$), while from the first equation we obtain a relation between the amplitudes of $\mathbf{E_k}$ and $\mathbf{P_k}$. As a result of this the polarization and field in this fluctuation wave may be written in the form

$$\delta\mathbf{P} = \mathbf{P_k}e^{-i\mathbf{kr}} + \text{c.c.}, \quad \delta\mathbf{E} = \mathbf{E_k}e^{-i\mathbf{kr}} + \text{c.c.}, \quad \mathbf{E_k} = -4\pi(\mathbf{P_k n})\,\mathbf{n}. \tag{10.2}$$

Putting these expressions into (10.1), we find that the minimum work necessary for creating the **k**-th fluctuation wave equals

$$R_\mathbf{k} = \frac{1}{2} V \varkappa_{ij}^{-1}(\mathbf{k})\,(P_{\mathbf{k}i}P_{\mathbf{k}j}^* + P_{\mathbf{k}i}^* P_{\mathbf{k}j}), \tag{10.3}$$

where

$$\varkappa_{ij}^{-1}(\mathbf{k}) = \varkappa_{ij}^{-1} + 4\pi n_i n_j. \tag{10.4}$$

Allowance for long-range forces of the dipole–dipole type thus results in the appearance of the last term in (10.4), which greatly changes the value of the minimum work required.

In the classical (not quantum) theory of fluctuations, it immediately follows from expressions (10.3) for the minimum work and from the Gaussian distribution of fluctuation probabilities (2.1), that

$$\frac{1}{2}\overline{(P_{\mathbf{k}i}P^*_{\mathbf{k}j}+P^*_{\mathbf{k}i}P_{\mathbf{k}j})}=\frac{k_BT}{V}\varkappa_{ij}(\mathbf{k}), \tag{10.5}$$

where $\varkappa(\mathbf{k})$ is the tensor reciprocal to the tensor $\varkappa^{-1}(\mathbf{k})$, which is given by formula (10.4). For the classical theory to be applicable, however, it is essential that for all the characteristic frequencies ω_i of the polarization oscillations (and for the effective frequencies of the diffusion motion of the dipoles) we should satisfy the condition

$$\hbar\omega_i \ll k_BT.$$

This type of condition is usually satisfied to a high accuracy for fluctuations of concentration and order parameters in solutions in which the change in fluctuations with time is determined by very slow diffusion processes. On the other hand, in the case of fluctuations in polarization, the condition $\hbar\omega_i \ll k_BT$ is only satisfied for fluctuational variations associated with relatively slow oscillations of the ions; for the part of the polarization corresponding to electron rather than ion excitations, however, the very opposite condition is usually satisfied: $\hbar\omega_i \gg k_BT$. The contribution of these high-frequency fluctuations must be taken into account by means of quantum theory.

In order to determine the mean squares of the fluctuations of polarization, allowing for the quantum character of a certain proportion of these fluctuations, we note that the mean products of the fluctuations given by formula (10.5), calculated on the classical theory of "static" fluctuations, may be put in the form of integrals

$$\frac{1}{2}\int_{-\infty}^{\infty}\overline{[P_{\mathbf{k}i}(\omega)P^*_{\mathbf{k}j}(\omega)+P^*_{\mathbf{k}i}(\omega)P_{\mathbf{k}j}(\omega)]}\,d\omega. \tag{10.6}$$

Here under the integral sign we have the mean products of the Fourier components

$$P_{\mathbf{k}i}(\omega) = \frac{1}{2\pi} \int_{-\infty}^{\infty} P_{\mathbf{k}i}(t) \exp(i\omega t)\, dt,$$

also calculated on the classical theory. This result follows from the theory of the time correlation of the fluctuations (see, for example, [1]). In actual fact, however, the probabilities of the high-frequency harmonics of the fluctuations $\mathbf{P}_{\mathbf{k}}(\omega)$, for which $\hbar\omega_i \gg k_B T$ cannot be determined from the formulas of the classical theory of fluctuations; these harmonics are "nonexcited," and it is permissible to neglect their contribution to the integral (10.6) over ω (neglecting the zero quantum oscillations). In order to determine the mean products of the genuinely existing fluctuations of polarization, we must subtract the contribution corresponding to these non-excited harmonics from (10.5) or (10.6).

Let us consider, for example, the case in which $k_B T \sim \hbar\omega'$, where ω' is considerably greater than the frequencies of the ions and considerably smaller than the electron frequencies. Let us use $\varkappa_{\infty ij}$ to denote the dielectric-susceptibility tensor for frequencies $\sim\omega'$, corresponding to electron polarization. Then the contribution from the high frequencies $\omega \geq \omega'$ in integral (10.6) (calculated from the classical-theory formulas) may be found from formula (10.5) if in the latter we replace $\varkappa(\mathbf{k})$ by the tensor $\varkappa_\infty(\mathbf{k})$ obtained from the $\varkappa_{\infty ij}$ of formula (10.4). As a result of this, on subtracting the contributions of the high-frequency fluctuations not excited at the temperature in question from (10.5), we obtain

$$\frac{1}{2}\overline{(P_{\mathbf{k}i}P^*_{\mathbf{k}j} + P^*_{\mathbf{k}i}P_{\mathbf{k}j})} = \frac{k_B T}{V}\left[\varkappa_{ij}(\mathbf{k}) - \varkappa_{\infty ij}(\mathbf{k})\right]. \qquad (10.7)$$

For lower temperatures, at which neither the electron branches nor certain of the branches of the ionic oscillations are excited, we may also use formula (10.7), if by $\varkappa_\infty$ we understand the tensor taking account of both the electronic and high-frequency ionic polarization. In deriving (10.7) it was assumed that the contribution of the low-frequency fluctuations considered was not anomalously small, so that it was permissible to neglect the quantum (zero) high-frequency fluctuations.

We see from (10.4) that all the quantities characterizing the mean products of the fluctuations (10.7) may be determined from experimental data relating to the static dielectric susceptibility ($\varkappa_{ij}$) and the refractive indices for infrared light (determining $\varkappa_{\infty ij}$). Since, as indicated by (10.4), $\varkappa(\mathbf{k})$ and $\varkappa_\infty(\mathbf{k})$ are generally speaking nonanalytic functions of $\mathbf{k}$ for small k [the limiting value of $\varkappa(\mathbf{k})$ as $\mathbf{k} \to 0$ depends on the direction of $\mathbf{k}$], expression (10.7) usually has a singularity as $\mathbf{k} \to 0$, in the same way as (9.4) (but $k \gg \Lambda^{-1}$).

In the particular case of cubic crystals $\varkappa_{ij} = [(\varepsilon - 1)/4\pi]\delta_{ij}$ (ε is the static dielectric constant) and $\varkappa_{\infty ij} = [(\varepsilon_\infty - 1)/4\pi]\delta_{ij}$. Taking the Z axis parallel to $\mathbf{k}$ and substituting these values in (10.4) and (10.7), we find that expression (10.7) vanishes for $i \neq j$, while for $i = j$

$$\overline{|P_{\mathbf{k}x}|^2} = \overline{|P_{\mathbf{k}y}|^2} = \frac{k_B T}{4\pi V}(\varepsilon - \varepsilon_\infty), \qquad \overline{|P_{\mathbf{k}z}|^2} = \frac{k_B T}{4\pi V}\frac{\varepsilon - \varepsilon_\infty}{\varepsilon\varepsilon_\infty}. \qquad (10.8)$$

Thus the probabilities of the development of longitudinal and transverse fluctuation waves may differ considerably. This difference is entirely due to the long-range dipole–dipole forces, which have no influence on $\overline{|P_{\mathbf{k}x}|^2}$ but reduce the probability of the development of longitudinal fluctuations and $\overline{|P_{\mathbf{k}z}|^2}$.

Formulas (10.7) and (10.4) are valid in the limiting case of long waves when $k \to 0$. For shorter waves, we must also allow for terms of the $\alpha_{ijlm}k_l k_m$ type in (10.4). It is clear that on allowing for quadrupole–quadrupole and dipole–octupole interaction forces α_{ijlm} will also depend on $\mathbf{n}$. (This effect should also occur on considering fluctuations of the parameters characterizing long-range order in antiferroelectrics.)

Expressions analogous to (10.7) and (10.8) are also clearly valid for fluctuations of magnetization on allowing for magnetic dipole–dipole interaction (in these formulas we need only replace the dielectric by the magnetic susceptibility). However, since the magnetic permeability of all substances differs very slightly from unity (even near the Curie point), effects associated with long-range forces appear considerably more weakly in this case than in that of polarization fluctuations.

Effects associated with dipole–dipole forces should appear especially sharply near the temperature of a phase transformation of the second kind in the ferroelectric state, when certain components of the tensor $\varkappa_{ij}$ tend to infinity and the fluctuations of polarization increase anomalously. Thus, for example, in cubic crystals, we see from (10.8) that, above the transformation temperature, as $\varepsilon \to \infty$, the fluctuations of the polarization-vector components in the plane perpendicular to **k** become anomalously large, as in the theory in which long-range forces are disregarded; however, in contrast to the predictions of this theory, the fluctuations in the polarization components along **k** remain finite. After the transformation of a cubic crystal into the ferroelectric state, the crystal symmetry is reduced, the components of the tensor $\varkappa_{ij}$ are no longer identical, and, as indicated by the general formula (10.7), the expressions for the fluctuations in polarization become more complicated than those in (10.8). However, our conclusion regarding the anomalous rise in fluctuations of polarization perpendicular to **k** (but not parallel to **k**) remains valid in this case also.

In noncubic crystals (i.e., crystals which are not cubic in the nonferroelectric phase) the probability of the fluctuation waves should depend very sharply on the orientation of the vector **k** if only one component $\varkappa_{zz}$ of the tensor $\varkappa_{ij}$ ($\varkappa_{zz} \gg 1$) rises anomalously near the transformation temperature. Then anomalously large fluctuations in polarization will only arise if **k** is practically perpendicular to the Z axis (if $n_z \ll 1$). If $\varkappa_{yy} = \varkappa_{xx}$ and $\varkappa_{ij} = 0$ for $i \neq j$, then in this case, on neglecting terms ~ 1 as compared with $\varkappa_{zz}$ or n_z^{-2}, we find from (10.4) and (10.7) that:

$$\overline{|P_{kz}|^2} = \frac{k_B T}{V} \frac{(1 + 4\pi\varkappa_{xx})\varkappa_{zz}}{1 + 4\pi\varkappa_{xx} + 4\pi\varkappa_{zz} n_z^2}, \tag{10.9}$$

i.e., $\overline{|P_{kz}|^2}$ reaches a maximum value proportional to $\varkappa_{zz}$ at $n_z = 0$ and falls as $1/n_z^2$ at $4\pi\varkappa_{zz} n_z^2 \gg 1 + 4\pi\varkappa_{xx}$. The squares and products of the other component of vector $\mathbf{P_k}$ do not become anomalously large under these conditions.

The above calculation of the polarization fluctuations was made for dielectric crystals. The presence of conductivity electrons or charged defects in the crystal leads to the screening of the field at distances of the order of the Debye radius r_d. As a result of this formulas (10.7) and (10.9) will only be valid for fluctuation waves of not too large a wavelength (less than r_d), for which $k^2r_d^2 \gg \varepsilon$. For smaller k we must simultaneously consider the fluctuations of polarization and electron concentration, which will lead to a sharp reduction in the influence of the dipole–dipole forces, in view of the fact that the field created by the distant dipoles is screened off. For such small k the $\varkappa_{ij}(\mathbf{k})$ in (10.7) will coincide with $\varkappa_{ij}$. On the other hand, for high frequencies corresponding to $\varkappa_\infty$ the electric charges will as a rule be unable to redistribute themselves and screen the electric fields of the high-frequency fluctuations of polarization, so that $\varkappa_{\infty ij}(\mathbf{k})$ will remain unaltered. Hence in accordance with formula (2.21), which was derived without considering long-range forces, (10.7) will take the form

$$\frac{1}{2}\overline{(P_{\mathbf{k}i}P^*_{\mathbf{k}j}+P^*_{\mathbf{k}i}P_{\mathbf{k}j})}=\frac{k_B T}{V}\left[\varkappa_{ij}-\varkappa_{\infty ij}(\mathbf{k})\right]. \tag{10.10}$$

If relaxation of the high-frequency fields were able to take place, the $\varkappa_{\infty ij}(\mathbf{k})$ in (10.10) would have to be replaced by $\varkappa_{\infty ij}$.

In order to illustrate the influence of screening effects on the k dependence of the mean squares of the fluctuations in the region $k \sim r_d^{-1}$, let us take, for example, the results for the simplest case of cubic crystals, in which $\varepsilon_\infty = 1$. In this case, allowing for Debye screening will not alter formulas (10.8) (with $\varepsilon_\infty = 1$) for $\overline{|P_{\mathbf{k}x}|^2} = \overline{|P_{\mathbf{k}y}|^2}$, while the expression for $\overline{|P_{\mathbf{k}z}|^2}$ will take the form

$$\overline{|P_{\mathbf{k}z}|^2}=\frac{k_B T}{4\pi V}\frac{\varepsilon-1}{\varepsilon}\frac{\varepsilon+k^2r_d^2}{1+k^2r_d^2}. \tag{10.11}$$

This expression coincides with (10.8) for $kr_d \gg \sqrt{\varepsilon}$, and then the screening is unimportant. If, however, $kr_d \ll 1$, then the screening eliminates the long-range dipole–dipole forces and $\overline{|P_{\mathbf{k}z}|^2}$ coincides with $\overline{|P_{\mathbf{k}x}|^2}$.

If elastic deformation arises as a result of the fluctuations in polarization (if there is a piezo-effect), then we must consider long-range forces of two types: dipole–dipole and elastic. Just as in the case of other internal parameters (of long-range order), allowance for the elastic energy when calculating polarization fluctuations results in the addition of terms of the $\varphi^y_{\mu\mu'}$ type to the second derivatives of the thermodynamic potential in (9.9), i.e., the elastic energy may be taken into account if in the formulas of this section we replace $\partial^2\varphi/\partial P_i \partial P_j \equiv \varkappa_{ij}^{-1}$ by the tensor $\varkappa_{ij}'^{-1}$:

$$\varkappa_{ij}'^{-1} = \varkappa_{ij}^{-1} + \lambda_{lmnp} L_{lm}^{i} (L_{np}^{j} - k n_n A_{\mathbf{k}p}^{j}). \tag{10.12}$$

Here λ is the tensor of the elastic moduli defined for constant polarization, $L_{lm}^{i} = \delta u_{lm}/\delta P_i$ characterizes the deformation δu_{lm} arising for a homogeneous change of δP_i in the i-th component of polarization, and the vector $\mathbf{A}_{\mathbf{k}}^{j}$ with components $A_{\mathbf{k}m}^{j}$ is given by a system of equations of the (5.8) type, in which the L_{lm} on the right-hand side is replaced by L_{lm}^{j}.

Hence, in cases in which the elastic energy is substantial, we must replace $\varkappa_{ij}(\mathbf{k})$ in formulas (10.7) for the fluctuations in polarization by the tensor $\varkappa'_{ij}(\mathbf{k})$, which is obtained from $\varkappa_{ij}'^{-1}$ by formulas (10.4) in the same way as $\varkappa_{ij}(\mathbf{k})$ is obtained from $\varkappa_{ij}^{-1}$. It is clear that in calculating the second term in (10.7), associated with high-frequency fluctuations, deformations varying comparatively slowly with time play no serious part.

Thus on considering elastic interaction

$$\frac{1}{2}\overline{(P_{\mathbf{k}i}P_{\mathbf{k}j}^{*} + P_{\mathbf{k}i}^{*}P_{\mathbf{k}j})} = \frac{k_B T}{V}[\varkappa'_{ij}(\mathbf{k}) - \varkappa_{\infty ij}(\mathbf{k})]. \tag{10.13}$$

In cases in which the length of the fluctuation wave is greater than the Debye radius ($kr_d \ll 1$), as indicated earlier, we must replace $\varkappa'_{ij}(\mathbf{k})$ by $\varkappa'_{ij}$ in (10.13).

§11. Fluctuations of Concentration of Charged Defects

In a number of cases defects in crystals are charged. Such charged defects include vacancies and interstitial ions in ionic crystals, impurity ions with differing valence (for example, Ca^{++} ions replacing the Na^{+} in NaCl crystals), ionized impurity atoms, and so on. Between the charged defects there is a strong Coulomb interaction, falling off slowly with distance.

This interaction greatly affects fluctuations, since fluctuations in the concentration of defects of one sign, embracing a large volume, lead to a sharp rise in the electrostatic energy and are energetically unfavorable. Correspondingly, the probability of such smooth fluctuations falls sharply. On the other hand, the electrostatic energy is greatly reduced if at the same time there is a fluctuational change in both the positive and negatively charged particles, leading to compensation of the charge fluctuations.

As a result of this there should be a strong static interaction between the fluctuations in the concentrations of charges of different sign. This effect corresponds to a peculiar kind of correlation between defects of different signs, and at large distances to Debye screening associated with the Coulomb interaction. As in other cases, this kind of correlation may be taken into account most conveniently by directly considering fluctuation waves in the concentrations of the defects of different sign [53].

Let us consider as a specific example a cubic ionic crystal containing positive and negative defects of the same valence. From considerations of electrical neutrality the mean concentrations c of these should be equal. Let there be one position s_1 in the unit cell accessible to a positive defect and one position s_2 accessible to a negative defect. The distribution of defects in these positions may be characterized by specifying the numbers c_{s1} and c_{s2} as unity if a defect is present in the corresponding position and zero if the defect is absent, or else by specifying their Fourier components $c_{\mathbf{k}1}$, $c_{\mathbf{k}2}$, defined by expansion (1.7). It is convenient to transform from the quantities $c_{\mathbf{k}1}$ and $c_{\mathbf{k}2}$ to their sum and difference

$$2c'_{\mathbf{k}} = c_{\mathbf{k}1} + c_{\mathbf{k}2}, \quad 2c''_{\mathbf{k}} = c_{\mathbf{k}1} - c_{\mathbf{k}2}. \tag{11.1}$$

A fluctuation wave of the difference (but not the sum) of the concentrations of positive and negative defects with amplitude will lead to the development of a wave of electric charge

$$\rho_{\mathbf{k}} = \frac{1}{V} \int \rho(\mathbf{r}) \exp(i\mathbf{kr})\, dV = \frac{2ez'}{v} c''_{\mathbf{k}} \tag{11.2}$$

and an associated wave of induction $\mathbf{D}$ (div $\mathbf{D} = -4\pi\rho$):

$$\mathbf{D}_{\mathbf{k}} = \frac{1}{V} \int \mathbf{D}(\mathbf{r}) \exp(i\mathbf{kr})\, dV = 4\pi i \rho_{\mathbf{k}} \frac{\mathbf{k}}{k^2} = \frac{8\pi i e z'}{v} c''_{\mathbf{k}} \frac{\mathbf{k}}{k^2}. \tag{11.3}$$

Here z' is the charge of defect and $e > 0$.

The concentration of charge defects will always be small, and on average they will lie at a considerable distance from each other, considerably exceeding the interatomic spacing. Hence in calculating the thermodynamic potential we may neglect all short-range forces and only consider the large Coulomb electrostatic energy. The change in this energy associated with the development of the **k**-th fluctuation wave, in accordance with (11.3), equals

$$\frac{1}{8\pi\varepsilon}\int \mathbf{D}^2(\mathbf{r})\, dV = \frac{V\mathbf{D}_{\mathbf{k}}\mathbf{D}_{\mathbf{k}}^*}{4\pi\varepsilon} = \frac{16\pi e^2 z'^2 V}{\varepsilon v^2 k^2}\,|\,c''_{\mathbf{k}}\,|^2. \tag{11.4}$$

The configuration part of the entropy in the case considered (case of small concentration) may be determined on the simplest approximation (omitting defect correlation):

$$S = -Nk_{\mathrm{B}}\,(c_1 \ln c_1 + c_2 \ln c_2).$$

The corresponding contribution of the entropy to the change in the thermodynamic potential associated with the development of the **k**-th wave equals

$$Nk_{\mathrm{B}}Tc^{-1}\,[\,|\,c_{\mathbf{k}1}\,|^2 + |\,c_{\mathbf{k}2}\,|^2] = 2Nk_{\mathrm{B}}Tc^{-1}\,[\,|\,c'_{\mathbf{k}}\,|^2 + |\,c''_{\mathbf{k}}\,|^2]. \tag{11.5}$$

As a result of this, the minimum work necessary for the creation of the **k**-th fluctuation wave, which is determined by the sum of expressions (11.4) and (11.5), will be equal to

$$R_{\mathbf{k}} = \frac{16\pi e^2 z'^2 V}{\varepsilon v^2 k^2}\,|\,c''_{\mathbf{k}}\,|^2 + \frac{2Nk_{\mathrm{B}}T}{c}\,(|\,c'_{\mathbf{k}}\,|^2 + |\,c''_{\mathbf{k}}\,|^2). \tag{11.6}$$

From (2.1) and (11.6) we obtain expressions for the mean squares of the fluctuations of $c'_{\mathbf{k}}$ and $c''_{\mathbf{k}}$ in the usual way:

$$\overline{|\,c'_{\mathbf{k}}\,|^2} = \frac{c}{2N}, \quad \overline{|\,c''_{\mathbf{k}}\,|^2} = \frac{c}{2N}\,\frac{r_d^2 k^2}{1 + r_d^2 k^2}, \quad \overline{c'_{\mathbf{k}} c''^*_{\mathbf{k}}} = 0, \tag{11.7}$$

where r_d is the Debye screening radius:

$$r_d^2 = \frac{\varepsilon k_{\mathrm{B}} T v}{8\pi e^2 z'^2 c}\,. \tag{11.8}$$

We see from (11.7) that the Coulomb interaction does not affect the fluctuations of the total change in the concentration of positively and negatively charged defects

$$c'_{\mathbf{k}} = \frac{1}{2}(c_{\mathbf{k}1} + c_{\mathbf{k}2}),$$

for which electrical neutrality is (on average) preserved. This interaction also has no effect on the fluctuations of the difference

$$c''_{\mathbf{k}} = \frac{1}{2}(c_{\mathbf{k}1} - c_{\mathbf{k}2})$$

for sufficiently small wavelengths of the fluctuation waves, i.e., waves shorter than the Debye radius ($kr_d \gg 1$). With increasing wavelength, however, as indicated by (11.4), the electrostatic energy increases as $1/k^2$. The result of this is that, for fairly small k ($kr_d \ll 1$), the Coulomb interaction prevents the development of fluctuation waves of $c''_{\mathbf{k}}$, such as would disturb the electrical neutrality, and, as indicated by (11.7), long-wave fluctuations of $c''_{\mathbf{k}}$ become improbable.

Formula (11.7) was derived for the case in which the screening of the field around a given defect was caused by other defects. However, the results will not change qualitatively if the Debye screening is effected by conductivity electrons. Only details of the **k** dependence will change (see, for example, [59]).

Chapter IV

General Theory of X-Ray and Thermal-Neutron Elastic Scattering by Nonideal Crystals

§12. General Expressions for Scattering Intensities

Strictly speaking, the problem of the scattering of x rays by crystals should be solved by means of the dynamic theory of scattering, by solving Maxwell's equations for the electromagnetic x radiation both inside and outside the crystal. There is a wide range of problems, however, which may be solved on the basis of the much simpler kinematic theory of scattering, neglecting multiple scattering and the complex interference interaction of the waves. The kinematic theory is applicable for studying regular Bragg reflections in not-very-perfect crystals, for which the dimensions of the "regions of coherent scattering" are not too large. The kinematic theory may be used for the diffuse (as distinct from Bragg) scattering of x rays with far greater justification. In future we shall confine ourselves to cases in which the concentration of defects is large enough for the kinematic theory to be applicable, and we shall consider the scattering of x rays and thermal neutrons on the basis of this theory.

For a fairly large ideal crystal the kinematic theory leads to a distribution of intensity in reciprocal-lattice space consisting of narrow δ-type peaks localized at the lattice points. Any disruptions of the ideal state of the crystal, associated, for example, with the introduction of defects into the crystal, substantially alter the x-ray-scattering intensity distribution. It is clear that the theory should give a general qualitative picture of the change in this distribution caused by introducing defects of one kind or another into the crystal, that it should give a quantitative account of the intensity in cases for which this is possible, and that it should determine what type of information regarding the nature and properties of the departures from ideal structure can be extracted from experimental data. These questions will be considered below.

In this section we shall present the general expressions of the kinematic theory for the x-ray and thermal-neutron scattering intensities associated with an arbitrary grouping of atoms which will be needed later.* We shall not consider Compton scattering, the intensity of which may be calculated in the usual way and added to the elastic (or quasielastic) scattering here considered.

The x-ray scattering intensity I is usually expressed in electron units. Here I denotes the ratio of the scattering intensity associated with the crystal (at distances large compared with its size) to the scattering intensity associated with the classical electron. In the kinematic theory of scattering the complex amplitudes of the scattering associated with different electrons (or different parts of the electron-density distribution) may be simply added (with appropriate phases). Accordingly the scattering intensity of monochromatic radiation, expressed in electron units, is determined by the well-known formula

$$I = \left| \int \rho(\mathbf{r}) \exp(i\mathbf{q}_1\mathbf{r})\, dV \right|^2, \qquad (12.1)$$

where $\rho(\mathbf{r})$ is the total electron-probability density at the point $\mathbf{r}$, $\mathbf{q}_1 = \mathbf{k}_2 - \mathbf{k}_1$ is the diffraction vector, equal to the difference of the wave vectors of the scattered and incident waves ($|\mathbf{k}_1| = |\mathbf{k}_2| = 2\pi/\lambda$, λ is the wavelength), and the integration extends over the whole volume of the crystal.

The density $\rho(\mathbf{r})$ may clearly be put in the form of a sum of terms corresponding to individual atoms, which may be numbered

*The general theory of the scattering of x rays by ideal and nonideal crystals is considered in detail in a number of monographs and textbooks [60-71]. We shall therefore only treat questions of this general theory briefly here.

by specifying the number of the cell s and the number of the point in the cell γ:

$$\rho(\mathbf{r}) = \sum_{s=1}^{N} \sum_{\gamma=1}^{\nu} \rho_{s\gamma}(\mathbf{r} - \mathbf{R}_{s\gamma} - \delta\mathbf{R}_{s\gamma}). \tag{12.2}$$

Putting (12.2) into (12.1) and carrying out a change of variables in each term

$$\mathbf{r}' = \mathbf{r} - \mathbf{R}_{s\gamma} - \delta\mathbf{R}_{s\gamma},$$

we write the scattering intensity in the form of the square of a sum over all the points in the crystal:

$$I = \left| \sum_{s=1}^{N} \sum_{\gamma=1}^{\nu} f_{s\gamma} e^{i\mathbf{q}_1\mathbf{R}_{s\gamma}} e^{i\mathbf{q}_1\delta\mathbf{R}_{s\gamma}} \right|^2, \tag{12.3}$$

where

$$f_{s\gamma} = \int \rho_{s\gamma}(\mathbf{r}') \exp(i\mathbf{q}_1\mathbf{r}')\, dV \tag{12.4}$$

is the atomic scattering factor of the atom $s\gamma$ [the integration in (12.4) is also taken over the whole volume of the crystal]. The electron density of the outer electrons of the atom in question depends on its displacement $\delta\mathbf{R}_{s\gamma}$ from the ideal lattice point (with radius vector $\mathbf{R}_{s\gamma}$) and on the type of atoms surrounding it. Hence $f_{s\gamma}$ should also, strictly speaking, depend on the displacement and surroundings of the atom $s\gamma$, and also on the composition and order in the solution. However, since the proportion of outer electrons is relatively small (except for the lightest atoms), and they contribute very little to $f_{s\gamma}$, these dependences may usually be neglected and we may consider that $f_{s\gamma}$ is determined by the actual type of the atom $s\gamma$ only.

Let us give the structure amplitude f_s of the s-th cell in the distorted crystal

$$f_s = \sum_{\gamma=1}^{\nu} f_{s\gamma} \exp[i\mathbf{q}_1(\mathbf{R}_{s\gamma} - \mathbf{R}_{s1})] \exp[i\mathbf{q}_1(\delta\mathbf{R}_{s\gamma} - \delta\mathbf{R}_{s1})], \tag{12.5}$$

allowing for the difference in the displacements of different atoms in the cell relative to the displacement of the first atom $\delta\mathbf{R}_{s1}$ (in undistorted crystals this definition coincides with the ordinary one). Then the expression for the scattering intensity may be written in the form of the square of a sum over the cells

$$I = \left| \sum_{s=1}^{N} f_s e^{i\mathbf{q}_1\mathbf{R}_s} e^{i\mathbf{q}_1\delta\mathbf{R}_s} \right|^2 = \sum_{s,\, s'=1}^{N} f_s f_{s'}^* e^{i\mathbf{q}_1(\mathbf{R}_s - \mathbf{R}_{s'})} e^{i\mathbf{q}_1(\delta\mathbf{R}_s - \delta\mathbf{R}_{s'})}, \qquad (12.6)$$

where $\mathbf{R}_s \equiv \mathbf{R}_{s1}$ and $\delta\mathbf{R}_s \equiv \delta\mathbf{R}_{s1}$ denote the radius vector of the first point of the s-th cell and the displacement of the atom from this point.

In nonideal crystals the structure amplitudes f_s and displacements $\delta\mathbf{R}_s$ are different for different cells and are determined by the detailed distribution of the atoms of different sorts and defects in the crystal. However, since the scattering volume always contains a fairly large number of atoms, the scattering intensity for such a detailed distribution of defects (neglecting the usually small effects of fluctuations) practically coincides with the mean value of the intensity for a statistical aggregate, corresponding to the different detailed distributions of atoms and defects, with specified values of the internal macroscopic parameters characterizing the composition, order, and correlation in the crystal.* Hence the expression for the scattering intensity (12.6) may be rewritten in the form

$$I \equiv I(\mathbf{q}_1) = \sum_{\boldsymbol{\rho}} I(\boldsymbol{\rho}) \exp(i\mathbf{q}_1\boldsymbol{\rho}), \qquad (12.7)$$

where

$$\boldsymbol{\rho} = \mathbf{R}_s - \mathbf{R}_{s'},$$

$$I(\boldsymbol{\rho}) = \sum_{s} \overline{f_s f_{s'}^* \exp[i\mathbf{q}_1(\delta\mathbf{R}_s - \delta\mathbf{R}_{s'})]}, \qquad (12.8)$$

in the sum (12.8) the points s and s' separated by the vector $\boldsymbol{\rho}$ must both lie within the crystal, and the stroke denotes averaging over the statistical aggregate in question. Thus the problem of x-ray scattering in the nonideal crystal reduces to the calculation of the average expression (12.8), which directly determines the Fourier component of scattering intensity, and hence the intensity itself.

*An estimate of effects associated with fluctuations in the number of defects is given in [72].

Expressions (12.3) and (12.6) [or (12.7)] determine the scattering intensity of monochromatic radiation by a single crystal as a function of the diffraction vector $\mathbf{q}_1$. The study of this intensity distribution, considered as a function of the position of the vector $\mathbf{q}_1/2\pi$ in reciprocal-lattice space (for different orientations of the single crystal and scattering angles), gives the most complete x-ray-diffraction information possible regarding the departure of the crystal from the ideal state. In practice, however, this method of study is extremely laborious, and experimentally one often uses simpler methods, analyzing certain averaged values of expressions (12.3), (12.6), and (12.7). Thus wide use is made of the Debye method of studying the scattering of monochromatic radiation by powders of polycrystalline samples. In this case we must average expressions (12.3) or (12.7) over all possible equally probable orientations of the crystals for a given direction of the vector $\mathbf{q}_1$. Instead of this we may clearly average over different orientations of the vector $\mathbf{q}_1$ (of given length) for a given orientation of the crystal. As a result of this averaging, the scattering-intensity distribution on the Debye photograph I_D may be expressed in terms of the scattering intensity associated with a single crystal $I \equiv I(\mathbf{q}_1)$ by the relation

$$I_D = \frac{1}{4\pi q_1^2} \int_S I(\mathbf{q}_1)\, dS, \tag{12.9}$$

where the integration is carried out over the surface of a sphere S of radius q_1 in reciprocal-lattice space. It immediately follows from the definition of $\mathbf{q}_1 = \mathbf{k}_2 - \mathbf{k}_1$ as the base of an isosceles triangle with sides $k = 2\pi/\lambda$ and vertical angle equal to the scattering angle 2θ that the length of the diffraction vector equals

$$q_1 = \frac{4\pi}{\lambda} \sin\theta. \tag{12.10}$$

The general expressions for the scattering cross section of thermal neutrons with wavelengths ~ 1 Å are largely analogous to the expression for the scattering intensity of x rays. The scattering of neutrons is due to their nuclear interaction with the nuclei of the atoms and their magnetic interaction with the electrons of the unfilled electron shells, which create uncompensated atomic magnetic moments. The cross section is usually determined by means of the Born approximation in the theory of scattering. This approximation is applicable if the interaction potential is weak and the wave function of the particle being scattered changes only a little. The magnetic interaction of neutrons is in fact weak, but the nuclear interaction clearly cannot be considered in any way as weak; the wave function of the neutron in the region of the atomic nucleus is strongly perturbed, as a result of which the ordinary basis of the Born approximation is inapplicable.

Instead of this, however, we may make use of the short-range character of the nuclear forces and consider that the strong perturbation of the neutron wave function is localized over a relatively negligible part of the volume, near the atomic nuclei. In this way, as shown by Fermi in [73] (see also [74]), the exact solution of Schrödinger's equation for the scattered wave, neglecting dynamic effects (multiple scattering), outside the region of the nuclei differs little from the approximate solution obtained on the Born approximation if we include an appropriately chosen perturbing potential, Fermi's quasipotential (generally speaking differing from the actual interaction potential). Since the radius of action of the nuclear forces is small, this quasipotential may be regarded as proportional to a δ function. For all the crystal nuclei taken together the quasipotential may be put in the form of a sum

$$V(\mathbf{r}) = \sum_{s\gamma} \{A_{s\gamma} + 2B_{s\gamma}(\mathbf{s}\mathbf{S}_{s\gamma})[S_{s\gamma}(S_{s\gamma}+1)]^{-1/2}\}\,\delta(\mathbf{r} - \mathbf{R}_{s\gamma} - \delta\mathbf{R}_{s\gamma}). \quad (12.11)$$

Here $\mathbf{s}$ and $\mathbf{S}_{s\gamma}$ are the spin operators of the neutron and the nucleus $s\gamma$, $S_{s\gamma}$ is the quantum number of the mechanical moment of this nucleus, $A_{s\gamma}$ and $B_{s\gamma}$ are constants describing the interactions independent of and dependent on the spins, respectively.

The cross section referred to unit solid angle

$$\frac{d\Sigma}{d\Omega} \equiv \sigma(\mathbf{q}_1)$$

for the quasielastic nuclear scattering of neutrons by immobile or slowly moving nuclei (the change of energy on scattering is considerably smaller than the energy of the incident particles) on the Born approximation of scattering theory is proportional to the mean (taken over the statistical aggregate) square of the matrix element of the interaction energy (12.11) based on the wave functions of the initial and final states. By averaging over the spin states of the nuclei we may put $\sigma(\mathbf{q}_1)$ in the form (see, for example, [75])

$$\sigma(\mathbf{q}_1) = \frac{m_n^2}{4\pi^2\hbar^4}\left|\sum_{s=1}^{N}\sum_{\gamma=1}^{\nu} A_{s\gamma}e^{i\mathbf{q}_1\mathbf{R}_{s\gamma}}e^{i\mathbf{q}_1\delta\mathbf{R}_{s\gamma}}\right|^2 + \frac{m_n^2}{4\pi^2\hbar^4}\sum_{s=1}^{N}\sum_{\gamma=1}^{\nu} B_{s\gamma}^2 \quad (12.12)$$

(m_n is the mass of a neutron).

The second term in (12.12) determines the scattering associated with the interaction potential depending on the spins. This scattering is purely incoherent, since there are no correlations between the spins of different nuclei (except for the case of very low temperatures). A purely incoherent scattering of another type is associated with the difference in the constants $A_{s\gamma}$ for different isotopes of the given element [76]. Writing $A_{s\gamma}$ in the form $A_{s\gamma} = \overline{A}_{s\gamma} + (A_{s\gamma}-\overline{A}_{s\gamma})$, where $\overline{A}_{s\gamma}$ is the value of $A_{s\gamma}$ averaged over the isotopes for the atom of the (A or B) component lying at the point $s\gamma$, and averaging over the isotopes with due allowance for the fact that correlation between them may practically always be neglected (so that the average $(A_{s\gamma}-\overline{A}_{s\gamma}) \times (A_{s'\gamma'}-\overline{A}_{s'\gamma'})$ for different points vanishes), we may rewrite (12.12) in the form

$$\sigma(\mathbf{q}_1) = \frac{m_n^2}{4\pi^2\hbar^4}\left|\sum_{s=1}^{N}\sum_{\gamma=1}^{\nu} \overline{A}_{s\gamma}e^{i\mathbf{q}_1\mathbf{R}_{s\gamma}}e^{i\mathbf{q}_1\delta\mathbf{R}_{s\gamma}}\right|^2 + $$

$$+ \frac{m_n^2}{4\pi^2\hbar^4}\sum_{s=1}^{N}\sum_{\gamma=1}^{\nu} \overline{[(A_{s\gamma}-\overline{A}_{s\gamma})^2 + B_{s\gamma}^2]}. \quad (12.13)$$

The quantities $\overline{A}_{s\gamma}$ take the values $\overline{A}^A$ and $\overline{A}^B$ according to which atom lies at the point $s\gamma$. These quantities and also the averages

$$\overline{(A_{s\gamma}^A - \overline{A}_{s\gamma}^A)^2} + \overline{(B_{s\gamma}^A)^2} \text{ and } \overline{(A_{s\gamma}^B - \overline{A}_{s\gamma}^B)^2} + \overline{(B_{s\gamma}^B)^2}$$

for the A and B atoms are expressed in terms of the integral cross sections of the coherent ($\sigma_{cA} = 4\pi b_A^2$ and σ_{cB}) or incoherent (σ_{iA} and σ_{iB}) scattering of neutrons by individual nuclei by means of relations (see, for example, [75]) of the type

$$\overline{A}^{A} = \frac{\hbar^2 \sqrt{\pi\sigma_{cA}}}{m_n}; \quad \overline{(A^{A}_{s\gamma} - \overline{A}^{A}_{s\gamma})^2} + \overline{(B^{A}_{s\gamma})^2} = \frac{\pi\hbar^4\sigma_{iA}}{m_n^2}. \qquad (12.14)$$

It should be noted that the quantities $\overline{A}^A$ and b_A may be either positive or negative. The values of the cross sections σ_c and σ_i and the amplitude b for different elements are given in tables (see, for example, [77]).

By comparing formulas (12.13), (12.14), and (12.3) we see that the scattering probabilities of neutrons and x rays are determined by expressions of similar types. In order to obtain the nuclear-scattering cross section of neutrons from the formulas for the intensity of x-ray scattering, it is sufficient in these formulas simply to make the exchange

$$f_A \to b_A, \qquad f_B \to b_B \qquad (12.15)$$

(i.e., to replace the atomic factor for x rays by the corresponding quantity for neutrons) and add the cross section for the incoherent scattering of neutrons

$$\sigma_i(\mathbf{q}_1) = \frac{N\nu}{4\pi}[c\sigma_{iA} + (1-c)\sigma_{iB}]. \qquad (12.16)$$

Hence in future we shall not consider the elastic scattering of neutrons separately, but shall restrict consideration to x-ray scattering, remembering that the results obtained are also applicable to the nuclear scattering of neutrons after the substitution (12.15). The magnetic scattering of neutrons, which appears only in the presence of atoms with uncompensated atomic moments, will not be considered.

§13. Scattering of X Rays by Crystals of Finite Dimensions

In a certain sense the simplest type of departure from ideal crystal structure is simply the finite size of the crystal, i.e., the fact that it possesses boundaries. The finite dimensions leads to "spreading" of the δ-type intensity distributions characterizing an infinite crystal. In order to discuss this effect, we shall consider that the existence of boundaries is the only "imperfect" aspect of the crystal, which in all other respects is ideal, i.e., all the atoms lie at lattice points ($\delta\mathbf{R}_s = 0$) and the structure amplitudes of different cells are identical ($f_s = f$). In particular, we shall neglect the smallish effect of the distortion of the crystal near the surface. Then the general expression (12.6) for the scattering intensity simplifies considerably

$$I = I_0 = |a|^2, \quad a = a(\mathbf{q}_1) = f\sum_{s=1}^{N} \exp(i\mathbf{q}_1\mathbf{R}_s). \tag{13.1}$$

The scattering amplitude a is conveniently calculated by means of an artificial approach, which reduces the sum over the points of the ideal lattice within the volume of the finite crystal to an integral over all space. Formula (13.1) may be identically rewritten in the form

$$a(\mathbf{q}_1) = f\int Y^{\infty}(\mathbf{r})\, s(\mathbf{r}) \exp(i\mathbf{q}_1\mathbf{r})\, dV, \quad Y^{\infty}(\mathbf{r}) = \sum_{s=1}^{\infty} \delta(\mathbf{r} - \mathbf{R}_s). \tag{13.2}$$

Here the summation with respect to s in $Y^{\infty}(\mathbf{r})$ is carried out over all points of an infinite ideal lattice with δ functions at the lattice points, i.e., $Y^{\infty}(\mathbf{r})$ is a periodic function. In the integral this function is multiplied by Ewald's [78] function $s(\mathbf{r})$, equal to unity inside the volume of the crystal and zero outside; this enables us to carry out the integration in (13.2) over all space.

In this form $a(\mathbf{q}_1)$ reduces to a Fourier integral of the product of $Y^{\infty}(\mathbf{r})$ and $s(\mathbf{r})$. From the theory of Fourier transformations it is known that the Fourier integral of a product of two functions is determined by the convolution of the Fourier integrals of the factors, i.e.,

$$a(\mathbf{q}_1) = \frac{f}{(2\pi)^3}\int Y^{\infty}(\mathbf{k})\, s(\mathbf{q}_1 - \mathbf{k})\, d\mathbf{k}, \tag{13.3}$$

where, for example, $s(\mathbf{q}_1 - \mathbf{k}) = s(\mathbf{q})$ is the Fourier integral of the function of the form

$$s(\mathbf{q}) = \int s(\mathbf{r}) \exp(-i\mathbf{q}\mathbf{r})\, dV \tag{13.4}$$

and the integration over d**k**, as well as that over dV, is carried out for all space.*

The periodic function $Y^{\infty}(\mathbf{r})$ $[Y^{\infty}(\mathbf{r}+\mathbf{R}_s) = Y^{\infty}(\mathbf{r})]$ may be expanded into a triple Fourier series:

$$Y^{\infty}(\mathbf{r}) = \sum_n Y_n^{\infty} \exp(-2\pi i \mathbf{K}_n \mathbf{r}),$$

$$Y_n^{\infty} = \frac{1}{v} \int_v Y^{\infty}(\mathbf{r}) \exp(2\pi i \mathbf{K}_n \mathbf{r})\, dV = \frac{1}{v}, \qquad (13.5)$$

where the integration is carried out over the volume of the unit cell v and, in accordance with (13.2), the $Y^{\infty}(\mathbf{r})$ in the integral is replaced by the δ function. For each term in the expansion (13.5) to satisfy the periodic condition

$$\exp[-2\pi i \mathbf{K}_n (\mathbf{r}+\mathbf{R}_s)] = \exp(-2\pi i \mathbf{K}_n \mathbf{r}),$$

it is necessary that $\mathbf{K}_n$ should be vectors of the reciprocal lattice (then for any $\mathbf{R}_s$ and $\mathbf{K}_n$ the product $\mathbf{K}_n\mathbf{R}_s$ will be a whole number). Putting expansion (13.5) in the definition of the Fourier integral and using the definition of the three-dimensional δ function (product of three one-dimensional functions)

$$\delta(\mathbf{q}) = (2\pi)^{-3} \int \exp(i\mathbf{q}\mathbf{r})\, dV,$$

we find that the Fourier integral for the function $Y^{\infty}(\mathbf{r})$ reduces to

*Relation (13.3) is immediately obtained if in the integral

$$\int Y^{\infty}(\mathbf{r})\, s(\mathbf{r}) \exp(-i\mathbf{q}\mathbf{r})\, dV$$

we substitute an expansion of the type

$$Y^{\infty}(\mathbf{r}) = (2\pi)^{-3} \int Y^{\infty}(\mathbf{k}) \exp(i\mathbf{k}\mathbf{r})\, d\mathbf{k}$$

and integrate over dV, allowing for the definition of the δ function

$$\delta(\mathbf{q}) = (2\pi)^{-3} \int \exp(i\mathbf{q}\mathbf{r})\, dV.$$

the sum of the δ functions:

$$Y^{\infty}(\mathbf{k}) = \int Y^{\infty}(\mathbf{r}) \exp(-i\mathbf{kr})\, dV = \frac{(2\pi)^3}{v} \sum_n \delta(\mathbf{k} - 2\pi \mathbf{K}_n). \qquad (13.6)$$

Here the summation with respect to n is carried out over all the reciprocal-lattice points.

If instead of $Y^{\infty}(\mathbf{k})$ in (13.3) we substitute the sum of the δ functions (13.6), then the integral in each term may immediately be calculated and the amplitude $a(\mathbf{q}_1)$ takes the form

$$a(\mathbf{q}_1) = \frac{f}{v} \sum_n s(\mathbf{q}_1 - 2\pi \mathbf{K}_n). \qquad (13.7)$$

In crystals of fairly large dimensions, considerably larger than the lattice constant, the Fourier transform of the functions $s(\mathbf{q})$ only has an appreciable value for smallish q, much smaller than the parameters of the reciprocal lattice (see below). Hence in squaring the sum (13.7) we may neglect double products (even if only one of the factors in the product is small) and retain only the squares of the terms. Thus according to (13.1) and (13.7) the intensity of the scattering by crystals of finite dimensions will be determined by the sum over the reciprocal-lattice points

$$I_0 = \frac{|f|^2}{v^2} \sum_n |s(\mathbf{q}_1 - 2\pi \mathbf{K}_n)|^2. \qquad (13.8)$$

For illustration let us consider, for example, a crystal having the form of a rectangular parallelepiped. Let the length of an edge along the x_i axis (x_i = x, y, z) equal Λ_i. Then the square of the Fourier transform of the form $s(\mathbf{q})$ will according to (13.4) equal

$$|s(\mathbf{q})|^2 = \prod_{i=1}^{3} \left| \int_0^{\Lambda_i} \exp(iq_i x_i)\, dx_i \right|^2 = \prod_{i=1}^{3} \frac{\sin^2(q_i \Lambda_i/2)}{(q_i/2)^2}. \qquad (13.9)$$

Each of the factors of this product takes a maximum value Λ_i^2 at $q_i = 0$ (expansion of the indeterminacy of $(1/x^2)\sin^2 ax$ as $x \to 0$ gives a^2) and falls rapidly from this maximum, vanishing at $q_i = \pm(2\pi/\Lambda_i)$. After this the function $(q_i/2)^{-2}\sin^2(q_i\Lambda_i/2)$ has subsidiary maxima (separated by minima), but these are much less intense than the principal one [the first subsidiary maxima lying at $q_i \approx \pm(3\pi/\Lambda_i), \pm(5\pi/\Lambda_i), \ldots$, equal 0.045, 0.016, ..., of the principal maximum], and on average it falls as $1/q_i^2$. Since

$$\int_{-\infty}^{\infty} \frac{\sin^2 (q_i\Lambda_i/2)}{(q_i/2)^2}\, dq_i = 2\pi\Lambda_i \tag{13.10}$$

and at $q_i = 0$ the function $(q_i/2)^{-2} \sin^2 (q_i \Lambda_i/2)$ equals Λ_i^2, the integral width of this function δq_i, i.e., the ratio of the area to the value at the maximum, is inversely proportional to Λ_i:

$$\delta q_i = \frac{2\pi}{\Lambda_i}\ . \tag{13.11}$$

Thus we see from (13.8), (13.9), and (13.11) that, when x rays are scattered by a rectangular parallelepiped with sides of Λ_1, Λ_2, Λ_3, symmetric intensity distributions develop for values of $\mathbf{q}_1/2\pi$ lying in the neighborhood of the reciprocal-lattice points; these distributions have effective dimensions of $2\pi/\Lambda_1$ and intensity maxima at $2\pi/\Lambda_2$, $2\pi/\Lambda_3$ and intensity maxima at $\mathbf{q}_1 = 2\pi\mathbf{K}_n$. The larger the dimensions of the crystal, the narrower are these distributions. If the dimensions of the crystal Λ_i are much larger than the lattice parameters d_i, then the widths of the peaks are much smaller than the distance between the reciprocal-lattice points ($\sim 2\pi/d_i$).

The shape of the intensity distributions, like their dimensions, is as it were inverse to the shape of the crystal itself. Thus if the crystal has a drawn-out, needle-shaped form, then the resultant intensity distribution are disc-shaped, and in the case of compressed, disc-shaped crystals, the distributions should have a rod-like shape. We see moreover from (13.8) that near each reciprocal-lattice point (including the zero point, corresponding to scattering through small angles), the intensity distribution I considered as a function of $\mathbf{q}_1/2\pi$ is absolutely identical, and I is a periodic function. This repeatability of the distributions is a characteristic of the broadening effect associated with the finite size of the crystal; effects associated with defects, however, lead to different distributions near different reciprocal-lattice points (see below).

The same qualitative picture of identical repeated distributions with dimensions of the order of the reciprocal dimensions of the crystal arises in crystals of any arbitrary shape. According to (13.8) the detailed shape of these distributions is determined by the Fourier components of the function (13.4). Calculations of s ($\mathbf{q}$) for crystals of different shapes, in particular for polyhedra with any type of crystallographic boundaries, are given in [79, 80, 81]. For any arbitrary form of the crystal, as in the example considered, the intensity takes its maximum value of f^2V^2/v^2 if the vector $\mathbf{q}_1/2\pi$ falls on a reciprocal-lattice point ($\mathbf{q}_1 = 2\pi\mathbf{K}_n$), and this point is the center of symmetry for the distribution I ($\mathbf{q}_1/2\pi$) [since according to (13.4) s ($-\mathbf{q}$) = s* ($\mathbf{q}$) and s (0) = V].

The form of the intensity distributions may only be studied experimentally in the case of very small crystals. If the crystal is fairly large, then owing to instrumental broadening and the natural width of the x-ray lines the distribution cannot be resolved, and it is perceived as an infinitely narrow δ distribution. Since, in accordance with (13.4),

$$\int |s(\mathbf{q})|^2 d\mathbf{q} = \int dV\, dV'\, s(\mathbf{r})\, s(\mathbf{r}') \int d\mathbf{q}\, e^{i\mathbf{q}(\mathbf{r}'-\mathbf{r})} =$$

$$= (2\pi)^3 \int dV\, s^2(\mathbf{r}) = (2\pi)^3 V \qquad (13.12)$$

[here it is remembered that $s^2(\mathbf{r}) = s(\mathbf{r})$], the integral of the distribution I for each reciprocal-lattice point equals $|f|^2(2\pi)^3 V v^{-2}$, and in the limit of a large crystal, with $\mathbf{q}_1 \approx 2\pi\mathbf{K}_n$, the expression for the intensity may be written in the form

$$I_0 = \lim_{N\to\infty} |f|^2 \left| \sum_{s=1}^{N} e^{i\mathbf{q}\mathbf{R}_s} \right|^2 = 8\pi^3 \frac{N}{v} |f|^2 \delta(\mathbf{q}_1 - 2\pi\mathbf{K}_n) =$$

$$= \frac{N}{v} |f|^2 \delta\left(\frac{\mathbf{q}_1}{2\pi} - \mathbf{K}_n\right). \qquad (13.13)$$

The relation between the dimensions of the crystals and the width of the intensity peaks makes it possible to estimate the dimensions of the scattering crystals experimentally. A single smallish crystal produces too small a scattering intensity, and for this reason it is always necessary to study a set of crystals oriented in different ways in space. Most frequently the Debye method of scattering by powders or polycrystalline samples is employed; then the scattering crystals have all possible different orientations with equal probabilities.

The scattering-intensity distribution on a Debye photograph may be obtained from the above distribution I ($\mathbf{q}_1$) for the scattering of an individual crystal by averaging (12.9) over the surface of a sphere of radius q_1 in reciprocal-lattice space. Let us carry out an averaging of this kind, for example, in the case of the (h00) reflections of identical crystals having a cubic shape and orthorhombic (or cubic) symmetry. Then supposing that the q_x axis is directed toward the point (h00) under consideration in reciprocal-lattice space, we find from (13.8) and (13.9) that the intensity distribution near this point has the form

$$I_0 = |f|^2 \frac{4\sin^2 \frac{Q\Lambda}{2}}{Q^2} \cdot \frac{4\sin^2 \frac{q_y\Lambda}{2}}{q_y^2} \frac{4\sin^2 \frac{q_z\Lambda}{2}}{q_z^2} . \qquad (13.14)$$

Here

$$\mathbf{q} = \mathbf{q}_1 - 2\pi\mathbf{K}_n \text{ and } Q = q_x.$$

It is clear that the quantity Q is the difference between the length of the given diffraction vector $\mathbf{q}_1$ and the length of the diffraction vector $\mathbf{q}_{10} = 2\pi\mathbf{K}_n$ corresponding to the Bragg reflection in an infinitely large crystal. Taking (12.10) into account and considering the closeness of q_1 and q_{10}, we may express Q in terms of the difference $2(\theta - \theta_0)$ between the given scattering angle 2θ and the scattering angle $2\theta_0$ corresponding to the infinite crystal:

$$Q = q_1 - q_{10} \approx \frac{2\pi}{\lambda} \cos\theta \cdot 2(\theta - \theta_0) . \qquad (13.15)$$

Since the width of the intensity distribution (shaded region in Fig. 5) is considerably smaller than the radius q_1 of the sphere of integration, we may (with only a slight error) replace the integration (12.9) over the surface of the sphere by an integration over a flat section in the plane $q_y q_z$, and then extend the limits of integration in this plane to infinity. Calculating the integrals with respect to dq_y, dq_z from formula (13.10) and remembering that p ends of different $2\pi\mathbf{K}_n$ vectors lie near the sphere of radius q_1 (p is the multiplicity factor), we find the following scattering-intensity distribution of the Debye photograph from (12.9) and (13.14):

$$I_{0D}(Q) = 4\pi^2 p\Lambda^2 |f|^2 \frac{4\sin^2 \frac{Q\Lambda}{2}}{Q^2}. \tag{13.16}$$

This distribution takes a maximum value of $4\pi^2 p\Lambda^4 |f|^2$ at $Q = 0$, when the scattering angle corresponds to the Bragg reflection from an infinite crystal (on the kinematic theory). For the integral width δQ in units of Q, or $2\delta\theta$ in angular units, we obtain from (13.10) and (13.15):

$$\delta Q = \frac{2\pi}{\Lambda}, \quad 2\delta\theta = \frac{\lambda}{\Lambda}\sec\theta = \frac{\lambda}{\sqrt[3]{V}}\sec\theta. \tag{13.17}$$

For crystallites having a more complicated form but of the same order of dimensions in three perpendicular directions, a numerical factor $\mathfrak{L}$ appears in the last equation (13.17), differing from unity by no more than 10 to 20%. For example, for spherical crystallites $\mathfrak{L} = \frac{4}{3}\sqrt[3]{\frac{\pi}{6}} \approx 1.075$. This factor depends on the direction of the vector $\mathbf{K}_n$, and for reflections of the (hhh) type of crystals of cubic form $\mathfrak{L} = 1.155$. In crystals of cubic symmetry having the form of a rectangular parallelepiped, for reflections of the (h00) type the lines are obtained by superimposing reflections of the (h00), (0h0), and (00h) types, so that instead of Λ in (13.17) we must put the arithmetic mean $\frac{1}{3}(\Lambda_1 + \Lambda_2 + \Lambda_3)$. For other reflections $\mathfrak{L}$ depends in a complicated manner on the lengths of the edges. Calculations of $\mathfrak{L}$ for various crystallite shapes are given in [80, 82,

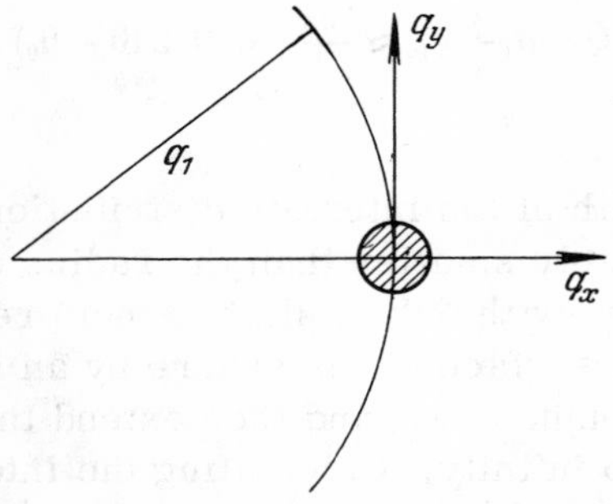

Fig. 5. Averaging the scattering intensity over the orientations of the crystals.

83] and are set out in detail in monographs [65, 67]. It should be remembered that different crystallites have differing dimensions, so that the form of the intensity distribution on the Debye photograph is complicated [in comparison with (13.16)], and formula (13.17) relates the line width to a certain averaged crystallite size.

Relation (13.17) makes it possible to determine the dimensions of the crystallites from experimental data relating to the widths of the x-ray lines in those cases in which the broadening is due to the finite dimensions of the crystals. It is an important point that the angular width is proportional to sec θ. This makes it possible in a number of cases to confirm that the broadening is associated with the finite dimensions of the crystals rather than with distortions (in the latter case the width varies with scattering angle as tan θ; see latter). This method has been used in a number of cases (see, for example, [84, 85]) to determine the dimensions of regions of coherent scattering (blocks), mutually disoriented by considerable angles, i.e., greater than λ/Λ. The necessity of having a considerable physical line broadening, greater than the width of the standard line, means that this method is only applicable for determining the size of relatively small blocks, $\lesssim 10^3$ Å. At the same time, in order to separate the actual x-ray lines from the background, the line width must be smaller than the distance between adjacent lines, and the block size must not be too small ($\Lambda \gtrsim 10^2$ Å).

The foregoing results for the scattering intensity of crystals of finite dimensions also enable us to study scattering by large crystals containing microscopic cavities (vacancies, pores) or particles of a new phase, if we neglect the distortions caused by these defects [86]. Let us consider, for example, a crystal containing N_c^0 similar and similarly oriented microscopic cavities. Neglecting distortions, the scattering amplitude for this crystal equals

$$a = f \sum{}' \exp(i\mathbf{q}_1 \mathbf{R}_s), \tag{13.18}$$

where Σ' denotes summation over all the cells in the volume of the crystal, but without the volume of the cavities. By adding and subtracting an analogous sum over the volumes of all the N_c^0 cavities, we may rewrite (13.18) in the form

$$a = f \sum \exp(i\mathbf{q}_1\mathbf{R}_s) - f \sum_{B=1}^{N_C^0} \exp(i\mathbf{q}_1\mathbf{R}_B) \sum{}'' \exp[i\mathbf{q}_1(\mathbf{R}_s - \mathbf{R}_B)]. \quad (13.19)$$

Here the first sum is the same as in the case of an ideal crystal not containing any microscopic cavities, and in the second sum $\mathbf{R}_B$ is the radius vector of cavity number B; in the sum Σ'' the summation is carried out over the volume of one of the cavities.

In accordance with the foregoing argument, the sum Σ differs from zero over very narrow regions of reciprocal-lattice space, where $|\mathbf{q}_1 - 2\pi\mathbf{K}_n| \lesssim 2\pi/\Lambda$ (Λ is the size of the whole crystal), while the sum Σ'' describes considerably wider distributions over regions $|\mathbf{q}_1 - 2\pi\mathbf{K}_n| \lesssim 2\pi/\Lambda_C$ (Λ_C is the size of the cavities). Hence if we exclude the values of $\mathbf{q}/2\pi = \mathbf{q}_1/2\pi - \mathbf{K}_n$ lying in the immediate neighborhood of the reciprocal-lattice points and consider q in the region

$$2\pi\Lambda^{-1} \ll q \lesssim 2\pi\Lambda_C^{-1},$$

we may neglect the first term in (13.19) and obtain a scattering amplitude which in effect represents scattering by a group of small crystals with negative structure amplitudes.

If there is no correlation in the arrangement of the cavities, these being distributed at random over the crystal, then interference between the radiation scattered by different defects may be neglected, and the scattering intensity of the aggregate of cavities equals the scattering intensity of one cavity multiplied by the number of cavities N_C^0. Hence the scattering intensity distribution of a crystal containing microscopic cavities has the form

$$I = N_C^0 |f|^2 \left|\sum{}'' \exp(i\mathbf{q}_1\mathbf{R}_s)\right|^2 = N_C^0 |f|^2 \sum_n |s(\mathbf{q}_1 - 2\pi\mathbf{K}_n)|^2 \quad (13.20)$$

and is in fact exactly the same as in scattering by an aggregate of N_C^0 crystals having the same dimensions, shape, and orientation as the cavities (for $q \gg 2\pi\Lambda^{-1}$) [86]. Intensity distributions of width $\sim 2\pi\Lambda_C^{-1}$ arise if $\mathbf{q}_1/2\pi$ falls in the neighborhood of any reciprocal-lattice point of the cavity-containing crystal under consideration. If the cavities may be oriented in λ different ways (for example, along three directions of the [100] type or four of the [111] type in a cubic crystal), then we must carry out an additional summation over these orientations, and

$$I = |f|^2 \sum_n \sum_{\delta=1}^{\lambda} N^0_{c\delta} \, |s_\delta(\mathbf{q}_1 - 2\pi\mathbf{K}_n)|^2, \tag{13.21}$$

where $s_\delta(\mathbf{q})$ is the Fourier transform of a function of the shape of the cavity for orientation δ, and $N^0_{c\delta}$ is the number of such cavities.

In the same way we may consider scattering by a crystal containing N^0_P precipitated particles of a new phase [86]. In this case, neglecting distortions

$$a = f \sum{}' \exp(i\mathbf{q}_1\mathbf{R}_s) + f' \sum_{B=1}^{N^0_P} \exp(i\mathbf{q}_1\mathbf{R}_B) \sum{}'' \exp[i\mathbf{q}_1(\mathbf{R}'_s - \mathbf{R}_B)] =$$
$$= f \sum \exp(i\mathbf{q}_1\mathbf{R}_s) - f \sum_{B=1}^{N^0_P} \exp(i\mathbf{q}_1\mathbf{R}_B) \sum{}'' \exp[i\mathbf{q}_1(\mathbf{R}_s - \mathbf{R}_B)] +$$
$$+ f' \sum_{B=1}^{N^0_P} \exp(i\mathbf{q}_1\mathbf{R}_B) \sum{}'' \exp[i\mathbf{q}_1(\mathbf{R}'_s - \mathbf{R}_B)]. \tag{13.22}$$

Here $\mathbf{R}'_S$ is the radius vector of a cell of the new phase, the structure of which, generally speaking, differs from that of the matrix, and f' is its structure amplitude; in the second equation we have added and subtracted a term making up the sum Σ' of the matrix crystal, excluding the volumes of the particles, to the sum corresponding to the ideal crystal.

Considering, as in the case of cavities, the range of values

$$\frac{2\pi}{\Lambda} \ll q \lesssim \frac{2\pi}{\Lambda_P}$$

(Λ_P is the size of a particle), we may neglect the first term in (13.22). If the structures of the matrix and the new phase differ and their reciprocal-lattice points ($\mathbf{K}_n$ and $\mathbf{K}'_n$) lie at a considerable distance from each other ($\gg \Lambda_P^{-1}$), then the distribution corresponding to the second and third terms in (13.22), concentrated respectively near $2\pi\mathbf{K}_n$ and $2\pi\mathbf{K}'_n$, do not overlap, so that the product of these terms is always small. Hence the scattering intensity of the crystal containing new-phase particles distributed at random with random orientations is determined by the expression

$$I(\mathbf{q}_1) = |f|^2 \sum_n \sum_{\delta=1}^{\lambda} N^0_{P\delta} |s_\delta(\mathbf{q}_1 - 2\pi \mathbf{K}_n)|^2 + \\ + |f'|^2 \sum_n \sum_{\delta=1}^{\lambda} N^0_{P\delta} |s_\delta(\mathbf{q}_1 - 2\pi \mathbf{K}'_{n\delta})|^2 \qquad (13.23)$$

($N^0_{P\delta}$ is the number of particles with orientation δ).

Thus intensity distributions $I(\mathbf{q}_1/2\pi)$ of width $\sim\Lambda_P^{-1}$ arise both near the reciprocal-lattice points of the matrix phase [first term in (13.23)], as in the case of microscopic cavities, and near the reciprocal-lattice points of the new phase [second term in (13.23)]. If, for example, the particles have the form of discs oriented in different ways, then near the reciprocal-lattice points there arise λ rod-shaped regions of high intensity, oriented perpendicularly to the discs. If the matrix and new phase have identical structures, the double product of the second and third terms in (13.22) becomes important, and the expression for the intensity becomes more complicated than (13.23). This distribution is also complicated if there is an impoverished layer in the matrix around the particles [87].

It should be emphasized that the intensity distributions given were obtained without considering the distortions around the microscopic cavities and new-phase particles. If any such distortions exist, then the picture of the intensity distribution changes considerably (see §29).

§14. Classification of Crystal Defects by Reference to the X-Ray Diffraction Effects which They Produce

It follows from the results derived in the preceding section that, for the elastic scattering of x rays by a fairly large ideal crystal in which the atoms are immovable and are situated at the points of a periodic lattice, the scattering intensity distribution $I(\mathbf{q}_1/2\pi)$ is described on the kinematic theory by δ-type functions (13.13) localized at the points of the reciprocal lattice. Any infringement of the ideal state of the crystal (the replacement of atoms of one sort by those of another, distortions of the crystal, etc.) leads to considerable changes in the intensity distribution. These changes in some cases include a displacement of the maxima of the δ-type peaks (i.e., of the reciprocal-lattice vectors), a change in their integral intensity, and the appearance of a smooth distribution of diffuse-scattering intensity outside these peaks, and in other cases diffuseness (broadening) of the δ-type intensity distributions.

As noted by Lifshits [88], the particular way in which the crystal imperfections influence the scattering depends on the nature of the fluctuations of the displacements in the nonideal crystal. The x-ray peaks become diffuse if, as the dimensions of the crystal are extended to infinity, the mean-square fluctuations of the displacements tend to infinity; crystal imperfections have no influence on the widths of the peaks if the fluctuations in the displacements remain finite.

Diffuse scattering and a weakening of the intensity of the x-ray lines are usually associated with distortions (stresses) of the third kind, embracing a smallish number of atoms, while line broadening is associated with distortions of the second kind embracing the volume of individual crystals. This kind of classification of distortions is of course largely formal, since, for example, distortions of the third kind may arise from different causes. The very concept of distortions of the third kind is not really very strict, since the displacements usually fall off quite slowly with distance instead of simply embracing a few neighboring atoms.

At the present time we are able to give a more detailed description of a nonideal crystal, based on considerations involving various different types of defect (impurity atoms, vacancies, new-phase particles, dislocations, stacking faults, and so on). With this kind of description, the problem of studying the elastic scattering of x rays by a nonideal crystal reduces to a study of the x-ray-diffraction effects created by different defects. Defects of different kinds lead to qualitatively different changes in the scattering intensity distribution, sometimes creating and sometimes not creating broadening of the lines (spots) on the x-ray-diffraction picture. Accordingly defects may be divided into two classes in accordance with the x-ray-diffraction effects which they produce. Clearly a theory of x-ray scattering by nonideal crystals should primarily establish criteria relating the characteristics of particular defects to the corresponding qualitative picture of intensity distribution, thus yielding some kind of classification of defects.

Let us therefore consider a crystal of arbitrary structure containing defects [72]. For simplicity we shall suppose that the concentration of defects is quite small (the number of defects is much smaller than the number of sites in which they may appear). Clearly this limitation does not reduce the generality of the qualitative results obtained. In this section we shall also confine ourselves to the case in which the defects are distributed at random over the crystal so that there is no correlation between them. We shall at first consider that only defects of one particular kind exist.

The intensity of the scattering of monochromatic radiation by a defect-containing single crystal may be determined from the general formula of the kinematic theory (12.6). The structure amplitudes f_s and displacements $\delta \mathbf{R}_s$ coming into this formula differ in different cells; they may be expressed in terms of the characteristics of individual defects and in terms of a quantity characterizing the detailed distribution of defects in the crystal. Let us consider for this purpose one of the defects in the crystal, lying at the position t (in the case of point defects the defect itself lies at t; in the case of rectilinear dislocations t gives the line of the dislocation, in the case of new-phase particles the center of the particle, and so on).

The introduction of a defect into the crystal produces a static displacement of the atoms and leads to a change in the atomic-scattering factors for the atoms at certain points (in which atoms of one sort are replaced by atoms of another sort or by vacancies). Let us denote the vector of the displacements of the first atom in the s-th cell, associated with the appearance of a defect at position t, by $\mathbf{u}_{ts}$, and the corresponding change in the structure amplitude by φ_{ts}. Usually φ_{ts} is only different from zero for cells close to the position t (for only one cell in the case of point defects, or for distances $|\mathbf{R}_t - \mathbf{R}_s| < r_0$, where r_0 is the radius of the particle, in the case of particles of a new phase) and $\mathbf{u}_{ts}$ usually falls off much more slowly with distance from the defect.

In the same way as the distribution of atoms at points of the solid solution in §1, the distribution of defects in the crystal may be characterized by making c_t equal to unity if a defect exists at position t, and equal to zero if it does not. The total static displacement of the first atom of the s-th cell due to all the defects in the crystal may be put in the form of a superposition of the displacements caused by individual defects:

$$\delta \mathbf{R}_s = \sum_t c_t \mathbf{u}_{ts}. \tag{14.1}$$

Here the summation is carried out over all positions, i.e., over all the lattice points in the case of substitution-type solutions, over the interstices in the case of interstitial solutions, over the points in a given plane at which dislocation lines may be found in the case of rectilinear dislocations, and so on. Owing to changes in the distance between t and s associated with the presence of other defects in the crystal, there may be slight deviations from the superposition law (14.1). However, it is not difficult to show that the corresponding corrections are quite small and tend to zero in the case of low defect concentration here considered.

In a number of cases, for example, in the case of point defects (see p. 81), effects associated with surface "image forces" are considerable. These have the result that, on introducing defects into the crystal, displacement fields appear around each defect, and there is also a homogeneous (apart from small fluctuations) deformation of the crystal. For future purposes it is convenient to take as the initial ideal lattice the lattice of a crystal homogeneously deformed by "image forces" of this kind. The displacement u_{ts} is reckoned from the radius vector $\mathbf{R}_s^0$ of the s-th cell of this lattice and does not include the terms associated with the surface forces. In those cases in which the homogeneous deformation in question does not take place, we may reckon distances from the lattice points of the defect-free crystal.

In an analogous way, allowing for the fact that, in the case of a small concentration of defects, configurations in which two or more defects lie close to the given s-th cell play a negligibly small part, the expression for the structure amplitude of the s-th cell may be written in the form

$$f_s = f + \sum_t c_t \varphi_{ts}, \tag{14.2}$$

where f is the structure amplitude of the defect-free crystal.

If we put (14.1) and (14.2) into (12.6), the expression for the scattering intensity corresponding to a given distribution of defects in the crystal, i.e., to given values of the numbers c_t, takes the following form

$$I = \sum_{s, s'} \left(f + \sum_t c_t \varphi_{ts}\right) \left(f^* + \sum_{t'} c_{t'} \varphi^*_{t's'}\right) e^{i\mathbf{q}_1(\mathbf{R}^0_s - \mathbf{R}^0_{s'})} \prod_{t''} e^{i\mathbf{q}_1(\mathbf{u}_{t''s} - \mathbf{u}_{t''s'}) c_t}. \quad (14.3)$$

Neglecting small fluctuations (in a crystal of fairly large dimensions), we may replace expression (14.3) by its mean value calculated for a random distribution of defects. This averaging process reduces to an averaging over the quantities c_t, considered as statistically independent quantities (no correlation), which take the value 1 with a probability c equal to the concentration of defects (the ratio of the number of defects to the numbers of sites in which these may occur), and the value 0 with a probability $1-c$.

Let us first carry out this averaging for the case in which the defects do not influence the structure amplitudes and $\varphi_{ts} = 0$. Then the problem reduces to the calculation of the mean of the products of the statistically independent factors $\exp[i\mathbf{q}_1(\mathbf{u}_{ts} - \mathbf{u}_{ts'})c_t]$. The means of each factor with respect to the numbers $c_t = 0, 1$ equal

$$\overline{\exp\left[i\mathbf{q}_1(\mathbf{u}_{ts} - \mathbf{u}_{ts'})\, c_t\right]} = c \exp\left[i\mathbf{q}_1(\mathbf{u}_{ts} - \mathbf{u}_{ts'})\right] + 1 - c. \quad (14.4)$$

Remembering that for small concentrations (to an accuracy of terms quadratic in c in the index of the exponential) the product equals

$$\prod_t \left[c e^{i\mathbf{q}_1(\mathbf{u}_{ts} - \mathbf{u}_{ts'})} + 1 - c\right] = \exp \sum_t \ln\left\{1 + c\left[e^{i\mathbf{q}_1(\mathbf{u}_{ts} - \mathbf{u}_{ts'})} - 1\right]\right\} = e^{-T}, \quad (14.5)$$

where

$$T = c \sum_t \left\{1 - \exp\left[i\mathbf{q}_1(\mathbf{u}_{ts} - \mathbf{u}_{ts'})\right]\right\}, \quad (14.6)$$

we find that, for $\varphi_{ts} = 0$, the formula for the scattering intensity has the form

$$I = f^2 \sum_{s, s'} e^{i\mathbf{q}_1(\mathbf{R}^0_s - \mathbf{R}^0_{s'})}\, e^{-T}. \quad (14.7)$$

In the more general case in which $\varphi_{ts} \neq 0$, it is not hard to find by an analogous calculation that for small c

$$I=\sum_{s,\,s'} e^{i\mathbf{q}_1(\mathbf{R}_s^0-\mathbf{R}_{s'}^0)}\left[|\bar{f}|^2+c\sum_t \varphi_{ts}\varphi_{ts'}^* e^{i\mathbf{q}_1(\mathbf{u}_{ts}-\mathbf{u}_{ts'})}\right]e^{-T'}, \qquad (14.8)$$

where

$$T'=c\sum_t\{1-\exp[i\mathbf{q}_1(\mathbf{u}_{ts}-\mathbf{u}_{ts'})]\}\left[1+\frac{1}{f}(\varphi_{ts}+\varphi_{ts'})\right] \qquad (14.9)$$

and $\bar{f}$ is the average structure amplitude of the crystal containing the defects:

$$\bar{f}=f+c\sum_t\varphi_{ts}. \qquad (14.10)$$

In a defect-free crystal expression (14.8) reduces to the δ functions $\delta\,(\mathbf{q}_1-2\pi\mathbf{K}_n)$ in an infinite crystal, as in formula (13.13), or to δ-type functions in a finite crystal, as in formula (13.8). If there are defects in the crystal, then generally speaking (14.8) also contains terms proportional to δ functions. It is clear that for a general analysis of the scattering-intensity distribution we must first of all separate out these terms. In the sum (14.8) over s and s', terms with neighboring s and s' give no contribution to the δ-type function (their number $\sim$N is much smaller than the total number N^2 of the terms in the double sum), and this function is determined by terms for which the distance $|\mathbf{R}_s-\mathbf{R}_{s'}|$ is very large. For these terms the second term in the square bracket of (14.8) vanishes, and the result is determined by the asymptotic behavior of the function T' at large $|\mathbf{R}_s-\mathbf{R}_{s'}|$.

Let us introduce the following notation for the limiting values (for $|R_s-R_{s'}|\to\infty$) of the real and imaginary parts of T':

$$2M=\operatorname{Re}T'=c\lim_{|\mathbf{R}_s-\mathbf{R}_{s'}|\to\infty}\sum_t\{1-\cos[\mathbf{q}_1(\mathbf{u}_{ts}-\mathbf{u}_{ts'})]\}\times$$

$$\times\left[1+\frac{1}{f}(\varphi_{ts}+\varphi_{ts'})\right], \qquad (14.11)$$

$$c\mathbf{q}_1\hat{\alpha}\,(\mathbf{R}_s^0-\mathbf{R}_{s'}^0)=-\operatorname{Im}T'=c\lim_{|\mathbf{R}_s-\mathbf{R}_{s'}|\to\infty}\sum_t\sin[\mathbf{q}_1(\mathbf{u}_{ts}-\mathbf{u}_{ts'})]. \qquad (14.12)$$

Here the tensor $\hat{\alpha}$ determines the changes in the size and shape of the "average" unit cell on introducing defects into the crystal (in addition to the homogeneous deformation associated with "image forces").

If the value of the displacements $\mathbf{u}_{ts}$ falls off rapidly with distance between t and s, tending toward zero, then in (14.11) we find that, of the pair of displacements $\mathbf{u}_{ts}$ and $\mathbf{u}_{ts'}$, only one differs markedly from zero (this also applies to the quantities φ_{ts}, $\varphi_{ts'}$), so that the expression for M becomes a little simpler:

$$M = c \sum_t [1 - \cos(\mathbf{q}_1 \mathbf{u}_{ts})] \left(1 + \frac{\varphi_{ts}}{f}\right). \tag{14.13}$$

Since

$$\mathbf{u}_{ts}(\mathbf{R}_s^0 - \mathbf{R}_t) = -\mathbf{u}_{ts}(\mathbf{R}_t - \mathbf{R}_s^0),$$

in the sum (14.12) the terms with t close to s or s' tend to cancel each other and there only remain terms corresponding to very remote defects ($|\mathbf{R}_t - \mathbf{R}_s| \gtrsim |\mathbf{R}_s - \mathbf{R}_{s'}| \to \infty$), so that for a rapid fall-off in the displacements with distance we may replace the sines in this sum by their arguments:

$$c\mathbf{q}_1 \hat{\alpha} (\mathbf{R}_s^0 - \mathbf{R}_{s'}^0) = c \lim_{|\mathbf{R}_s - \mathbf{R}_{s'}| \to \infty} \sum_t \mathbf{q}_1 (\mathbf{u}_{ts} - \mathbf{u}_{ts'}). \tag{14.14}$$

Let us write expression (14.8) in the form of a sum of two terms, one of which (I_0), in the limit of an infinite crystal, is proportional to a δ function while the other (I_1) contains no δ function:

$$I = I_0 + I_1. \tag{14.15}$$

The term proportional to the δ function may be separated out from (14.8) by considering that, in all the terms of the sum over s and s', the values of T' is determined by the same expressions (14.11) and (14.12) as in the previous case of large distances $|\mathbf{R}_s - \mathbf{R}_{s'}|$. Then, remembering (14.11), (14.12), and (13.3), we find that for an infinite crystal (to an accuracy of terms of higher order in

c) I_0 will equal

$$I_0 = |\bar{f}|^2 e^{-2M} \sum_{s,\, s'} \exp [i\mathbf{q}_1 (\mathbf{R}_s^0 - \mathbf{R}_{s'}^0) + ic\mathbf{q}_1 \hat{\alpha} (\mathbf{R}_s^0 - \mathbf{R}_{s'}^0)] = \frac{N}{v} |\bar{f}|^2 e^{-2M} \delta \left(\frac{\mathbf{q}}{2\pi}\right),$$

$$\mathbf{q} = \mathbf{q}_1 - 2\pi \mathbf{K}_n. \qquad (14.16)$$

Here $\mathbf{K}_n$ is the reciprocal-lattice vector corresponding to the "average" periodic lattice of the crystal containing defects (with point vectors $\mathbf{R}_s = \mathbf{R}_s^0 + c\hat{\alpha}\mathbf{R}_s^0$), and $\mathbf{q}/2\pi$ characterizes the deviation of the end of vector $\mathbf{q}_1/2\pi$ from the nearest reciprocal-lattice point. In a crystal of finite dimensions we must replace the $\delta(\mathbf{q}/2\pi)$ by a δ-type function $|s(\mathbf{q})|^2/V$ corresponding to the given shape of the crystal. Expression (14.16) differs from the analogous expression (13.13) determining the intensity of the regular Bragg reflections in ideal crystals in that f is replaced by the average structure amplitude $\bar{f}$, and that there is a factor $\exp(-2M)$ determining the weakening of the intensity of the regular reflections due to the static distortions created by the defects, as well as a change in the vectors $\mathbf{K}_n$ resulting from the average deformation of the lattice, which arises on introducing defects and leads to a displacement of the Bragg maxima.

The second term I_1 in (14.15) is obtained by subtracting from the total expression for the intensity (14.8) the isolated δ-type distribution (14.16):

$$I_1 = \sum_{s,\, s'} e^{i\mathbf{q}_1(\mathbf{R}_s^0 - \mathbf{R}_{s'}^0)} \{[|\bar{f}|^2 + c \sum_t \varphi_{ts}\varphi_{ts'}^* e^{i\mathbf{q}_1(\mathbf{u}_{ts} - \mathbf{u}_{ts'})}] e^{-T'} -$$

$$- |\bar{f}|^2 e^{-2M} \exp [ic\mathbf{q}_1 \hat{\alpha} (\mathbf{R}_s^0 - \mathbf{R}_{s'}^0)]\}. \qquad (14.17)$$

It is an important point that I_1 does not contain any δ function in any of its terms. It follows from this that as $|\mathbf{R}_s - \mathbf{R}_{s'}| \to \infty$ the expression in curly brackets of (14.17) tends to zero and not to any finite limit.

The results obtained enable us to determine whether the defects in question lead to any line or spot broadening on the x-ray-diffraction picture. Strictly speaking, we can only separate the scattered radiation into regular reflections (giving lines on the Debye diffraction picture) and diffuse scattering (giving diffuse background) for an infinite crystal. In this case the terms proportional to δ functions in the expressions for the scattering intensity describe regular reflections and the terms not containing any δ function as a factor describe the smooth distribution of diffuse scattering. As indicated earlier, only the term I_0 in (14.15) is proportional to a δ function and this therefore defines the intensity of the regular reflections.

Defects of different types may be divided into two classes. For defects of the first class expressions (14.11) and (14.13) for M are finite. In this case the introduction of defects into the crystal does not alter the δ-type form of the intensity distribution of the regular reflection (does not lead to any line broadening). The defects thus lead to a displacement of the lines [in accordance with formula (14.12)], to a change in their integral intensity, on account of the change in the mean atomic scattering factor [see (14.10)] and the appearance of the intensity-weakening factor $\exp(-2M)$ associated with distortions [see (14.11), (14.13)], and also to the appearance of diffuse scattering, the intensity of which is given by formula (14.17) for I_1. We notice that, according to (14.13), the attenuation factor $\exp(-2M)$ is determined not by the mean squares of the displacements but by a more complicated formula, based on the detailed behavior of the distortions near the defect (more details of this in §24).

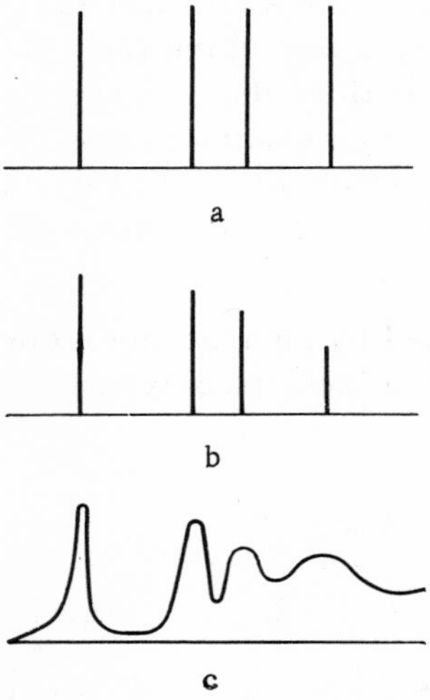

Fig. 6. Influence of defects of the first and second classes on the scattering intensity distribution on an x-ray-diffraction photograph. a) Ideal crystal (line intensities in arbitrary units divided by $p|f|^2$, i.e., reduced to the same intensity); b) crystal with defects of the first class; c) crystal with defects of the second class.

For defects of the second class the quantity M defined by formulas (14.11) and (14.13) passes to infinite. The term I_0 vanishes and the expression for the scattering intensity, now only determined by the term I_1, no longer contains any δ functions. The scattering-intensity distribution becomes smooth, and even in the limit of an infinite crystal cannot be split into lines and background. For small defect concentrations, as we shall demonstrate for various specific types of defects (see Chapter VII), these distributions have narrow, sharp maxima in the neighborhood of the reciprocal-lattice points, the widths of which are proportional to the defect concentration. It is natural to call the sharp peaks obtained "broadened regular reflections" and speak of a "broadening" of the lines on the x-ray-diffraction picture on introducing defects into the crystal.* In this case I_1 no longer determines the diffuse-scattering intensity distribution, but a single intensity distribution corresponding to the broadened line on the x-ray-diffraction picture together with its "wings." The influence of defects of the first and second classes on the intensity distribution is shown schematically in Fig. 6.

Thus whether a defect belongs to the first or second classes is determined by whether the sum (14.11) or (14.13) is finite or infinite. It is clear that in expression (14.13), which is valid if at large distances $\mathbf{u}_{ts} \to 0$, the sum of a finite number of initial terms in t, corresponding to small distances between t and s, is always finite, so that it is only required to study the "residue" of the sum, corresponding to large $|\mathbf{R}_s - \mathbf{R}_t|$. For these terms we may put $\varphi_{ts} = 0$ and replace $1 - \cos(\mathbf{q}_1\mathbf{u}_{ts})$ by the first term of the expansion $1/2\ (\mathbf{q}_1\mathbf{u}_{ts})^2$. In addition to this, since $\mathbf{u}_{ts}$ for large $|\mathbf{R}_s - \mathbf{R}_t|$ is a smooth function of distance, we may replace the sum by an integral (multiplying by $1/v$). Thus in the case of displacements tending to zero with distance the problem reduces to studying the convergence of the integral

$$\int_{r > R_0} (\mathbf{q}_1\mathbf{u}_{ts})^2\, dV. \tag{14.18}$$

Here R_0 is a distance greatly exceeding the lattice constant, so that the replacement of the cosine by the first two terms of its expansion and the continuum approximation are legitimate. This convergence is clearly determined by the behavior of the quantity $\mathbf{u}_{ts}$, considered as a function of the difference $\mathbf{r} = \mathbf{R}_t - \mathbf{R}_s$ at large distances.

*Qualitatively, this picture of intensity distribution as a function of the type of defect is valid not only for scattering by a single crystal but also for polycrystalline or powder samples. In fact, on averaging over the orientations of the crystals the δ function in reciprocal-lattice space reduces to a δ function of the scattering angle giving the line on the Debye photograph, and the smooth distribution remains smooth even after averaging.

Thus whether the defects belong to the first or the second class is determined by the asymptotic law of variation of the displacements at large distances from the defects.

In the case of point defects, as may be seen from (7.2), the displacements $\mathbf{u}_{ts} \equiv \delta\mathbf{R}_s(\mathbf{r})$ at large distances from the defect fall off as the inverse square of the distance. In this case the integral (14.18) converges, i.e., the point defects belong to the first class. As noted in §7, it follows from elasticity theory that for the quite general case of an arbitrary defect, the dimensions of which are finite in all three directions, the displacements also fall off in accordance with (7.2) at distances considerably exceeding these dimensions. Hence all defects of such a type (especially isolated particles of a new phase) in the classification under consideration are also defects of the first class and produce no line broadening in the x-ray diffraction picture (but see p. 144).

On the other hand, for infinitely extended defects the integral (14.18) and the sum (14.13) diverge. Thus, for example, if the defect is an infinitely long cylinder of impurity atoms in the crystal or a point defect in a two-dimensional lattice, the displacements will fall off as the inverse first power of the distance to the axis of the cylinder. Integral (14.18) will thus clearly diverge logarithmically, i.e., such defects belong to the second class. This divergence, however, only appears in an infinite crystal, and in a crystal of finite dimensions Λ the logarithmic factor arising $\ln(\Lambda/d)$ is usually about 10, and M remains finite.

The sum (14.11) diverges more rapidly in the case of point defects in a linear chain or the analogous plane defects in a space lattice [in this case the displacements do not fall off with distance at all, and the transformation from (14.11) to formulas (14.13) and (14.18) is illegitimate]. Hence, in the linear case, in the presence of point defects (for example, where atoms of different sorts have different dimensions) there should be a broadening of the lines on the x-ray diffraction picture. This result was obtained directly for a linear chain in [89, 90].* It follows in particular from the foregoing that, in the case considered, results obtained for a linear model cannot be extended even qualitatively to a three-dimensional crystal.

*Thermal vibrations also give line broadening in the one-dimensional case [91] but a weakening of line intensity in the three-dimensional case [92, 93].

Dislocations for which the dislocation line is a straight line passing through the whole crystal also constitute infinitely extended defects. The displacements do not fall off with increasing distance from the line of such a dislocation, and the sum (14.11) diverges (see §27). Rectilinear dislocations are therefore defects of the second class and produce line broadening. Clearly, in a finite crystal, M does not become infinite. However, for dislocations or point defects in a linear chain M becomes so large (order of N_g, where N_g is the total number of defects in the crystal) that $\exp(-2M)$ is practically equal to zero.

It also follows from the results presented that such infinitely extended defects as randomly distributed stacking faults in the crystal or systems of dislocations forming block boundaries in an infinite crystal also lead to line broadening on an x-ray diffraction picture. On the other hand, if a dislocation line is not infinitely extended, but closed, as in the case of dislocation loops, the dimensions of the defect are limited, and according to the foregoing classification should lead to weakening of the line rather than line broadening (see §28).

In the same way we may make a qualitative study of x-ray effects associated with any other form of crystal defect. Whether such defects belong to the first or second class depends on whether their dimensions are limited or infinitely large in one or two directions. In other words we may say that defects in the crystal belong to the first class if the displacements which they create fall off as $1/r^2$ (or faster) and to the second class if the displacements fall off more slowly than $1/r^{3/2}$.

In using the results obtained we must remember two facts.

First, our discussion relates to the case of randomly distributed defects, while in a real crystal there may be quite a high degree of correlation in their positions. In principle it is possible that correlation will lead to the screening of the field of displacements of a particular defect by other defects, so that defects of the second class will be converted into defects of the first class. Such a complete screening of the field of displacements may only take place, however, in extremely special cases, for example, for charged defects in piezoelectric crystals (see §21). In particular, this effect cannot take place in ordinary solid solutions or deformed crystals. In the latter case the arrangement of the defects is in general determined by a kinetic rather than a thermodynamic process, and the very special type of correlation indicated is impossible. No other type of correlation qualitatively alters the results.

Secondly, our considerations related to a set of equivalent defects. Even in the case of a set of defects of the same type, however, individual defects may differ markedly from each other. For example, edge or screw dislocations may differ in the shapes of their lines, which are generally speaking not straight. It is clear, however, that the existence of a certain bending in such lines on passing from one end of the grain to the other does not alter the qualitative conclusions regarding the broadening of lines on the x-ray diffraction photograph.

One reservation must be made regarding the above division of defects into two classes. It is possible to have cases in which the value of M is finite but much greater than unity. Then in the expression for I there is a term containing a δ function, and yet this term has a small exponential coefficient of the $\exp(-2M)$ type. In principle a term with a δ function, however small, may be distinguished from a smoothly varying term I_1. In practice, however, owing to the finite dimensions of the crystal, the δ-type intensity distribution becomes diffuse. On the other hand, for large M the diffuse-scattering intensity distribution concentrates into a narrow bell-shaped distribution (see Chapter VII). Hence for $M \gg 1$ the term I_0 may not appear, and the x-ray photograph will only appreciably show a broadened, bell-shaped distribution corresponding to I_1, interpreted experimentally as a "quasi-line." This means that, although for finite but very large M, defects belong theoretically to the first class, in an experimental investigation they will be interpreted as defects of the second class.

Thus, for different defect concentrations and parameter values, the same defects may be regarded as belonging either to the second class (leading to line broadening) or to the first class (not leading to broadening). In some cases the precipitated particles of a new phase (see §29) or dislocation loops (see §28) may form defects of this type.

Since, in the case of defects of the first class, the expression for I contains a term proportional to a δ function and also a term smoothly varying with scattering angle, for fairly large crystals containing such defects it is quite easy to separate the background from the lines on the x-ray photograph experimentally, and to determine the weakening in the intensity of the regular reflections associated with defects. However, when there are defects of the second class present in the crystal, the expression for I does not contain any δ functions but only describes a smooth (though sharp) intensity distribution. If the crystal contains randomly distributed defects of the second class of only one type, then the resultant intensity distribution describing the broadened line and its "wings" is characterized by only one parameter, determined by the properties of the defects and their concentration (we may take, for example, the line width as representing this parameter). Such an intensity distribution will occur, for example, in crystals containing randomly distributed dislocations of one type, the lines of which pass through the whole crystal. It is clear that in this case the separation of a single intensity distribution into lines and background may only be carried out quite arbitrarily and will have no real meaning.

If, however, the crystal contains defects of various types, for example, dislocations and vacancies or other point defects, then such a separation acquires a specific meaning. The intensity distribution may be divided into a narrow distribution (corresponding to a line) and a smooth distribution corresponding to diffuse scattering at point defects, giving the background. The accuracy of separating the line from the background in this case clearly increases on increasing the ratio of the widths of these distributions.

The above analysis related to defects in infinite crystals. Allowing for their finite dimensions leads to blurring (spreading) of the δ-type intensity distributions describing the regular reflections. The separation of the scattered radiation into lines and background cannot be carried out strictly in this case, even for crystals only containing defects of the first class; separation becomes to a certain extent arbitrary. With increasing crystal size, and hence sharper lines, the error in this separation clearly diminishes, tending to zero in the limit of an infinite crystal. In practice the separation may be reliable if the intensity of the background is much smaller than that of the line maxima.

In the case of scattering by a set of crystals of finite dimensions, there is yet another effect leading to line broadening; this is associated with fluctuations of the number of defects in different crystals.* In view of these fluctuations, the mean deformations and displacements of the maxima of the regular reflections will be different for different crystals on introducing defects into the crystal. If reflections from different crystals merge on a Debye photograph, the resultant intensity distribution will be broadened. The estimate made in [72] shows that the extent of the broadening is negligibly small in the case of homogeneous solid solutions, but may become considerable if precipitated new-phase particles are present. Fluctuations in the number of dislocations lead to a very small change in the line width (since dislocations have a relatively slight effect on the density of the crystal) but may considerably change the line shape.

It is clear that the above method may be used not only for the qualitative but also for the quantitative study of scattering-intensity distribution. The formulas obtained express the intensity of scattering by a distorted crystal in terms of the characteristics of individual defects. It is an important point that, in deriving these formulas, we did not use the (generally speaking, illegitimate) expansion of the general expression (12.6) in powers of the displacements $\delta\mathbf{R}_s$ (containing divergences in the case of defects of the second class) nor did we assume that the displacement $\delta\mathbf{R}_s$ was created simply by the defect closest to the s-th cell. Hence it is precisely this type of method which must be used in those cases in which the displacements are large and represent a superposition of contributions from a large number of defects, especially when calculating scattering at defects of the second class. Examples of scattering-intensity calculations carried out by this method will be given in Chapter VII.

On the other hand, on considering scattering by point defects created by smallish local displacements, expansion in powers of the displacement becomes legitimate, and only the first terms of this expansion have to be taken. This method, set out in Chapter V, makes it possible to take account of correlation quite easily, and is more convenient in studying scattering in solid solutions.

*All the effects earlier considered also involve fluctuations, but fluctuations of the distribution of defects in small volume elements rather than the total number of defects in the crystal (for an infinite crystal these fluctuations vanish).

§15. Harmonic Analysis of the Shape of X-Ray Lines

In the case of crystal containing defects of the second class, broadened intensity distributions arise in the neighborhood of the reciprocal-lattice points corresponding to regular Bragg reflections and broadened lines occur in the Debye diffraction photograph. The nature of this broadening is determined by the probabilities of differences in the displacements of different cells in the crystal $\delta\mathbf{R}_s - \delta\mathbf{R}_{s'}$, in particular by the probabilities of deformations. It is interesting to consider how to obtain information regarding the distribution of these probabilities, and also the dimensions of the crystallites, from x-ray diffraction data, without requiring additional detailed assumptions regarding the imperfections of the crystal, for example, the type of defects present in the crystal and their distribution. Such information may be obtained from data relating to the widths of the x-ray lines and more particularly their shapes. In principle, the best method of making a general analysis of the distribution of distortions in crystallites and crystallite dimensions on the basis of x-ray scattering by polycrystalline samples is that of carrying out a harmonic analysis of the line shapes on the Debye photograph in the manner proposed by Warren and Averbach [94], and developed subsequently in a number of other papers; see, for example, reviews [95–97, 85]).*

In order to illustrate the method of harmonic analysis, we shall follow [94] in considering crystals with a cubic lattice. In these crystals we may always choose a system of orthogonal axes in such a way that the Bragg reflection under consideration will be a reflection of the (h00) type. The edges of the corresponding cell, which has the shape of a rectangular parallelepiped, may be denoted d_x, d_y, d_z. It is clear that the results will also be applicable to reflections of the (h00) type from crystals of orthorhombic or tetragonal symmetry.

Let us confine ourselves to the case in which variation in the structure amplitudes may be neglected and the "nonideal" state of the crystal is simply represented by static displacements of the

*Useful, though less complete, information may also be obtained by studying the moments of the intensity distribution of the x-ray lines [251, 252].

atoms created by defects of the second type. The scattering intensity for a powder is determined by the integral of (12.9) taken over the surface of a sphere in reciprocal-lattice space. Since the intensity distribution forms sharp peaks for values of $\mathbf{q}_1/2\pi$ falling in the neighborhood of reciprocal-lattice points (see Fig. 5), integration over the surface of the sphere may be replaced by integration over p plane sections perpendicular to the vectors $2\pi\mathbf{K}_n$, which lie on the surface of this sphere. Then in accordance with (12.9) and (12.6) the scattering-intensity distribution on the Debye photograph will be given by the expression

$$I_D(q_1) = \frac{f^2}{4\pi q_1^2} \sum_{s, s'=1}^{N} e^{i\mathbf{q}_1(\mathbf{R}_{sx} - \mathbf{R}_{s'x})} \times$$

$$\times \iint dq_y \, dq_z \, e^{iq_y(R_{sy} - R_{s'y}) + iq_z(R_{sz} - R_{s'z})} \exp\left[i\mathbf{q}_1(\delta\mathbf{R}_s - \delta\mathbf{R}_{s'})\right]. \tag{15.1}$$

The integration with respect to q_y and q_z may be taken over the plane rectangular section

$$-\frac{\pi}{d_y} < q_y < \frac{\pi}{d_y} \text{ and } -\frac{\pi}{d_z} < q_z < \frac{\pi}{d_z}.$$

Since the differences $R_{sy} - R_{s'y} \equiv R_{ss'y}$ and $R_{sz} - R_{s'z} \equiv R_{ss'z}$ contain whole numbers of sections d_y and d_z, the result of this integration, summed over s and s', eliminates all terms for which these differences are other than zero, only terms with zero differences remaining. Hence expression (15.1) may be put in the form

$$I_D(q_1) = a \sum_{s, s'=1}^{N} \exp\left[iq_1(R_{sx} - R_{s'x})\right] \exp\left[i\mathbf{q}_1(\delta\mathbf{R}_s - \delta\mathbf{R}_{s'})\right] \delta_{ss'y}\delta_{ss'z},$$

$$a = \frac{I_i}{q_1}\frac{h}{N}. \tag{15.2}$$

Here $\delta_{ss'y}$ is the δ-symbol, equal to unity for $R_{ss'y} = 0$ and zero for $R_{ss'y} \neq 0$, while the constant a is taken in such a way that the integral of I_D over q_1 equals the integral intensity of the line I_i; this integral is most conveniently taken in the range

$$2\pi K_n - \frac{\pi}{d_x} < q_1 < 2\pi K_n + \frac{\pi}{d_x},$$

and then the only terms left in the sum are those with $\mathbf{R}_s = \mathbf{R}_{s'}$, so that, allowing for the equation $2\pi K_n = 2\pi h/d_x$ we immediately obtain (15.2) for *a*.

The difference $R_{sx} - R_{s'x}$ may be written in the form

$$R_{sx} - R_{s'x} = nd_x,$$

where n is a whole number. The diffraction vector q_1 we put as $q_1 = (2\pi/d_x)H$. If $q_1 = (4\pi/\lambda)\sin\theta$ corresponds to the position of an x-ray line in the ideal crystal, then H coincides with the whole number h (i.e., with the Miller index), while the other q_1 corresponding to the broadened line in the distorted crystal, H takes values close to h (differing from h by an amount small compared with unity). The quantity H is directly related to the scattering angle by the equation

$$H = \frac{2d_x}{\lambda}\sin\theta. \tag{15.3}$$

It is clear that I_D may be considered either as a function of q_1, or as a function of the scattering angle 2θ, or else as a function of H. In the new variables the first exponential in (15.2) takes the form

$$\exp[iq_1(R_{sx} - R_{s'x})] = \exp(2\pi inH) = \cos(2\pi nH) + i\sin(2\pi nH). \tag{15.4}$$

For the scalar product of $\mathbf{q}_1$ by the difference $\delta\mathbf{R}_s - \delta\mathbf{R}_{s'}$ in the displacements of the atoms lying in a single straight line parallel to the X axis and separated by n sections of length d_x, we introduce the notation

$$\mathbf{q}_1(\delta\mathbf{R}_s - \delta\mathbf{R}_{s'}) = 2\pi hX_n \quad \text{for} \quad R_{ss'y} = R_{ss'z} = 0. \tag{15.5}$$

Here X_n determines the relative change in the distance between s and s'. Since $[i\mathbf{q}_1(\delta\mathbf{R}_s - \delta\mathbf{R}_{s'})]$ is a smooth function of H, we may replace H in (15.5) by the neighboring whole number h.

Since (15.2) involves the δ symbols $\delta_{ss'y}$ and $\delta_{ss'z}$, the summation over s and s' is essentially carried out with respect to the discrete variables R_{sx}, R_{sy}, R_{sz}, and $R_{s'x}$. Summation over $R_{s'x}$ may be replaced by summation over the distance $R_{s'x} - R_{sx}$, i.e., with respect to n. Changing the order of the summation, remembering (15.4) and (15.5), and considering that I_D is real ($X_n = -X_{-n}$), we may express equation (15.2) for the scattering intensity, considered as a function of H, in the form of an ordinary expansion in Fourier series:

$$I_D(H) = aN \sum_{n=-\infty}^{\infty} (A_n \cos 2\pi Hn + B_n \sin 2\pi Hn), \tag{15.6}$$

where the Fourier coefficients are defined by the formulas

$$A_n = \frac{1}{N} \sum_{R_{sy}, R_{sz}} \sum_{R_{sx}}^{(n)} \cos 2\pi h X_n, \tag{15.7}$$

$$B_n = -\frac{1}{N} \sum_{R_{sy}, R_{sz}} \sum_{R_{sx}}^{(n)} \sin 2\pi h X_n. \tag{15.8}$$

Here the index (n) on the sum means that the summation over R_{sx} is only carried out for those R_{sx} for which both points, s and s', with given $R_{s'y} = R_{sy}$ and $R_{s'z} = R_{sz}$, lying at a distance of $R_{sx} - R_{s'x} = nd_x$ from each other along the X axis, lie within the volume of the crystal. We see at once from (15.7) that the zero Fourier coefficient equals unity in every case:

$$A_0 = 1. \tag{15.9}$$

This condition makes it possible to determine the normalizing constant *a* from experimental data.

Analysis of the expressions obtained for the Fourier coefficients will be treated first for the case in which distortions are absent and the line broadening is due solely to the finite dimensions of the crystallites. Then in formulas (15.7) and (15.8) we must put $X_n = 0$, the coefficients B_n vanish immediately, and in the formula for the A_n coefficients the cosines must be replaced by unity. If a column of unit cells parallel to the X axis contains m cells, then

$$\sum_{R_{sx}}^{(n)} 1 = m - |n|. \tag{15.10}$$

Here it is considered that for n cells lying at one of the extremities of the column the point s' lying at a distance of nd_x from s is outside the crystal, and the corresponding terms in the sum $\Sigma^{(n)}$ over s are absent.

Let us denote by p_m the number of columns parallel to the X axis in the crystal containing m cells. It follows from (15.7) and (15.10) that the Fourier coefficients $A_n = A_n^g$ in the case considered are determined by the size distribution of such columns:

$$A_n^g = \frac{1}{N} \sum_{m=1+|n|}^{\infty} (m - |n|)\, p_m \approx \frac{1}{N} \int_{1+|n|}^{\infty} (m - |n|)\, p_m\, dm. \qquad (15.11)$$

In the latter approximate equation it is considered that $m \gg 1$ ($m \sim 10^2 - 10^3$) and p_m is a smooth function of m.

It follows from the definition of the function p_m that

$$\sum_{m=1}^{\infty} m p_m \approx \int_1^{\infty} m p_m\, dm = N$$

and

$$\frac{1}{N} \sum_{m=1}^{\infty} p_m \approx \frac{1}{N} \int_1^{\infty} p_m\, dm = \frac{N_k}{N} = \frac{1}{\overline{m}}. \qquad (15.12)$$

If in (15.11) we put n = 0, then the first equation of (15.12), requiring that the total number of cells in all the columns should equal the number of cells in the crystal, leads to formula (15.9) for the coefficient A_0. In the second equation of (15.12) N_k determines the total number of columns and $\overline{m} = N/N_k$ is the average number of cells in one column. Differentiating expression (15.11) for A_n^g with respect to n and bearing this equation in mind, we find that at the point n = 0 the derivative equals

$$\left.\frac{dA_n^g}{dn}\right|_{n=0} = -\frac{1}{N} \int_1^{\infty} p_m\, dm = -\frac{1}{\overline{m}}. \qquad (15.13)$$

Here it is considered that $\sum_m p_m \gg p_1$.

Thus the initial slope of the curve relating A_n^g to n determines the average number of cells in the column $\overline{m}$, and hence also the average size of the crystal $\overline{m}d_X$ measured along the X axis [98]. The second derivative of (15.11) with respect to n

$$\frac{d^2A_n^g}{dn^2}=\frac{p_n}{N} \tag{15.14}$$

is expressed directly in terms of p_n. Hence a study of the curvature of the curve $A_n^g(n)$ for different n (for the case in which the line broadening is determined solely by the crystal size) in principle makes it possible to determine the size distribution of the columns along the X axis. It is clear that the character of this distribution is determined both by the shape of the individual crystallites and by the size distribution of the latter.

In the opposite case of fairly large, distorted crystals, when the line broadening is entirely determined by the distortions, the coefficients $A_n = A_n^u$ become negligibly small for values of n considerably smaller than the number of cells in the column $\overline{m}$. Hence for calculating A_n^u in the actual range of n values from formula (15.7) it is permissible, in the sum $\sum\limits_{R_{sx}}^{(n)}$ over R_{sx}, to disregard the limitation imposed by the index (n), which was associated with the finite dimensions of the crystal, and to carry out the $\mathbf{R}_s$ summation over all the cells s. Then the coefficients A_n^u

$$A_n^u=\frac{1}{N}\sum_s \cos 2\pi h X_n=\overline{\cos 2\pi h X_n} \tag{15.15}$$

will be determined by the distributions of the relative differences of the displacements X_n of the cells s and s' for various distances nd_X between these cells. For fairly small n the values of X_n are also small, so that $\cos 2\pi h X_n$ may be expanded in series and restricted to the first two terms of the expansion

$$A_n^u=1-2\pi^2h^2\overline{X_n^2};\quad \ln A_n^u=-2\pi^2h^2\overline{X_n^2}. \tag{15.16}$$

Thus the coefficients A_n^u for small n are determined by the mean-square distortions $\overline{X_n^2}$. If the probability distribution X_n is Gaussian, then formula (15.16) for $\ln A_n^u$ is valid not only for small but also for any n. However, as we shall show in Chapter VII, this distribution is by no means always Gaussian.

If distortions are present, not only are the A_n coefficients, generally speaking, nonzero in the expansion (15.6), but so are the B_n coefficients. The sine terms in the Fourier expansion describe the displacement of the x-ray lines due to the distortion and also their asymmetry. These terms are often not considered when analyzing broadened lines in plastically deformed metals; however, in some case effects of line displacement and asymmetry should in fact appear (see Chapter VII).

If the broadening of the x-ray line is due both to the finite dimensions of the crystallites and to distortions, then, by using the convolution theorem (see p. 122), it is easy to see that the A_n coefficients are in general equal to the product of the A_n^g and A_n^u coefficients given by formulas (15.11) and (15.15):

$$A_n = A_n^g A_n^u. \tag{15.17}$$

In particular, for small n, allowing for (15.16)

$$\ln A_n = \ln A_n^g - 2\pi^2 h^2 \overline{X_n^2}. \tag{15.18}$$

When the distortions of the crystallites and their finite dimensions are both important, the question of the separation of the x-ray-diffraction effects associated with these two factors arises. In order to achieve a separation of this kind, one frequently assumes that $\overline{X_n^2}$ depends on n in accordance with a law of the $\overline{X_n^2} \sim n^2$ type. Since $\ln A_n^g = -n/\overline{m}$ for small n, according to (15.13) and (15.9), the foregoing assumptions means that the first and second terms in (15.18) will depend on n in accordance with different laws (linear and quadratic, respectively). This enables us to separate the effects associated with the finite size of the crystallites and the distortions by distinguishing between the linear and quadratic terms in the graph of $\ln A_n$ against n for small n.

In actual fact, however, the assumption regarding the $\ln A_n^u \sim n^2$ relationship may not be justified. We see from the results given in §§26 and 28 that in some cases, in the important range of comparatively small n, the value of $\ln A_n^u$ is proportional to n rather than n^2, i.e., this term depends on n in the same way as $\ln A_n^g$. For this reason, and also because of certain experimental difficulties in determining A_n for small n, this approach to the separation of the effects is not very reliable.

A considerably more reliable method of separating the effects of finite crystallite size and distortions is based on using data relating to the shape of not one but several x-ray lines, corresponding to different orders of reflections from a single set of Bragg planes (with different h) [99]. Equations (15.11) and (15.15) show that only the $\ln A_n^u$ term in $\ln A_n$ depends on h, while $\ln A_n^g$ does not; hence extrapolation of the values of $\ln A_n$ for a given n and different h to zero h enables us to determine $\ln A_n^g$, i.e., to separate out the effect associated with the finite dimensions of the crystallites.

For fairly small n, for which formula (15.18) is valid, $\ln A_n$ depends quadratically on h, so that the graph relating $\ln A_n$ to h^2 (for a given n) is represented by a straight line. The section cut off by this straight line on the axis of ordinates determines $\ln A_n^g$, while the slope of the straight line determines the mean square of the relative displacements of the cells separated by a distance of nd_x, i.e., $\overline{X_n^2}$. From these data we may in principle determine both the mean size of the crystallites $\bar{m}d_x$ and the size distribution of the columns, and also the relation between $\overline{X_n^2}$ and n for small n.

It must be noted, however, that there may be cases in which, for comparatively small values of n, the value of $\ln A_n$ depends linearly on h rather than quadratically [see formulas (26.13) and (28.21)]. In these cases, for an extrapolation-based determination of $\ln A_n^g$, it is better to use a graph of $\ln A_n$ as a function of h (and not h^2).

If we were able to determine the values of $\ln A_n^u = \ln A_n - \ln A_n^g$ for a large number of orders of reflection, then, as indicated by (15.15), we could in principle find the distribution of distortions X_n (by reference to their mean Fourier components) [100]. In practice, however, we can only make an experimental study of lines corresponding to a small number of orders of reflections from a given Bragg plane. The use of reflections from different Bragg planes is usually troublesome, since for different orientations of these planes the distributions of the distortions and column may in general vary considerably.

In the practical application of the method of harmonic analysis, it is necessary to determine the Fourier coefficients of the intensity distributions of the x-ray lines, introduce a correction for instrumental broadening [101], and (in order to normalize the system) divide the resultant coefficients by the zero coefficient. We shall not consider the practical details of harmonic analysis here, especially the part played by the "wings" of the lines, nor the many experimental papers which have been written on the basis of this method, which are considered in detail in review articles [85, 95, 96].

In concluding this section we would emphasize that the dimensions of the crystallites obtained from data relating to line widths or the method of harmonic analysis are usually an order smaller than the actual sizes of the powders or grains in a polycrystalline sample. Such crystallites constitute regions of coherent scattering (blocks) considerably disoriented with respect to each other. The very existence of these is in fact associated with distortions of a special kind, which are created by such defects as small-angle boundaries or stacking faults. A characteristic of these defects is the fact that, for any reflection, when a defect (for example, a sharply-defined small-angle boundary) occurs, a large change in phase shift immediately develops between the pair of cells under consideration. As a result of this the A_n coefficients are not dependent on h, as in the case of the broadening associated with the finite dimensions of the actual crystals.

Hence, strictly speaking, the whole broadening of the x-ray lines should be associated simply with distortions, including those created by such defects as small-angle boundaries. In practice, however, it is convenient to describe effects associated with sharply-defined small-angle boundaries, antiphase (domain) boundaries in ordered solutions, and stacking faults by introducing the concept of regions of coherent scattering (blocks, ordered domains, and so on) and regarding deformations within these regions (for example, those created by randomly distributed dislocations) as "true" distortions.

Chapter V

Diffuse Scattering of X Rays and Neutrons at Fluctuation Inhomogeneities of Crystals

§16. Scattering of X Rays by Solid Solutions

A solid solution may be regarded as an ideal crystal consisting of "average" atoms with a superimposed "inhomogeneity" represented by variations in the atomic scattering factors and static displacements, due to the difference between the real atoms of the solution and the "average" ones. The distortions arising in the solution around the impurity atoms are associated with point defects, i.e., defects of the first class according to the classification proposed in §14. As we shall see from the results of this section, therefore, no x-ray line broadening should occur in solid solutions. X-ray diffraction effects which arise on passing from a single-component crystal to a solid solution include a displacement of the lines on the x-ray diffraction picture, a weakening of their intensity, and the appearance of diffuse scattering at static inhomogeneities.

Let us consider these effects individually, starting with the most general features.

The displacement of the lines on the x-ray-diffraction picture on introducing point defects into the crystal corresponds to a change in the lattice parameters of the ideal "average" crystal determined by formula (14.14). This displacement was considered in [102–104, 52]. It was shown that, if the number of lattice points remains unaltered on introducing the defects into the crystal (for example, on replacing atoms at some points by impurity atoms or introducing impurity atoms into the interstices), then the relative change in the lattice constant of a cubic lattice $\Delta d/d$ determined from the displacement of the lines in the diffraction picture will be exactly equal to the relative change in the macroscopic dimensions of the sample determined dilatometrically.

In some cases, however, the number of lattice points does change on introducing defects. For example, on the formation of N_g vacancies (without changing the number of atoms) the number of lattice points increases by N_g, while if N_g of the genuine crystal atoms pass into the interstices (without forming vacancies) the number of points falls by N_g. In this case the macroscopic dimensions change as a result of the change in both the lattice constant and the total number of lattice points. For example, when vacancies are formed in a monatomic crystal, the total volume V will equal

$$V = v(N + N_g) = V_0 + vN_g,$$

where v is the average atomic volume of the crystal with the vacancies, determined from the positions of the x-ray lines ($\Delta v/v = 3(\Delta d/d)$, N is the total number of atoms in the crystal, determined by weighing, and $V_0 = vN$. It thus follows that

$$\frac{V - V_0}{V_0} = \frac{N_g}{N} \quad \text{or} \quad 3\frac{\Delta\Lambda}{\Lambda} - 3\frac{\Delta d}{d} = \frac{N_g}{N}. \qquad (16.1)$$

For the case of the formation of interstitial atoms, we must put a minus sign in front of the N_g/N in (16.1).

Thus a simultaneous x-ray-diffraction and dilatometric study of the quantities $\Delta d/d$ and $\Delta\Lambda/\Lambda$ makes it possible to determine the type of defects formed (if $\Delta\Lambda/\Lambda > \Delta d/d$, these are vacancies and if $\Delta\Lambda/\Lambda < \Delta d/d$ interstitial atoms) and their concentration independently. It is an important point that this method, which was developed and used for studying defects at high temperatures in a number of metals [105–107], is not based on any supplementary assumptions (for example, regarding the volume of the vacancies) but constitutes a direct method of determining the concentration of the defects (if only defects of one type are formed).

Let us now consider the weakening in the intensity of regular reflections associated with the static displacements of the atoms in solid solutions.

The intensity of the scattering of x rays by a solid solution is given by formula (12.3). The atomic factor $f_{s\gamma}$ in a binary solution takes the values f_A or f_B according to whether the A or B type of atom lies at the γ point of the s-th cell. The quantities

$$f_{s\gamma} = c_{s\gamma} f_A + (1 - c_{s\gamma}) f_B$$

may be expressed in terms of the numbers $c_{s\gamma}$ defined by formula (1.1). Then the expression (12.3) for the intensity of monochromatic radiation scattered from a single crystal may be put in the form

$$I = \left| \sum_{s=1}^{N} \sum_{\gamma=1}^{\nu} [c_{s\gamma} f_A + (1 - c_{s\gamma}) f_B] \exp (i\mathbf{q}_1 \mathbf{R}_{s\gamma}) \exp (i\mathbf{q}_1 \delta \mathbf{R}_{s\gamma}) \right|^2. \quad (16.2)$$

For regular reflections $\mathbf{q}_1 = 2\pi \mathbf{K}_n$ and the factor $\exp (i\mathbf{q}_1 \mathbf{R}_{s\gamma}) = \exp (i\mathbf{q}_1 \mathbf{R}_\gamma)$ is the same for all cells ($\mathbf{R}_{s\gamma} = \mathbf{R}_s + \mathbf{R}_\gamma$ and the product $\mathbf{R}_s \mathbf{K}_n$ is a whole number). Hence the product

$$[c_{s\gamma} f_A + (1 - c_{s\gamma}) f_B] \exp (i\mathbf{q}_1 \delta \mathbf{R}_{s\gamma}),$$

arising in the sum over s (for given γ) with identical coefficients may be replaced by its average value f_γ:

$$f_\gamma = \overline{[c_{s\gamma} f_A + (1 - c_{s\gamma}) f_B] \exp (i\mathbf{q}_1 \delta \mathbf{R}_{s\gamma})} = c_\gamma f_A e^{-M_{A\gamma}} + (1 - c_\gamma) f_B e^{-M_{B\gamma}}. \quad (16.3)$$

Here $c_\gamma = \overline{c}_{s\gamma}$ is the concentration of A atoms at the points of the sublattice γ, and $\exp(-M_{A\gamma})$ and $\exp(-M_{B\gamma})$ are attenuation factors for the scattering amplitude of the A and B atoms, this attenuation being produced by the static distortions. These factors are defined as the averages of $\exp (i\mathbf{q}_1 \delta \mathbf{R}_{s\gamma})$ over the A and B atoms respectively in the sublattice γ:

$$\exp (-M_{A\gamma}) = \overline{\exp (i\mathbf{q}_1 \delta \mathbf{R}_{s\gamma})}^{A\gamma}, \quad \exp (-M_{B\gamma}) = \overline{\exp (i\mathbf{q}_1 \delta \mathbf{R}_{s\gamma})}^{B\gamma}. \quad (16.4)$$

It is clear that the quantities M are generally speaking different, both for atoms of different types at the points of the same sublattice, and for atoms of the same type in different sublattices. The scattering-amplitude attenuation factors and regular-reflection intensities associated with the static displacements will be discussed in more detail in Chapter VI.

If we introduce the average structure amplitude

$$f = \sum_{\gamma=1}^{\nu} f_\gamma \exp(i\mathbf{q}_1\mathbf{R}_\gamma), \tag{16.5}$$

where the average atomic scattering factors f_γ are given by formula (16.3), allowing for distortions, then for regular reflections the expression for the scattering intensity (16.2) formally takes the same form (13.1) as for scattering by ideal crystals. Hence the intensity of the regular reflections for solid solutions is described by the same distributions (13.8) (broadened as a result of the finite dimensions of the crystal) as for ideal crystals, and in the limit of an infinite crystal by an infinitely narrow distribution corresponding to a δ function (13.13). The difference from the ideal crystal lies simply in the fact that now, in accordance with (16.5) and (16.3), the structure amplitude depends on the concentration, long-range-order parameters, and static distortions.

The most complete information regarding the character of the nonideal features of the solid solution may be obtained from data relating to diffuse scattering. Diffuse scattering occurs for angles differing from the Bragg angle ($\mathbf{q}_1 \neq 2\pi\mathbf{K}_n$) as a result of perturbations in the periodicity of the crystal. In solid solutions, the diffuse scattering is due to two causes: the different scattering factors of the two atoms (A and B) lying at points of a given type γ, and the static displacements. Both these factors arise from concentration inhomogeneities in the solutions and may be considered at the same time.

In considering scattering by solid solutions, two approaches are possible. In the first of these, we consider scattering at the inhomogeneity created by each atom (the change in the atomic factor and the resultant field of static distortions), use (16.2) to determine the interference picture created by the secondary waves scattered by the different atoms for a given atomic configuration, and then average over the various possible configurations. It is by precisely this method that the majority of work has been done on x-ray and neutron scattering theory for solid solutions, some authors neglecting the static displacements of the atoms in the solution [76, 89, 108–115] and some taking account of such displacements [116–122].

In the second approach, the crystal is considered as a periodic structure consisting of effective "average" atoms, on which fluctuations of composition and order parameters are superimposed. The periodic structure results in the appearance of regular reflections and the fluctuations produce diffuse scattering. In this method, the diffuse scattering is associated not with individual scattering centers but with fluctuation waves of concentration and internal parameters, and with the waves of static displacements resulting from these. As a result of this, the scattering probability is directly related to the thermodynamic characteristics of the solution.

This approach leads to considerable simplification when considering some more complicated problems in the theory of diffuse scattering, for example, when studying the scattering of x rays near critical points or phase transformations of the second kind, when considering long-range forces, and so on. The method is especially suitable for considering scattering with due allowance for distortions, since the equations of elastic theory or the atomic theory of crystals simplify considerably on transforming to Fourier components.

A study of x-ray and neutron scattering by the method of fluctuation waves in undistorted crystals was made in [3, 6, 23] and with due allowance for distortions in [27, 30, 32, 35, 37, 41, 53, 55, 123, 124]. In what follows, diffuse scattering will always be considered by this method, using the results of the theory of fluctuation waves set out in Chapters I to III.

In considering diffuse scattering ($\mathbf{q}_1 \neq 2\pi\mathbf{K}_n$), the constant average component of the product

$$[c_{s\gamma} f_A + (1 - c_{s\gamma}) f_B] \exp(i\mathbf{q}_1 \delta\mathbf{R}_{s\gamma})$$

in (16.2), determining the intensity of the regular reflections, falls out of the expression for the scattering amplitude, and we need only consider the fluctuation component of this quantity, associated with the deviation of the quantities $c_{s\gamma}$ from their mean values c_γ and with the deviation of the displacements $\delta\mathbf{R}_{s\gamma}$ from zero. The fluctuations of $c_{s\gamma}-c_\gamma$ and $\delta\mathbf{R}_{s\gamma}$ may be defined by their Fourier expansions (1.7) and (5.1).

The static distortions in homogeneous solid solutions are associated with defects of the first class (by the classification of §14) and are usually not large. Hence we may expand expression (16.2) in powers of $\mathbf{q}_1\delta\mathbf{R}_{s\gamma}$ and confine attention to the first few terms in the expansion (the case of large displacements, resulting from concentration inhomogeneities, for which this expansion converges only slowly, may arise in inhomogeneous solutions, and will be considered in Chapter VII).

Carrying out this expansion, let us confine ourselves first to linear terms in $f_A - f_B$ and $\mathbf{q}_1\delta\mathbf{R}_{s\gamma}$ in the expression for the scattering amplitude. Replacing $c_{s\gamma}-c$ and $\delta\mathbf{R}_{s\gamma}$ by their Fourier expansions (1.7) and (5.1) and putting $\mathbf{q}_1$ in the form of a sum $\mathbf{q}_1 = 2\pi\mathbf{K}_n + \mathbf{q}$ ($\mathbf{K}_n$ is the reciprocal-lattice vector closest to $\mathbf{q}_1/2\pi$) and $\mathbf{R}_{s\gamma}$ in the form of a sum $\mathbf{R}_{s\gamma} = \mathbf{R}_s + \mathbf{R}_\gamma$, we write this expression in the form

$$I = \left| \sum_{\gamma=1}^{\nu} e^{2\pi i \mathbf{K}_n \mathbf{R}_\gamma} \sum_{s=1}^{N} \left\{ f_\gamma + \sum_{\mathbf{k}} \left[(f_A - f_B)\, c_{\mathbf{k}\gamma} - f_\gamma \mathbf{q}_1 \mathbf{R}_{\mathbf{k}\gamma} \right] e^{-i\mathbf{k}\mathbf{R}_{s\gamma}} \right\} e^{i\mathbf{q}\mathbf{R}_{s\gamma}} \right|^2 . \tag{16.6}$$

Strictly speaking, it would have been more consistent in (16.6) to replace f_γ by the average of $c_\gamma f_A + (1-c_\gamma) f_B$. For small displacements, however, the difference between these quantities may (in the approximation taken) be neglected, in accordance with (16.3). In the case of small q, however, the factors $\exp(-M_{A\gamma})$ and $\exp(-M_{B\gamma})$ in (16.3) lead to a refinement of the formula for I, which in effect takes a more proper account of the higher terms of the expansion in powers of the displacement for this region.*

Remembering that in the limit of an infinite crystal the sum $\sum_s \exp[i(\mathbf{q}-\mathbf{k})\mathbf{R}_{s\gamma}]$ equals zero for $\mathbf{q} \neq \mathbf{k}$ and N for $\mathbf{q} = \mathbf{k}$ (for sim-

*It is clear that the attenuation factors for scattering by a wave of distortions with a long wavelength should be the same as for regular reflections. This is confirmed by direct calculation, allowing for the higher terms in the expansion.

plicity we consider that $\mathbf{q}$ satisfies the cyclical conditions), we may write $I = I_0 + I_1$ in the form of a sum of two terms. The first of these (I_0) describes the intensity of the regular reflections and is determined by the formulas of §13 [with f values allowing for distortions in accordance with formulas (16.4) and (16.3)]; the second (I_1) describes diffuse scattering and is given by the expression

$$I_1 = N^2 \left| \sum_{\gamma=1}^{\nu} \exp(2\pi i \mathbf{K}_n \mathbf{R}_\gamma) [f_\gamma \mathbf{q}_1 \mathbf{R}_{q\gamma} - (f_A - f_B) c_{q\gamma}] \right|^2. \tag{16.7}$$

The square of the first term in (16.7) determines the scattering due to the distortions, the square of the second term gives the scattering due to the difference in the atomic factors, and the double product gives the interference term associated both with the distortions and the difference between f_A and f_B. In formulas (16.7) and (16.6) we understand averaging over the atomic configurations corresponding to given values of c_γ and correlation parameters.

Consideration of the higher terms of the expansion of I_1 in powers of the displacements enables us to formulate criteria indicating the conditions under which we may confine attention to the quadratic terms of the expansion and use formula (16.7). According to [124] such criteria may be written in the form*

$$M_\gamma \frac{q}{k_m} \ll 1, \quad \frac{M_\gamma}{c_\gamma (1 - c_\gamma)} \left(\frac{q}{k_m} \right)^2 \ll 1. \tag{16.8}$$

These criteria are satisfied in slightly distorted crystals for which $M_\gamma \ll c_\gamma (1 - c_\gamma)$ and also in severely distorted crystals if the vector $\mathbf{q}_1/2\pi$ falls in the neighborhood of any reciprocal-lattice point and q is much smaller than the maximum wave vector in the unit cell $k_m \sim (2\pi/d)$ ($q \ll k_m$). For large q, when condition (16.8) is satisfied by virtue of $M \ll 1$, the square of the first term in

*In (16.8) it is assumed that $|f_A - f_B|$ has the same order as the f_γ or is much smaller than these. If $|f_A - f_B| \gg f_\gamma$ (this condition is only satisfied for special cases in neutron scattering but not for x rays) the left-hand side of (16.8) must be multiplied by $f_\gamma |f_A - f_B|^{-1}$.

(16.7) is much smaller than the square of the second term and has the same order of magnitude as the terms rejected in the derivation of (16.7) (considered in [124]). Hence in this case it would be consistent to retain only the terms linear in the displacements. However, for fairly small q, even in weakly distorted crystals ($M \ll 1$), the square of the first term in (16.7) becomes the principal term in the expression for I_1 (see §18) and is considerably greater than the discarded terms. Hence in (16.7) we must then consider the terms quadratic in the displacements as well.

We see from (16.7) that the intensity of the diffuse scattering is expressed in terms of the squares and products of the Fourier components of the fluctuations of the concentrations c_γ and displacements of the atoms (for the wave vector $\mathbf{q}$), which were considered in Chapters I to III. The expression for the intensity is greatly simplified in the case of disordered solutions with one atom per unit cell ($\nu = 1$), in which the static displacements are only due to fluctuations of concentration. In this case, as may be seen from (5.2), $\mathbf{R}_\mathbf{k} \sim c_\mathbf{k}$ and expression (16.7) takes the form

$$I_1 = N^2 \overline{|c_\mathbf{q}|^2} [f\mathbf{q}_1\mathbf{A}_\mathbf{q} - (f_A - f_B)]^2. \tag{16.9}$$

In order to study diffuse scattering by disordered solutions, we must use the expressions derived in §§1 to 3 and 9 for $\overline{|c_\mathbf{q}|^2}$ and those derived in §§5 and 6 for the proportionality factor $\mathbf{A}_\mathbf{q}$ between the amplitudes of the fluctuation waves of displacements and concentration. A study of this kind will be made in §17 for the case of undistorted crystals and in §18 with due allowance for static displacements.

§17. Diffuse Scattering at Concentration Inhomogeneities in Undistorted Solutions

In the absence of distortions, we must put $\mathbf{A}_\mathbf{q} = 0$ in expression (16.9) for the intensity of diffuse scattering by disordered solutions with one atom per unit cell. Defining the square of the Fourier component $\overline{|c_\mathbf{q}|^2}$ in accordance with formula (1.13), we may express I_1 in terms of the correlation parameters $\varepsilon(\boldsymbol{\rho})$:

$$I_1 = N (f_A - f_B)^2 \left[c(1-c) + \sum_{\boldsymbol{\rho} \neq 0} \varepsilon(\boldsymbol{\rho}) \cos \mathbf{q}\boldsymbol{\rho}\right]. \tag{17.1}$$

If there is no correlation in the solution, $\varepsilon(\boldsymbol{\rho}) = 0$, and the intensity of diffuse scattering by such an ideal solution is determined by the Laue formula [108]:

$$I_1 = N(f_A - f_B)^2 c(1-c). \tag{17.2}$$

It is a characteristic feature that in an ideal solution the ratio $I_1/(f_A - f_B)^2$ does not depend on the diffraction vector $\mathbf{q}_1$ and is the same at all points in reciprocal-lattice space. If, however, the solution is not ideal and the correlation parameters differ from zero, then, as may be seen from (17.1), this ratio will depend on $\mathbf{q}_1$. It is an important fact that, according to (17.1), $I_1(f_A - f_B)^{-2}$ is a periodic function of $\mathbf{q}_1/2\pi$, with the periods of the reciprocal lattice (on changing $\mathbf{q}_1/2\pi$ by any vector $\mathbf{K}$ of the reciprocal lattice, $\mathbf{q}_1\boldsymbol{\rho} = \cos \mathbf{q}\boldsymbol{\rho}$ remains unaltered, since $\mathbf{K}\boldsymbol{\rho}$ is a whole number). The diffuse scattering has this property of periodicity in undistorted crystals only (see §18), and the observation of such periodicity in experiment may serve as an indication that distortions are very small or absent.

In essence formula (17.1) constitutes an expansion of the function $I_1(f_A - f_B)^{-2}N^{-1}$ in Fourier series, in which the Fourier coefficients are the correlation parameters $\varepsilon(\boldsymbol{\rho})$. This expansion may be used for determining $\varepsilon(\boldsymbol{\rho})$ at all $\boldsymbol{\rho}$ from experimental data relating to the distribution of diffuse-scattering intensity $I_1(\mathbf{q}_1/2\pi)$ in any cell of the reciprocal lattice [113, 125]. In fact, carrying out a Fourier transformation, we obtain from (17.1)

$$\varepsilon(\boldsymbol{\rho}) = \frac{v}{8\pi^3} \int_{1/v} d\mathbf{k} \frac{I_1}{N} (f_A - f_B)^{-2} \cos \mathbf{k}\boldsymbol{\rho}, \tag{17.3}$$

where for integration in the region $1/v$ the quantities $\mathbf{k}/2\pi$ take values lying within the unit cell of the reciprocal lattice. For $\boldsymbol{\rho} = 0$ we may put $\varepsilon(0) = c(1-c)$ in (17.3) and use this relation as a normalization condition, but caution must be exercised in so doing [129].

The details of the practical use of formula (17.3) may be found in Cowley's articles [113] (see also [71, 128]). A modification of this formula in the presence of distortions (the role of which may be considerable) is considered in §18.

The results given for disordered solutions may easily be converted to the case of ordered solutions in which, after disordering (keeping the lattice geometry unaltered), the unit cell contains one atom. If in this case we reckon $\mathbf{q}/2\pi = \mathbf{q}_1/2\pi - \mathbf{K}_n$ from the reciprocal-lattice vector (corresponding to a "structurally" regular reflection) for which $\mathbf{K}_n\mathbf{R}_\gamma$ are whole numbers for all $\mathbf{R}_\gamma$, then in (16.7) $\exp(2\pi i\mathbf{K}_n\mathbf{R}_\gamma) = 1$ and I_1 is proportional to $|\sum_\gamma c_{q\gamma}|^2$. Defining this quantity from formulas (1.11) and (1.12), we may express I_1 in a form analogous to (17.1):

$$I_1 = N\nu (f_A - f_B)^2 \left[\frac{1}{\nu}\sum_{\gamma=1}^{\nu} c_\gamma (1 - c_\gamma) + \sum_{\boldsymbol{\rho}\neq 0} \varepsilon(\boldsymbol{\rho}) \cos \mathbf{q}\boldsymbol{\rho}\right], \qquad (17.4)$$

where the correlation parameters $\varepsilon(\boldsymbol{\rho})$ are given by formula (1.5). It follows from this, in particular, that in ordered solutions $\varepsilon(\boldsymbol{\rho})$ may be determined from formula (17.3), in which, however, the integration is now carried out over the volume ν/v of the ν unit cells of the reciprocal lattice of the ordered solution (over the volume of one unit cell for the disordered solution), N is replaced by $N\nu$, v by v/ν, and

$$\varepsilon(0) = \frac{1}{\nu}\sum_{\gamma=1}^{\nu} c_\gamma (1 - c_\gamma).$$

In order to obtain the diffuse-scattering intensity distribution on a Debye photograph, we must average expression (17.1) or (17.4) in accordance with formula (12.9). Since the sphere of radius q_1 in (12.9) passes through several unit cells in reciprocal-lattice space, it is more convenient in (17.4) to replace $\mathbf{q}\boldsymbol{\rho}$ by the equal quantity $\mathbf{q}_1\boldsymbol{\rho}$. Since

$$\int \cos \mathbf{q}_1\boldsymbol{\rho}\, dS = q_1^2 \int\int \cos(q_1\rho\cos\vartheta)\sin\vartheta\, d\vartheta\, d\varphi = 4\pi q_1^2 \frac{\sin q_1\rho}{q_1\rho}$$

(ϑ is the angle between $\mathbf{q}_1$ and $\boldsymbol{\rho}$), after putting (17.4) into (12.9) we obtain an expression for the diffuse-scattering intensity on the Debye picture of an undistorted crystal

$$I_{1D} = N\nu (f_A - f_B)^2 \left[\frac{1}{\nu}\sum_{\gamma=1}^{\nu} c_\gamma (1 - c_\gamma) + \sum_{l=1}^{\infty} z_l \frac{\sin q_1\rho_l}{q_1\rho_l} \varepsilon(\rho_l)\right], \qquad (17.5)$$

where ρ_l is the radius of the l-th coordination sphere with coordination number z_l. In view of the fact that $q_1 = (4\pi/\lambda)\sin\theta$ only varies in the finite interval $q_1 < 4\pi/\lambda$, we cannot carry out an inversion of expansion (17.5) and determine all the $\varepsilon(\rho_l)$ from data simply relating to the diffuse scattering on the Debye photograph. If, however, we may regard just a small number (one to three) of the correlation parameters for the first coordination spheres as differing from zero, then formula (17.5) enables us to determine these parameters from experimental data, for example, by the method of least squares [126] (but, generally speaking, less accurately than by studying the scattering from a single crystal).

By using the formulas of §§2 and 3 for $\overline{|c_{\mathbf{q}}|^2}$, we may express the diffuse scattering intensity, not in terms of the correlation parameters, but directly in terms of quantities characterizing the thermodynamic properties of the solution. Thus, if a disordered solution may be described by means of a pair-interaction model, then, by putting expression (3.3) into (16.9) instead of $\overline{|c_{\mathbf{q}}|^2}$ and supposing that for undistorted solutions $\mathbf{A}_{\mathbf{q}} = 0$, we may express I_1 in terms of the quantities $\chi(\boldsymbol{\rho})$ determined by the ordering energies $w_{\boldsymbol{\rho}}$ for different coordination spheres [23]:

$$I_1 = \frac{N(f_A - f_B)^2}{\sum\limits_{\boldsymbol{\rho}} x(\boldsymbol{\rho}) \cos \mathbf{q}\boldsymbol{\rho}}. \tag{17.6}$$

In cases of high temperatures or small concentrations, the quantities $\chi(\boldsymbol{\rho})$ are expressed in terms of the ordering energies for the same lattice vectors $\boldsymbol{\rho}$ by means of the simple relations (3.6) or (3.8).

Formula (17.6) may be used for the direct determination of the ordering energies of various coordination spheres by reference to experimental data relating to the distribution of $I_1(\mathbf{q}_1/2\pi)$ in reciprocal-lattice space. For this purpose we must carry out a Fourier transformation not of the actual scattering intensity [divided by $(f_A - f_B)^2$], as in determining the correlation parameters, but of the inverse quantity. This method was proposed in [23] and independently in [434]. Then we see from (17.6) that

$$x(\boldsymbol{\rho}) = \frac{v}{8\pi^3} \int\limits_{1/v} d\mathbf{k} \frac{N}{I_1} (f_A - f_B)^2 \cos \mathbf{k}\boldsymbol{\rho}. \tag{17.7}$$

Remembering relations (3.6) and (3.8) (or the more detailed relations (3.10) and (3.11) for the nearest-neighbor approximation) relating $\chi(\boldsymbol{\rho})$ and w_{ρ}, we may use (17.7) to determine w_{ρ} for all $\boldsymbol{\rho}$ [the formula for $\chi(0)$ may be used to normalize the I_1 distribution]. It is an interesting point that the values of w_{ρ} determined in this way for an Ag–Al alloy fall off relatively slowly with distance [127].

Formula (17.6) enables us to study the scattering intensity I_1 as a function of the position of the vector $\mathbf{q}_1/2\pi$ in the reciprocal-lattice cell for various temperatures and concentrations of the solution. Thus, for example, in the nearest-neighbor approximation, and at high temperatures, when only expressions (3.6) for $\boldsymbol{\rho} = 0$ and for z atoms of the first coordination sphere with $\boldsymbol{\rho} = \boldsymbol{\rho}_{\pi}$ ($\pi = 1, \ldots, z$), differ from zero, I_1 is determined by the simple formula

$$I_1 = N(f_A - f_B)^2 \frac{c(1-c)}{1 + c(1-c)\frac{w}{k_B T}\sum_{\pi=1}^{z}\cos \mathbf{q}\boldsymbol{\rho}_{\pi}}. \tag{17.8}$$

For lower temperatures, according to (3.9) to (3.11) and (16.9), I_1 becomes a more complex function of the ordering energy w for the first coordination sphere. In the case of small concentrations and arbitrary temperatures, it follows from (3.8) that we must replace w/k_BT by $1-\exp(-w/k_BT)$ in (17.8).

We see from (17.8) that in the nearest-neighbor approximation the dependence of I_1 on $\mathbf{q}$ is determined simply by the sum $\Sigma \cos \mathbf{q}\boldsymbol{\rho}_{\pi}$ over the points of the first coordination sphere. This sum takes the maximum value of z for $\mathbf{q} = 0$, i.e., at the reciprocal-lattice points of the disordered solution. The minimum value of this sum, equal to -8, for crystals with body-centered cubic lattices, occurs in the middles of the edges and at the centers of the cubic cells of the reciprocal lattice (at points of the type $q_x = 2\pi/d$, $q_y = q_z = 0$ or $q_x = q_y = q_z = 2\pi/d$), i.e., for values of $\mathbf{q}/2\pi$ falling at the "superstructural" points of the reciprocal lattice which would arise on forming an ordered structure of the β brass type. In crystals with a face-centered cubic lattice, the sum $\Sigma \cos \mathbf{q}\boldsymbol{\rho}_{\pi}$ takes a minimum value equal to -4 at the middles of the edges and in the centers of the faces of the cubic cells of the reciprocal lattice, i.e., at points of the type $q_x = q_y = 2\pi/d$, $q_z = 0$ or $q_x = 2\pi/d$, $q_y = q_z = 0$, which correspond to "superstructural" points of the reciprocal lattice which appear on forming an ordered structure of the Cu_3Au type.

We thus see from (17.8) that, on the pair-interaction model, and in decomposing solutions, the function $I_1 (f_A - f_B)^{-2}$ takes maximum values if $\mathbf{q}_1/2\pi$ falls at the reciprocal-lattice points of the disordered solution, and minimum values near points at which lattice points corresponding to superstructural reflections would appear on ordering. In solutions undergoing an ordering process, the picture is the reverse. This kind of intensity distribution has been observed experimentally in a number of papers [113, 119, 127–129].

We see from (17.8), or from the more exact formulas (17.6), (3.6), (3.8), (3.9)–(3.11), that, either on raising the temperature or on reducing the concentration of one of the components, $x(\boldsymbol{\rho})/x(0)$ falls, the short-range order becomes less important, and the intensity distribution approaches the distribution (17.2) corresponding to an ideal solution. For small c we see from (3.8) that the inhomogeneity of the background in decomposing solutions appears more sharply than in those undergoing an ordering process (for the same $|w|/k_BT$).

The diffuse-scattering intensity distribution is usually characterized by specifying the surfaces of equal diffuse-scattering intensity in reciprocal-lattice space, i.e., the surfaces on which $I_1 (\mathbf{q}_1/2\pi)$ is constant, or else by specifying the curves of equal diffuse-scattering intensity obtained when these surfaces intersect some reciprocal-lattice plane. For small q, for which $\mathbf{q}\boldsymbol{\rho} \approx 1 - \frac{1}{2} (\mathbf{q}\boldsymbol{\rho})^2$, we find from (17.8) or (17.6), in the case of undistorted crystals considered, that the surfaces of equal diffuse-scattering intensity are spheres with centers at the reciprocal-lattice points. For large q, the form of these surfaces becomes much more complicated, in accordance with (17.8); in particular, they may become closed in the middles of the cells and not around the lattice points. Depending on whether the solution is decomposing or becoming ordered, the curves of equal diffuse scattering corresponding to high scattering intensities will either be gathered together around the lattice points or in the middles of the cells.

Fig. 7. Curves of equal diffuse-scattering intensity (in arbitrary units) in the (100) plane of the reciprocal lattice of a Cu_3Au alloy at a temperature of 405°C [113]. Thermal and Compton scattering excluded.

An example of the appearance of the curves of equal diffuse scattering in an ordering Cu_3Au alloy with a face-centered cubic lattice above the ordering temperature ($T_C \approx 390°C$) is given in Fig. 7. We should also mention here that allowing for distortions qualitatively changes the form of the curves of equal diffuse scattering, especially near the reciprocal-lattice points (in Fig. 7 the curves are not shown in these regions).

It follows from (16.7), (1.11), and the formulas of §3 for $\overline{|c_\mathbf{k}|^2}$, that expression (17.8) is valid not only for disordered but also for undistorted, ordered solutions of stoichiometric composition AB if we reckon the vector $\mathbf{q}/2\pi$ from the reciprocal-lattice vector corresponding to a "structural" reflection (see p. 49). In this case we need only replace N by $N\nu = N_0$ in (17.8), and for completely ordered solutions determine $x(\boldsymbol{\rho})$ from formulas (3.13) and (3.14). Hence formula (17.7) (replacing N by N_0) is valid even for ordered AB solutions, enabling us to determine the quantities $x(\boldsymbol{\rho})$ and hence also the ordering energy w_ρ, from experimental data relating to the diffuse-scattering intensity distribution. In the nearest-neighbor approximation, in almost completely ordered AB solutions of the β brass or NaCl type, $\overline{|c_\mathbf{k}|^2}$ is determined by formula (3.16). Putting this formula into (16.7) for $\mathbf{R}_{q\gamma} = 0$, we find

$$I_1 = \frac{1}{2} N (f_A - f_B)^2 \frac{1-\eta^2}{1 + \frac{1}{4}(1-\eta^2)\left(\exp\frac{w}{k_B T} - 1\right) \sum_{\pi=1}^{z} \cos \mathbf{q}\boldsymbol{\rho}_\pi}. \quad (17.9)$$

As already noted on p. 50, on reducing the temperature $1-\eta^2$ falls off exponentially more rapidly than $w/k_B T$ increases. Hence in the case of almost completely ordered solutions at fairly low temperatures, we may reject the second term associated with correlation in the denominator of (17.9), since in this case (as in the case of high temperatures), this term becomes very small. The scattering intensity $I_1 \sim (1-\eta^2)$ for a solution in a state of equilibrium falls off exponentially as $\exp(-zw/2k_B T)$ with falling temperature. Expressions for the scattering intensity arising from ordered solutions of other structures and compositions are given in [23].

If $\mathbf{q}_1/2\pi$ falls in the neighborhood of a reciprocal-lattice point and q is small, we see from (16.9) that the diffuse-scattering intensity is determined by the probability of long-wave concentration fluctuations. In order to determine these probabilities we may use the strict formulas of the macroscopic theory of fluctuations (§2), which are not based on the simplified model of pair interaction. Thus, on determining $\overline{|c_\mathbf{q}|^2}$ for small q by means of formula (2.10), we find from (16.9) or (16.7) that the diffuse-scattering intensity in the neighborhood of the reciprocal-lattice points (or, for ordered solutions, in the neighborhood of points corresponding to structural reflections, for which $\mathbf{K}_n\mathbf{R}_\gamma$ are whole numbers) and in the absence of distortions is determined by the formula [6]

$$I_1 = N_0 \frac{k_B T}{v_0} (f_A - f_B)^2 \frac{1}{\frac{d^2\varphi}{dc^2} + \beta_{ij} q_i q_j} \quad (17.10)$$

($v_0 = V/N\nu$ is the atomic volume). For fairly small q the second term in the denominator of (17.10) may be neglected in comparison with the first term and the diffuse-scattering intensity depends only on the second derivative of the thermodynamic potential with respect to the concentration $d^2\varphi/dc^2$, which may be determined from independent thermodynamic data relating to the concentration dependence of the chemical potentials [see (2.3)]. We see from (17.10) that, in the absence of distortions, the same intensity distributions [divided by $(f_A - f_B)^2$] occur in the neighborhood of all the reciprocal-lattice points mentioned, and also at small scattering angles (when $\mathbf{q}$ coincides with $\mathbf{q}_1$).

In the same way, in the neighborhood of the reciprocal-lattice points of ordered solutions corresponding to superstructural reflections, we may express I_1 in terms of the derivatives of the thermodynamic potential with respect to the long-range-order parameters (and concentration parameters). Thus, for example, if the unit cell contains two points, and the long-range order is characterized by a single parameter η, then for superstructural reflections we may put

$$\exp(2\pi i \mathbf{K}_n \mathbf{R}_\gamma) = (-1)^{\gamma+1},$$

in (16.7) and the difference $c_{\mathbf{q}1} - c_{\mathbf{q}2}$ may be replaced, in accordance with (1.3) (for $\nu_1 = \nu_2 = \nu/2$), by the Fourier component of the long-range-order parameter $\eta_\mathbf{q}$. Putting $\mathbf{R}_{\mathbf{q}\gamma} = 0$ for undistorted crystals in (16.7) and defining $\overline{|\eta_\mathbf{q}|^2}$ by formula (2.23) of the macroscopic theory of fluctuations, we may write I_1 near the superstructural reflections (for cubic crystals) in the form

$$I_1 = \frac{N_0^2}{4}(f_A - f_B)^2 \overline{|\eta_\mathbf{q}|^2} =$$

$$= \frac{N_0^2}{4}\frac{k_B T}{V}(f_A - f_B)^2 \frac{\varphi_{cc} + \beta' q^2}{\varphi_{\eta\eta}\varphi_{cc} - \varphi_{c\eta}^2 + (\alpha\varphi_{cc} + \beta'\varphi_{\eta\eta} - 2\gamma\varphi_{c\eta})\, q^2}\,. \tag{17.11}$$

Here $\mathbf{q}/2\pi$ characterizes the distance from the reciprocal-lattice point corresponding to a superstructural reflection. As in the neighborhood of structural reflections, the intensity I_1 for small q is expressed solely in terms of thermodynamic quantities.

If in the respective cases of weak, ideal, and almost completely ordered solutions, we use the general thermodynamic formulas (2.25), (2.27), and (2.29) for φ or the corresponding formulas (2.26), (2.28), and (2.30) for $\overline{|c_\mathbf{k}|^2}$ and $\overline{|\eta_\mathbf{k}|^2}$, it is not hard to discover that in the general theory, as in the pair-interaction model, correlation no longer influences the diffuse scattering, and expressions (17.2) [or (17.4) for $\varepsilon(\boldsymbol{\rho}) = 0$] become valid.

The characteristic singularities in the expressions relating I_1 to the concentration and the diffraction vector are associated with the electronic part of the energy of a metallic solution discussed in §3 [426]. In particular, near the concentration c^k, at which the Fermi energy ξ_e coincides with the critical energy E_{cr} corresponding to the appearance of new hollows on the isoenergy surfaces, according to [430] φ_{cc} will have a diffuse (blurred) singularity of the radical type. As a result of this, and in accordance with (17.10), the concentration dependence of I_1 on one side of the point c^k (for the concentrations at which new hollows develop) will acquire a term proportional to $\sqrt{|c-c^k|}$, while on the other side of c^k no such term will occur.

The "Kohn" singularities of the function w_k^e considered in §3, as indicated by (3.24) and (16.9), should lead to analogous singularities in the relation between I_1 and the diffraction vector for values of q corresponding to $\mathbf{q} + K_n$ vectors connecting points on the Fermi surface with antiparallel normals. The character of these singularities is the same as that of the function P(k) [see formulas (3.21) to (3.23)], and for ellipsoidal, cylindrical, and plane sections of the Fermi surface corresponds, respectively, to a logarithmic singularity of the derivative of I_1, and to a radical or logarithmic singularity of the function I_1 itself. As in the case of thermal scattering, these singularities of the scattering at static inhomogeneities may be observed experimentally.

The "troughs" of the function $\overline{|c_k|^2}$ discussed in §3, corresponding to small hollows or grooves in the Fermi surface, should also lead to "troughs" in the relation between I_1 and $\mathbf{q}$. These lie near values of $\mathbf{q}$ connecting two different hollows or grooves.

Thus a study of diffuse scattering may be used not only in order to determine short-range order and ordering energy but also in order to investigate certain electronic characteristics of metallic solid solutions; in particular, it may provide certain information regarding the shape of the Fermi surface.

§18. Diffuse Scattering at Concentration Inhomogeneities in Distorted, Disordered Solutions

Allowing for the static displacements associated with the difference in the atomic radii of the components of a solution qualitatively changes the character of the diffuse-scattering intensity distribution. In order to study aspects of scattering due to distortions, let us first consider the simplest case of ideal, disordered solutions of the substitution type with one atom per cell. We shall at first consider that the distortions are not very large [criterion (16.8) is satisfied] and that they are related only to fluctuations of concentration [criterion (8.14) satisfied], so that I_1 may be determined from formula (16.9).

Putting expression (1.14) into formula (16.9) instead of $\overline{|c_{\mathbf{q}}|^2}$ and writing $\mathbf{A_q}$ in the form (5.9), we find that in this case I_1 is determined by the formula [30]

$$I_1 = Nc(1-c)\left[fa_{\mathbf{q}}\frac{\mathbf{q}_1\mathbf{e}_{\mathbf{q}}}{q} - (f_A - f_B)\right]^2. \tag{18.1}$$

Here the square of the first term is associated with scattering due to distortions only, and the square of the second is associated with scattering arising from the difference in the atomic factors, while the double product constitutes an interference term due to both sources. Explicit expressions for the quantities $a_{\mathbf{q}}$, characterizing the distortions and for the unitary vector $\mathbf{e_q}$ are given in §5.

If distortions are absent ($a_{\mathbf{q}} = 0$), then (18.1) passes into the Laue formula (17.2). Allowing for distortions is equivalent to the substitution of

$$f_A - f_B \to f_A - f_B - fa_{\mathbf{q}}\frac{\mathbf{q}_1\mathbf{e}_{\mathbf{q}}}{q} \tag{18.2}$$

in the formula for the scattering intensity. Distortions are especially important if the lattice parameters depend greatly on the concentration ($|a_{\mathbf{q}}|$ is large) or if f_A and f_B are close together. However, even if $|a_{\mathbf{q}}| \ll 1$ and $|f_A - f_B| \sim f$, nevertheless, for fairly small q values, for which the vector $\mathbf{q}_1/2\pi$ falls in the neighborhood of a reciprocal-lattice point, the first term in the square brackets of (18.1) becomes dominant. Thus I_1 rises on approaching the reciprocal-lattice point in accordance with the law $I_1 \sim 1/q^2$ first established by Huang [102] (who considered the case of an isotropic continuum).

In the approximation of an elastic isotropic continuum, according to (5.14), the unit vector $\mathbf{e_q} = \mathbf{n} = \mathbf{q}/q$ is parallel to $\mathbf{q}$ and $a_{\mathbf{q}} = a^0$ does not depend on $\mathbf{q}$. The term proportional to q^{-2} in I_1

then contains a factor $\cos^2\varphi$, where φ is the angle between $\mathbf{q}$ and $\mathbf{q}_1$. Hence for fairly small q, for which the second term in the square brackets of (18.1) may be neglected in comparison with the first, the surfaces of equal diffuse scattering (for which $|\mathbf{q}| \sim \cos\varphi$) have the form of two spheres which touch at a point of the reciprocal lattice; the tangent plane is perpendicular to the vector $\mathbf{q}_1 \approx 2\pi\mathbf{K}_n$, which constitutes an axis of symmetry for the two spheres (in contrast to the spherical surfaces of equal diffuse scattering with centers at the reciprocal-lattice points in undistorted crystals). Then the curves of equal diffuse scattering in a plane passing through the reciprocal-lattice point and the origin of coordinates consist of two circles, i.e., they have a lemniscate shape (curves 1 in Figs. 8 and 9).

On taking account of elastic anisotropy, $\mathbf{e}_q$ no longer coincides with $\mathbf{n}$, while a_q is no longer a constant quantity but depends on $\mathbf{n}$; hence the angular variation of I_1 for small q will be more complicated than in elastically anisotropic crystals. This relationship will be completely defined by formula (5.11) for cubic crystals and by the formulas of Appendix II [or (5.8)] for crystals of other symmetries.

Elastic anisotropy may lead to considerable deviations from the bispherical form of the surfaces of equal diffuse scattering, and these will take different forms for different reciprocal-lattice points. However, it may be shown that, as in the approximation of the isotropic continuum, for certain directions of $\mathbf{q}$ the scattering intensity due to the distortions vanishes. In the neighborhood of reciprocal-lattice points of the (h00), (hh0), and (hhh) type in cubic

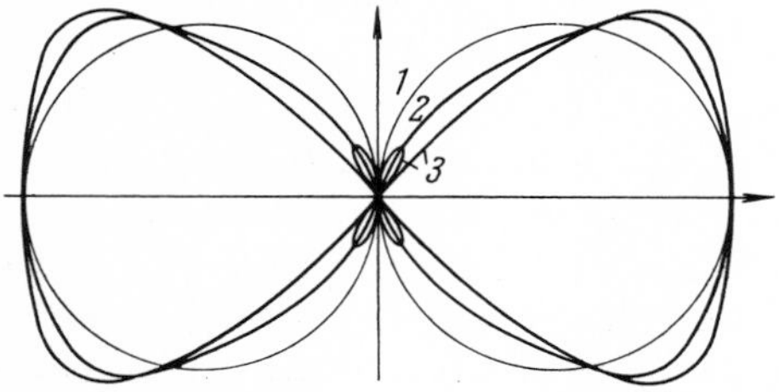

Fig. 8. Curves of equal diffuse scattering in the (001) plane near the (h00) point for small q and different anisotropy constants of a cubic crystal (in arbitrary units).

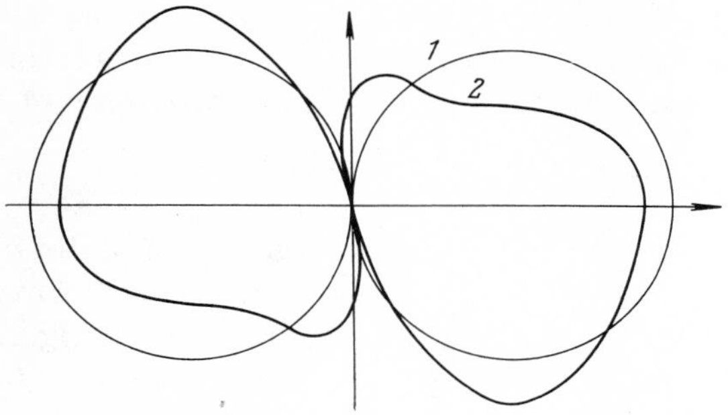

Fig. 9. Curves of equal diffuse scattering in the (001) plane near the point (2hh0) for small q in the case of isotropic and elastically anisotropic cubic crystals (in arbitrary units).

crystals, the curves of equal diffuse scattering plotted in planes passing through the point in question and the origin of coordinates have a symmetry axis coinciding with the vector $\mathbf{q}_1$. However, in general, these curves may be sharply asymmetric with respect to the direction $\mathbf{q}_1$ for the term proportional to q^{-2} in I_1.

In order to illustrate the influence of elastic anisotropy on the form of the curves of equal diffuse scattering, Figs. 8 and 9 show these curves in the (001) plane near the (h00) point (Fig. 8) and the (2hh0) point (Fig. 9) of cubic crystals for the case in which $f_A \approx f_B$, so that in (18.1) we need only retain the term associated with distortions. The curves of equal diffuse scattering are plotted from formulas (18.1) and (5.11). Curves 1, i.e., the circles, correspond to elastically isotropic crystals ($\xi = 0$), curves 2 correspond to an anisotropy constant of $\xi = -1$, and curves 3 to a constant of $\xi = -1.5$. In the last case, as indicated by Fig. 8, I_1 vanishes for certain directions of $\mathbf{q}$.

For reasonably large values of q, we must also consider the second term in the square brackets of (18.1) when considering intensity distributions. The double product obtained by squaring the binomial in (18.1) changes sign on replacing $\mathbf{q}$ by $-\mathbf{q}$ and this leads to asymmetry of the diffuse-scattering intensity distribution in relation to the reciprocal-lattice point. A typical relationship between I_1 and q for a given direction of the vector $\mathbf{q}$ is shown in

Fig. 10. One result of allowing for the square of the second term in (18.1) is that the curves of equal diffuse scattering (for not-too-small values of q) cannot vanish for any directions of vector $\mathbf{q}$.

We see from (18.1) that the coefficient of q^{-2} is proportional to $q_1^2 = (4\pi\lambda^{-1}\sin\theta)^2$. Hence, in contrast to the case of undistorted solutions considered in §17, in the presence of distortions the function $I_1(f_A - f_B)^{-2}$ is not periodically repeated in different cells of the reciprocal lattice, but increases with increasing scattering angle 2θ and with falling wavelength λ, i.e., on passing to more distant cells. For small scattering angles, the intensity distribution in the distorted crystal in the neighborhood of the zero point of the reciprocal lattice, for which $\mathbf{q}_1 = \mathbf{q}$, is qualitatively different from the distributions near other points, since according to (18.1) the quantity I_1 tends to a constant limit as $\mathbf{q}_1 \to 0$, and does not vary in proportion to q^{-2}.

The concentration dependence of I_1 for ideal solutions is simple in two limiting cases, namely, that in which, for the range of $\mathbf{q}$ values considered, we may neglect distortions ($|fa_{\mathbf{q}}(\mathbf{e_q q}_1/q)| \ll |f_A - f_B|$), and that in which f_A and f_B are similar and we may neglect the dependence of f on c. Remembering that in the approximation considered [when criterion (8.14) is satisfied] $a_q\mathbf{e}_q$ does not depend on c, we may conclude that in both these cases I_1 depends

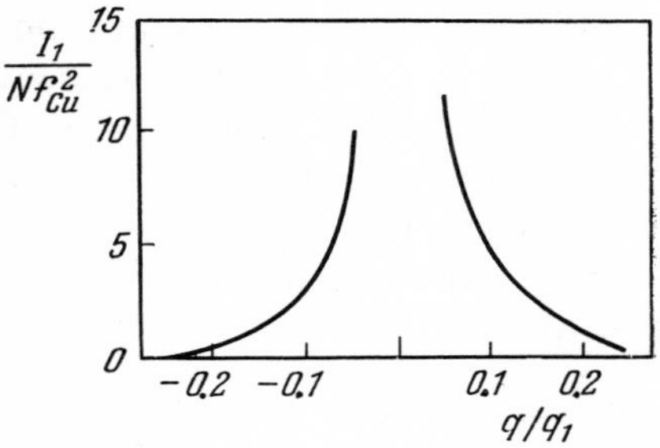

Fig. 10. Diffuse-scattering intensity as a function of q/q_1 for the [100] direction in the reciprocal lattice in the neighborhood of the (200) reflection, as taken from the results of [119] for a disordered Cu_3Au alloy quenched from 600°C.

quadratically on c, i.e., varies as c(1−c). In the more general case we must also consider the (almost linear) dependence of f on c in (18.1).

In nonideal solutions, allowing for correlation leads to a modification of the expressions for $\overline{|c_{\mathbf{q}}|^2}$ and the diffuse-scattering intensity. If $\mathbf{q}_1/2\pi$ falls in the neighborhood of a reciprocal-lattice point and q is small, then, as in undistorted solutions, $\overline{|c_{\mathbf{q}}|^2}$ may be determined from the general formula of the macroscopic theory for long-wave fluctuations. In the presence of distortions, however, the long-range elastic forces are important, and these change the expression for $\overline{|c_{\mathbf{q}}|^2}$. Allowing for these forces, the value of $\overline{|c_{\mathbf{q}}|^2}$ for small q is given by formula (9.4). Putting (9.4) into (16.9), we write the expression for the diffuse-scattering intensity in the neighborhood of a reciprocal-lattice point in the form

$$I_1 = \frac{N}{v}\frac{k_B T}{\varphi_{cc}(\mathbf{q})}\left[f a_{\mathbf{q}} \frac{\mathbf{q}_1 \mathbf{e}_{\mathbf{q}}}{q} - (f_A - f_B)\right]^2 . \qquad (18.3)$$

We see from this formula that, in nonideal solutions, the difference in the atomic radii influences the diffuse scattering both directly, by producing scattering at distortions [the amplitude of this is described by the first term in the brackets of (18.3)], and indirectly, by creating an elastic energy φ^{y}_{cc} (associated with long-range forces), which influences the probability of the development of fluctuations and also the diffuse scattering by changing the value of $\varphi_{cc}(\mathbf{q})$ in (18.3).

The quantities $a_{\mathbf{q}}\mathbf{e}_{\mathbf{q}}$ (or $\mathbf{A}_{\mathbf{q}}$) in the case of small q may be determined on the macroscopic approximation of elastic theory from the formulas of §5 or Appendix II, if we know the elastic moduli of the solution and the concentration dependence of the shape and size of the cell. The contribution of the elastic interaction φ^{y}_{cc} to $\varphi_{cc}(\mathbf{q})$ is determined in the same way, as indicated by (9.4). The other term in $\varphi_{cc}(\mathbf{q})$, the second derivative $d^2\varphi/dc^2$, may according to (2.3) be determined from the concentration dependence of the chemical potential (or the activity) of one of the components of the solution. Thus for small q all the quantities in formula (18.3) may be determined from independent experimental data, after which we may calculate the intensity distribution in the neighborhood of the reciprocal-lattice points.

If the contribution of the elastic energy φ^{y}_{cc} to $\varphi_{cc}(\mathbf{q})$ is small compared with $d^2\varphi/dc^2$, then $\varphi_{cc}(\mathbf{q})$ is almost constant, and, as may be seen by comparing (18.3) and (18.1), the form of the curves of equal diffuse scattering for small q is in general the same as in the previously considered case of ideal solutions. Only the numerical value of I_1 changes. Moreover, in ordering solutions $\varphi_{cc}(\mathbf{q})$ is usually greater than the value of $k_BT/vc(1-c)$ corresponding to ideal solutions, i.e., when short-range order is established in these, I_1 falls in the region of small q. In decomposing solutions, as a rule, $\varphi_{cc}(\mathbf{q}) < k_BT/vc(1-c)$, and after the establishment of correlation I_1 rises for small q (there may be some exceptions to this rule). If, however, the lattice parameters depend substantially on the composition and φ^{y}_{cc} is comparable with $d^2\varphi/dc^2$, then in severely-anisotropic crystals $\varphi_{cc}(\mathbf{q})$ may depend considerably on the direction of the vector $\mathbf{q}$, so that the shape of the curves of equal diffuse scattering become more complicated than in the case of ideal solutions.

For large values of q, as in undistorted solutions, the diffuse-scattering intensity may be expressed either in terms of the correlation parameters or (on the pair-interaction model) directly in terms of the ordering energy. Substituting (1.13) into (16.9), we obtain a generalization of formula (17.1) relating the scattering intensity and correlation in the solution for the case of distorted solutions:

$$I_1 = N\left[c(1-c) + \sum_{\boldsymbol{\rho}\neq 0} \varepsilon(\boldsymbol{\rho})\cos\mathbf{q}\boldsymbol{\rho}\right]\left[fa_{\mathbf{q}}\frac{\mathbf{q}_1\mathbf{e}_{\mathbf{q}}}{q} - (f_A - f_B)\right]^2. \quad (18.4)$$

On the other hand, assuming the applicability of the pair-interaction model, we may determine $\overline{|c_{\mathbf{q}}|^2}$ in (16.9) from formula (3.3) and express the diffuse-scattering intensity

$$I_1 = N\left[\sum_{\boldsymbol{\rho}} x(\boldsymbol{\rho})\cos\mathbf{q}\boldsymbol{\rho}\right]^{-1}\left[fa_{\mathbf{q}}\frac{\mathbf{q}_1\mathbf{e}_{\mathbf{q}}}{q} - (f_A - f_B)\right]^2 \quad (18.4a)$$

in terms of the quantities $x(\boldsymbol{\rho})$ associated with the ordering energies w_{ρ} by relations (3.6) (for high temperatures) or (3.8) (for low concentrations). In the presence of distortions, the energies w_{ρ} include, in particular, the elastic-interaction energy in elastically anisotropic crystals, which falls off fairly slowly with distance (as $1/\rho^3$).

The form of the curves of equal diffuse scattering in general becomes extremely complicated for large q, both because of the relationship between $a_{\mathbf{q}}\mathbf{e}_{\mathbf{q}}$ and $\mathbf{q}$, which is much more complex than in the case of small q, being determined by the formulas of the microscopic theory given in §6 rather than the macroscopic expressions, and also because of the appearance of an additional $\mathbf{q}$-dependent second factor in (18.4) and (18.4a). For scattering at distortions (for $f_A \approx f_B$), the form of the surfaces of equal diffuse scattering may differ considerably from the bispherical shape, even in elastically isotropic crystals. As before, however, there are certain directions of $\mathbf{q}$ for which $\mathbf{e}_{\mathbf{q}} \perp \mathbf{q}_1$ and the scattering intensity at the distortions vanishes.

For large q, distortions clearly play a relatively small part. If the lattice parameters are not very greatly dependent on composition ($|a_{\mathbf{q}}| \ll 1$) and the atomic factors f_A and f_B are not very close, then for large q we may have the condition

$$\left| f a_{\mathbf{q}} \frac{\mathbf{q}_1 \mathbf{e}_{\mathbf{q}}}{q} \right| \ll |f_A - f_B|$$

and the effects associated with distortions may be neglected. The expression for the scattering and the form of the curves of equal diffuse scattering are thus the same as in the case of undistorted crystals considered in §17.

By carrying out a Fourier transformation and using (18.4), we may obtain a relation determining the different correlation parameters $\varepsilon(\boldsymbol{\rho})$ by reference to the intensity distribution $I_1(\mathbf{q}_1/2\pi)$ in any cell of the reciprocal lattice [30]:

$$\varepsilon(\boldsymbol{\rho}) = \frac{v}{8\pi^3} \int_{1/v} d\mathbf{k} \frac{I_1}{N} \left[f a_{\mathbf{k}} \frac{\mathbf{q}_1 \mathbf{e}_{\mathbf{k}}}{k} - (f_A - f_B) \right]^{-2} \cos \mathbf{k}\boldsymbol{\rho}. \qquad (18.5)$$

In an analogous way (18.4a) yields the relation

$$x(\boldsymbol{\rho}) = \frac{v}{8\pi^3} \int_{1/v} d\mathbf{k} \frac{N}{I_1} \left[f a_{\mathbf{k}} \frac{\mathbf{q}_1 \mathbf{e}_{\mathbf{k}}}{k} - (f_A - f_B) \right]^{2} \cos \mathbf{k}\boldsymbol{\rho}, \qquad (18.6)$$

enabling us to determine the ordering energy $w_{\boldsymbol{\rho}}$.

Formulas (18.5) and (18.6) for $a_{\mathbf{k}} = 0$ coincide with formulas (17.3) and (17.7) and constitute a generalization of the latter to the case of distorted crystals. Allowance for the distortions may considerably affect the determination of the correlation parameters, especially in solutions with greatly differing atomic radii, such as Cu–Au.

The correction for distortions in (18.5) and (18.6) is especially considerable for small k; in this case, in order to determine $a_{\mathbf{k}}\mathbf{e}_{\mathbf{k}}$, we may use the exact formulas of the macroscopic theory given in §5 and Appendix II, for example, formula (5.11) for cubic crystals. For large k the distortions usually lead to a relatively small correction in the integrands of (18.5) and (18.6). In this region, the correction may be made by approximate formulas such as (6.3), (6.5), and (6.6) without introducing any serious error. After introducing this correction for distortion, equivalent to the substitution (18.2), the determination of the correlation parameters or ordering energies may be carried out in the same way as in the case of undistorted solutions considered in §17, by numerical integration with respect to values of $\mathbf{k}/2\pi$ lying in the reciprocal-lattice cell.*

The averaging of expression (18.4) over the orientations of the crystals, carried out in accordance with formula (12.9), enables us to determine the scattering intensity distribution on a Debye photograph I_{1D}. In distorted crystals I_{1D} depends linearly on the correlation parameters $\varepsilon(\rho_l)$, the coefficients of $\varepsilon(\rho_l)$ being the

*In discussing experimental data, the effect of distortions on scattering is often considered on the basis of [116]. This paper, however, incorporated the unrealistic assumption that the distance between two atoms in the solution only depended on the nature of these atoms. Yet clearly the nature of other nearby atoms, e.g., those lying between the pair considered, will exert no less influence.

Moreover [116] only considered terms linear with respect to the displacements in the expression for the scattering intensity, ignoring the quadratic terms, although in some cases, e.g., near reciprocal-lattice points, as indicated by the foregoing results, these may produce the strongest scattering (especially if the atomic factors are close together).

Hence the intensity distribution given in [116] may differ greatly from the genuine one. The attempt to refine the arguments of [116] by allowing for terms quadratic in the displacements made in [119] is also not very well-founded, since no allowance was made for the strong influence of correlation on the corresponding scattering.

complicated functions of scattering angle considered in [130, 131]. Knowing these functions, we may determine the correlation in the solution, with due allowance for distortions, from the distribution of the background on a Debye photograph, although with considerably lower accuracy than when using single crystals.

As mentioned earlier in §5, interstitial solutions should, strictly speaking, be considered as a particular case of ordered solutions, in which impurity atoms and vacancies occur in certain sub-lattices. In practice, however, since the concentration of the interstitial atoms is usually low and their atomic factors much smaller than those of the lattice atoms, we may neglect scattering at the impurity atoms and consider simply the displacements which they produce in the atoms normally situated at lattice points. Then if the impurity atoms in the pure crystal A lie in interstices of one type, the diffuse scattering intensity is easily seen (see [35]) to be given by the formula

$$I_1 = Nf^2 \left[c(1-c) + \sum_{\boldsymbol{\rho}} \varepsilon'(\boldsymbol{\rho}) \cos \mathbf{q}\boldsymbol{\rho}\right] (\mathbf{q}_1 \mathbf{A}_\mathbf{q})^2, \tag{18.7}$$

where $f = f_A \exp(-M_A)$, $\varepsilon'(\boldsymbol{\rho})$ are the correlation parameters for the interstitial atoms, and $\mathbf{A}_\mathbf{q}$ is the proportionality factor between the $\mathbf{q}$-th Fourier component of the displacements of the atoms from the lattice points and the concentration of the impurity atoms in the interstices. For small q the scattering intensity may in this case be written in the form

$$I_1 = Nf^2 \frac{k_B T}{v\varphi_{cc}(\mathbf{q})} (\mathbf{q}_1 \mathbf{A}_\mathbf{q})^2. \tag{18.8}$$

For small q the values of $\mathbf{A}_\mathbf{q}$ in interstitial solutions with impurity atoms in interstices of one type are determined by the same formulas of the macroscopic theory as in solutions of the substitution type (see §5). Thus, for example, impurity atoms in the octahedral interstices of a face-centered cubic lattice (having cubic symmetry) cause scattering characterized by the same curves of equal diffuse-scattering intensity as in the case of cubic substitution-type solid solutions. If, however, impurity atoms in a cubic crystal fall in interstices of the same type but without cubic symmetry (thus infringing the cubic symmetry of the solution), the form

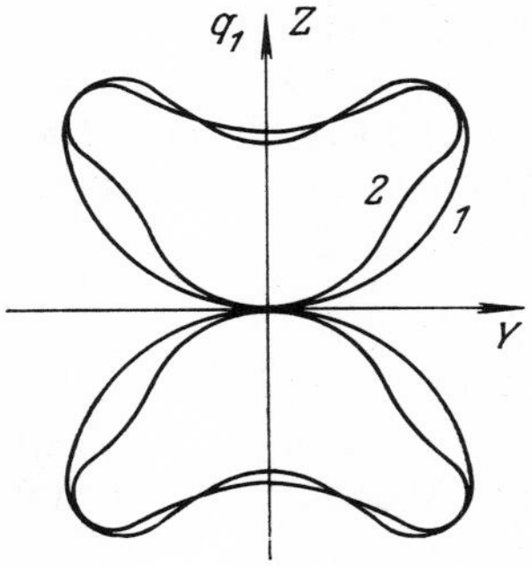

Fig. 11. Curves of equal diffuse scattering in the (100) plane near the (00h) point of a crystal of the martensite type.

of the surfaces of equal diffuse scattering is not at all like that corresponding to substitution-type solutions (for example, in elastically isotropic crystals these surfaces are not of the bispherical variety).

For illustration, Fig. 11 shows the curves of equal diffuse scattering in the neighborhood of the (00h) point in crystals of the martensite type, which are formed on introducing impurity atoms into the octahedral interstices (with tetragonal symmetry) of one type (Z) in crystals with a body-centered cubic lattice. The curves were plotted by means of formulas (18.7) (with $\varepsilon' = 0$) and (II.6) and (II.7). Curve 1 corresponds to an elastically isotropic crystal with $\sigma = 0.3$ and $(1/d_Z)(\partial d_Z/\partial c)[(1/d_X)(\partial d_X/\partial c)]^{-1} = -8$; curve 2 corresponds to the parameters of martensite $[(1/d_X)(\partial d_X/\partial c) = 0.12$, $(1/d_Z)(\partial d_Z/\partial c) = 0.92$ [34], $c_{11} = 2.4$, $c_{12} = 1.4$, $c_{44} = 1.2 \cdot 10^{12}$ dyne/cm$^2]$. For other points of the reciprocal lattice the curves of equal diffuse scattering corresponding to this case become sharply asymmetric with respect to the vector $\mathbf{q}_1$, but for small q they also pass through the points.

The curves of equal diffuse scattering in cubic crystals should have a qualitatively different form if the interstitial atoms occupy positions of several types (rather than one type), not having cubic symmetry. This case occurs, for example, in interstitial solutions with a body-centered cubic lattice, in which the impurity atoms may occupy octahedral positions of three types (X, Y, and Z) with equal probabilities. Adding the intensities (18.7) for scattering at the defects of each type, we find that in such solutions, neglecting correlation,

$$I_1 = Nf^2 c(1-c) \sum_{X,Y,Z} (\mathbf{q}_1 \mathbf{A}_\mathbf{q}^X)^2, \tag{18.9}$$

where $c = N_c/3N$ (N_c is the number of interstitial atoms) and $\mathbf{A}_\mathbf{q}^X$ are determined by equations (II.6) and (II.7). The vectors $\mathbf{A}_\mathbf{q}^X$, $\mathbf{A}_\mathbf{q}^Y$,

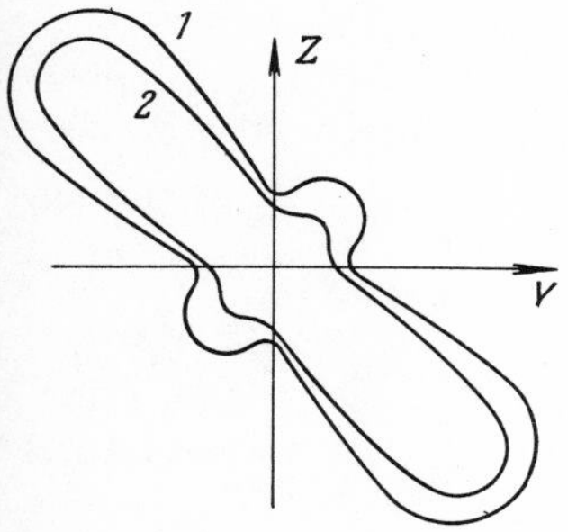

Fig. 12. Curves of equal diffuse scattering in the (100) plane near the (hhh) point of an interstitial solution with a body-centered cubic lattice. Curves 1 and 2 correspond to the same parameters as in Fig. 11.

and $\mathbf{A}_q^Z$, generally speaking, become perpendicular to $\mathbf{q}_1$ for different directions of $\mathbf{q}$. Hence I_1 does not vanish for any values of $\mathbf{q}/q$, and the overall surface of equal diffuse scattering for small q does not pass through the reciprocal-lattice point [except for points of the (h00) and (hh0) type]. Examples of the corresponding curves of equal diffuse scattering are shown in Fig. 12.

The curves of equal diffuse scattering will also not pass through the points of the reciprocal lattice in other cases, in which the interstitial atoms lie in interstices of several types, for example, in the tetrahedral pores of a face-centered cubic lattice. The qualitative difference in the form of the curves of equal diffuse scattering for different positions of the impurity atoms may be used as an additional method of determining the structure of the solution and the type of defects [35].

In the foregoing consideration of diffuse scattering we only considered the first terms in the expansion of I_1 in powers of the displacements. In effect we only took account of scattering at one wave of concentration fluctuations corresponding to the given $\mathbf{q}$. As the extent of the distortions increases, however, a greater and greater part should be played by the higher terms in the expansion of I_1 in powers of the displacements; these produce scattering associated with two or several fluctuation waves, to some extent analogous to multiphonon scattering at thermal vibrations. This scattering was considered in [124].

In order to illustrate the role of the higher terms of the expansion, let us give some results obtained on the approximation of an elastically isotropic continuum, relating to the simplest manner in which the reciprocal-lattice points may be surrounded in ideal solutions. Then allowing for terms up to the fourth order in $\mathbf{R}_k$ and c_k in the expansion of I_1 leads to the appearance of additional terms

$I_1' + I_1''$ as well as the earlier-considered expression (18.1) for I_1

$$I_1' = 2Nf^2(1-2c)a^0M\frac{\mathbf{q}_1\mathbf{q}}{q^2} + \frac{1}{512}Nf^2c^2(1-c)^2(a^0)^4v\frac{q_1^4}{q}(8\cos^2\varphi + 3\sin^4\varphi), \tag{18.10}$$

$$I_1'' = -Nf(f_A - f_B)\left[2(1-2c)M + \frac{1}{64}c^2(1-c)^2(a^0)^3q_1^3v\cos\varphi(1+\cos^2\varphi)\right]. \tag{18.11}$$

Here M is determined by formula (24.9) ($M \sim q_1^2$).

We see from (18.10) that as $q \to 0$ the quantity I_1' tends to infinity; however, it remains proportional to q^{-1} and not q^{-2} like I_1. The first term in (18.10) changes sign on replacing $\mathbf{q}$ by $-\mathbf{q}$ and leads to a certain additional asymmetry in the intensity distribution relative to the reciprocal-lattice point. The second term in (18.10) does not vanish for any values of the angle φ between $\mathbf{q}$ and $\mathbf{q}_1$, and should lead to deviations from the lemniscate form of the curves of equal diffuse scattering shown in Figs. 8 and 9 (these cannot now pass through the point). These effects, however, will only appear in remote cells of the reciprocal lattice (for large q_1) and for moderately large q in severely distorted solutions.

By way of example, let us make an estimate for the case of $f_A \approx f_B (a^0)^2 = 0.1$ (severely distorted lattice), with high reflection indices $\Sigma h_i^2 \sim 60$ [so that for a face-centered lattice, according to (24.13), $2M \sim 0.6$], $q = {}^1/_5(2\pi/d)$ and $\varphi = 0$. Then the ratio of the second term in (18.10) to I_1 with $c = {}^1/_2$ equals 0.3 (for $\varphi = 90°$ the second term falls by a factor of three), and the ratio of the first term to I_1 with $c = {}^1/_4$ equals 0.1 (-0.1 for $\varphi = 180°$). We note that comparison of (18.10) and (18.1) leads to the criterion (16.8) (for disordered solutions).

It should be noted that the role of the higher terms of the expansion in powers of displacements may be large in nonideal solutions, especially when the impurity atoms are united into groups in the initial stages of aging. Here the series in powers of the displacements may be only slowly convergent, and the scattering intensity must be determined without using this expansion. This case of severely distorted crystals will be considered in §26.

§19. Diffuse Scattering at Fluctuations of Correlation Parameters

Strictly speaking, the results derived in §18 are only applicable to solutions in which the lattice parameter does not depend on the correlation, or in which the concentration is small [condition (8.14) is satisfied]. If in a concentrated solution the deviations from Vegard's rule are considerable and the lattice constant depends considerably on order, then, in accordance with the results of §8 static distortions are created not only by fluctuations of concentration but also by fluctuations of correlation parameters, so that according to (8.6) $\mathbf{R}_\mathbf{k}$ will depend linearly both on the Fourier components of concentration $c_\mathbf{k}$, and on the Fourier components of the correlation parameters $\varepsilon_\mathbf{k}(\rho)$. As a result of this, there is an additional diffuse scattering at the distortions associated with fluctuations in the correlation parameters; this may be considerable in such solutions and may greatly affect the scattering intensity distribution [27].

Let us consider scattering at fluctuations of the correlation parameters in the case of ideal disordered solutions with one atom in the cell. In this case, as indicated by (4.3), the fluctuations of concentration and correlation parameters and also the fluctuations of different correlation parameters $\varepsilon(\boldsymbol{\rho})$ and $\varepsilon(\boldsymbol{\rho}')$ with $\boldsymbol{\rho}' \neq \pm\boldsymbol{\rho}$ are statistically independent, which greatly simplifies the results. In order to determine the diffuse scattering intensity, let us put expression (8.6) instead of $\mathbf{R}_\mathbf{q}$ in formula (16.7) (with $\nu = 1$) and average in accordance with formula (4.3). As a result of this, the expression for the diffuse scattering intensity will consist of two terms:

$$I_1 = I_1^c + I_1^\varepsilon.$$

One of these, I_1^c, determined the scattering at concentration fluctuations and coincides with (18.1).*

The other term, I_1^ε, is related to the fluctuations of the cor-

*If the lattice constant depends on the correlation, then in determining the $A_\mathbf{q}$ in (18.1) from the formulas of §§5 and 6 we must use the derivatives with respect to concentration taken for constant correlation parameters.

relation parameters and is determined by the expression

$$I_1^{\varepsilon} = Nc^2(1-c)^2 f^2 \sum_{\rho} (\mathbf{q}_1 \mathbf{A_q}(\boldsymbol{\rho}))^2 (1 - \cos \mathbf{q}\boldsymbol{\rho}), \tag{19.1}$$

where the $\mathbf{A_q}(\boldsymbol{\rho})$ are solutions of equations (8.7).

It follows from (8.7) and (6.4) that, for small q, the coefficients $\mathbf{A_q}(\boldsymbol{\rho})$ are proportional to $1/q^2$. Hence in the neighborhood of the reciprocal-lattice points, as $q \to 0$, the value of I_1^{ε}, like that of I_1^c tends to infinity as q^{-2}. Using formula (8.11), in this region I_1^{ε} may be written in the form

$$I_1^{\varepsilon} = Nc^2(1-c)^2 f^2 \frac{1}{q^2} \sum_{i,\, j=1}^{3} q_{1i} q_{1j} f_{ij}(\mathbf{n}), \tag{19.2}$$

where the functions $f_{ij}(\mathbf{n})$ only depend on the direction of $\mathbf{n}$, but not on the modulus of the vector $\mathbf{q}$. In the nearest-neighbor approximation, these functions are determined by formulas (8.12) in elastically isotropic crystals with face-centered cubic lattices (the corresponding expressions for elastically anisotropic crystals are given in [27]).

Although for small q the quantity I_1^{ε}, like I_1^c, increases in proportion to $1/q^2$, the ways in which these two types of scattering depend on the orientation of the vector $\mathbf{q}$ are very different: I_1^{ε}, in

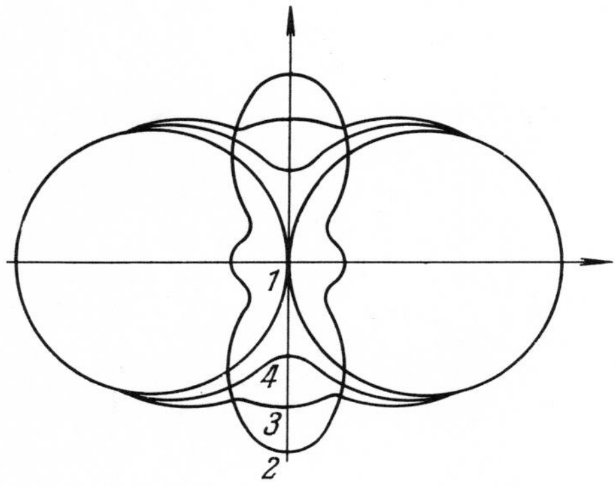

Fig. 13. Curves of equal diffuse scattering in the (001) plane of reciprocal-lattice space near the (h00) point, allowing for fluctuations of correlation parameters.

contrast to I_1^c, does not vanish for any directions of $\mathbf{q}$, and the corresponding curves of equal diffuse scattering have a form reminiscent of an oval rather than a lemniscate-like shape.

For illustration, Fig. 13 shows (in arbitrary units) the curves of equal diffuse scattering for I_1^c (with $f_A \approx f_B$) and I_1^ε (curves 1 and 2) in the (001) plane of reciprocal-lattice space near the (h00) point, and also the corresponding curves for the total scattering intensity $I_1 = I_1^c + I_1^\varepsilon$ for values of $c(1-c)(\partial v/\partial \varepsilon)^2(\partial v/\partial c)^{-2} = 0.2$ (curve 3) and $c(1-c)(\partial v/\partial \varepsilon)^2(\partial v/\partial c)^{-2} = 0.08$ (curve 4). The curves are plotted for elastically isotropic crystals with a body-centered cubic lattice and with a Poisson's ratio of $\sigma = 0.3$. The functions $f_{ij}(\mathbf{n})$ in (19.2) were determined on the nearest-neighbor approximation.

In order to make a quantitative estimate of the relative role of scattering at fluctuations of correlation parameters and fluctuations of concentration, let us, for a given q, and close to the point (h00), compare the maximum value of the term proportional to q^{-2} in I_1^c (associated with distortions) with the maximum value of I_1^ε. It follows from (18.1), (5.14), (19.2), and (8.12) that in the isotropic case the second value is much smaller than the first if inequality (8.13) or the equivalent criterion (8.14) is satisfied. Thus scattering at fluctuations of the correlation parameters is relatively small if the lattice constant is only slightly dependent on correlation or (less exactly) if its concentration dependence differs little from linear (deviations from Vegard's rule only slight), and also if there is a low concentration of one of the components of the solution.

There may nevertheless be cases in which inequalities (8.13) are not satisfied and I_1^ε becomes comparable with I_1^c. We may expect that I_1^ε plays a significant part in those solutions in which deviations from Vegard's rule are substantial, especially near the maxima and minima of the curve relating c and v [when $(\partial v/\partial c)_\varepsilon = 0$]. It should be remembered that, even for relatively small values of the dimensionless parameter $c(1-c)(\partial v/\partial \varepsilon)^2(\partial v/\partial c)^{-2}$ determining the validity or otherwise of criterion (8.13), allowing for fluctuations of the correlation parameters may greatly change the character of the angular distribution of the total diffuse-scattering intensity in reciprocal-lattice space (see curve 4 in Fig. 13).

Deviations from the lemniscate-like shape of the curves of equal diffuse scattering, as noted earlier, also arise in severely distorted crystals and in interstitial solutions in which the interstitial atoms lie in unsymmetrical positions of several types. The reason for these deviations may in a number of cases be deduced experimentally, if we consider that effects associated with fluctuations in the correlation parameters vanish as concentration falls, while effects associated with the large magnitude of the distortions play a relatively small part for small q and q_1.

In nonideal solutions the expressions for I_1^{ε} are complicated and contain unknown correlation parameters for threes and fours of atoms. Without giving the cumbersome formulas in question, we would simply note that in nonideal solutions the scattering at fluctuations of correlation parameters may in a number of cases be considerably greater than in ideal solutions. For instance, if in dilute solutions the impurity atoms form pairs ("diatomic molecules") or groups of several atoms, then I_1^{ε} is proportional to c and not c^2, as in ideal solutions. Such groups of defects, corresponding to large fluctuations of correlation parameters, are formed, in particular, on irradiating crystals with fast particles. The distortions around the resultant relatively large distorted regions should be considerable. Both these factors, as well as the interstitial atoms formed on irradiation, lead to deviations from the lemniscate form of the curves of equal diffuse scattering, and these curves may take an oval form.

§20. Diffuse Scattering at Fluctuations of Long-Range Order

Fluctuations of long-range order produce diffuse scattering of x rays, both in solid solutions and in single-component crystals. In one particular case (undistorted crystals, in which the long-range order is characterized by one parameter only) this scattering was in effect considered in §17 [formula (17.11)]. In the presence of several parameters, and especially when considering static distortions, the results may nevertheless be considerably modified [123, 55]. Hence in this section we shall consider diffuse scattering in the general case.

Let us confine ourselves to the most interesting range of values of $\mathbf{q}_1/2\pi$, i.e., those falling in the neighborhood of reciprocal-lattice points, for which the macroscopic treatment of long-range-order parameters is permissible and the scattering intensity may be expressed in terms of quantities determinable from independent experiments (for example, in terms of the dielectric susceptibility in ferroelectrics).

20.1. Single-Component Crystals. Let us first consider the case of single-component crystals in which the long-range order is characterized by r parameters η_μ. The intensity of x-ray scattering in the distorted crystals may be determined from the general formula (12.6). The long-wave fluctuations of long-range-order parameters $\delta\eta_\mu(\mathbf{r})$ here considered lead to a change in the structure amplitudes of the cells f_s and to statistical displacements $\delta\mathbf{R}_s$. The change in the structure amplitude of the s-th cell δf_s corresponding to fluctuations of long-range order may be written in the form

$$\delta f_s = \chi_\mu \delta\eta_\mu$$

(here and subsequently we shall understand that summation is to be carried out over all twice-repeated indices μ, μ'). The quantities χ_μ corresponding to the neighborhood of a given reciprocal-lattice point are determined from the relation between the mean structure amplitude (characterizing the intensity of the regular Bragg reflections) and the long-range-order parameters η_μ (for certain reciprocal-lattice points $\chi_\mu = 0$).

The static displacement of the first point of the s-th cell $\delta\mathbf{R}_s$ (neglecting distortions associated with fluctuations in the correlation parameters) may be written in the form of an expansion analogous to (5.2)*

$$\delta\mathbf{R}_s = i\sum_{\mathbf{k}} \mathbf{A}_{\mathbf{k}}^{\mu}\eta_{\mu\mathbf{k}}e^{-i\mathbf{k}\mathbf{R}_s}, \quad \mathbf{A}_{\mathbf{k}}^{\mu} = \frac{a_{\mathbf{k}}^{\mu}\mathbf{e}_{\mathbf{k}}^{\mu}}{k}. \tag{20.1}$$

*Strictly speaking, (20.1) should also include terms quadratic in $\eta_{\mu\mathbf{k}}$, or equivalent terms linear with respect to the Fourier components of the fluctuations in correlation parameters. In some cases the relation between the displacements and the fluctuations in the correlation parameters is characterized by the same small parameters as that between the displacements and the long-range-order parameters, so that it is not really consistent simply to allow for the latter. In many interesting cases, however, especially near phase transformations of the second kind, when the long-range-order fluctuations lead to anomalously large scattering, the scattering at fluctuations of the correlation parameters plays a relatively small part and may be neglected.

Here the proportionality factors $\mathbf{A}_{\mathbf{k}}^{\mu}$ between the Fourier components of the displacements and the Fourier components $\eta_{\mu\mathbf{k}}$ of the fluctuations in the parameter η_μ are determined by the same equations of type (5.8) as in the case of displacements created by fluctuations in concentration. In these equations we must simply replace $L_{ij} = \delta u_{ij}/\delta c$ [see (5.5)] by the analogous quantities $L_{ij}^{\mu} = \delta u_{ij}/\delta \eta_\mu$. For long-wave fluctuations and small k, as in the case of concentration waves, $\mathbf{A}_{\mathbf{k}}^{\mu} \sim 1/k$, i.e., as k → 0 the quantities only depend on the direction of $\mathbf{k}$ ($\mathbf{e}_{\mathbf{k}}^{\mu}$ are unit vectors).

Remembering both the change in structure amplitude and the static displacements, the contribution to the scattering amplitude arising from the s-th unit cell may in accordance with (12.6) be written in the form

$$\left[f + \sum_{\mathbf{k}} \left(\chi_\mu - f\,\frac{a_{\mathbf{k}}^{\mu}\,\mathbf{q}_1\mathbf{e}_{\mathbf{k}}^{\mu}}{k}\right)\eta_{\mu\mathbf{k}} e^{-i\mathbf{k}\mathbf{R}_s}\right] e^{i\mathbf{q}_1\mathbf{R}_s}, \tag{20.2}$$

where f is the average structure amplitude for the regular reflection (the neighborhood of which is under consideration), calculated with due allowance for distortions. It is assumed in (20.2) that the distortions are not very large [conditions of the (16.8) type are satisfied], so that in the expansion in powers of displacements we may confine attention to the linear terms.

Summing expression (20.2) over the unit cells (with respect to s) and squaring the resultant sum in accordance with (12.6), we find that in the limit of an infinite crystal the scattering intensity equals

$$I = 8\pi^3 \frac{N}{v} f^2 \delta(\mathbf{q}) + N^2 \overline{\left|\left(f a_{\mathbf{q}}^{\mu} \frac{\mathbf{q}_1\mathbf{e}_{\mathbf{q}}^{\mu}}{q} - \chi_\mu\right)\eta_{\mu\mathbf{q}}\right|^2}. \tag{20.3}$$

Here the first term determines the intensity of the regular reflections and the second term determines the diffuse scattering I_1.

In the region of small q considered, the mean squares and products of the Fourier components of the long-wave fluctuations of long-range-order parameters η_μ in undistorted crystals are determined by formulas (2.18) of the macroscopic theory of fluctuations, and in the presence of distortions by formulas (9.9), which allow for long-range elastic forces. Remembering (9.9), we write the diffuse-scattering intensity [second term in (20.3)] in the form

$$I_1 = \frac{Nk_BT}{v}\left(fa_{\mathbf{q}}^{\mu}\frac{\mathbf{q}_1\mathbf{e}_{\mathbf{q}}^{\mu}}{q} - \chi_{\mu}\right)\left(fa_{\mathbf{q}}^{\mu'}\frac{\mathbf{q}_1\mathbf{e}_{\mathbf{q}}^{\mu'}}{q} - \chi_{\mu'}\right)\varphi_{\mu\mu'}^{-1}(\mathbf{q}). \qquad (20.4)$$

In essence expression (20.4) is not only applicable to single-component crystals but may also be used for describing scattering at fluctuations of concentration and long-range-order parameters in solid solutions. In this case we must simply regard the concentration c as being one of the quantities η_{μ}.

In the particular case in which the long-range order is characterized by a single parameter η, the double summation over μ, μ' in (20.4) falls out and the expression for I_1 is simplified:

$$I_1 = \frac{Nk_BT}{v\varphi_{\eta\eta}(\mathbf{q})}\left(fa_{\mathbf{q}}^{\eta}\frac{\mathbf{q}_1\mathbf{e}_{\mathbf{q}}^{\eta}}{q} - \chi_{\eta}\right)^2. \qquad (20.5)$$

Here

$$\varphi_{\eta\eta}(\mathbf{q}) = \frac{\partial^2\varphi}{\partial\eta^2} + \varphi_{\eta\eta}^{y} + \alpha_{ij}q_iq_j$$

is determined by formula (9.8). Usually the dependence of the lattice parameters on the long-range order is weak and the contribution of the elastic energy $\varphi_{\eta\eta}^{y}$ to $\varphi_{\eta\eta}(\mathbf{q})$ is quantitatively small (much smaller than in the case of concentration fluctuations), appearing only in the region of very small $\partial^2\varphi/\partial\eta^2$. If, in the case considered, distortions may in general be neglected ($a_{\mathbf{q}}^{\eta} = 0$), then expression (20.5) takes a simple form [3]:

$$I_1 = \frac{Nk_BT}{v}\,\frac{\chi_{\eta}^2}{\dfrac{\partial^2\varphi}{\partial\eta^2} + \alpha_{ij}q_iq_j}. \qquad (20.6)$$

20.2. Solid Solutions. The general expression (20.4) for the diffuse scattering intensity may also be written in more explicit form for the case of solid solutions with a structure characterized by a single parameter of long-range order, in which the lattice points are centers of symmetry (solution with two sublattices of the β brass type, the NaCl type, and so on). We shall consider that the criterion (8.14) is satisfied, i.e., that the lattice parameter depends much more strongly on the concentration than on the parameter of long-range order. Then we may neglect the distortions caused by the fluctuations in long-range order in the same way as the distortions caused by fluctuations in correlation parameters, and simply consider the concentration distortions. In the case under consideration, the part of fluctuating internal parameters η_μ in (20.4) is played by the parameter of long-range order $\eta \equiv \eta_1$ and the concentration $c \equiv \eta_2$.

Since the distortions caused by fluctuations of η are not considered, we must put $a_{\mathbf{q}}^1 = 0$, in (20.4), while $a_{\mathbf{q}}^2 \mathbf{e}_{\mathbf{q}}^2 \equiv a_{\mathbf{q}} \mathbf{e}_{\mathbf{q}}$ are determined by the general formulas of §5 for the amplitudes of the waves of concentration distortions. For structural reflections [for which $\exp(2\pi i \mathbf{K}_n \mathbf{R}_\gamma) = 1$] with $M \ll 1$, the structure amplitude of the cell is, according to (16.3) and (16.5), determined by a formula ($f = 2[cf_A + (1-c)f_B]$) of the same type as in disordered solutions, and is unaffected by fluctuations of long-range order, i.e., $\chi_1 = 0$. The change in f associated with fluctuations of concentration corresponds to the value $\chi_2 = 2(f_A - f_B)$. Hence, in the sum of (20.4) over μ, $\mu' = 1, 2$, only the term with $\mu = \mu' = 2$ remains, and in the neighborhood of the reciprocal-lattice points corresponding to structural reflections the diffuse-scattering intensity in cubic crystals is equal to

$$I_1 = \frac{N}{v} \frac{k_B T (\varphi_{\eta\eta} + \alpha q^2)}{\varphi_{\eta\eta}\varphi_{cc}(\mathbf{q}) - \varphi_{c\eta}^2 + \alpha\varphi_{cc}(\mathbf{q}) q^2} \left(f a_{\mathbf{q}} \frac{\mathbf{q}_1 \mathbf{e}_{\mathbf{q}}}{q} - 2f_A + 2f_B \right)^2. \quad (20.7)$$

Here v is the volume of the cell, and in $\varphi_{\eta\eta}$ and $\varphi_{cc}(\mathbf{q})$ the partial derivatives with respect to η and c are respectively calculated for constant c and η. Remembering that

$$\frac{d^2\varphi}{dc^2} = \varphi_{cc} - \frac{\varphi_{c\eta}^2}{\varphi_{\eta\eta}},$$

it is easy to see that for small q the expression for I_1 in this region is the same as in the case of disordered solutions [cf. (18.3)].

For superstructural reflections [for which $\exp(2\pi i \mathbf{K}_n \mathbf{R}_\gamma) = (-1)^{\gamma+1}$] with $M \ll 1$, we see from (16.3) and (16.5) that the structure amplitude equals $f = \eta(f_A - f_B)$. The quantities χ_1 and χ_2 determining the changes in the structure amplitudes of the cells for fluctuations of order and composition will be equal to

$$\chi_1 = f_A - f_B \text{ and } \chi_2 = 0.$$

Hence it follows from (20.4) that, in the neighborhood of "superstructural" points of the reciprocal lattice (the difference $\mathbf{q}/2\pi = \mathbf{q}_1/2\pi - \mathbf{K}_n$ reckoned from these points is small), the diffuse-scattering intensity is determined by the formula

$$I_1 = \frac{N}{v}(f_A - f_B)^2 \frac{k_B T}{\varphi_{\eta\eta}\varphi_{cc}(\mathbf{q}) - \varphi_{c\eta}^2 + \alpha\varphi_{cc}(\mathbf{q})\, q^2} \times$$

$$\times \left[\varphi_{cc}(\mathbf{q}) + 2(\varphi_{c\eta} + \gamma q^2)\,\eta a_{\mathbf{q}} \frac{\mathbf{q}_1\mathbf{e}_{\mathbf{q}}}{q} + (\varphi_{\eta\eta} + \alpha q^2)\,\eta^2 a_{\mathbf{q}}^2 \frac{(\mathbf{q}_1\mathbf{e}_{\mathbf{q}})^2}{q^2}\right]. \quad (20.8)$$

In (20.7) and (20.8) the terms proportional to q^2 are only retained alongside the derivatives $\varphi_{\eta\eta}$ and $\varphi_{c\eta}$, which become small near phase transformation points of the second kind. In the absence of distortion ($a_{\mathbf{q}} = 0$) formula (20.8) transforms into (17.11).

In distorted solid solutions, in which the long-range order is associated with the redistribution of atoms of different sorts at the crystal-lattice points, it is also quite easy to express the diffuse-scattering intensity in terms of correlation parameters rather than thermodynamic characteristics. For this purpose it is convenient to start from the general expression (16.7) for I_1 and determine the $\mathbf{R}_{\mathbf{q}\gamma}$ in this expression in terms of the Fourier components $c_{\mathbf{q}\gamma'}$ in accordance with formula (5.15). Then, remembering (1.9) and (1.10), we may express I_1 in terms of the correlation parameters $\varepsilon_{\gamma\gamma'}(\boldsymbol{\rho})$ and concentrations c_γ of the A atoms in different sublattices:

$$I_1 = N \sum_{\gamma,\gamma'=1}^{\nu} \left[c_\gamma(1 - c_\gamma)\,\delta_{\gamma\gamma'} + \sum_{\boldsymbol{\rho}\neq 0} \varepsilon_{\gamma\gamma'}(\boldsymbol{\rho}) \cos \mathbf{q}\boldsymbol{\rho}\right] \times$$

$$\times \left[f_A - f_B - \sum_{\gamma_1=1}^{\nu} \exp(2\pi i \mathbf{K}_n \mathbf{R}_{\gamma_1})\, f_{\gamma_1}\mathbf{q}_1\mathbf{A}_{\mathbf{q}\gamma_1\gamma}\right] \times$$

$$\times \left[f_A - f_B - \sum_{\gamma_2=1}^{\nu} \exp(-2\pi i \mathbf{K}_n \mathbf{R}_{\gamma_2})\, f_{\gamma_2}\mathbf{q}_1\mathbf{A}_{\mathbf{q}\gamma_2\gamma}\right]. \quad (20.9)$$

This expression is valid for all values of $\mathbf{q}_1/2\pi$ and not only for values corresponding to the neighborhoods of the reciprocal-lattice points. In particular, for solutions with two sub-lattices of stoichiometric composition AB

$$c_\gamma (1 - c_\gamma) = \frac{1}{4} (1 - \eta^2),$$

and, if we may neglect correlation, then as in undistorted crystals, I_1 depends on long-range order in accordance with the law

$$I_1 \sim (1 - \eta^2).$$

20.3. Ferroelectric Crystals. The majority of the parameters in expression (20.4) for the diffuse-scattering intensity may be determined from independent experimental data. Thus the quantities f and χ_μ for the reciprocal-lattice point considered may easily be calculated if we know the atomic scattering factors and the structure of the crystal. The quantities $a_\mathbf{q}^\mu \mathbf{e}_\mathbf{q}^\mu$, as mentioned earlier, are determined by reference to data relating to the elastic moduli and the relationship between the shape and size of the cell and the long-range-order parameters.

Only the derivatives $\varphi_{\mu\mu'} \equiv \partial^2\varphi/\partial\eta_\mu\partial\eta_{\mu'}$ are in general difficult to determine from independent experiments. There are some interesting particular cases, however, in which even these derivatives may be determined independently by reference to experiment. Such a determination of $\varphi_{\mu\mu'}$ and $\varphi^{-1}_{\mu\mu'}(\mathbf{q})$ is possible in ferroelectric crystals if the long-range order in these is unambiguously characterized by specifying the polarization vector P_i [55, 123]. Then we may take these components P_i as long-range-order parameters, and the corresponding derivatives $\varphi_{ij} \equiv \partial^2\varphi/\partial P_i \partial P_j$ according to (2.20) are determined by the components of the dielectric-susceptibility tensor $\varkappa_{ij}$ of the ferroelectric.

The form of the expressions for the mean squares and products of the Fourier components of the polarization fluctuations, i.e., for the functions $\varphi^{-1}_{\mu\mu'}(\mathbf{q})$ in (20.4), depends greatly on whether or not dipole–dipole and elastic forces play any part. If the influence of elastic interaction on the probability of the fluctuations may be neglected, then for fairly small q, for which the length of the fluctuation wave is considerably greater than the Debye radius r_d ($qr_d \ll 1$), and the dipole – dipole interaction is screened, the fluctuations of polarization may be calculated from formula (2.21) (see also the note on p. 22) which was derived without accounting for the interaction. Then by considering the second term in (20.3) for the diffuse scattering at polarization fluctuations in ferroelectric crystals

$(\eta_{\mu\mathbf{q}} \to P_{\mathbf{q}i})$, we may write the expression for I_1 in the form

$$I_1 = \frac{Nk_BT}{v}[\varkappa_{ij} - \varkappa_{\infty ij}(\mathbf{q})]\left(fa_{\mathbf{q}}^i \frac{\mathbf{q}_1\mathbf{e}_{\mathbf{q}}^i}{q} - \chi_i\right)\left(fa_{\mathbf{q}}^j \frac{\mathbf{q}_1\mathbf{e}_{\mathbf{q}}^j}{q} - \chi_j\right). \quad (20.10)$$

Here $\chi_i = \partial f/\partial P_i$ and $a_{\mathbf{q}}^i \mathbf{e}_{\mathbf{q}}^i$ determine the change in the structure amplitude and the distortions arising from fluctuations of the polarization-vector component P_i. All the quantities entering into formula (20.10) may be determined from independent experiments, after which the calculated value of I_1 may be compared with the experimental limiting value as $q \to 0$.

For large q values, for which $qr_d \gg \sqrt{\varepsilon}$ (but $qd \ll 1$), Debye screening cannot arise within a wavelength, and long-range dipole–dipole forces become appreciable. Then the polarization fluctuations must be determined with due allowance for these forces by means of formula (10.7), and the diffuse-scattering intensity will be equal to

$$I_1 = \frac{Nk_BT}{v}[\varkappa_{ij}(\mathbf{q}) - \varkappa_{\infty ij}(\mathbf{q})]\left(fa_{\mathbf{q}}^i \frac{\mathbf{q}_1\mathbf{e}_{\mathbf{q}}^i}{q} - \chi_i\right)\left(fa_{\mathbf{q}}^j \frac{\mathbf{q}_1\mathbf{e}_{\mathbf{q}}^j}{q} - \chi_j\right). \quad (20.11)$$

It follows moreover from (20.10), (20.11), and (10.4) that dipole–dipole forces greatly influence the value of I_1 and its dependence on $\mathbf{q}$. As a result of this, we should expect some special behavior of $I_1(\mathbf{q})$ in the region in which the dipole–dipole interaction is "switched on," with $q \sim 1/r_d$, and the scattering intensity may vary as the concentration of screening charges (i.e., r_d) varies.

If the distortions associated with polarization fluctuations are relatively large and the influence of long-range elastic forces on the probability of fluctuations cannot be neglected, then in (20.10) we must replace $\varkappa_{ij}$ by $\varkappa'_{ij}$, defined, with due allowance for these forces, by formula (10.12); then in (20.11), in accordance with (10.13), we must replace $\varkappa_{ij}(\mathbf{q})$ by $\varkappa'_{ij}(\mathbf{q})$, as a result of which the scattering intensity will fall. In these cases, allowing for (10.4) and (10.13), all the quantities entering into the expression for I_1 may also be determined from independent experimental data, after which the intensity distribution $I_1(\mathbf{q})$ may be calculated in each specific case.

Scattering at fluctuations of the long-range-order parameters should take place both in the ordered and disordered phases (in the latter case, as mentioned earlier in §2, the fluctuational changes take place around the zero values of η_μ). In single-component crystals, the character of the scattering-intensity distribution in reciprocal-lattice space differs considerably according to whether the fluctuations cause distortions or not, i.e., $a_q^\mu = 0$ or $a_q^\mu \neq 0$.

It follows in particular from symmetry considerations that, in a number of structures, for example, in crystals with a center of symmetry, $a_q^\mu = 0$ identically in the disordered phase. In other cases, however (for example, if there is a piezo effect in a non-ferroelectric phase), symmetry considerations do not prevent there from being nonzero values of a_q^μ in the disordered phase. In the ordered phase, generally speaking, the a_q^μ are always nonzero (although thay may be numerically small).

If the a_q^μ are different from zero, then for regular reflections with $f \neq 0$, the function I_1 in the neighborhoods of the corresponding reciprocal-lattice points with small q contains a term proportional to q^{-2}, tending to infinity on approaching the point. The dependence of I_1 on q (for a given direction of $\mathbf{q}$) will then be described by a hyperbolic curve (see Fig. 10). In the case in which only one order parameter fluctuates, we see from comparing (20.5) and (18.1) that the curves of equal diffuse scattering will be qualitatively the same as in the case of scattering at concentration fluctuations in disordered solutions, and for small q will pass through the reciprocal-lattice point. However, in the case in which fluctuations of several order parameters are considerable, the e_q^μ generally speaking become perpendicular to $\mathbf{q}_1$ for different $\mathbf{q}$, and, as may be seen from the general formula (20.4), I_1 does not vanish for any $\mathbf{q}$ ($q \to 0$), i.e., the curves of equal diffuse scattering do not pass through the lattice point (unless the reciprocal-lattice point possesses special symmetry).

In weakly-distorted crystals, for which $\chi_\mu \neq 0$, and for not-too-small values of q, we may, on the other hand, neglect the first terms in the brackets of (20.4) and (20.5) in comparison with χ_μ. The intensity distribution will have the same character near reciprocal-lattice points for which the structure amplitude f equals zero (as in the disordered phase for points corresponding to structural reflections), and also in undistorted crystals with zero values of a_q^μ (resulting, for example, from symmetry requirements). We see from (20.6) that in these cases the dependence of I_1 on q for a given direction of **q** is described by bell-shaped and not hyperbolic curves. The surfaces of equal diffuse scattering surround the reciprocal-lattice points without passing through them; in contrast to the case of distorted crystals, the intensity distribution repeats itself periodically in each cell of the reciprocal lattice.

In solid solutions, if criterion (8.14) is satisfied, the distortions are mainly associated with fluctuations of concentration and not of long-range order. We see from (20.7) and (20.8) that the term proportional to q^{-2} in I_1 contains the square of the structure amplitude as a factor here also, and in the disordered phase it only appears in the neighborhood of "structural" lattice points.

The temperature dependence of the diffuse-scattering intensity should have special characteristics near a phase-transformation point of the second kind. These questions are discussed in §22.

§21. Diffuse Scattering by Ionic Crystals Containing Charged Defects or Impurities

The above results obtained for scattering by solid solutions are clearly applicable to crystals containing any point defects. All such defects produce deformation inversely proportional to the cube of the distance to the defect, r, and static displacements $\sim 1/r^2$; this gives rise to scattering at the distortions, increasing as $1/q^2$ on approaching a reciprocal-lattice point.

Here it has been tacitly assumed that the defects are electrically neutral. If, however, the impurity atoms (or other point defects) in ionic crystals are charged, then there should be some new aspects of diffuse scattering [53] which should make it possible to determine whether the effects observed are due to neutral or charged defects. These features or aspects are associated with long-range Coulomb forces which lead not only to deformation of the lattice but also to its polarization (to the displacement of the atoms in the cell relative to one another). Hence in crystals with a center of symmetry the relations between the coefficients of $1/q^2$ in the expressions for I_1 in the neighborhoods of "structural" and "superstructural" reciprocal-lattice points may differ considerably for neutral and charged defects, respectively.

In addition to this, the slowly diminishing Coulomb interaction produces a sharp rise in the energy of the long-wave fluctuations and leads to the singularities in the fluctuations of charged defects discussed in §11. Hence in the neighborhood of $q \sim 1/r_d$ there should also be some special features in the diffuse-scattering intensity distribution.

A specially sharp difference between scattering at neutral and charged defects should occur in piezoelectric crystals. The Coulomb field of a charged defect in a piezoelectric produces a deformation proportional to the field, i.e., proportional to $1/r^2$ and not $1/r^3$ as in other crystals, or in the case of neutral defects in piezoelectric crystals. Hence the diffuse-scattering intensity at charged defects should increase as $1/q^4$ and not $1/q^2$ (as in other cases) on approaching a reciprocal-lattice point with $q > 1/r_d$.

Since the effects in question appear most sharply for small q, let us confine ourselves to studying this region, corresponding to scattering at long-wave fluctuations, which may be considered by means of the macroscopic approximation. We shall suppose that the concentration of impurity centers is quite small ($c \ll 1$).

As in §12, let us first consider an ionic, nonpiezoelectric crystal AB with two ions in the unit cell (crystals with lattices of the NaCl or CsCl type). Suppose that the crystal contains positive and negative defects of the same valence (vacancies, interstitial ions, impurity ions of differing valence, etc.), the concentration c of which must, from considerations of electrical neutrality, be exactly the same. Using indices s_1 and s_2 to denote the positions which may be occupied by the positive and negative defects, respectively, let us characterize the defect distribution in these positions by assigning numbers $c_{s\gamma'}$ ($\gamma' = 1, 2$) equal to 1 or 0, as in §11. We shall confine ourselves to the case in which the unit cell contains one s_1 and one s_2 position.

In determining the diffuse-scattering intensity I_1 we shall start from the general formula (12.3) (for $\mathbf{q} \neq 0$). Let us denote the change in the scattering amplitude on introducing a positive defect into the s-th cell by

$$f_1' \exp[i\mathbf{q}_1(\mathbf{R}_s + \mathbf{R}_1')],$$

and that associated with introducing a negative defect by

$$f_2' \exp[i\mathbf{q}_1(\mathbf{R}_s + \mathbf{R}_2')]$$

($\mathbf{R}'_{\gamma'} = \mathbf{R}'_1, \mathbf{R}'_2$ are vectors drawn from the first point of the s-th cell to the positions s_1 and s_2). As earlier, let us expand expression (12.3) in powers of $\mathbf{q}_1\delta\mathbf{R}_{s\gamma}$ and confine attention to the linear terms of the expansion. For $c \ll 1$ we may neglect the displacements of the defects themselves and in the linear terms carry out the summation over the lattice atoms only. Thus γ in (12.3) takes the values $\gamma = 1, 2$, and $f_{s\gamma}$ takes the two values f_1 and f_2. Then the expression for I_1 takes the form

$$I_1 = \left| \sum_s \left[\sum_{\gamma'=1,2} f'_{\gamma'} c_{s\gamma'} e^{i\mathbf{q}_1\mathbf{R}'_{\gamma'}} + \sum_{\gamma=1,2} i\mathbf{q}_1 \delta\mathbf{R}_{s\gamma} f_\gamma e^{i\mathbf{q}_1\mathbf{R}_\gamma} \right] e^{i\mathbf{q}\mathbf{R}_s} \right|^2. \qquad (21.1)$$

It is convenient to transform from the quantities $c_{s\gamma'}$ to their Fourier components (1.7) and then to their sum and difference (11.1), i.e., to $c'_{\mathbf{k}}$ and $c''_{\mathbf{k}}$. In an analogous way, instead of the Fourier components (5.1) $\mathbf{R}_{\mathbf{k}\gamma}$ of the quantities $\delta\mathbf{R}_{s\gamma}$, it is more convenient to introduce the sum and difference

$$2\mathbf{R}'_{\mathbf{k}} = \mathbf{R}_{\mathbf{k}1} + \mathbf{R}_{\mathbf{k}2}; \qquad 2\mathbf{R}''_{\mathbf{k}} = \mathbf{R}_{\mathbf{k}1} - \mathbf{R}_{\mathbf{k}2}. \qquad (21.2)$$

Here $\mathbf{R}'_{\mathbf{k}}$ gives the deformation (strain) and $\mathbf{R}''_{\mathbf{k}}$ the polarization displacements of the atoms in the crystal.

The Fourier components of the displacements $\mathbf{R}'_{\mathbf{k}}$ and $\mathbf{R}''_{\mathbf{k}}$ are linear functions of the Fourier components of the fluctuations in the defect concentration:

$$\mathbf{R}'_{\mathbf{k}} = \mathbf{A}'_{\mathbf{k}} c'_{\mathbf{k}} + \mathbf{A}''_{\mathbf{k}} c''_{\mathbf{k}}; \qquad \mathbf{R}''_{\mathbf{k}} = \mathbf{B}'_{\mathbf{k}} c'_{\mathbf{k}} + \mathbf{B}''_{\mathbf{k}} c''_{\mathbf{k}}. \qquad (21.3)$$

For small k, in the long-wave approximation, the coefficients $\mathbf{A}_{\mathbf{k}}$ and $\mathbf{B}_{\mathbf{k}}$ may be expressed in terms of macroscopic constants determinable from independent experiments. Thus the coefficients $\mathbf{A}_{\mathbf{k}}$, which determine the strain distortions may be found from the equations of elastic theory describing the stresses associated with smooth fluctuational changes

$$\delta c' = \frac{1}{2}(\delta c_1 + \delta c_2) \qquad \text{or} \qquad \delta c'' = \frac{1}{2}(\delta c_1 - \delta c_2).$$

As a result of this we obtain equations of the (5.8) type for $\mathbf{A}'_{\mathbf{k}}$ and $\mathbf{A}''_{\mathbf{k}}$, in which we must simply replace L_{lm} by $L'_{lm} = \delta u_{lm}/\delta c'$ or $L''_{lm} = \delta u_{lm}/\delta c''$ [in cubic crystals we may use formulas (5.11), replacing ∂v/∂c by ∂v/∂c' or ∂v/∂c"]. The Fourier components of the polarization displacements $\mathbf{R}''_{\mathbf{k}}$ and also $c''_{\mathbf{k}}$ may be related to the Fourier components of the waves of electric charge and induction (11.2) and (11.3) for small k. For the coefficients $\mathbf{B}_{\mathbf{k}}$ we obtain the simple expressions [53]:

$$\mathbf{B}'_{\mathbf{k}}=0; \qquad \mathbf{B}''_{\mathbf{k}}=\frac{3(\varepsilon-\varepsilon_{\infty})}{\varepsilon(2+\varepsilon_{\infty})}\frac{z'}{z}\frac{\mathbf{k}}{k^2}, \tag{21.4}$$

where z is the effective charge of the crystal ions (z' is the charge of the defects). The equation $\mathbf{B}'_{\mathbf{k}}=0$ in (21.4) allows for the fact that in the macroscopic approximation the fluctuations of $c'_{\mathbf{k}}$ do not create an electric field or polarization displacements of the ions. In the same way as $\mathbf{A}_{\mathbf{k}}$, $\mathbf{B}''_{\mathbf{k}} \sim 1/k$.

Substituting (11.1), (21.2), and (21.3) in (21.1), we write the expression for the diffuse-scattering intensity in the form

$$I_1=N^2\,|\,(f'_c-\mathbf{q}_1\mathbf{A}'_{\mathbf{q}}f_c)\,c'_{\mathbf{q}}+(f'_p-\mathbf{q}_1\mathbf{A}''_{\mathbf{q}}f_c-\mathbf{q}_1\mathbf{B}''_{\mathbf{q}}f_p)\,c''_{\mathbf{q}}\,|^2, \tag{21.5}$$

where we have introduced the notations

$$\begin{aligned}
f_c&=f_1+f_2\exp(2\pi i\mathbf{K}_n\mathbf{R}_2),\\
f_p&=f_1-f_2\exp(2\pi i\mathbf{K}_n\mathbf{R}_2),\\
f'_c&=f'_1\exp(2\pi i\mathbf{K}_n\mathbf{R}'_1)+f'_2\exp(2\pi i\mathbf{K}_n\mathbf{R}'_2),\\
f'_p&=f'_1\exp(2\pi i\mathbf{K}_n\mathbf{R}'_1)-f'_2\exp(2\pi i\mathbf{K}_n\mathbf{R}'_2).
\end{aligned} \tag{21.6}$$

In formulas (21.5) [as in (21.1)], we understand that averaging is carried out over different configurations of defects. The corresponding mean squares and products of the Fourier components were calculated in §11 and are given by formula (11.7). Substituting these expressions in (21.5), we obtain a formula for I_1 in the final form:

$$I_1=\frac{1}{2}cN(f'_c-\mathbf{q}_1\mathbf{A}'_{\mathbf{q}}f_c)^2+\frac{1}{2}cN(f'_p-\mathbf{q}_1\mathbf{A}''_{\mathbf{q}}f_c-\mathbf{q}_1\mathbf{B}''_{\mathbf{q}}f_p)^2\frac{r_d^2q^2}{1+r_d^2q^2}. \tag{21.7}$$

In the case of scattering at neutral centers of two types, it follows from the results of §18 that the intensity I_1 is described by an analogous formula, in which, however, we must omit the last factor in the second term, which allows for Debye screening, and put $\mathbf{B}''_q = 0$. As a result of this the dependence of I_1 on $\mathbf{q}$ for scattering at neutral and charged defects, respectively, may differ considerably, which raises the possibility of deciding (experimentally) whether the centers under consideration in a particular case are charged or not.

If in the range of $\mathbf{q}$ values considered we may neglect distortions, i.e., put $\mathbf{A}_q = \mathbf{B}_q = 0$, then we find from (21.7) that for $r_d q \gg 1$

$$I_1 = \frac{1}{2} cN (f_c'^2 + f_p'^2),$$

and for $r_d q \ll 1$

$$I_1 = \frac{1}{2} cN f_c'^2.$$

For $q \sim 1/r_d$, the scattering intensity may thus vary considerably. Since $\mathbf{A}_q$ and $\mathbf{B}_q$ are proportional to $1/q$ for small q, in the majority of cases we may, on the other hand, neglect terms containing f_c' and f_p' not associated with distortions. Then $I_1 \sim 1/q^2$ both for $r_d q \gg 1$ and for $r_d q \ll 1$, except for the fact that the proportionality factors are different in these two regions.

Especially sharp effects associated with the charges of defects should occur in the neighborhood of "superstructural" reciprocal-lattice points $[\exp(2\pi i \mathbf{K}_n \mathbf{R}_\gamma) = (-1)^{\gamma+1}]$ if f_1 and f_2 are close together (as in KCl, for example). Then we see from (21.6) that $f_c \ll f_p$. Putting $f_c = 0$, we find in this case that

$$I_1 \sim 1/q^2 \quad \text{for} \quad r_d q \gg 1,$$
$$I_1 = \text{const} \quad \text{for} \quad r_d q \ll 1$$

(because $f_c \neq 0$ for very small q, the quantity I_1 again starts rising as $1/q^2$, but with a very small coefficient). In the case of neutral centers near "superstructural" points there would in general be no scattering component proportional to $1/q^2$ at all under these conditions. Substantial singularities in the relation between I_1 and q should thus occur for $q \sim 1/r_d$, and in principle this raises the possibility of estimating the Debye radius by reference to x-ray-diffraction data.

If, for example, $\varepsilon = 10$, $z' = 1$, $T = 1000°K$, $v = \text{Å}^3$, $c = 10^{-4}$, then $r_d = 4 \cdot 10^{-7}$ cm.

Let us now consider the special features of the diffuse scattering at charged defects in piezoelectric crystals. The electric fields of such defects produce elastic stresses in piezoelectric crystals. Hence in the expression for the stress tensor of the (5.4) type we must supplement the terms proportional to the strain and the variations in concentration by a term proportional to the induction:

$$\sigma_{ij} = \lambda_{ijlm} u_{lm} - \lambda_{ijlm} (L'_{lm} \delta c' + L''_{lm} \delta c'') - h_{ijl} D_l. \tag{21.8}$$

Here h_{ijl} are the components of a third-order tensor, and the term $\lambda_{ijlm} L''_{lm} \delta c''$ allows for the stresses associated with changes $\delta c''$ but not associated with the induction **D** (these stresses remain when the induction is compensated by an oppositely directed field).

As in the derivation of (5.8) we now substitute for δc and u_{lm} their values corresponding to the **k**-th fluctuation wave; remembering (11.3) and the equilibrium conditions $\partial \sigma_{ij}/\partial x_j = 0$, we find that as before the $\mathbf{A}'_k$ are determined by equations (5.8) (replacing L_{lm} by L'_{lm}) and the $\mathbf{A}''_k$ by the equations

$$k \lambda_{ijlm} n_j n_l A''_{km} = \lambda_{ijlm} L''_{lm} n_j + \frac{8\pi e i z'}{vk} h_{ijl} n_j n_l \quad (i = 1, 2, 3). \tag{21.9}$$

For fairly small k, we may neglect the first term on the right-hand side of (21.9). In this case $\mathbf{A}''_k$ rises as k falls, varying in proportion to $1/k^2$, as does $\mathbf{A}'_k$ (or $\mathbf{A}''_k$ in nonpiezoelectric crystals), i.e.,

$$\mathbf{A}'_k = \frac{a'_k \mathbf{e}'_k}{k}, \qquad \mathbf{A}''_k = \frac{a''_k \mathbf{e}''_k}{k^2}, \tag{21.10}$$

where $\mathbf{e}'_k$, $\mathbf{e}''_k$ are unit vectors and a'_k and a''_k (for small k) only on the direction (and not the magnitude) of vector **k**. We note that all the coefficients in the equations (21.9) are determined from independent data.

For fairly small q, i.e., near a reciprocal-lattice point, we need only retain the terms containing $\mathbf{A}'_q$ and $\mathbf{A}''_q$. in expression (21.7) for the scattering intensity. Considering (21.10), we obtain

$$I_1 = \frac{1}{2} cNf_c^2 \left[\frac{a_q'^2 (\mathbf{q}_1 \mathbf{e}_q')^2}{q^2} + \frac{a_q''^2 (\mathbf{q}_1 \mathbf{e}_q'')^2}{q^4} \frac{r_d^2 q^2}{1 + r_d^2 q^2} \right]. \tag{21.11}$$

We note that formula (21.11) is applicable not only to crystals with two ions in the cell but also in the general case [then f_c is determined by the general formula (16.5) for the structure amplitude f].

If the Debye radius is quite large and a_q' small, then the second term in (21.11) plays the major part. Thus in the region $r_d q \gg 1$ the quantity I_1 increases as $1/q^4$ with falling q, and in the region $r_d q \ll 1$ as $1/q^2$, i.e., there is an extra factor of q^{-2} as compared with the analogous term in the case of nonferroelectric crystals.

Charged defects in ionic crystals should also lead to some sharp singularities in diffuse electron scattering as studied by electron-diffraction methods [53].

§22. Anomalous Scattering near Critical Points on the Decomposition Curves and Phase Transformations of the Second Kind

Near critical points on decomposition curves and phase transformation points of the second kind there may be a sharp rise in the probabilities of long-wave fluctuation waves of concentration and long-range-order parameters, as already discussed in §2.4 and in Chapter III. The unusually large fluctuational inhomogeneities thus arising in the crystals should lead to an anomalous increase in the intensity of diffuse x-ray and neutron scattering at such long-wave fluctuations (i.e., for values of $\mathbf{q}_1/2\pi$ situated in the neighborhood of reciprocal-lattice points).

The study of anomalous scattering may in principle give valuable information regarding the singularities of various thermodynamic quantities (considered as functions of not only the temperature but also the wave vector), which is difficult to obtain by other methods, and may prove useful when studying another interesting question, namely, that of the character of phase transformations of the second kind. In this connection we shall now give some rather more detailed attention to scattering in the neighborhood of critical points and phase transformation points of the second kind by using the above results on diffuse scattering.

22.1. Anomalous Scattering by Undistorted Crystals. Let us first consider anomalous scattering in undistorted crystals in the absence of static distortions. Then the probabilities of the fluctuations may be determined without considering long-range elastic forces, and in the expressions for the diffuse-scattering intensity I_1 we may neglect terms which describe scattering due to static displacements. The scattering intensity at concentration inhomogeneities in solid solutions will be determined by the formulas of §17, and in particular, in the neighborhoods of the reciprocal-lattice points of disordered solutions ("structural" points in ordered solutions), by formula (17.10).

Since according to (2.33) the derivative $d^2\varphi/dc^2$ vanishes at critical points on the decomposition curves, we find that, near these points, for small q, i.e., in the neighborhood of reciprocal-lattice points with small scattering angles, the diffuse-scattering intensity becomes anomalously large, as indicated by (17.10). In the absence of distortions, similar bell-shaped symmetrical intensity distributions $I_1(f_A - f_B)^{-2}$ arise around each point (including the zero one), with maxima at the lattice points themselves. On approaching the critical point, for which $d^2\varphi/dc^2 \to 0$, these distributions become still sharper and higher (Fig. 14). The critical x-ray scattering thus arising (which is discussed in [6, 30, 132]) is largely analogous to the well-known phenomenon of the critical scattering of light [2, 8].

In particular, the intensity at the maximum of the distribution

$$I_{1\max} = N_0 \frac{k_B T}{v} (f_A - f_B)^2 \left(\frac{d^2\varphi}{dc^2}\right)^{-1} \quad (22.1)$$

is completely determined by independent thermodynamic data relating to activities (i.e., $d^2\varphi/dc^2$), and near the maximum the intensity falls off in accordance with formula (17.10). It should nevertheless be remembered that on approaching the critical point $\beta \to \infty$, and the range of applicability of the expansion in the denominator of (17.10) is limited to smaller q.

If we wish to study the dependence of the critical scattering on temperature and on $\mathbf{q}$ in explicit form, we may use the results given in §2.4 for fluctuations in the critical region, which were obtained by analyzing the high-temperature expansions in the nearest-neighbor model of the statistical theory of solutions. Thus, sub-

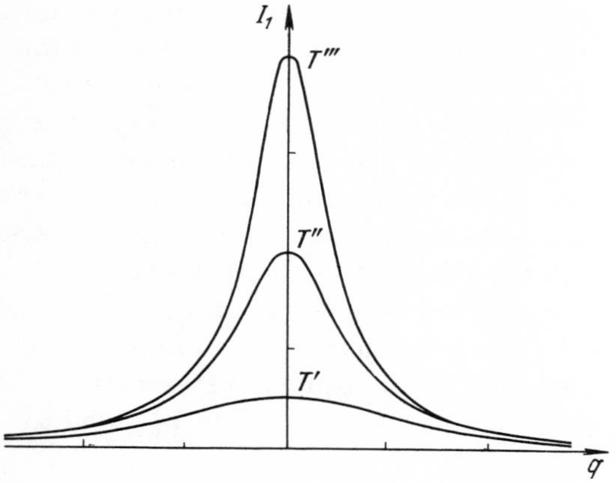

Fig. 14. Intensity distribution of the critical scattering in undistorted solutions near a critical point or a phase transformation of the second kind (schematic). T' > T" > T"' > T_k.

stituting expressions (2.49) and (2.51) (which give the square of the Fourier component of the fluctuation in a cubic solution of critical composition slightly above the critical temperature T_k) into (16.9) (for $\mathbf{A}_q = 0$), we find that the critical-scattering intensity in two ranges of q values is given by the formulas

$$I_1 = N(f_A - f_B)^2 \frac{1}{\zeta\left(\frac{T-T_k}{T_k}\right)^{5/4} + \zeta_2\left(\frac{T-T_k}{T_k}\right)^{-\frac{5\psi}{4(2-\psi)}} q^2}$$

$$\left(q \ll h\,(T-T_k)^{\frac{5}{4(2-\psi)}}\right), \tag{22.2}$$

$$I_1 = N(f_A - f_B)^2 \frac{\text{const}}{q^{2-\psi}} \quad \left(h\,(T-T_k)^{\frac{5}{4(2-\psi)}} \ll q \ll \frac{2\pi}{d}\right). \tag{22.3}$$

$$I_1 = N(f_A - f_B)^2\,\zeta^{-1}\left(\frac{T-T_k}{T_k}\right)^{-\gamma} \frac{\left[1 + \varphi''(ak)^2\left(\frac{T-T_k}{T_k}\right)^{-2\sigma}\right]^{\psi/2}}{1 + \varphi'(ak)^2\left(\frac{T-T_k}{T_k}\right)^{-2\sigma}} \tag{22.4}$$

We see from (22.2) to (22.4) that, near the critical point, the intensity distribution is determined by a curve of the Lorentz type, with the one difference that for large q the quantity I_1 falls off not as $1/q^2$ but rather more slowly, as $1/q^{2-\psi}$ [see (2.46)]. On approaching the critical point the intensity at the maximum rises as $[(T-T_k)/T_k]^{-5/4}$. At the same time the range of q values in which expression (22.2) is applicable contracts, and at the actual critical point expression (22.3) describes the dependence of I_1 on q, i.e., $I_1 \sim 1/q^{2-\psi}$ over the whole range $q \ll 2\pi/d$. We note that, as indicated by formula (22.4), the maximum T_m on the curve of the temperature dependence of I_1 for a given q lies rather above the critical temperature T_k. Only as $q \to 0$ does T_m tend to T_k ($T_m - T_k \sim q^2$).

If in the solution under consideration the radius of interatomic interaction R_0 is large (compared with r_0), then, as noted on p. 39, the results of the thermodynamic theory of phase transformations of the second kind [1, 11] or the analogous theory of decomposition [6] are applicable over a comparatively wide temperature range $T_k(r_0/R_0)^6 \ll |T-T_k| \ll T_k$ [424]. Using expansions of the (2.36) type for φ_{cc} and remembering (17.10), we find that for $T > T_k$ the I_1 of a cubic crystal in this range is given by the formula

$$I_1 = N_0 \frac{k_B T}{v_0} (f_A - f_B)^2 \frac{1}{a(T - T_k) + \beta q^2} . \tag{22.5}$$

Here the dependence of I_1 on both **q** and temperature deviates considerably from the analogous relationships in formula (22.4). It is important to note that, near the actual critical point (or phase transformation point of the second kind), formula (22.5) ceases to be valid, even for a large radius of interatomic interaction.

Near the point corresponding to a phase transformation of the second kind in the solid solution, the long-wave antiphase fluctuations of concentration in the different sublattices become anomalously large, i.e., fluctuations in the long-range-order parameters (see §2.4) become large. In undistorted crystals these produce anomalous diffuse scattering $I_1(\mathbf{q}_1/2\pi)$ in the neighborhoods of the "superstructural" but not the "structural" reciprocal lattice points, as before [3, 6, 23, 26, 30, 123].

In actual fact, at short distances $\mathbf{q}/2\pi = \mathbf{q}_1/2\pi - \mathbf{K}_n$ from "superstructural" points, the scattering intensity arising from ordering solutions with two sublattices (long-range order characterized by one parameter η) is determined by formula (17.11). According to (2.34), at the actual point corresponding to a phase transformation of the second kind the derivatives $\varphi_{\eta\eta}$ and $\varphi_{c\eta}$ vanish (but φ_{cc} remains finite). Near the transformation point, both in the ordered and disordered phases, $\varphi_{\eta\eta}$ and $\varphi_{c\eta}$ are small, and for small q, i.e., in the neighborhoods of the superstructural reciprocal-lattice points, I_1 increases anomalously, as indicated by (17.11). The bell-shaped intensity distributions $I_1(f_A-f_B)^{-2}$ arising in the neighborhoods of different superstructural reciprocal-lattice points are identical, and are similar to the previously considered intensity distributions in the neighborhoods of the "structural" points near the critical point of a decomposition curve (see Fig. 14). We see from (20.6) that the same type of anomalously large scattering should arise not only in solid solutions but also in single-component crystals near a phase transformation point of the second kind (at which $\varphi_{\eta\eta} = 0$).

The temperature dependence of the anomalous-scattering intensity distribution above and below the transformation point T_0 may be studied on the nearest-neighbor approximation. Above the transformation point the derivative $\varphi_{c\eta}$ equals zero identically, $\varphi_{\eta\eta}$ varies in proportion to $[(T-T_0)/T_0]^{5/4}$ in accordance with (2.43), and $\overline{|\eta_k|^2}$ in this model is determined by formulas (2.47), (2.48), and (2.50). Substituting these expressions for $\overline{|\eta_q|^2}$ into (17.11), we immediately see that the intensity distributions in the neighborhoods of the superstructural reciprocal-lattice points near a phase-transformation point of the second kind are described for $T > T_0$ by the same formulas, (22.2) to (22.5), as the distributions in the neighborhoods of "structural" points near the critical point. We only need to replace T_k by T_0 and remember that q is reckoned from the "superstructural" point.

Thus (on the nearest-neighbor approximation) the intensity in the "tails" of the distribution falls off as $1/q^{2-\psi}$, and in the central range (the size of which diminishes on approaching the transformation point) is described by curve (22.2), the maximum of which increases in proportion to $[(T-T_0)/T_0]^{-5/4}$ as $T \to T_0$.

Below the transformation point the derivative $\varphi_{c\eta}$ equals zero for a concentration corresponding to the maximum on the curve $T_0(c)$ (for $c = 1/2$ in the model taken). According to [14], the derivative $\varphi_{\eta\eta}$ for such a concentration is proportional to $|(T-T_0)/T_0|^{5/4}$, in the same way as above the transformation point, but with a much smaller coefficient of proportionality [the constant $\xi \approx 10$ in (2.43) for cubic lattices is more than five times as large for $T > T_0$ than for $T < T_0$]. According to [133], however, the power index in the temperature dependence of $\varphi_{\eta\eta}$ above and below the transformation temperature differs very little, and for $T < T_0$ we have $\varphi_{\eta\eta} \sim [(T_0-T)/T_0]^{31/16}$. In any case, the graph of the temperature dependence of $1/\varphi_{\eta\eta}$, i.e., the temperature dependence of I_1 for a given $q \ll h|T-T_0|^{5/4(2-\psi)}$, should be sharply asymmetric with respect to the point T_0, and for the same $|T-T_0|$ the values of the intensity for $T > T_0$ should be much greater than for $T < T_0$.

Such a graph of the temperature dependence of the maximum intensity I_{1max} (for $q \to 0$), plotted for crystals with lattices of the β brass type in the nearest-neighbor approximation from data of [14], is presented on a semilogarithmic scale in Fig. 15 (curve a).

If the concentration of the solution does not correspond to the maximum on the $T_0(c)$ curve, then in the ordered phase the deriv-

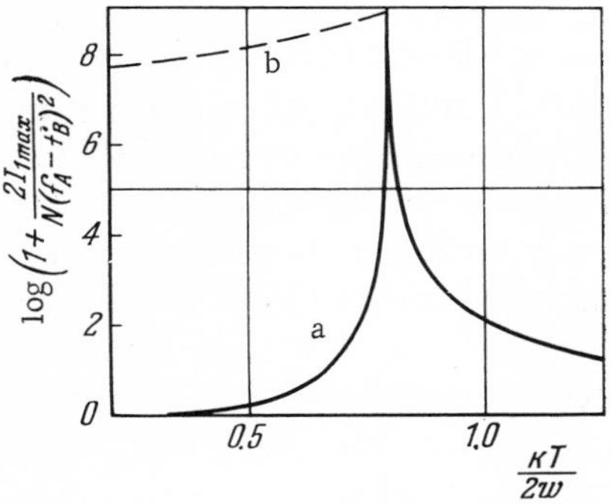

Fig. 15. Temperature dependence of the diffuse-scattering intensity at the maximum of the distribution for crystals with a body-centered cubic lattice of the β brass type, obtained on nearest-neighbor approximation. Curve a is for a solution of stoichiometric composition [$T_0(c)$ maximum]; curve b is for a solution of critical composition (schematic).

ative $\varphi_{c\eta}$ is different from zero (for $T > T_0$ $\varphi_{c\eta} \equiv 0$). Since

$$\varphi_{cc} > 0 \quad \text{and} \quad \varphi_{\eta\eta} - \frac{\varphi_{c\eta}^2}{\varphi_{cc}} < \varphi_{\eta\eta},$$

we see from (17.11) that this circumstance leads to a relative increase in the scattering intensity below the transformation point. As a result of this, on moving away from the extremal concentration in question, the ratio of the diffuse-scattering intensities at $T < T_0$ and $T > T_0$ corresponding to the same values of $|T-T_0|$ will increase and the asymmetry of the curve of the temperature dependence of I_1 will diminish.

Finally, in the neighborhood of the critical point, at which the curve of phase transformations of the second kind passes into the curve of decomposition (point K in Fig. 4), on passing away from the transformation point, I_1 should fall off more slowly in the ordered than in the disordered phase [6]. This follows from (7.11) if we consider that, according to (2.52), at this type of critical point $\varphi_{cc} - \varphi_{c\eta}^2/\varphi_{\eta\eta} = 0$ in the ordered phase but differs from zero in the disordered phase. The corresponding temperature dependence is shown schematically in Fig. 15 (curve b).

Another characteristic feature of diffuse scattering near the critical points is the fact that, as already mentioned in §2, not only fluctuations of long-range order but also fluctuations of concentration increase sharply in the neighborhood of these points (in the disordered phase in undistorted crystals). As a result of this we should observe the interesting phenomenon of a simultaneous anomalous rise in scattering intensity near both the "superstructural" and "structural" reciprocal-lattice points.

In fact we see, for example, from formulas (20.7) [in an undistorted crystal $a_q = 0$ and $\varphi_{cc}(\mathbf{q}) = \varphi_{cc}$] and (2.52), that on approaching the critical point there is a sharp rise in intensity in the ordered phase for fairly small q (when $\alpha q^2 \ll \varphi_{\eta\eta} - \varphi_{c\eta}^2/\varphi_{cc}$) in the neighborhood of the structural points, i.e., $I_1 \sim (\varphi_{cc} - \varphi_{c\eta}^2/\varphi_{\eta\eta})^{-1}$ increases sharply and the same type of anomalous-scattering intensity distribution arises as in the previously considered case of the critical point on the decomposition curve. However, in contrast to the latter, in the present case the anomalous rise of I_1 in the neighborhood of the "structural" points only takes place in one of the phases (the ordered phase). In the disordered phase, for

$T \geq T_0$, and also in the ordered phase slightly below the transformation temperature for $\varphi_{\eta\eta} - \varphi_{c\eta}^2/\varphi_{\eta\eta} \ll \alpha q^2$, this rise in I_1 near the "structural" points should not [according to (20.7)] take place. A long way from the critical point the fluctuations in concentration remain finite, so that in the neighborhoods of these points, near the phase-transformation point, I_1 varies sharply with temperature, without growing anomalously large.

22.2. Consideration of Static Distortions. Let us now consider the influence of the static displacements of the atoms on the diffuse scattering near the critical points and phase-transformation points of the second kind. On considering distortions, the diffuse-scattering intensity in the neighborhood of the "structural" reciprocal-lattice points will be determined by the more general formula (18.3) instead of (17.10). In this generalized formula for I_1 we replace φ_{cc} by $\varphi_{cc}(\mathbf{q}) = \varphi_{cc} + \varphi_{cc}^{y}$ [see (9.4)], allowing for the influence of long-range elastic forces on the fluctuations of concentration, and take account of the scattering at distortions described by the first term in the square brackets of (18.3). Allowing for these two effects associated with distortions greatly changes the picture of the critical-scattering intensity distribution near the critical point on the decomposition curve.

In fact, whereas in undistorted crystals $\varphi_{cc}(\mathbf{q})$ coincides with the derivative $d^2\varphi/dc^2$ and vanishes at the critical point, on taking account of the elastic energy in the distorted crystal in accordance with (9.4) $\varphi_{cc}(\mathbf{q})$ does not vanish at the critical point. Hence the first factor in (18.3) describing the temperature dependence of the diffuse scattering does not tend to infinity at the critical point as $q \to 0$, but remains finite, although it certainly becomes quite large if the distortions are small.

As noted earlier in §9, the quantity $\varphi_{cc}(\mathbf{q})$ vanishes and the scattering intensity becomes anomalously large in the nonequilibrium region at lower temperatures [close to the temperatures $T_0'(c)$ at which $\varphi_{cc}(\mathbf{k}_{min}) = 0$] for solutions which have been unable to decompose (i.e., solutions with a small number of defects). In elastically anisotropic crystals $\varphi_{cc}(\mathbf{q})$ only vanishes for certain directions of $\mathbf{q}$, while for other directions it has finite (though frequently small) values. Hence we should expect to observe some additional special characteristics in the angular dependence of this critical scattering. The temperature dependence of the critical scattering changes after allowing for distortions, firstly on account of the direct influence of the elastic energy on $\varphi_{cc}(\mathbf{q})$ and secondly on account of the fact that the character of the singularities in the thermodynamic quantities near the critical point differs from that given by the nearest-neighbor model when long-range elastic forces are taken into consideration.

We see from (18.3) that, for fairly small q, the scattering at distortions described by the first term in the square brackets of (18.3) becomes dominant. As a result of this, the critical-scattering intensity distribution in the neighborhood of the reciprocal-lattice points for a given direction of vector $\mathbf{q}$ will no longer have a bell-shaped form as in Fig. 14, but a hyperbolic form. If the distortions are fairly small

$$|a_{\mathbf{q}}\mathbf{q}_1\mathbf{e}_{\mathbf{q}}|\frac{f}{|f_A-f_B|} \ll \sqrt{\frac{\varphi_{cc}(\mathbf{q})}{\beta}},$$

then the hyperbolic curve only replaces the bell-shaped curve for very small q; if the distortions are not small, then in general no bell-shaped distribution occurs at all.

The intensity distribution in distorted crystals is asymmetric; on one side of the lattice point the intensity I_1 vanishes for a certain value of q, and the curve of this distribution touches the axis of abscissas. In contrast to the case of undistorted crystals, the critical-scattering distribution will not be the same in the neighborhood of different reciprocal-lattice points. We note that, even in slightly distorted crystals, for which the contribution of the elastic energy to $\varphi_{cc}(\mathbf{q})$ may be neglected (except for the region of very small $|T-T_k|$), for fairly small q the distortions should qualitatively alter the character of the critical-scattering distribution.

Distortions have a rather less pronounced effect on anomalous scattering near a phase transformation point of the second kind. Thus in solid solutions in which long-range order is characterized by a single parameter η and only distortions due to fluctuations of concentration (and not of order) are appreciable, the diffuse-scattering intensity in the neighborhood of "superstructural" reciprocal-lattice points is determined (allowing for distortions) by formula (20.8). Moreover in a disordered phase with $\eta = 0$ the terms proportional to 1/q and $1/q^2$ due to distortion fall out of expression (20.8) [for $\eta = 0$ we also have $a_{\mathbf{q}}^{\eta} = 0$ and $\varphi_{\eta\eta}(\mathbf{q}) \equiv \varphi_{\eta\eta}$] and a bell-shaped anomalous-scattering intensity distribution is obtained, as in undistorted crystals (see Fig. 14). In an ordered phase, since η, $\varphi_{\eta\eta}$, and $\varphi_{c\eta}$ are very small near the transformation point, terms proportional to $1/q$ and $1/q^2$ only start playing an appreciable part for very small q; the smaller the closer the solution is to the transformation point.

For this reason, in practice, the influence of distortions on the anomalous scattering near the transformation point is not very great. The only exception is the case of the critical point in which the curve of phase transformations of the second kind transforms into the decomposition curve. The difference $\varphi_{cc}(\mathbf{q})-\varphi^2_{c\eta}/\varphi_{\eta\eta}$, unlike $\varphi_{cc}-\varphi^2_{c\eta}/\varphi_{\eta\eta}$, does not vanish at this point, but remains positive. Hence, as in the case of the critical point on the decomposition curve, anomalous scattering in the neighborhood of "structural" reciprocal-lattice points and singularities of the temperature dependence of I_1 in the neighborhood of "superstructural" points will in fact appear, not in the immediate neighborhood of this critical point, but in the two-phase region of nonequilibrium solutions, close to the point on the phase diagram at which

$$\varphi_{cc}(\mathbf{q})-\frac{\varphi^2_{c\eta}}{\varphi_{\eta\eta}}=0.$$

In single-component crystals, and in the more detailed consideration of solid solutions, we must consider distortions associated with fluctuations of order (and not only of concentration). Allowing for these distortions, the diffuse scattering near reciprocal-lattice points associated with single-component crystals having one long-range-order parameter is given by formula (20.5), and in the general case, in which the long-range order is characterized by r parameters, by formula (20.4).

As mentioned earlier in §20, the diffuse-scattering intensity distribution, especially anomalous scattering near phase transformation points of the second kind, depends substantially on the symmetry of the crystal, which determines whether L^{μ}_{ij} and a^{μ}_{q} (i.e., the distortions) are identically equal to zero in the disordered phase and small (proportional to η) in the ordered phase, or whether these quantities differ from zero in both phases.

In the first case we see from (9.9) that, in the disordered phase, the contribution $\varphi^{y}_{\mu\mu'}$ of the long-range elastic forces to

$\varphi_{\mu\mu'}$ (k) vanishes, the coefficients a_q^{μ} in (20.4) or (20.5) are also equal to zero, and the distortions have no effect on the diffuse scattering. Since the derivative $\partial^2\varphi/\partial\eta^2$, or, in the case of several order parameters, the derivatives $\varphi_{\mu\mu'} = \partial^2\varphi/\partial\eta_\mu\partial\eta_{\mu'}$ with respect to the parameters η_μ, corresponding to any irreducible representation of the symmetry group of the disordered phase, vanish at a transformation point of the second kind, some of the matrix elements of the reciprocal matrix $\varphi^{-1}_{\mu\mu'}$ tend to infinity at the transformation point. Hence, in the neighborhood of reciprocal-lattice points for which $\chi \neq 0$, the same bell-shaped anomalous-scattering intensity distributions as in the earlier-discussed case of solid solutions (not associated with distortions) should arise in the disordered phase near the transformation point.

Below the transformation point in the case considered, L_{ij} and a_q^{μ} are proportional to η, and the contribution of the elastic energy $\varphi^{y}_{\mu\mu'}$ according to (9.8) and (9.9) is proportional to η^2. Hence, in the ordered phase, as $T \to T_0$ the quantity $\varphi_{\mu\mu'}(\mathbf{q})$ also vanishes, and as for $T > T_0$ the diffuse scattering should show an anomalous rise. Since $a_q \sim \eta$ are small near the transformation point, the scattering at distortions will only appear for very small q, as indicated by (20.4) and (20.5).

Distortions play a relatively larger part near the critical point in single-component crystals, in which the curve of phase transformations of the second kind passes into the curve of phase transformations of the first kind. Near such points the ratio $\eta^2/\varphi_{\eta\eta}$ should be much larger for the same $T_0 - T$ than near an ordinary phase transformation point of the second kind [134]. Hence the relative contribution of $\varphi^{y}_{\eta\eta} \sim \eta^2$ rises in comparison with $\varphi_{\eta\eta}$, the quantity $\varphi_{\eta\eta}(\mathbf{q})$ increases, and hence for $T < T_0$ the intensity I_1 will diminish. However, since distortions associated with fluctuations of order are in the majority of cases quantitatively small (much smaller than distortions associated with fluctuations of concentration), even in this case, on allowing for distortions, $\varphi^{-1}_{\mu\mu'}(\mathbf{q})$ usually keeps the same order of magnitude, so that anomalous scattering takes place.

On the other hand, for fairly small distances q from "structural" points of the reciprocal lattice ($f \neq 0$), the first terms in the brackets of (20.5) or (20.4) play the principal part, so that near the critical point there will be an anomalous rise in the diffuse scattering at distortions (proportional to $1/q^2$ and $\eta^2/\varphi_{\eta\eta}$) with an intensity distribution of the hyperbolic and not of the bell-shaped type. In the disordered phase in this case, distortions associated with fluctuations of long-range order will not arise, and the scattering term proportional to $1/q^2$ may only be associated with fluctuations in correlation parameters, and should thus be less intense, so that for $T > T_0$ the anomalous-scattering intensity distribution around points with $\chi \neq 0$ will have a bell-shaped form.

If the crystal has no center of symmetry, and even in the disordered phase the L_{ij}^{μ} differ from zero, then allowing for elastic energy will in accordance with (9.9) reduce the value of $\varphi_{\mu\mu'}^{-1}(\mathbf{q})$ near the transformation point (at which some derivatives $\varphi_{\mu\mu'}$ are equal to zero) and lead to a weakening of the scattering intensity in the neighborhood of the reciprocal-lattice points. If, however, as often occurs, the L_{ij}^{μ} are numerically small, then the diffuse scattering will rise sharply near the transformation point, as in the absence of long-range elastic forces. As indicated by (20.4), near "structural" points ($f \neq 0$), the intensity distribution both above and below the transformation point will have a hyperbolic form for fairly small q [terms in I_1 proportional to q^{-2} and $\varphi_{\mu\mu'}^{-1}(\mathbf{q})$]. If, however, for $T > T_0$ $f = 0$, then, in the disordered phase, near such "superstructural" points the intensity distribution will have a bell-shaped form.

22.3. Anomalous Scattering at Fluctuations of Polarization. The temperature dependence of the derivatives $\varphi_{\mu\mu'}$, the order parameters η_μ, and hence also the anomalous-scattering intensity in single-component crystals may only be determined after calculating the statistical model of the ordering of these crystals near the transformation point. We must also remember that the corresponding temperature relationships may differ in details (especially when allowing for long-range forces) from those given earlier for the nearest-interaction model in solutions.

Although in general these temperature relationships cannot at present be predicted, they may be determined in ferroelectric crystals, in which the long-range order is uniquely characterized by specifying the polarization vector components P_i, by using independent experimental data relating to the dielectric susceptibility $\varkappa_{ij}$, which in this case gives $\varphi_{\mu\mu'}$ directly. Depending on the relation between q and the reciprocal of the Debye radius $1/r_d$, the diffuse-scattering intensity, neglecting elastic interaction, is determined by formulas (20.10) (for $qr_d \ll 1$) or (20.11) (for $qr_d \gg \sqrt{\varepsilon}$). All the quantities entering into these formulas may be found for fairly small q from independent experiments, and this offers the possibility of establishing the temperature dependence of the scattering intensity distribution in every particular case.

For a large carrier concentration, the Debye radius is small, the dipole–dipole interactions for long wavelengths of the fluctuation waves ($qr_d \ll 1$) are screened, and the anomalous-scattering intensity near the phase transformation into the ferroelectric state is exactly the same as in the cases considered earlier, in agreement with (20.10). However, for large Debye radii and not-too-small q values, characteristic ferroelectric effects (associated with the considerable influence of long-range dipole–dipole forces on the fluctuation of polarization) should become manifest. As a result of this the magnitude of the scattering intensity, and especially its angular dependence, may change considerably.

In cubic (i.e., cubic in the nonferroelectric phase) crystals, moreover, on allowing for the dipole–dipole interaction, the scattering intensity for $q \to 0$ increases anomalously on approaching the transformation point for any directions of $\mathbf{q}$. Expressing $\varkappa_{ij}(\mathbf{q}) - \varkappa_{\infty ij}(\mathbf{q})$ in (20.11) in terms of the dielectric constants ε and ε_∞ for low and high frequencies in accordance with formulas (10.7) and (10.8) [in so doing we must transform from the special coordinate system used in (10.8) to the natural system in which the axes are directed along directions of the [100] type], we may obtain an explicit expression for the scattering intensity in this case:

$$I_1 = \frac{Nk_BT}{4\pi v}\left[(\varepsilon - \varepsilon_\infty)(\delta_{ij} - n_i n_j) + \frac{\varepsilon - \varepsilon_\infty}{\varepsilon\varepsilon_\infty} n_i n_j\right] \times$$

$$\times \left(f a_{\mathbf{q}}^i \frac{\mathbf{q}_1 \mathbf{e}_{\mathbf{q}}^i}{q} - \chi_i\right)\left(f a_{\mathbf{q}}^j \frac{\mathbf{q}_1 \mathbf{e}_{\mathbf{q}}^j}{q} - \chi_j\right). \qquad (22.6)$$

If the dipole–dipole interaction were screened, then the square bracket in (22.6) would have to be replaced by $(\varepsilon - \varepsilon_\infty)\delta_{ij}$, i.e., allowing for this interaction in fact greatly changes the angular dependence of the diffuse scattering distribution. The angular dependence of I_1 is still further complicated in such ferroelectrics below the transformation point in the ferroelectric phase (where the crystal does not have cubic symmetry), but, as before, in the case of the nonferroelectric phase, anomalous scattering should be observed for all directions of **q**.

Dipole–dipole interaction has an especially sharp influence on anomalous scattering in noncubic (in the nonferroelectric phase) crystals. If only one component $\varkappa_{zz}$ of the tensor $\varkappa_{ij}$ tends to infinity near the phase transformation and $\varkappa_{xx} = \varkappa_{yy}$, $\varkappa_{ij} = 0$ for $i \neq j$, it then follows from (20.11), (10.7), and (10.9) that, neglecting terms which remain finite on approaching the transformation point, the anomalous-scattering intensity for $qr_d \gg \sqrt{4\pi\varkappa_{zz}}$ will be equal to

$$I_1 = \frac{Nk_BT}{v} \frac{(1+4\pi\varkappa_{xx})\,\varkappa_{zz}}{1+4\pi\varkappa_{xx}+4\pi\varkappa_{zz}n_z^2} \left(f a_{\mathbf{q}}^z \frac{\mathbf{q}_1 \mathbf{e}_{\mathbf{q}}^z}{q} - \chi_z \right)^2 . \qquad (22.7)$$

We see from formula (22.7) that, in this case, diffuse scattering will only increase anomalously if the vector $\mathbf{n} = \mathbf{q}/q$ is almost perpendicular to the Z axis ($n_z \ll 1$), while for other directions of **q** an anomalous rise in I_1 should only occur for $qr_d \ll 1$, when the dipole–dipole interaction is eliminated.

In order to take account of elastic long-range forces, we must replace $\varkappa_{ij}$ by $\varkappa'_{ij}$ or $\varkappa_{ij}(\mathbf{q})$ by $\varkappa'_{ij}(\mathbf{q})$ in formulas (20.10) and (20.11), or (22.6) and (22.7) [see (10.12)]. The substitution leads to a weakening of the diffuse scattering near the transformation point, as in the general case considered above, if the crystal is a piezoelectric in the nonferroelectric phase.

22.4. Some Experimental Results. A comparatively small amount of attention has been devoted to the experimental study of anomalous scattering. Walker and Keating [135] studied this scattering in β brass (β-CuZn), constituting a classical alloy in which the transformation to the ordered phase is a phase transformation of the second kind. Since in the case of x rays the atomic factors for Cu and Zn are close together, the intensity of the diffuse scattering associated with short-range order will be relatively small even near the phase-transformation point. For this reason the authors of [135] studied the diffuse scattering of neutrons in order to observe anomalous-scattering effects; the scattering amplitudes of neutrons interacting with the nuclei of Cu and Zn differ considerably, especially if the isotope Cu^{65} is used instead of a natural mixture of Cu isotopes (this was done in [135]).

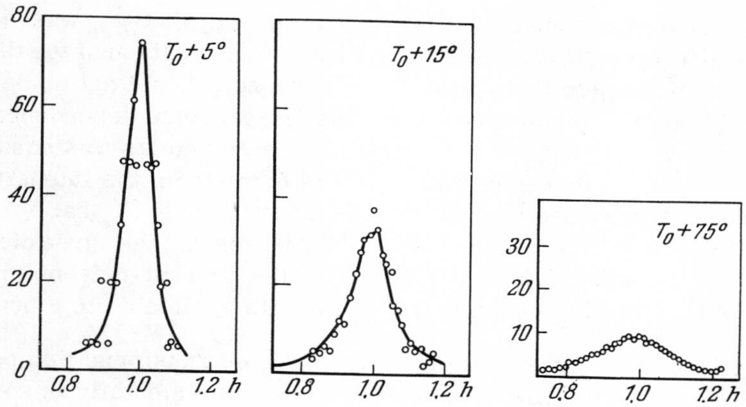

Fig. 16. Intensity of the diffuse scattering of neutrons in β brass (in arbitrary units) along the [100] direction near the (100) reciprocal-lattice point at various temperatures. The y axis gives the ratio of the scattering intensity for fluctuations of long-range order (other types of scattering excluded) to the scattering intensity for an ideal solution of the same composition.

It was found that, in agreement with the theoretical conclusions discussed above, the diffuse-scattering distribution in a Cu-46.8 at.% Zn alloy contracted into narrower and higher peaks around the superstructural point of the reciprocal lattice on approaching the temperature of the phase transformation. Such distributions of scattering intensity along the [100] axis near the (100) reciprocal-lattice point are shown in Fig. 16 for several temperatures above the ordering temperature T_0 (T_0 = 741°K). The ratio of the peak intensities for $T = T_0 + 75°K$ and $T = T_0 + 175°K$ agrees closely with the law $I_{1max} \sim [(T-T_0)/T_0]^{-5/4}$; full confirmation of this temperature relationship for lower temperatures is difficult, however, owing to the errors associated with instrumental broadening and the inaccuracy of determining (and maintaining) the temperature.

More detailed study of the anomalous diffuse scattering of neutrons by single crystals of β brass near the temperature T_0 was carried out by Als-Nielsen and Dietrich [435]. This work was carried out over a temperature range between 2 and 25°C above T_0 with fairly accurate temperature control (accuracy ±0.05°C) and with the careful introduction of corrections for instrumental broadening. It was found from the temperature dependence of the intensity I_1 at the maxima of the peaks ($q \to 0$) that $\varphi_{\eta\eta}$ was described by formula (2.43) with $\gamma = 1.25 \pm 0.02$. Although the difference of the φ in (2.45) and (2.50) from zero could not be determined reliably, it was found from the temperature dependence of the peak widths that the value of σ in these formulas was equal to 0.65 ± 0.02. In addition to this, it was found from the intensities of the Bragg reflections below the temperature T_0 that $\eta \sim T-T_0)^{0.305 \pm 0.005}$. All these values of the power indices agree closely with the theoretical values obtained on the nearest-neighbor model (see §3), indicating that this model is quite applicable to β brass.

The anomalous scattering near phase-transformation points of the second kind has also been studied experimentally in some more complicated single-component crystals. This effect is revealed, for example, in the scattering of x rays in $NaNO_2$ near the temperature T_0 of the transformation into the ferroelectric state [136–138]. We see from Fig. 17, which is taken from [137] and shows the temperature dependence of the diffuse scattering for several values of q ($q_1 < q_2 < q_3$) in the [010] direction in the neighborhood of the (002) reciprocal-lattice point (c is the polar axis), that there is a sharp peak on this curve near the transformation temperature for fairly small q.

In order to explain all the details of the careful study of the diffuse-scattering intensity distribution carried out by Canut and Mendiola [137], we must clearly have greater information regarding the character of the ordering in $NaNO_2$ (in particular, regarding the appearance of the antiferroelectric phase and the "microdomain" structure [139–142], and also regarding the electron and ion concentrations, i.e., the Debye screening radius). An analogous anomalous rise in x-ray scattering intensity near a phase transformation of the second kind has also been found in triglycine sulfate [143].

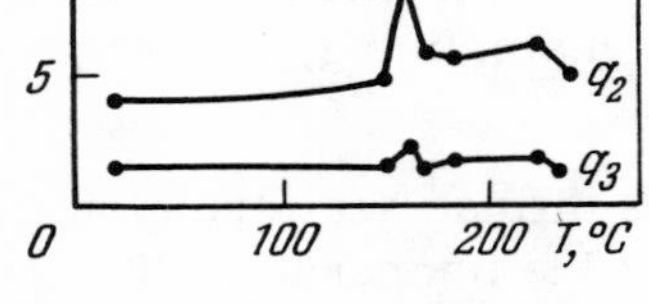

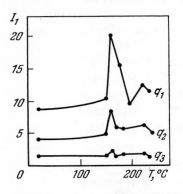

Fig. 17. Temperature dependence of the diffuse-scattering intensity of x rays in an $NaNO_2$ crystal for **q** parallel to the [010] axis close to the (002) point of the reciprocal lattice.

Critical scattering near the critical point on the decomposition curve in the neighborhood of nonzero

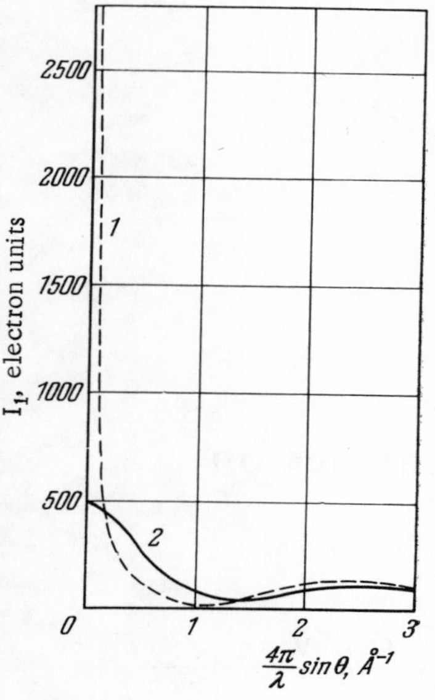

Fig. 18. Angular dependence of the intensity of low-angle scattering by an Al–Zn solution of critical composition for T = 352°C (curve 1) and T = 360°C (curve 2).

reciprocal-lattice points has apparently not yet been studied. Only low-angle critical scattering in solid and liquid solutions has been considered (at small angles critical scattering by liquid solutions is clearly described by formulas of the same type as undistorted solid solutions). Münster and Sagel [144] observed an anomalous rise in low-angle scattering in Al–Zn alloys near the critical decomposition point (T_k = 351.5°C, c_k = 0.395). We see from Fig. 18 that on approaching the critical point the scattering intensity does in fact rise sharply. Values of the derivatives $d^2\varphi/dc^2$ determined from these results by using a formula of the (17.10) type agree with the results of thermodynamic measurements [145]. It is nevertheless a little difficult to understand why this agreement is achieved without considering distortions rather than on the more consistent theory [formula (18.3)] which allows for the influence of elastic interaction on the fluctuations.

In liquid solutions the critical low-angle scattering of x rays near the critical point was observed in [146, 147]. The anomalous low-angle scattering of x rays at critical fluctuations of density in single-component liquids near the gas-liquid critical point has also been studied (see, for example, [148]).

Here we have only discussed the anomalous scattering of x rays and neutrons. Analogous effects should also be observed, however, for the scattering of other waves near critical points and phase transformations of the second kind, e.g., in the scattering of light [2, 5, 8, 149–154], elastic waves (leading to anomalies of phonon thermal conductivity in undistorted crystals [155]), and electrons (leading to anomalies in the mobility of conduction electrons in the neighborhood of critical points and phase transformations of the second kind [156]).

Chapter VI

Weakening of the Line Intensities on the X-Ray Diffraction Picture

§23. Debye–Waller Factor of the Weakening of Intensity in Ideal Crystals

In addition to diffuse scattering, defects of the first class (especially impurity atoms) also produce weakening in the intensity of the regular Bragg reflections (lines on the x-ray diffraction photograph), in accordance with the general results discussed in §14; a study of these may give additional information regarding distortions in the crystal. The intensity of the x-ray lines is weakened by not only static but also thermal displacements of the atoms; in solid solutions these also exhibit certain characteristic features contrasting with the case of ideal crystals.

In this chapter we shall consider the weakening in the intensity of regular reflections resulting from both thermal and static displacements of the atoms, first taking the simplest case of ideal crystals, then (§24) effects associated with static displacements, and finally (§25) effects associated with thermal vibrations in solid solutions.

The Debye–Waller factor $\exp(-M_\gamma)$ representing the weakening in the scattering amplitude of x rays scattered by atoms of the γ sublattice resulting from thermal vibrations is determined in accordance with (16.4) by the mean value of the exponential function of the thermal displacements. In the harmonic approximation of the theory of vibrations, this mean value is most simply calculated if we consider that, in this approximation, the probability distribution of the thermal displacements $\mathbf{u}_\gamma$ of the atoms belonging to sublattice γ, and hence also that of the scalar product $\mathbf{q}_1\mathbf{u}_\gamma$, is Gaussian* and has the form

$$w(\mathbf{q}_1\mathbf{u}_\gamma) \sim \exp\left[-\frac{(\mathbf{q}_1\mathbf{u}_\gamma)^2}{2\langle(\mathbf{q}_1\mathbf{u}_\gamma)^2\rangle}\right], \tag{23.1}$$

the dispersion of the distribution being determined by the mean (with respect to the thermal vibrations) square of the scalar product $(\mathbf{q}_1\mathbf{u}_\gamma)^2$. Averaging the exponential function $\exp(i\mathbf{q}_1\mathbf{u}_\gamma)$ with respect to the thermal vibrations ($\langle\ldots\rangle$) by means of the distribution (23.1), we obtain an expression for the Debye–Waller factor:

$$e^{-M_\gamma} = \langle\exp(i\mathbf{q}_1\mathbf{u}_\gamma)\rangle = \exp\left[-\frac{1}{2}\langle(\mathbf{q}_1\mathbf{u}_\gamma)^2\rangle\right], \quad 2M_\gamma = \langle(\mathbf{q}_1\mathbf{u}_\gamma)^2\rangle. \tag{23.2}$$

The quantity $2M_\gamma$ may be put in the form of a sum over the Cartesian coordinates

$$2M_\gamma = q_{1i}q_{1j}\langle u_{\gamma i}u_{\gamma j}\rangle,$$

where the means $\langle u_{\gamma i}u_{\gamma j}\rangle$ form a symmetric tensor of the second order (since $\mathbf{u}_\gamma$ is a vector), and, generally speaking, it depends on the direction of the vector $\mathbf{q}_1$ and the number of the sublattice γ. However, in cubic crystals with one atom per cell $M_\gamma \equiv M$ are the same for all atoms, the tensor $\langle u_i u_j\rangle$ degenerates into a scalar, and

$$2M = q_1^2\langle u_x^2\rangle = \frac{1}{3}q_1^2\langle\mathbf{u}^2\rangle \tag{23.3}$$

depends only on the length and not the orientation of the vector $\mathbf{q}_1$.

* This assertion is based on the fact that, for each oscillator corresponding to any normal coordinate, the probability distribution of the displacements on both the classical and quantum theory is Gaussian [1]. It is also known from the theory of probabilities that, if the probability distribution of each term is Gaussian, then the probability of the sum of the statistically independent quantities (on the harmonic approximation the normal coordinates are not connected) also obeys a Gaussian distribution (see, for example, [157]).

The theory of the Debye–Waller factor is usually constructed by introducing normal coordinates [92, 93, 158–161]. In a single-atom crystal the expansion of the thermal displacements $\mathbf{u}_s$ of any s-th atom with respect to the dimensionless normal coordinates $q_{\mathbf{k}n}$, characterized by wave vectors $\mathbf{k}$ and branch number n (n = 1, 2, 3) may be written in the form (see, for example, [162–164])

$$\mathbf{u}_s = \sum_{\mathbf{k}n} \left(\frac{4\hbar}{Nm\omega_{\mathbf{k}n}}\right)^{1/2} \mathbf{e}_{\mathbf{k}n}\chi_{\mathbf{k}}(\mathbf{R}_s)\, q_{\mathbf{k}n},$$
$$\chi_{\mathbf{k}}(\mathbf{R}_s) = \begin{cases} \cos \mathbf{k}\mathbf{R}_s, & k_x \geqslant 0, \\ \sin \mathbf{k}\mathbf{R}_s, & k_x < 0, \end{cases} \qquad (23.4)$$

where m is the mass of an atom. Substituting (23.4) into (23.3) and remembering that for the selected dimensionless coordinates

$$\langle q_{\mathbf{k}n} q_{\mathbf{k}'n'}\rangle = \frac{1}{2}\left(n_{\mathbf{k}n} + \frac{1}{2}\right)\delta_{\mathbf{k}\mathbf{k}'}\delta_{nn'},$$

where

$$n_{\mathbf{k}n} = \left(\exp\frac{\hbar\omega_{\mathbf{k}n}}{k_B T} - 1\right)^{-1},$$
$$\chi_{\mathbf{k}}^2(\mathbf{R}_s) + \chi_{-\mathbf{k}}^2(\mathbf{R}_s) = 1$$

and that for cubic crystals

$$\sum_n (\mathbf{q}_1\mathbf{e}_{\mathbf{k}n})^2 = q_1^2$$

(the three unit polarization vectors $\mathbf{e}_{\mathbf{k}n}$ with different n are orthogonal), we express the quantity 2M in terms of the frequency of the normal vibrations $\omega_{\mathbf{k}n}$:

$$2M = \frac{\hbar q_1^2}{6mN}\sum_{\mathbf{k}n}\frac{2n_{\mathbf{k}n}+1}{\omega_{\mathbf{k}n}} = \frac{v\hbar q_1^2}{48\pi^3 m}\sum_{n=1}^{3}\int d\mathbf{k}\,\frac{2n_{\mathbf{k}n}+1}{\omega_{\mathbf{k}n}}, \qquad (23.5)$$

where $\mathbf{k}/2\pi$ run through values lying in the unit cell of the reciprocal lattice.

At high temperatures ($\hbar\omega_{\mathbf{k}n} \ll k_B T$)

$$n_{\mathbf{k}n} + \frac{1}{2} \approx \frac{k_B T}{\hbar\omega_{\mathbf{k}n}}$$

and in accordance with the results of the classical theory the mean square of the thermal displacements and 2M are proportional to T. Moreover

$$2M = q_1^2 k_B T m^{-1} \overline{\omega_{\mathbf{k}n}^{-2}}$$

is determined by the mean value (averaged over the spectrum) of the inverse square of the frequency. As temperature falls there are deviations from the linear relationship, and at T = 0 the quantity 2M tends to a nonzero limiting value of

$$2M = \hbar q_1^2 (2m)^{-1} \overline{\omega_{\mathbf{k}n}^{-1}},$$

proportional to the mean inverse frequency and to the corresponding purely quantum effect of the zero vibrations of the atoms.

Integral (23.5) may be calculated in explicit form by means of the Debye approximation, in which it is assumed that the frequencies of all three branches of vibrations depend in the same way on $|\mathbf{k}|$:

$$\omega_{\mathbf{k}n} = wk.$$

In this approximation, instead of integrating over the cell of the reciprocal lattice, we integrate over the volume of a sphere of equal size with radius $k_m = (6\pi^2/v)^{1/3}$. As a result of this the integral (23.5) becomes equal to

$$2M = \frac{3\hbar^2 q_1^2}{m k_B \theta}\left[\frac{1}{4} + \frac{T}{\theta}\Phi\left(\frac{\theta}{T}\right)\right], \quad \Phi(x) = \frac{1}{x}\int_0^x \frac{t\,dt}{e^t - 1}, \qquad (23.6)$$

where the Debye temperature θ in the Debye approximation is determined by the maximum vibration frequency $\omega_m = wk_m$,

$$\theta = \frac{\hbar\omega_m}{k_B},$$

and is simply expressed in terms of the elastic modulus of the (elastically isotropic) crystal. Using the expansion of $\Phi(x)$ for small x and its asymptotic expression for large x, we obtain the approximations

$$2M = \frac{3\hbar^2 q_1^2 T}{m k_B \theta^2}\left[1 + \frac{1}{36}\left(\frac{\theta}{T}\right)^2 + \dots\right] \text{ for } T > \theta$$

and

$$2M = \frac{3\hbar^2 q_1^2}{4mk_B\theta}\left[1 + \frac{3\pi^2}{2}\left(\frac{T}{\theta}\right)^2 + \ldots\right] \text{ for } T \ll \theta.$$

For intermediate temperatures the function $\Phi(x)$ is tabulated in [92] (Table 2).

In real crystals the assumption of the Debye approximation regarding the linear, isotropic dependence of $\omega_{\mathbf{k}n}$ on $\mathbf{k}$ is clearly not satisfied, especially in the high-frequency range (which gives a substantial contribution in the calculation of 2M). Hence the actual values of 2M at different temperatures will differ from the values obtained by formula (23.6) on the Debye approximation. In practice, however, it is convenient, instead of giving 2M (or $\langle \mathbf{u}^2 \rangle$), to give θ for each temperature, since this determines 2M unambiguously from formula (23.6).

The "x-ray-diffraction" Debye temperature θ determined in this way will in general depend on the (actual) temperature. It is clear that θ may differ substantially from the "calorimetric" Debye temperature θ_D describing the temperature dependence of the specific heat, which for $T \to 0$ is determined simply by the long-wave part of the spectrum and also varies with temperature.

In order to calculate the Debye–Waller factor in real crystals, as indicated by (23.5), we must know the whole spectrum of vibrations (or the frequency-distribution function). Only in a few cases is this spectrum known to a fair accuracy from experiment.

Table 2. Table of Values of the Function $\Phi(x)$

x	$\Phi(x)$	x	$\Phi(x)$	x	$\Phi(x)$	x	$\Phi(x)$
0.0	1	1.2	0.740	3	0.483	9	0.183
0.2	0.951	1.4	0.704	4	0.388	10	0.164
0.4	0.904	1.6	0.669	5	0.321	12	0.137
0.6	0.860	1.8	0.637	6	0.271	14	0.114
0.8	0.818	2.0	0.607	7	0.234	16	0.103
1.0	0.778	2.5	0.540	8	0.205	20	0.0822

Hence 2M is often calculated by means of a semi-phenomenological vibration model, in which only interactions with the atoms of the first or first few coordination spheres are considered. The corresponding force constants are determined by comparing the calculated elastic moduli (or $\omega_{\mathbf{k}n}$) with the experimental data. After this the secular equations are solved numerically, the $\omega_{\mathbf{k}n}$ are found, and then a numerical summation over **k** is carried out in order to determine 2M.

Such calculations have been carried out, for example, in the case of Al [165–168] and Cu [169, 167], which have face-centered cubic lattices, and for white tin, which has a more complicated tetragonal lattice with two atoms in the cell [170]. It was found in particular that, in the crystals with the face-centered cubic lattices, θ (as distinct from θ_D) was almost independent of temperature (on passing from T = 0°K to high temperatures, the θ of Al rose by less than 10° and that of Cu by 5°).

Since θ depends only slightly on temperature, it is sufficient in a number of cases to determine simply the limiting high-temperature value of the Debye temperature θ_∞. For this the quantum effects are not severe, and in determining θ_∞ we may avoid the cumbersome calculations of normal coordinates by using the result of Leontovich [171, 172], which reduces the calculation of the mean-square thermal displacements to a classical problem of mechanics. According to [171], the mean square of the projection of the thermal displacement of an atom in a given direction equals the projection (in the same direction) of the static displacement of this atom produced by a force equal in magnitude to k_BT, applied to the same atom and acting in this direction. The solution of the corresponding static problem is easily obtained by means of Fourier series (see §6). Using this method, we obtained a formula [173] giving θ_∞ for any crystal with a face-centered cubic lattice on the noncentral-interaction model.

Table 3 presents the values of θ_∞ calculated by this formula for six metals with face-centered cubic lattices, for which the elastic moduli c_{ij} are known. We used the values of c_{ij} for room temperature given in [174] (for Au, values from a later paper [175] were taken). The penultimate column of the table gives the experimental x-ray-diffraction values of θ for $T \approx \theta$, determined to an

Table 3. Debye Temperatures of Metals with Face-Centered Cubic Lattices

Metal	Elastic moduli, 10^{11} dyne/cm²			θ_∞, °K [173]	θ_{expt}, °K	θ_D, °K
	c_{11}	c_{12}	c_{44}			
Ag	12.40	9.34	4.61	196	210 [178], 191 [179], 212 [180]	226
Al	10.82	6.13	2.85	362	395 [181], 400 [178], 382 [182], 393 [436]	428
Au	19.23	16.31	4.20	145	155 [181]	162
Cu	16.84	12.14	7.54	301	315 [169], 307 [183]	344
Ni	24.65	14.73	12.47	407	420 [184], 400 [185], 418 [186]	476
Pb	4.66	3.92	1.44	85	93 [182], 76 [187]	

accuracy of 5 to 10%* while the last column gives the values of the "calorimetric" Debye temperature θ_D corresponding to the limit $T \rightarrow 0$ and calculated from the elastic moduli with due allowance for elastic anisotropy [177] (these agree with experimental specific-heat data).

We see from Table 3 that the values of θ_∞ may differ considerably (by some 20%) from the values of θ_D calculated from data relating to the elastic constants or the low-temperature specific heat (with increasing temperature, the θ_D vary rapidly and their values may approach θ_∞). We note that the approximations involved in the calculation and the model used in obtaining such integral characteristics of the spectrum as θ lead to relatively small errors, probably not exceeding 5 to 10%.† The slight difference in the calculated and experimental values of θ may be associated with

*A detailed list of experimental θ values for crystals of various structures appears in Herbstein's review [176].

†For the elastic moduli of Al and Cu used in [165, 168, 169], the formula of [173] gives θ_∞ values, respectively, 10 to 15 and 12°K below the values obtained in [165, 168, 169] by means of considerably more complicated calculations. The low sensitivity of the calculated value of θ to the details of the model is demonstrated in [167], where, despite the great difference of the force constants in the different models, very close values of M were obtained.

experimental and calculating errors, and also with the effect of anharmonicity (which was not allowed for very accurately in calculating θ_∞ by using the elastic moduli corresponding to room temperature rather than 0°K).

In polyatomic crystals with several atoms in the unit cell, the Debye–Waller factors for the atoms of different sublattices will clearly differ. The existence of optical branches of vibrations will lead to a change in the temperature dependence of M as compared with the case of monatomic crystals. Calculations of M for diatomic crystals were carried out, in particular, in [188–191].

At high temperatures, corrections to the Debye–Waller factor due to anharmonicity become considerable [192–194]. The existence of anharmonicity leads, first, to a change in the temperature dependence of the square of the thermal displacements of the atoms (at high temperatures $\langle \mathbf{u}^2 \rangle$ will contain terms both linear and quadratic with respect to T), and secondly to a non-Gaussian probability distribution of the displacements, as a result of which 2M will be determined not only by the square but also by the fourth and subsequent powers of the displacements (and $\mathbf{q}_1$).

According to [193], if the anharmonicity is small, the expression for M in a monatomic crystal may be put in the form

$$M = M_0 + M_1 + M_2. \tag{23.7}$$

Here $2(M_0 + M_1) = \langle (\mathbf{q}_1 \mathbf{u})^2 \rangle$, $M_0 = M_0^0 + M_0'$ is calculated from formula (23.5) of harmonic theory, in which, however, we must allow for the temperature dependence of the frequencies associated with thermal expansion, i.e., M_0 contains a term $M_0' \sim T^2$; in the Grüneisen approximation

$$\frac{M_0'}{M_0} \approx -\frac{2}{\omega_{av}} \frac{\partial \omega_{av}}{\partial V} V \alpha T \approx 2 \frac{C_p - C_v}{C_v},$$

where α is the thermal-expansion coefficient, ω_{av} is some average vibration frequency, and C_p and C_v are the specific heats at constant pressure and volume.

For $T > \theta$, M_1 is proportional to T^2 and may be estimated from the formula

$$\frac{M_1}{M_0} = \mathfrak{w} \overline{\overline{\omega^{-2}}} (\overline{\omega^{-2}})^{-1} \frac{C'}{C_v}. \tag{23.8}$$

Here $\overline{\overline{\omega^{-2}}} \approx \overline{\omega^{-2}}$ are the mean values of $\omega_{\mathbf{k}n}^{-2}$, taken from several sums, C' is the high-temperature correction to the specific heat C_V due to anharmonicity, $\mathfrak{w}$ is a dimensionless factor of the order or unity ($\mathfrak{w} = 2$ and $\mathfrak{w} = 3$ if the main contribution comes from anharmonicity of the fourth order in the first approximation or the third order in the second, respectively; in a few rare cases $\mathfrak{w} < 2$ or $\mathfrak{w} > 3$).

Calculation by this formula, using experimental data for C_p and C_V, shows that

$$\frac{M_0' + M_1}{M_0} \approx 2\frac{C_p - C_v}{C_v} + \mathfrak{w}\frac{C'}{C_v}$$

may be of the order of several tens. This estimate agrees with the experimental data (see, for example, [181, 182, 195–197]). For low temperatures $M_1/M_0 \sim 10^{-2}$. The sign of M_1 should as a rule be positive, which corresponds to a reduction in the effective x-ray-diffraction Debye temperature with increasing T. The term M_2 associated with the non-Gaussian probability distribution is proportional to q_1^4 and T^3 (for $T > \theta$). According to the estimates of [193, 194] this is only manifest at very high temperatures and large q_1 (hard radiation).

§24. Effect of Static Displacements of the Atoms in Solutions on the Intensity of X-Ray Lines

Experimental investigations have shown (see, for example, 84, 198–203] that static distortions in solutions associated with a difference in atomic radii lead in a number of cases to a weakening of the intensity of the x-ray lines as substantial as that caused by thermal vibrations. In considering this effect theoretically, we must remember two important facts, which lead to a difference in the results obtained for the attenuation factors associated with static and thermal displacements, respectively, and also to the failure of formulas of the (23.2) and (23.3) type in the case of static distortions. First, the factors (16.4) determining the weakening of the scattering amplitude are, generally speaking, different for different atoms (and for lattice points of different types), and are not determined by the mean-square displacements of all the atoms in the crystal, as in (23.3). Secondly, the probability distribution of the static displacements is described, in contrast to the often-expressed view,* not by a Gaussian distribution (as in the case of thermal displacements in the harmonic approximation), but by a more complicated distribution (in some cases by a generalized binomial Poisson distribution). These facts lead to a modification of the formulas for the attenuation or weakening factor [204].

For simplicity, we shall consider mainly disordered solutions with one atom per cell, and in this section we shall only consider static distortions (a simultaneous calculation of thermal and static displacements will be given in §25). Thus the general formulas (16.3) and (16.4) for the structure amplitude and attenuation factors of the scattering amplitudes for the A and B atoms, $\exp(-M_A)$ and $\exp(-M_B)$, take the form

$$f = cf_A \exp(-M_A) + (1-c) f_B \exp(-M_B), \tag{24.1}$$

$$\begin{aligned} \exp(-M_A) &= \overline{\exp(i\mathbf{q}_1 \delta \mathbf{R}_s)}^A, \\ \exp(-M_B) &= \overline{\exp(i\mathbf{q}_1 \delta \mathbf{R}_s)}^B. \end{aligned} \tag{24.2}$$

Instead of M_A and M_B it is convenient to introduce the mean value of these $M = cM_A + (1-c)M_B$ and $c(1-c)$ times their difference $M' = c(1-c) \times (M_A - M_B)$:

$$M_A = M + \frac{1}{c} M', \quad M_B = M - \frac{1}{1-c} M'. \tag{24.3}$$

*In order to justify the application of the Gaussian distribution to static displacements authors sometimes [118] put δR_s in the form of the sum of a large number of displacements created by different defects and refer to the central-limit theorem of the theory of probability. However, for this theorem to be applicable, we must be able to divide the quantity in question into a large number of statistically independent terms. It is also important that no group of terms should be "preferred." This condition requires that the dispersion of the sum should tend to infinity (if the dispersion of the terms is not infinitely small; see, for example, [157]).

We can easily see, however, that the latter condition is not satisfied in the case under consideration, since the displacements of the atoms fall off quite rapidly on moving away from a point defect, so that the role of the closest defects is a "preferred" or dominant one.

Then expression (24.1) will take the form

$$f = e^{-M}\left[cf_A \exp\left(-\frac{M'}{c}\right) + (1-c) f_B \exp\left(\frac{M'}{1-c}\right)\right] \approx$$

$$\approx e^{-M}\left[cf_A + (1-c) f_B - M'(f_A - f_B)\right], \qquad (24.4)$$

where the "approximately equals" sign refers to the frequently satisfied case of small $|M_A - M_B|$. If the atomic factors f_A and f_B are close together and $|M_A - M_B| \ll 1$, or if $|M_A - M_B| \ll M$, we may neglect the difference between M_A and M_B, and the problem of calculating the attenuation factor reduces to calculating the mean value of M (with respect to the A and B atoms).

Let us first consider the simplest case of ideal solutions with one atom per unit cell, in which the lattice constant does not depend on the correlation parameters. Then in expression (8.6) for the Fourier components of the displacements it is permissible to retain only the first term. Transforming by means of formulas (5.1) and (1.7) from the Fourier components $\mathbf{R_k}$ and $c_\mathbf{k}$ to the actual displacements and numbers c_s, we may write down the displacement of the zero atom under consideration from the lattice point lying at the origin of coordinates, $\delta\mathbf{R}_0$ (s = 0), in the form of a sum

$$\delta\mathbf{R}_0 = \sum_s \mathbf{u}_{s0}(c_s - c) = \sum_s \mathbf{u}_s c_s \qquad (24.5)$$

($\mathbf{u}_{s0} = -\mathbf{u}_{-s0}$). Here the quantities $\mathbf{u}_s \equiv \mathbf{u}_{s0}$ determine the difference in the displacements of the atom at the zero lattice point (irrespective of whether this is A or B) on replacing the B atom at the s-th lattice point by an A atom. Since the solution is ideal, the probabilities of zero or unit values of c_s do not depend on whether an A or a B atom lies at the zero lattice point. Hence the probabilities of the displacements (24.5) are the same for the A and B atoms, M_A and M_B are equal ($M_A = M_B = M$), and in determining these quantities from (24.2) we may average over all the lattice points.

In an ideal solution, according to (24.5), $\delta\mathbf{R}_s$ is the sum of statistically independent terms, i.e., the probability of $\delta\mathbf{R}_s$ is described by a generalized binomial distribution. In this case the mean of $\exp(i\mathbf{q}_1\delta\mathbf{R}_0)$ in (24.2) is divided into the product of means corresponding to different terms, and with due allowance for (14.4)

M may be calculated in an elementary way:

$$e^{-M} = \prod_s |ce^{i\mathbf{q}_1\mathbf{u}_s} + (1-c)|,$$
$$M = -\frac{1}{2}\sum_s \ln[1 + 2c(1-c)(\cos\mathbf{q}_1\mathbf{u}_s - 1)]. \qquad (24.6)$$

Formula (24.6) is also valid in weak solutions, for which the assumption that the lattice constant is independent of the correlation parameters is unnecessary. For a fairly small concentration of A atoms, for which $cf_A \ll f_B$, we may neglect the direct contribution of the impurity atoms to the scattering amplitude and consider that the influence of the impurity is only manifested by way of distortions. Thus only the magnitude of M_B is of interest. In the case of small c we may always calculate this by means of formula (24.5) (configurations in which two or more impurity atoms lie close to the lattice point in question do not occur in practice), in which now $\mathbf{u}_s$ means the displacement of the B atom at the zero lattice point caused by introducing an impurity atom into position s (this is not, generally speaking, equal to the displacement of the A atom). In view of this, formula (24.6) is applicable to the calculation of M_B in weak solutions. It is valid, in particular, for interstitial solutions ($cf_A \ll f_B$), although in these the summation over s is carried out not over the lattice points but over the interstices around the atom under consideration.

Formula (24.6) is simplified in various limiting cases. For small concentrations ($c \ll 1$) it takes the following form*

$$M = c\sum_s (1 - \cos\mathbf{q}_1\mathbf{u}_s). \qquad (24.7)$$

In the case of not-very-severely distorted crystals and not-too-large reflection indices (small q_1), we find by expanding (24.6) in powers of $\mathbf{q}_1\mathbf{u}_s$ that

$$2M = c(1-c)\sum_s (\mathbf{q}_1\mathbf{u}_s)^2 - \frac{1}{12}c(1-c)[1 - 6c(1-c)]\sum_s (\mathbf{q}_1\mathbf{u}_s)^4 + \ldots =$$

* This expression agrees with the general formula (14.13) if one remembers that for impurity atoms in (14.13) we only have $\varphi \neq 0$ for t = s when $\mathbf{u}_{ts} \equiv \mathbf{u}_{ss} = 0$.

$$= c(1-c)q_1^2\sum_s u_{sx}^2 - \frac{1}{12}c(1-c)[1-6c(1-c)]\Big[(q_{1x}^4+q_{1y}^4+q_{1z}^4)\times$$

$$\times\sum_s u_{sx}^4 + 6(q_{1x}^2q_{1y}^2 + q_{1x}^2q_{1z}^2 + q_{1y}^2q_{1z}^2)\sum_s u_{sx}^2u_{sy}^2\Big] + \dots \qquad (24.8)$$

The last part of the formula is written for the case of cubic crystals.

For fairly small q_1 and a slightly distorted crystal, it is permissible to retain only the first term in (24.8), so that the expression for 2M

$$2M = \overline{(\mathbf{q}_1\delta\mathbf{R}_0)^2} = c(1-c)\sum_s(\mathbf{q}_1\mathbf{u}_s)^2 \qquad (24.9)$$

agrees with the analogous expression (23.3) for the case of thermal vibrations. The deviation of the probability distribution of the displacements from the Gaussian distribution has no effect on M.

However, in the general case in which the distortions are not small, the fact that the distribution in question is not Gaussian has the result that formulas (24.6) and (24.7) bear no resemblance to (24.9). It is an important point, as may be seen from (24.7) and (24.8), that, in order to satisfy the criterion of "small" distortions, the local distortions in the neighborhood of each defect, and not simply the mean-square displacements, should be small. Even for small concentrations of defect, when M is small, there may be some vary marked deviations from (24.9).

We see from (24.8) that the expression for M contains not only terms quadratic in $\mathbf{u}_s$ but also terms of the fourth and higher powers. The corrections associated with these should lead to a deviation of the graph relating M to q_1^2 from the straight line characteristic of the Debye–Waller factor in ideal crystals. In contrast to the term quadratic in $\mathbf{q}_1$, the fourth-order term depends, even in cubic crystals, not only on the length of the vector $\mathbf{q}_1$ but also in its direction in reciprocal-lattice space. Hence for regular reflections with the same (or almost the same) sum of the squares of the indices, the factor exp(−M) may differ considerably.

For large q_1, expansion (24.8) starts converging slowly. The convergence may be considerably improved if in the sum of (24.6) we separate out the first few coordination spheres and only carry out the expansion with respect to $\mathbf{q}_1\mathbf{u}_s$ for lattice points lying outside these spheres. Then

$$2M = -\sum_s^{(1)} \ln[1 + 2c(1-c)(\cos \mathbf{q}_1\mathbf{u}_s - 1)] + c(1-c)\sum_s^{(2)} (\mathbf{q}_1\mathbf{u}_s)^2 -$$

$$-\frac{1}{12}c(1-c)[1-6c(1-c)]\sum_s^{(2)} (\mathbf{q}_1\mathbf{u}_s)^4 + \ldots, \qquad (24.10)$$

where the indices (1) and (2) attached to the sums mean that the summation is carried out respectively over the points of the separated-out coordination spheres and the points lying outside these spheres. For fairly large $\mathbf{q}_1\mathbf{u}_s$, the first terms in (24.10) may give contributions to the $M : q_1^2$ graph oscillating with increasing q_1.

Let us further consider the asymptotic form of the expression for M in the case of large q_1 values in a severely distorted crystal. For simplicity we shall confine ourselves to the case of small concentrations, for which M is determined by formula (24.7). For a large distance r_s of the point considered from the defect, $\mathbf{u}_s$ is determined by formula (7.2). Let us divide the sum over s into two sums Σ' and Σ'' in such a way that, for the terms in the second sum, the asymptotic law is satisfied for the displacements, and also so that in this sum we may replace summation by integration outside a certain sphere of radius r_1. In the case of fairly large q_1, for which the condition $|C|q_1/r_1^2 \gg 1$ is satisfied, after carrying out the integration we obtain the following asymptotic expression for M:

$$M = c\sum_s{}' (1 - \cos \mathbf{q}_1\mathbf{u}_s) + cYq_1^{3/2} \qquad \left(\frac{|C|q_1}{r_1^2} \gg 1\right), \qquad (24.11)$$

where

$$Y = \frac{\sqrt{2\pi}}{3v}\int \left|\frac{\mathbf{q}_1\mathbf{e}(\mathbf{m})}{q_1}\right|^{3/2} |C(\mathbf{m})|^{3/2}\, d\Omega = \frac{8\pi\sqrt{2\pi}}{15v}|C|^{3/2} \qquad (24.12)$$

[the second expression for Y is valid in the isotropic case for which C does not depend on $\mathbf{m}$ and $\mathbf{e}(\mathbf{m}) = \mathbf{m}$].

Since the first term in (24.11) is limited, for large q_1 the value of M increases asymptotically in proportion to $q_1^{3/2}$ (and not in proportion to q_1^2 as in the case of small q_1). It should be noted that, in homogeneous solutions, for the values of q_1 used in ordinary experiments, this limiting case is not reached. However, it may be reached in the initial stages of aging, when considerable local displacements may develop around the nuclei of the newly formed phase (see Chapter VII).

In order to estimate the extent of the effects associated with deviations from formula (24.9) we may use the model of Huang [102], according to which the displacements are determined on the approximation of an isotropic continuum, i.e., by formula (7.4) in the case of defects with cubic symmetry. Substituting this expression into (24.8) and using the values of the resultant lattice sums calculated for substitution-type solutions in [205], we write M in the form

$$2M = a_1 c(1-c)\left(\frac{1+\sigma}{1-\sigma}\right)^2\left(\frac{1}{v}\frac{\partial v}{\partial c}\right)^2\sum_{i=1}^{3} h_i^2 -$$

$$-10^{-5}c(1-c)[1-6c(1-c)]\left(\frac{1+\sigma}{1-\sigma}\right)^4\left(\frac{1}{v}\frac{\partial v}{\partial c}\right)^4\times$$

$$\times\left[a_2\sum_{i=1}^{3} h_i^4 + a_3\sum_{i<j=1}^{3} h_i^2 h_j^2\right]. \tag{24.13}$$

Here h_i are the Miller indices, and for substitution-type solutions with a face-centered cubic lattice $a_1 = 0.0587$, $a_2 = 0.884$, $a_3 = 2.49$. For a body-centered cubic lattice $a_1 = 0.0932$, $a_2 = 2.04$, $a_3 = 7.04$. It follows from this that for homogeneous substitution-type solutions the corrections to M associated with deviations of the probability distribution of the displacements from a Gaussian distribution are very small. Thus, for example, if $c = 0.1$, $\sigma = 0.3$, and $(1/v)(\partial v/\partial c) = 0.5$ (severely distorted solution), for large reflection indices in a body-centered lattice, the first term in (24.13) equals 0.46, while the second equals 0.0026, about 0.6% of the first. Thus in this case the calculation of M from formula (24.9) is justified.*

*Considerably larger effects in substitution-type solutions may be expected in cases in which the impurity atoms or other defects are collected in groups (for example, in the initial stages of aging or in irradiated crystals). If the number of particles in the group equals n, then for $c \ll 1$ the first term in (24.8) or (24.13) increases as $n^{2/3}$ for large n,

In interstitial solutions, the crystal is usually distorted a great deal around an interstitial atom, and the corrections associated with the deviation of the probability distribution from Gaussian form play a considerably greater part than in solutions of the substitution type. If, for example, the impurity atoms lie in the octahedral pores of a crystal with a face-centered cubic lattice, the constants in (24.13) equal $a_1 = 0.095$, $a_2 = 13.0$, $a_3 = 0.526$. For $c = 0.05$, $\sigma = 0.3$, $(1/v)(\partial v/\partial c) = 1$ (this value approximately corresponds to the relation between the lattice constant of austenite and carbon concentration) for the (800) reflection the first term in (24.13) equals 1.0, while the second equals -0.22. For the (553) reflection, which has almost the same sum of the squares of the indices, the correction is -0.08. Thus for large reflection indices the correction may be 10 to 30% of M and the values of M for reflections with almost equal sums of the squares of the indices (Σh^2) may differ considerably.

These corrections should have a still greater effect in the case in which atoms of the principal element fall into the interstices (in irradiated crystals), or in interstitial solutions with a body-centered cubic lattice (having "tighter" interstices). In such cases, even for low orders of reflection, $\mathbf{q}_1\mathbf{u}_s \sim 1$ for neighboring positions, and the calculation of M must be carried out by means of formula (24.10). For example, in the case of martensite, a calculation of this kind, made on the basis of displacements obtained from the atomic model of the crystal, with $c = 0.045$, led to the following values of M for three (00h) order of reflection: $M_{002} = 0.41$, $M_{004} = 0.56$, $M_{006} = 0.46$ [35]. Thus M does not increase as h_3^2 as indicated by (24.9), but may even fall with increasing h_3. A detailed study of the influence of static displacements on the intensity of the regular reflections in martensite was carried out recently by Moss [437]. The results of this investigation agree with the conclusions of theory [35]. In particular, the experimentally determined displacement of the Fe atoms in the first coordination sphere around an impurity C atom, namely, 0.53 ± 0.03 Å, agrees with the theoretical value obtained in [35], i.e., 0.49 Å.

---

while the second term increases as $n^{4/3}$. Hence, on the formation of such groups, in addition to a general rise in M, there should be sharper deviations from formula (24.9).

In estimating the different terms in M by formula (24.13), the static displacements were determined by means of the obviously coarse approximation of an isotropic continuum. This estimate may be refined by using values of the displacements obtained with due allowance for the atomic structure (see §7). If the displacements are not very large and M is determined by formula (24.9), then in accordance with (7.12) M may be written in the form

$$2M = \frac{1}{3} q_1^2 \overline{(\delta \mathbf{R}_0)^2} = c\,(1-c)\, M^0 \sum_{i=1}^{3} h_i^2. \tag{24.14}$$

An explicit expression for M^0 as a function of $(1/v)(\partial v/\partial c)$ and the elastic moduli is given in [42], and for a number of specific metals with face-centered cubic lattices the values of M^0 are given in Table 1 (p. 83). In substitution-type solutions these values are almost the same as on the approximation of an isotropic continuum (differing by less than 20%), but, in interstitial solutions, allowing for the atomic structure greatly increases M^0 (by a factor of 1.7 in aluminum-base solutions).

The results here presented may easily be generalized to ordered solutions in which correlation may be neglected, i.e., we may consider that in each sublattice the atoms are distributed chaotically (at random). If the lattice constant does not depend on the correlation parameters, the quantities M_γ are identical for the A and B atoms, but generally speaking they differ for different sublattices. Following arguments analogous to those used in deriving (24.6), we easily obtain

$$2M_\gamma = \sum_{\gamma'} \sum_{s} \ln\left[1 + 2c_{\gamma'}(1-c_{\gamma'})(\cos \mathbf{q}_1 \mathbf{u}_{s\gamma'} - 1)\right] \approx$$

$$\approx \sum_{\gamma'} c_{\gamma'}(1-c_{\gamma'}) \sum_{s} (\mathbf{q}_1 \mathbf{u}_{s\gamma'})^2. \tag{24.15}$$

Here $\mathbf{u}_{s\gamma'}$ is the displacement of an atom lying at a point of sublattice γ of the zeroth cell due to the replacement of a B atom by an A atom at the point γ' of the s-th cell, and the second formula is valid for small $|\mathbf{q}_1 \mathbf{u}_{s\gamma'}|$.

We see from (24.15) that M_γ depends greatly on long-range order. If the ordered solution consists of two equivalent sublattices (for example, solutions of the β brass or AuCu type), then in solutions of stoichiometric composition AB the quantities M_γ are identical for both sublattices, and on neglecting the terms $\sim q_1^4$ the formulas for M in ordered solutions only differ from the foregoing formulas for ideal solutions by virtue of addition of a factor $1-\eta^2$.

In solutions of different compositions, and also in the case of nonequivalent sublattices, the M_γ may nevertheless differ considerably. The difference may be illustrated by the example of crystals of the (NaK)Cl type, in which all the points of the first sublattice are filled with identical atoms ($c_1 = 0$), while the points of the second sublattice have a random distribution of two types of atoms with a concentration $c_2 = c$. In this case the constant a_1 in formula (24.13) for M_1 equals $a_1 = 0.0948$, while for M_2 it is $a_1 = 0.0587$ [37]. In an analogous way, in body-centered lattices of the Cs(ClBr) type (or the Fe_3Al type), for M_1 we have $a_1 = 0.0549$ and for M_2 we have $a_1 = 0.0383$. Thus in both cases M_1 is 1.5 times greater than M_2.

Let us now consider the case of solutions in which the correlation is substantial. If we confine ourselves to the case of disordered solutions of the substitution type with one atom per cell and consider that the lattice constant does not depend on correlation, then, as before, the displacements are determined by an additive expression (24.5). The individual terms in this expression, however, are not statistically independent in the presence of correlation, and their probabilities depend on the type of atom considered. In view of this M_A and M_B will generally speaking, be different.

In solutions of the substitution type, as indicated above, the terms $\sim q_1^4$ in M are negligibly small and we may confine attention to the quadratic terms in the expansion of (24.1) with respect to q_1. Here M_A and M_B are determined by formulas (24.3), in which, according to (24.1) and (24.5), M and M' may be written in the form

$$2M = \overline{(\mathbf{q}_1\delta\mathbf{R}_s)^2} = \sum_{s's''} (\mathbf{q}_1\mathbf{u}_{s'})(\mathbf{q}_1\mathbf{u}_{s''})\overline{(c_{s'}-c)(c_{s''}-c)} = \sum_{\mathbf{k}} (\mathbf{q}_1\mathbf{A}_\mathbf{k})^2\overline{|c_\mathbf{k}|^2}, \qquad (24.16)$$

$$2M' = \overline{(c_s-c)(\mathbf{q}_1\delta\mathbf{R}_s)^2} = \sum_{s's''} (\mathbf{q}_1\mathbf{u}_{s'})(\mathbf{q}_1\mathbf{u}_{s''})\overline{(c_0-c)(c_{s'}-c)(c_{s''}-c)} \qquad (24.17)$$

(c_0 corresponds to c_s for $s = 0$).

Since $\mathbf{u}_s = 0$ for s = 0, we see from (24.17) that, in accordance with the foregoing argument, M' = 0 in ideal solutions. For estimating the value of M' in nonideal solutions, let us consider the case of a slightly nonideal state in which we need only allow for correlation between the closest atoms and may neglect terms quadratic with respect to the correlation parameters. Then in the sum of (24.17) we need only retain terms with s' = s". Thus

$$2M' = (1-2c)\,\varepsilon_1 \sum_{s'}{}' (\mathbf{q}_1 \mathbf{u}_{s'})^2, \qquad (24.18)$$

where the summation over s' is carried out for atoms in the first coordination sphere and ε_1 is the correlation parameter for this sphere.

In order to estimate the correlation parameter at high temperatures we may use the formula obtained on the model of pair interaction [206]

$$\varepsilon_1 = -c^2 (1-c)^2 \frac{w}{k_B T},$$

and then we find from (24.18) and (24.9) that

$$|M'| \ll M,$$

i.e., the difference between M_A and M_B may be neglected if

$$c(1-c)\,|1-2c|\,\frac{|w|}{k_B T} \ll 1,$$

i.e., in the case of solutions the concentration of which is either small or close to $c = 1/2$, and also in the case of high temperatures. In the general case of nonideal solutions, however, the value of M' may not be small. We see from (24.4) that, for terms containing M' to stand out clearly in the expression for the scattering amplitude, it is also necessary that the ratio $|f_A - f_B|/f$ should not be small. Owing to the fact that $f_A - f_B$ and $cf_A + (1-c)f_B$, generally speaking, depend in different ways on q_1, the presence of a term containing M' in f may lead to deviations from the linear relationship between the logarithm of the ratio $f[cf_A + (1-c)f_B]^{-1}$ and q_1^2 in weakly distorted crystals also.

Even in ideal solutions, M_A and M_B may differ ($M' \neq 0$) if the lattice constant depends on the correlation parameters. Without stopping to deal with this question here (see [27]), we simply note that the corresponding correction to M' is proportional to $c^2(1-c)^2$ and is not very substantial at low concentrations.

If the atomic factors f_A and f_B are close together, then we see from (24.4) that the difference between M_A and M_B is not very great and the weakening of the intensity is determined by the value of M, i.e., according to (24.16), by the mean-square displacements of the atoms. It follows from (7.11) and (1.13) that in nonideal solutions M is a linear function of the correlation parameters. Estimates show [42] that the establishment of correlation may greatly change the value of M in a disordered alloy, usually increasing it in decomposing solutions and reducing it in ordering solutions.

It follows in particular from the preceding results that, in severely distorted crystals (i.e., in interstitial solutions, in aging alloys, in crystals irradiated with fast particles, and so on) and for large q_1 (i.e., for large scattering angles in hard radiation), there should be considerable deviations from formula (24.9), associated with the difference between the probability distribution of $\delta\mathbf{R}_s$ and the Gaussian distribution. These effects should lead to deviations from a straight line on the graph relating M to q_1^2 and to different values of these deviations for points lying on different straight lines in reciprocal-lattice space.

The deviations from linearity may be small, and over a fairly wide range of scattering angles the graph of M against q_1^2 may be closely approximated by a straight line. However, the slopes of the straight lines will differ for very different ranges of scattering angle or for different wavelengths. This may be seen in particular in Fig. 20 (p. 286), which gives the relation between M and $\sum_{i=1}^{3} h_i^2$ for crystals containing precipitates comprising particles of a newly formed phase. Over a fairly wide range of values of $\sum_{i=1}^{3} h_i^2$, the graph may be approximated by a straight line with only a slight error (no greater than the errors incurred experimentally). However, the slope of this approximating straight line will differ considerably (by several tens of percents) from the slope of the tangent to the curve at the origin of coordinates, which corresponds to regions of small $\sum_{i=1}^{3} h_i^2$ (or soft radiation). On analyzing the experimental data in the usual way by means of formula (24.9), the resultant nonquadratic relationship between M and 1/λ, will appear as a relationship between the mean-square displacements and the wavelength.

This effect has actually been observed in several investigations; in accordance with (24.8), the mean-square displacements proved to be smaller for harder radiation. Also in accordance with theory, a nonquadratic relation between M and 1/λ [described as a relation between $\overline{(\delta \mathbf{R}_S)^2}$ and 1/λ] was observed in precisely those cases for which the local distortions were large (for example, in martensite [207] or in an aging Fe–Nb alloy containing Nb 0.8%, this concentration being greater than the limit of solubility at room temperature [178]).

§25. Effect of Thermal Vibrations in Solid Solutions on the Intensity of X-Ray Lines

The nonideal state of a crystal not only leads to additional weakening of the x-ray line intensity as a result of static distortions but also modifies the expression for the Debye–Waller attenuation factor associated with thermal vibrations.

Certain special features of the Debye–Waller factor arise in the case of nonideal crystals (for example, in solutions); these are attributable to the difference in the mean-square thermal displacements relating to different atoms of a given type (lying at different distances from the defect), which leads to deviations from the Gaussian probability distribution of the thermal displacements (of any atom not specified in advance), even in the harmonic approximation. The effects due to static and thermal displacements are, generally speaking, not independent, and may be considered together. Let us consider these effects first in the simplest case of weak, disordered solutions with one atom per unit cell (the more general case is discussed in [209]).

As in the case of static displacements, the attenuation factor $\exp(-M_B)$ for the B atoms is determined by a formula of the (24.2) type:

$$\exp(-M_B) = \overline{\langle \exp(i\mathbf{q}_1 \delta \mathbf{R}_s) \rangle}^{B}. \tag{25.1}$$

However, $\delta \mathbf{R}_S$ is now the sum of the static displacement $\delta \mathbf{R}_S^S$ (the deviation of the equilibrium position for the vibrations of the atom from the point of the "average" lattice) and the thermal displacement $\mathbf{u}_S^T$, which is reckoned from this equilibrium position:

$$\delta \mathbf{R}_s = \delta \mathbf{R}_s^S + \mathbf{u}_s^T, \tag{25.2}$$

while the averaging in (25.1) is carried out both over the thermal vibrations (mean <...>) and over the different B atoms in the crystal, or else over the configurations of the defects around a given B atom (this averaging is indicated by a stroke).

Let us first carry out the averaging over the thermal vibrations. Since the thermal displacement $\mathbf{u}_S^T$ in a solution, as in an ideal crystal, may be expressed in the form of a sum of terms corresponding to individual normal coordinates, the probability distribution of these displacements for each given atom in the harmonic approximation is Gaussian and is determined by a formula of the (23.1) type. However, the mean value of $\langle(\mathbf{q}_1\mathbf{u}_S^T)^2\rangle$ in the solid solution, in contrast to the ideal crystal, depends on the number s of the B atom considered (i.e., on the distance to the defect). (It is precisely because of this that the probabilities of the thermal displacements of any atom not specified in advance do not obey the Gaussian distribution, although for each individual atom the probability distribution of these displacements is Gaussian.) Remembering (25.2) and averaging over the thermal vibrations in (25.1) by means of this Gaussian probability distribution, we immediately obtain

$$\exp(-M_B) = \overline{\exp\left[i\mathbf{q}_1\delta \mathbf{R}_s^S - \frac{1}{2}\langle(\mathbf{q}_1\mathbf{u}_s^T)^2\rangle\right]}. \tag{25.3}$$

In the present case of small concentrations, for which we may neglect configurations in which two or more impurity atoms lie near a given lattice point, the static displacements $\delta \mathbf{R}_S^S$ may be written in the form of a sum (24.5), while the mean squares of the thermal displacements of the B atom at the zero point may be written as an analogous sum

$$\langle(\mathbf{q}_1\mathbf{u}_0^T)^2\rangle = \overline{(\mathbf{q}_1\mathbf{u}_s^T)^2}^B + \sum_{s'} \Delta\,(\mathbf{q}_1\mathbf{v}_{s'})^2\,(c_{s'} - c). \tag{25.4}$$

Here $\overline{(\mathbf{q}_1\mathbf{u}_s^T)^2}^B$ is given by the mean-square thermal displacements of all the B atoms, while $a\Delta\,(\mathbf{q}_1\mathbf{v}_{s'})^2$ gives the change in the mean square $\langle(\mathbf{q}_1\mathbf{u}_0^T)^2\rangle$ for the thermal displacement of the B atom at the zero point when an impurity atom appears at the point s'.

Since in weak solutions the impurity atoms may be regarded as distributed at random over the lattice points, the average (25.3) may be calculated, after allowing for (24.5) and (25.4), in the same way as in the derivation of formula (24.6), by dividing the exponential into the product of statistically independent factors. Expanding the resultant expression for M_B in powers of c and retaining only the linear terms of the expansion, we may write M_B in the form

$$M_B = \frac{1}{2}\,\overline{(\mathbf{q}_1\mathbf{u}_s^T)^2}^B + c\sum_{s'}\left[1 - \cos(\mathbf{q}_1\mathbf{u}_{s'})\exp\left\{-\frac{1}{2}\Delta\,(\mathbf{q}_1\mathbf{v}_{s'})^2\right\} - \frac{1}{2}\Delta\,(\mathbf{q}_1\mathbf{v}_{s'})^2\right]. \tag{25.5}$$

An analogous formula also holds for M_A.

In the case of not-very-severely-distorted crystals and small q_1, expression (25.5) may be expanded in series in powers of $\mathbf{q}_1$, and attention may be confined to the first terms in the expansion:

$$2M_B = \overline{(\mathbf{q}_1\mathbf{u}_s^T)^2}^B + c\sum_{s'}(\mathbf{q}_1\mathbf{u}_s)^2 - \frac{1}{12}c\sum_{s'}(\mathbf{q}_1\mathbf{u}_s)^4 - $$

$$- \frac{1}{4}c\sum_{s'}[\Delta\,(\mathbf{q}_1\mathbf{v}_{s'})^2]^2 - \frac{1}{2}c\sum_{s'}(\mathbf{q}_1\mathbf{u}_{s'})^2\,\Delta\,(\mathbf{q}_1\mathbf{v}_{s'})^2. \tag{25.6}$$

In the more general case, in which $\Delta\,(\mathbf{q}_1\mathbf{v}_{s'})^2$ are small (so that we may discard $[\Delta\,(\mathbf{q}_1\mathbf{v}_{s'})^2]^2$), but $\mathbf{q}_1\mathbf{u}_{s'}$ may have an arbitrary magnitude, the following expression holds for M_B:

$$M_B = \frac{1}{2}\,\overline{(\mathbf{q}_1\mathbf{u}_s^T)^2}^B + c\sum_{s'}(1 - \cos\mathbf{q}_1\mathbf{u}_{s'})\left[1 - \frac{1}{2}\Delta\,(\mathbf{q}_1\mathbf{v}_{s'})^2\right]. \tag{25.7}$$

It follows from the formulas presented that, in contrast to ideal crystals, M_B is (generally speaking) not proportional to q_1^2 even in the harmonic approximation, and is not simply determined by the mean-square displacements of the atoms. Only the first terms in the expansion of (25.6) are proportional to q_1^2. The third, fourth, and fifth terms in this expansion, respectively, associated with static displacements, thermal displacements, and product of the squares of the static and thermal displacements, are functions of the fourth order with respect to $\mathbf{q}_1$ and the displacements, and are due to deviations from the Gaussian probability distribution.

Just as in the case of static displacements, these terms should lead to deviations from the straight line on the graph relating M to q_1^2, and a difference should arise between the values of M corresponding to almost identical $\sum_{i=1}^{3} h_i^2$ in cubic crystals. At high temperatures ($T > \theta$), the fourth term in (25.6) is proportional to T^2, and corresponding effects (associated with thermal vibrations in the solutions) appear at high temperatures. The last term in (25.6), like the first, is proportional to T for $T > \theta$. The presence of this term is responsible for the nonadditive contributions of the static and thermal displacements to M.

These effects (the nonquadratic dependence of M on $\mathbf{q}_1$ and the nonadditive effects of the static and thermal displacements), which are associated with the non-Gaussian probability distribution, should appear in the case of large local distortions in the crystals, i.e., large values of $\mathbf{q}_1\mathbf{u}_{S'}$ and $\Delta(\mathbf{q}_1\mathbf{v}_{S'})^2$. As mentioned earlier in §24, the occurrence of such effects may be expected in interstitial solutions, in crystals subjected to irradiation, and in aging alloys in the initial stages of aging.

The variations in $\Delta(\mathbf{q}_1\mathbf{v}_{S'})^2$ near defects at $T > \theta$ may clearly be determined most conveniently by the method mentioned in §23 of reducing the dynamic problem to a static one. Without considering this problem in detail here (see [209]), we simply note that at large distances from a point defect $\Delta(\mathbf{q}_1\mathbf{v}_{S'})^2$ falls off rapidly, as the inverse fourth power of the distance. We also note that (as may quite easily be shown), when impurity atoms unite into groups of n atoms within a homogeneous solution, the third term in (25.6) rises as $n^{4/3}$, and the second and last as $n^{2/3}$. Hence, when groups of atoms are formed, we should observe, in particular, an increase in the effect associated with the nonadditive contribution of the static and thermal displacements to M.

In describing the results of an experimental investigation into the weakening of the intensities of x-ray lines, it is customary to use a formula derived on the assumption of a Gaussian distribution of displacement probabilities, i.e., only the first two terms in (25.6) are considered. The temperature-independent part of M is associated with static displacements, while the temperature-dependent part is described by the Debye function (23.6) and the effective Debye temperature θ is determined. The third term in (25.6), as already mentioned in §24, leads in the case of severely distorted crystals to a dependence of the static displacements so determined on the wavelength λ, while the fourth term may cause the θ determined by this method to depend on λ and T [the effects associated with this term will only appear when the force constants associated with atoms of different sorts differ considerably, i.e., for large $\Delta(\mathbf{q}_1\mathbf{v}_{s'})^2$; in weak solutions they are numerically quite small]. Finally, the fifth term in (25.6) may lead to a considerable apparent change in θ when static distortions occur (this change will depend greatly on the radiation employed).

The latter effect may appear, in particular, after the union of impurity atoms into groups, when (as already mentioned) the magnitude of the fifth term in (25.6) will increase considerably, leading to a sharp change in the value of θ determined by the method in question for a slight change in the constants of interatomic interaction (elastic moduli). It is not impossible that the sharp change in θ (tens of percents) observed in a number of cases [210] during the annealing of plastically deformed (worked) or quenched alloys for slight changes of elastic moduli (about 1%) may be due to precisely this last term in (25.6) [or (25.7)], the contribution of which increases sharply when groups of atoms are formed, i.e., when a high degree of short-range order (disrupted by plastic deformation) is reestablished.

We also note that, as a result of anharmonicity, the equilibrium positions of the atoms around defects, i.e., distortions, also in general depend on the temperature. The associated temperature dependence of the second term (25.6) may clearly lead to certain errors in the x-ray determination of θ in solutions [211, 212].

The results given in this section relate to weak solutions. Of no less interest is the study of the Debye–Waller factor in concentrated solutions, especially in view of the fact that, in a number of papers (see, for example, [202, 210, 213–216]), experimental workers have observed that, in various alloys, composition and order have a considerable influence on the intensity of the x-ray lines. In essence this effect is associated with the change in the frequencies and amplitudes of normal vibrations on increasing the concentration and redistributing the atoms over the lattice points. The change in the vibration spectrum is due to the difference in the masses of the atoms and the force constants of interatomic interaction. The character of the normal vibrations in nonideal crystals is extremely complicated [217, 218], and they may only be calculated in concentrated solutions for slight differences in the masses of the atoms and the force constants (by using perturbation theory).

Remembering that in many solutions the masses of the atoms differ much more than the force constants, we may follow [219] in considering the mean squares of the thermal vibrations and the Debye–Waller factor in solutions by confining attention to terms linear with respect to the force constants and quadratic with respect to the mass differences inclusively. This approximation enables us, in particular, to allow for the effect of fluctuational inhomogeneities of concentration in solutions, which make a contribution to the mean-square displacements of the same order of magnitude as the whole effect associated with the establishment of order in the solution.*

Let us here confine ourselves to the case in which the static distortions are fairly small, so that terms in the expression for M associated with both static and thermal displacements [the last term in (25.6)] may be neglected, and the contribution of the static and thermal displacements to M is additive. We shall only consider effects associated with thermal vibrations, considering that the terms in M due to static displacements are small or that the corresponding attenuation factors are included in f_A and f_B. Then, denoting the attenuation factors of the scattering amplitudes associated with thermal vibrations only by $\exp(-M_A)$ and $\exp(-M_B)$, we may write down the expression for the structure amplitude of a

*In view of this the approximation taken is more accurate than the "average-atom method" [220, 188], in which the solid solution is replaced by a completely ordered crystal, with masses equal to the average masses for each sublattice. The latter approximation only enables us to calculate to an accuracy of terms linear with respect to the mass differences, and prevents us from consistently considering the influence of order on $\langle \overline{\mathbf{u}^2} \rangle$ in solutions with different masses.

disordered solution, analogous to (24.1), in the form

$$f = f_{av}e^{-M} = cf_A e^{-M_A} + (1-c) f_B e^{-M_B} = \overline{[c_s f_A + (1-c_s) f_B] \langle \exp (i\mathbf{q}_1 \mathbf{u}_s^{\mathrm{T}}) \rangle}. \tag{25.8}$$

Here

$$f_{av} = cf_A + (1-c) f_B.$$

In calculating the averages over the thermal vibrations in (25.8) we may avoid the rather complicated calculations of the frequencies and amplitudes of the normal vibrations in a nonideal crystal by representing the corresponding mean as the spur of some operator and calculating it by means of perturbation theory [219]. By way of zero approximation, we may take a crystal with average force constants and an average reciprocal mass

$$m^{-1} = cm_A^{-1} + (1-c)\, m_B^{-1}$$

(m_A and m_B are the masses of the A and B atoms). The result of such a calculation of M (to an accuracy of terms of the order of $\sim (m_A - m_B/m)^2$ and $(f_A - f_B/f)$ inclusively in an ideal, disordered solution at T = 0 may be put in the form of a sum

$$M = M^0 + M' + M''. \tag{25.9}$$

Here M^0 is given by formula (23.5) with T = 0 (and with the values of m indicated above), and corresponds to the ideal crystal of the zero approximation; the term M' equals

$$M' = -\frac{\hbar}{8N^2} \frac{m (m_A - m_B)^2}{m_A^2 m_B^2} c(1-c) \sum_{\mathbf{k}n\mathbf{k}'n'n''} (\mathbf{q}_1 \mathbf{e}_{\mathbf{k}n}^*)(\mathbf{q}_1 \mathbf{e}_{\mathbf{k}n''})(\mathbf{e}_{\mathbf{k}n}\mathbf{e}_{\mathbf{k}'n'}) \times$$

$$\times (\mathbf{e}_{\mathbf{k}'n'}\mathbf{e}_{\mathbf{k}n''}^*) \left[\frac{2\omega_{\mathbf{k}'n'}}{(\omega_{\mathbf{k}n''} + \omega_{\mathbf{k}'n'})(\omega_{\mathbf{k}n} + \omega_{\mathbf{k}n''})} - \frac{\omega_{\mathbf{k}'n'}}{(\omega_{\mathbf{k}'n'} + \omega_{\mathbf{k}n})(\omega_{\mathbf{k}'n'} + \omega_{\mathbf{k}n''})} \right] -$$

$$-\frac{\hbar}{4N^2} \frac{f_A - f_B}{f_{cp}} \frac{m_A - m_B}{m_A m_B} c(1-c) \times$$

$$\times \sum_{\mathbf{k}n\mathbf{k}'n'} (\mathbf{q}_1 \mathbf{e}_{\mathbf{k}n}^*)(\mathbf{q}_1 \mathbf{e}_{\mathbf{k}'n'})(\mathbf{e}_{\mathbf{k}n}\mathbf{e}_{\mathbf{k}'n'}^*) \frac{1}{\omega_{\mathbf{k}n} + \omega_{\mathbf{k}'n'}}. \tag{25.10}$$

The term M", in contrast to M^0 and M', is proportional to q_1^4 and not q_1^2.

At high temperatures, higher than the Debye value ($T > \theta$), for which we may neglect quantum effects, M' and M" vanish. The Debye–Waller factor in this case does not in general depend on the masses of the atoms but is determined simply by the force constants. If the force constants for different pairs of atoms are the same, then any change in composition and order in the solution at $T > \theta$ leaves M unaltered. This result is an obvious consequence of classical statistics in which the probabilities of the displacements and momenta are statistically independent, i.e., the probabilities of the displacements and their mean squares are independent of the masses.

In order to estimate M' for T = 0 we may, for example, calculate the sums (25.10) in the approximation of an elastically isotropic continuum. Considering that the velocity of longitudinal vibrations is twice that of transverse vibrations and that

$$\frac{f_A - f_B}{f_{av}} \approx \frac{m_A - m_B}{m} = \varepsilon,$$

we thus find that

$$\frac{M'}{M^0} \approx -0.6c(1-c)\varepsilon^2.$$

If as zero approximation we take a crystal consisting of identical atoms with mass $m = cm_A + (1-c)m_B$, and not with the mean reciprocal mass as taken above, the expression for the correction M' changes [in accordance with the change in the value M^0 defined in (23.5)], and for the example given

$$\frac{M'}{M^0} \approx -0.1c(1-c)\varepsilon^2.$$

For example, with $c \sim 1/2$, $\varepsilon \sim 1$ the correction M'/M^0 is about 15% for the first choice of m and about 2.5% for the second. As a result of this, the value of θ at low temperatures will be rather lower than in an ideal crystal with the same force constants and average mass (or reciprocal mass). At high temperatures this difference in θ vanishes, so that we find an additional reason for the fall in θ with temperature in the solution.

An extremely coarse estimate of M" (see [219]) shows that in a cubic crystal at T = 0

$$M'' \sim 0.1c\,(1-c)\,\varepsilon^2\,(M^0)^2$$

for reflections of the (h00) type, and it may be considerably larger for reflections of other types. This correction is proportional to q_1^4 and can only become large for high reflection indices.

Without here considering the question as to the influence of correlation and long-range order on the Debye–Waller factor (see [219]), we simply note that, in the case in which these effects are associated with different masses of the atoms (the force constants for pairs of atoms of different sorts being the same), they can only appear at low temperatures ($T \ll \theta$). At high temperatures a change in the short- and long-range order should not affect M.

In view of this, if order has no effect on the force constants, then the increase observed experimentally in a number of cases in the difference between the values of M corresponding to room temperature and low temperature, respectively [213–215], is associated not with a reduction in θ for the whole temperature range, but with the fact that at low temperature M falls on ordering (θ increases), while at high temperature M remains unaltered. Clearly, however, an important part in these experiments is played by the change in the force constants, which leads to a change in θ at any temperature. The effects attributable to differences in masses and force constants, respectively, could be separated by measuring M and θ in ordered and disordered solutions at different temperatures, including very low values [$T < (\theta/5)$].

Chapter VII

Scattering of X Rays by Severely Distorted Crystals

§26. Asymptote of the Scattering-Intensity Distribution in the Case of Strong Coulomb Fields of Displacements

Around impurity atoms or other spatially limited defects, fields of static displacements arise; these fall off on an anisotropic Coulomb law (7.2) on moving away to large distances from the defects. The scattering of x rays at this kind of distortion was considered in §18 for the case in which the displacements created by the defects were not very large, so that it was permissible to expand the expression for the scattering intensity in powers of the displacements and confine attention to the first terms in the expansion. This approximation is applicable for weakly distorted crystals provided that criterion (16.8) is satisfied.

As the distortions increase [for example, as the constant C in (7.2) becomes greater], the higher terms in the expansion in powers of the displacements start playing a more important part, so that when criterion (16.8) is no longer satisfied, but rather reversed in the form of

$$M \gg 1 \tag{26.1}$$

(here M is only associated with the static distortions), we must use a different approach in order to study the scattering-intensity distribution. The character of the distribution in fact changes qualitatively as compared with the case considered in §16. It is clearly interesting to study the intensity distribution in the limiting case of severely distorted crystals also. Although, as indicated by the results presented in §24, the criterion (26.1) is not satisfied in homogeneous solid solutions, the study of severely distorted crystals is not simply of academic interest, since severely distorted crystals in the sense in question may arise, for example, in aging alloys at the initial stages of aging or in crystals containing dislocation loops.

Let us first of all follow [221] in considering the asymptotic intensity distribution in the simplest case of defects in elastically isotropic crystals, where at distances greater than r_0 these defects create spherically symmetric Coulomb fields of displacements of the (7.2) type:

$$\mathbf{u}_{ts} = \delta\mathbf{R}_s = C\frac{\mathbf{r}_{ts}}{r_{ts}^3} \quad \text{for} \quad r_{ts} > r_0, \tag{26.2}$$

where $\mathbf{r}_{ts}$ is a vector drawn from the defect (lying at position t) to the s-th atom under consideration, and the constant C is independent of the direction. For $\mathbf{r}_{ts} < r_0$ the displacements may change in a more complicated way. In addition to the displacements (26.2), the defects in question also produce a homogeneous deformation of the lattice as a result of "image forces" (see p. 81); this deformation, however, may most simply be taken into account by regarding the crystal homogeneously deformed in this manner as representing the original ideal crystal (with lattice vectors $\mathbf{R}_s^0$).

We shall consider that the defect concentration c is small and that the defects are distributed at random through the crystal. For small defect concentrations, it follows from the results of §24 that condition (26.1) may only be satisfied for large values of the constant C in (26.2), for which the local distortions around each defect are large and M is determined by the second term in (24.11) ($M \sim q_1^{3/2}$). The model of severely distorted crystals in question thus corresponds to the asymptotic case of large $|C|$.

If condition (26.1) is satisfied, the intensity of the regular reflections $I_0 \sim \exp(-2M)$ becomes exponentially small. The terms proportional to q^{-2} and q^{-1} considered in §18 in the expression for the diffuse-scattering intensity, which tend to infinity on approaching a reciprocal-lattice point, also fall off as exp (−2M) [or as exp (−M)] [according to (16.3) the structure amplitude f in the formulas of §18 includes a factor of the exp (−M) type]. However, since the total intensity of the regular reflections plus the diffuse scattering should remain unaltered with increasing |C|, the total intensity of the diffuse scattering will increase sharply and there will be a qualitative redistribution in scattering intensity.

In order to study scattering by severely distorted crystals with a random distribution of defects, we use the method set out in §14, which is not based on any expansion in powers of the displacements. Since the intensity I_0 is in this case exponentially small, our main interest lies in studying the I_1 given by formula (14.17). Since in this section we are considering a model problem, in which the defects only produce static displacements and have no effect on the structure amplitudes of neighboring cells, in this formula we put $\varphi_{ts} = 0$. For $q \neq 0$, in the limit of an infinite crystal, the sum over s and s' represented by the second term in (14.17) vanishes (in a finite crystal it may be neglected for $q \gg 1/\Lambda$). Then, remembering (14.9) and (14.6), we may rewrite expression (14.17) for I_1 in the form

$$I_1 = f^2 \sum_{s,\, s'} e^{i\mathbf{q}_1 (\mathbf{R}_s^0 - \mathbf{R}_{s'}^0)} e^{-T},$$

$$T = c \sum_t \{1 - \exp[i\mathbf{q}_1 (\mathbf{u}_{ts} - \mathbf{u}_{ts'})]\}, \tag{26.3}$$

where $\mathbf{u}_{ts}$ is given by formula (26.2).

In calculating expression (26.3) for I_1 we must remember that, for large values of the modulus of the vector $\mathbf{R}_{ss'} = \mathbf{R}_s^0 - \mathbf{R}_{s'}^0$, exp (−T) tends [according to (14.11) to the exponentially small limiting value of exp (−2M). Hence in the summation over s and s' in (26.3) the main contribution is given by terms corresponding to small $R_{ss'}$. In order to determine T in this region, we expand $\mathbf{q}_1 (\mathbf{u}_{ts} - \mathbf{u}_{ts'})$ [with due allowance for (26.2)] in series in powers of $\mathbf{R}_{ss'}$ and confine attention to cubic terms of the expansion:

$$\mathbf{q}_1 (\mathbf{u}_{ts} - \mathbf{u}_{ts'}) = \frac{3Cq_1R_{ss'}}{r^3} \psi_1 + \frac{Cq_1R_{ss'}^3}{8r^5} \psi_2 \quad (r \gg r_0), \tag{26.4}$$

$$\psi_1 = \frac{1}{3}\cos\gamma_1 - \cos\theta\cos\chi,$$

$$\psi_2 = 15\cos\theta\cos\chi - 35\cos^3\theta\cos\chi - 3\cos\gamma_1 + 15\cos^2\theta\cos\gamma_1.$$

Here $\mathbf{r}$ is a vector drawn to position t from a point lying halfway between s and s'; θ, χ, and γ_1 are the angles between $\mathbf{r}$ and $\mathbf{R}_{ss'}$, $\mathbf{q}_1$ and $\mathbf{r}$, and $\mathbf{q}_1$ and $\mathbf{R}_{ss'}$, respectively.

It should be noted that expansion (26.4) is only applicable if the position t is a fair distance from the points s and s' (at a distance much greater than $R_{ss'}$ and r_0), and it becomes invalid over small regions near the points s and s' for which

$$|\mathbf{R}_t - \mathbf{R}_s^0| \lesssim R_{ss'},\ r_0 \text{ or } |\mathbf{R}_t - \mathbf{R}_{s'}^0| \lesssim R_{ss'},\ r_0.$$

These regions, however, give a small contribution $\sim cR_{ss'}^3/v$ or $\sim cr_0^3/v$, and in the approximation of large M considered this may be neglected (see below).

The sum over t in (26.3) may be replaced by an integral over $\mathbf{r}$, (multiplied by 1/v; here it is considered that there is only one position t in the cell). Carrying out the integration in spherical coordinates [it is convenient, for given values of the angular coordinates, to transform from variable r to variable $\mathbf{q}_1(\mathbf{u}_{ts} - \mathbf{u}_{ts'})$], and again neglecting terms $\sim cR_{ss'}^3/v$, for not too small values of $R_{ss'}$ we easily obtain the following expression for T

$$T = BR_{ss'}\varphi_1(\gamma_1) + 1.5\cdot 10^{-2}(BR_{ss'})^{1/3}R_{ss'}^2 v^{-2/3}c^{2/3} \times \left[\varphi_2(\gamma_1) - i\frac{C}{|C|}\varphi_3(\gamma_1)\right],$$

$$\frac{|C| q_1 R_{ss'}}{r_0^3} \gg 1, \tag{26.5}$$

$$B = \frac{\pi}{2}\frac{c|C|q_1}{v},$$

$$\varphi_1(\gamma_1) = \int |\psi_1|\, d\Omega,$$

$$\varphi_2(\gamma_1) = \int \frac{\psi_2}{\psi_1}|\psi_1|^{1/3}\, d\Omega, \quad \varphi_3(\gamma_1) = \frac{1}{\sqrt{3}}\int \psi_2\psi_1^{-2/3}\, d\Omega$$

($d\Omega = \sin\theta\, d\theta\, d\varphi$ is an element of solid angle).

For small $R_{ss'}$ it is permissible to retain only the first term in (26.5). Substituting this approximate expression for T in (26.3) and passing from a sum over s and s' to an integral, we write I_1 in the form

$$I_1 = \frac{N}{v} f^2 \int d\mathbf{R}_{ss'} \exp(i\mathbf{q}'\mathbf{R}_{ss'}) \exp[-BR_{ss'}\varphi_1(\gamma_1)], \tag{26.6}$$

where $\mathbf{q}' = \mathbf{q}_1 - 2\pi\mathbf{K}_n^0$, $\mathbf{K}_n^0$ is a vector of the reciprocal lattice of the crystal homogeneously deformed by "image forces" (the closest to $\mathbf{q}_1/2\pi$). In (26.6) we have discarded the exponentially small terms $\sim \exp(-2M)$, including terms proportional to $q^{-2}\exp(-2M)$, which are associated with large values of $R_{ss'}$ in the integral, where the approximate expression (26.5) for T ceases to be valid and T is close to the limiting value of 2M.

For small q' ($q' \lesssim B$) the main part in integral (26.6) is played by the range of values $R_{ss'} \lesssim B^{-1}$. The terms discarded above when calculating T, i.e., terms $\sim cR_{ss'}^3/v$, are according to (24.11) and (24.12) of the order of $1/M^2$ in this region and according to (26.1) need not in fact be considered in this approximation. For $M \gg 1$ we may also omit [in the same way as in (26.6)] the second term in formula (26.6) for T, which for $BR_{ss'} \sim 1$ is $M^{4/3}$ times smaller than the first term (the corrections associated with this term are discussed below).

Expression (26.5) for T ceases to be valid not only for large but also for very small $R_{ss'}$ on account of the fact that, for $r_{ts} < r_0$, the expression (26.2) relating $\mathbf{u}_{ts}$ to distance is infringed. Such deviations from formula (26.5) will appear for $|C| q_1 R_{ss'} \lesssim r_0^3$. For small q' ($q' \lesssim B$), for which the region $R_{ss'} \lesssim B^{-1}$ in (26.6) is important, the change in the expression for T in the region of small $R_{ss'} \lesssim r_0^3/(|C| q_1)$ may be neglected if

$$c\frac{r_0^3}{v} \ll 1. \tag{26.7}$$

This condition is always satisfied for small enough concentrations. However, for fairly large q' ($q' \gg B$), integral (26.6) is determined by the region of small $R_{ss'}$ ($R_{ss'} \lesssim q'^{-1}$), in which the above-mentioned deviations from formula (26.5) for T have an appreciable effect. Hence expression (26.6) for I_1 will only be valid for not-too-large values of q', for which the condition

$$q' \ll \frac{|C|\, q_1}{r_0^3} \sim B\left(c\,\frac{r_0^3}{v}\right)^{-1} \qquad (26.8)$$

is satisfied. For small concentrations, when condition (26.7) is satisfied, this range of q' values is quite large and embraces the whole region of appreciable intensity I_1.

It is not hard to study the general character of the intensity distribution (26.6) given in integral form. According to (26.6), the intensity $I_1(\mathbf{q}_1/2\pi)$ takes a maximum value for $\mathbf{q}' = 0$, i.e., at the reciprocal-lattice points of the crystal deformed by "image" forces only. It is easy to show that a comparatively narrow bell-shaped intensity distribution is formed around each point, reminiscent of a diffuse regular reflection.

The integral intensity of the distribution $I_1(\mathbf{q}_1)$ around the extremum point $\mathbf{q}_1 = 2\pi\mathbf{K}_n^0$ is in fact equal to $8\pi^3(N/v)f^2(1-e^{-2M})$, as it should be, and is approximately the same as in a crystal containing no defects [see (13.13)]. The value of the intensity at the maximum point with $\mathbf{q}' = 0$ is determined from (26.6) by numerical calculation of the function $\varphi_1(\gamma_1)$ and numerical integration:

$$I_1^{\max} = \frac{2Nf^2}{vB^3}\int \varphi_1^{-3}(\gamma_1)\, d\Omega = 0.51\,\frac{Nf^2}{vB^3}.$$

It follows from this that the integral half-width $2q_i$, defined as the width of the distribution enclosed within a sphere of radius q_i, with constant intensity $I_1^{\max}$ and the same integral intensity as that of the distribution under consideration, equals

$$2q_i = 9.6B. \qquad (26.9)$$

According to (26.5), (24.11), and (24.12), the quantity B may be related to M:

$$B = \frac{30^{2/3}}{16}\left(\frac{cM^2}{v}\right)^{1/3} = 0.60\left(\frac{cM^2}{v}\right)^{1/3}, \qquad (26.10)$$

for example, for $M = 10$, $c = 10^{-8}$ we have $B = 6\cdot10^{-3}\,v^{-1/3}$ and $2q_i = 9\cdot10^{-3}\,(2\pi/v^{1/3})$.

Here the distribution $I_1(\mathbf{q}_1/2\pi)$ occupies a small part of the reciprocal-lattice cell and in an experimental study may be interpreted as a broadened Bragg distribution. For larger q', for which $q' \gg q_i$ (but $q' \ll q_i[c(r_0^3/v)^{-1}]$,

$$I_1 = \frac{4\pi N f^2 B}{v q'^4} \overline{\varphi_1(\gamma_1)},$$

where $\overline{\varphi_1(\gamma_1)}$ is the average value of $\varphi_1(\gamma_1)$ in a plane perpendicular to $\mathbf{q}'$, i.e., I_1 falls as $1/q'^4$. Since $\overline{\varphi_1(\gamma_1)} = 8/3$ for $\mathbf{q}' \| \mathbf{q}_1$ and $\overline{\varphi_1(\gamma_1)} = 3.10$ for $\mathbf{q}' \perp \mathbf{q}_1$, the intensity distribution is very slightly compressed in the $\mathbf{q}_1$ direction.

For small scattering angles (i.e., for the zero point of the reciprocal lattice), condition (26.1) is not satisfied and the diffuse scattering intensity is determined from the formulas of §18, as in weakly distorted crystals.

In weakly distorted crystals I_1 describes diffuse scattering with intensity distributed over the whole cell of the reciprocal lattice. It follows from the results presented that, as the distortions (26.2) created by individual defects increase, the diffuse-scattering intensity distribution undergoes a qualitative modification, and for small defect concentrations it contracts into narrow bell-shaped peaks (in the case of high concentrations of strong Coulomb defects, which are never found in practice, the value of B might, according to (26.5), be large, and the width of the distribution (26.9) might be comparable with the size of the reciprocal-lattice cell).

These bell-shaped distributions are not connected directly with regular Bragg reflections.* Their intensity maxima lie at the points $\mathbf{q}' = 0$ and correspond to a lattice distorted by "image forces" but not by localized displacements. The maxima for the regular reflections, however, lie at points $\mathbf{q} = 0$ and correspond to the "average" lattice of a crystal containing defects and also deformed by local distortions. In elastically isotropic crystals, in particular, it follows from the results of [102] that

$$\mathbf{q} = \mathbf{q}' + \frac{4\pi}{3} \frac{cC}{v} \mathbf{q}_1,$$

*Whereas Bragg reflections arise as a result of correlation at infinity in an (on average) periodic structure and correspond to terms with $R_{ss'} \to \infty$ in the sum of (26.3), for the bell-shaped distributions in question, correlation at large but finite distances $R_{ss'} \sim 1/B$ plays an important part.

i.e., the maxima corresponding to the broadened intensity distributions in severely distorted crystals are displaced relative to the Bragg maxima by a distance of the order of the broadening itself. As a result of this, if the broadened distribution is described as a "quasi-line" on the x-ray diffraction picture, the corresponding x-ray-diffraction value of the lattice constant will differ from the dilatometric value.

In addition to the bell-shaped intensity distribution I_1 for $\mathbf{q}' = 0$, we may also in principle have Bragg distributions I_0 for $\mathbf{q}=0$, with an exponentially small integral intensity [exp (2M) times smaller than I_1], and with a width $\sim 2\pi/\Lambda$ determined by the dimensions of the crystallites Λ.

The intensity distribution (26.6) in reciprocal-lattice space, after averaging over the orientations of the crystals, leads to a simple scattering-intensity distribution in the Debye photograph I_{1D}. Carrying out this averaging in accordance with formula (12.9) and allowing for (13.15), we easily find that the distribution I_{1D} is described by a Lorentz curve:

$$I_{1D}(q_1) \sim \frac{\varphi_1 B}{(\varphi_1 B)^2 + Q^2} \quad \left(\text{for } Q \ll B\left(\frac{cr_0^3}{v}\right)^{-1}\right),$$

$$\varphi_1 \equiv \varphi_1(0) = \frac{16\pi}{9\sqrt{3}} \approx 3.2 . \qquad (26.11)$$

The integral width of this curve equals

$$\delta Q = \pi\varphi_1 B \approx 10B$$

in units of Q, or

$$2\delta\theta = \frac{\lambda}{2\pi}\sec\theta\,\delta Q = \frac{\lambda\varphi_1}{2} B \sec\theta = \frac{16\pi^3}{9\sqrt{3}}\frac{c\,|C|}{v}\tan\theta \qquad (26.12)$$

in angular units. Thus $\delta\theta$ increases with increasing scattering angle 2θ in proportion to $\tan\theta$.

The intensity distribution of a "quasi-line" on the Debye photograph (26.11) may be expanded into a Fourier series (15.6). Remembering that for the (h00) reflection $Q = 2\pi(H-h)/d_x$, we find that the coefficients A_n^u associated with the distortions in this expansion depend on n in accordance with the law

$$A_n^u \sim \exp(-\varphi_1 B d_x |n|) \tag{26.13}$$

and $B_n = 0$. Since the Lorentz intensity distribution (26.11) becomes invalid for very large Q, when $Q \gtrsim B(cr_0^3/v)^{-1}$ (in this region I_{1D} should fall off more rapidly in the wings of the distribution), formula (26.13) for A_n^u is also invalid for very small $|n|$ when

$$|n| \lesssim \frac{1}{Bd_x}\frac{cr_0^3}{v}$$

(in this region of very small $|n|$, in agreement with the general formulas of §15, $\ln A_n^u \sim n^2h^2$). It is an important point, however, that, in the case under consideration, on satisfying criterion (26.7), there is a considerable range of n values (including small $|n|$) for which $\ln A_n^u$ depends linearly (and not quadratically) both on the number of the coefficients n and on the order of reflection h. This fact must clearly be taken into account in separating the effects due to distortions and the finite size of the crystallites by harmonic analysis.

If the magnitude of M is not very great, the second term in expansion (26.5) for T becomes important. By considering this term in the expression for I_1 to a first approximation, we may find the correction to the scattering intensity distribution. In the Debye photograph the corresponding distribution takes the form:

$$I_{1D} \sim \frac{\varphi_1 B}{\varphi_1^2 B^2 + Q^2} + 1.0\left(\frac{Bc^2}{v^2}\right)^{1/3}\frac{(\varphi_1 B + iQ)^{10/3} + (\varphi_1 B - iQ)^{10/3}}{(\varphi_1^2 B^2 + Q^2)^{10/3}} +$$

$$+ 0.48i\left(\frac{Bc^2}{v^2}\right)^{1/3}\frac{(\varphi_1 B + iQ)^{10/3} - (\varphi_1 B - iQ)^{10/3}}{(\varphi_1^2 B^2 + Q^2)^{10/3}}. \tag{26.14}$$

On passing from the distribution (26.11) to (26.14), the integral intensity of the "quasi-line" remains unaltered, but it becomes asymmetric (the intensity falls off more slowly in the direction of large scattering angles), its maximum shifts by a distance

$$\Delta Q \approx -3.2B(2M)^{-4/3}\frac{C}{|C|}$$

(much less than the line width), and the width changes by $12.8B(2M)^{-4/3}$.

In addition to the "quasi-lines" on the Debye photograph, there are of course the ordinary Bragg lines, the position of which corresponds to the average lattice constant. Since their integral intensity is very low [exp (2M) times lower than that of the "quasi-lines"], these can only appear in the case of very small widths (determined by the dimensions of the crystallites). In this case we should observe some peculiar doublets, in which the distance between the lines is smaller than the half-width of the wide line, while the intensity of the narrow line falls off rapidly with increasing reflection indices (i.e., M).

Thus the scattering intensity distribution for defects surrounded by Coulomb fields of displacements is qualitatively different in the cases of slightly and severely distorted crystals. As the constant $|C|$ in (26.2) increases, first (for $M \ll 1$) the defects lead to a greater and greater attenuation in the intensity of the regular reflections (without broadening these) and to an increase in the diffuse scattering as given by the formulas of §18; then for $M \gg 1$ the diffuse scattering condenses into narrow, bell-shaped distributions, which may be interpreted as broadened "quasi-lines" with the same integral intensity as in the undistorted crystal. Since M depends on the Miller indices h_i, we may find in a given crystal that for some lines the criterion $M \ll 1$ is satisfied (the lines are not broadened), while for other lines, with larger h_i, $M \gg 1$ is satisfied (the lines are broadened).

§27. Scattering of X Rays by Crystals Containing Chaotically Distributed Linear Dislocations

In order to understand the x-ray-diffraction effects arising from the plastic deformation (working) of metals or from the annealing of metals after working on the basis of defect theory, we must make a theoretical study of the scattering of x rays by crystals containing various types of dislocation systems. The determination of the scattering intensity in the case of a distribution of dislocations of different types is a difficult problem, hardly soluble in explicit form. Hence calculations based on certain (necessarily simplified) models of dislocation distributions are of special interest. The results of such calculations should facilitate a qualitative interpretation of experimental data relating to the scattering of x rays by crystals containing dislocations.

In view of this we shall here consider the scattering-intensity distribution for a model corresponding to a chaotic (random) distribution of screw or edge dislocations with straight dislocation lines in crystals of large dimensions (large compared with the average distance between dislocations) [222].* In the next section we shall consider scattering by chaotically distributed dislocation loops [227].

In the absence of correlation between the dislocations, we may calculate the scattering intensity by means of the method set out in §14. Dislocations with straight dislocation lines may be distinguished both by type (by the orientation of the line and the Burgers vector) and by position in the crystal. We shall characterize the type of a dislocation by an index δ and its position by the number t of the point† in the atomic plane perpendicular to the lines of the dislocation system of number δ. The detailed distribution of dislocations in the crystal is characterized by giving the numbers $c_{t\delta}$ as equal to 1 or 0 according to whether the dislocation line of system number δ passes through the point t or not. The concentration of dislocations of a given type, i.e., the ratio of the number of dislocations to the number of positions which they may occupy, is denoted by c_δ, and the overall concentration by $c = \sum_\delta c_\delta$.

*A number of authors [223–226] have closely studied the intensity distribution in the scattering of x rays by a cylindrical crystal containing one dislocation. These results, however, cannot be directly used (as is sometimes done) for scattering by a real crystal with many dislocations by dividing it into coherent cylindrical blocks containing single dislocations and assuming that the displacements inside each cylinder are due to one dislocation only. This artificial division of the crystal into incoherent blocks may lead to an incorrect relation between the x-ray line widths and the scattering angle.

Owing to the slow fall-off in deformation with distance from the line of the dislocation, it is dislocated a long way from the point under consideration rather than neighboring dislocations which have the most important effect when considering scattering. We must thus pay special attention to the superposition of displacements arising from all dislocations in the crystals (this is in fact done below).

†It is more convenient to number the lattice points rather than the atoms, since atoms may move from one point to another as dislocations move.

The averaging over the random values of the numbers $c_{t\delta} = 1, 0$ may be carried out in the same way as in §14 for defects of arbitrary type (since even for very large degrees of deformation $c < 10^{-3}$; the concentration of defects may in this case also be considered small). It is only necessary to consider that now an additional summation over the systems of dislocations δ will appear.

According to the classification presented in §14, dislocations with straight dislocation lines belong to the second class of defects. Accordingly the scattering intensity I_0 (14.16) corresponding to a δ-shaped intensity distribution in a crystal of large dimensions vanishes ($M = \infty$), and the scattering intensity is described by the broadened distribution $I_1 = I$ (14.17). Neglecting unimportant effects associated with the nucleus of the dislocation (leading to insignificant scattering with an integral intensity of the order of c), we may set the change in the structure amplitude φ_{ts} equal to zero. Then the expression for the scattering intensity of crystals containing dislocations takes the form

$$I = f^2 \sum_{s,\, s'} e^{i\mathbf{q}_1\mathbf{R}_{ss'}} e^{-T},$$

$$T = \sum_{\delta} c_\delta \sum_t \{1 - \exp[i\mathbf{q}_1(\mathbf{u}_{ts\delta} - \mathbf{u}_{ts'\delta})]\}. \qquad (27.1)$$

The scattering-intensity distribution $I(\mathbf{q}_1/2\pi)$ around the reciprocal-lattice points, as may be seen from this formula, is determined by the dependence of T on the difference $\mathbf{R}_{ss'} = \mathbf{R}_s^0 - \mathbf{R}_{s'}^0$ ($\mathbf{R}_s^0$ corresponds to the crystal without defects). The explicit form of this relationship is determined by the field of displacements around the dislocations $\mathbf{u}_{ts\delta}$, and must be studied separately for every type of dislocation.

Let us first consider the simplest case of a cylindrical crystal of radius R containing screw dislocations, the Burgers vectors of which $\mathbf{b}_\delta$ ($\delta = 1, 2$) are parallel to the axis of the cylinder. We shall consider that the concentrations of dislocations with Burgers vectors $\mathbf{b}_1 = \mathbf{b}$ and $\mathbf{b}_2 = -\mathbf{b}$ are the same ($c_\delta = c/2$).

If the line of the dislocation passes through the X axis at a distance x_0 from the axis of the cylinder (the Z axis), then, on the approximation of an elastically isotropic continuum, the displacements around the dislocations are determined [228] by the formula

$$\mathbf{u}_{ts\delta} = \frac{\mathbf{b}_\delta}{2\pi}\left[\arctan\frac{y}{x-x_0} - \arctan\frac{y}{x-R^2/x_0}\right], \tag{27.2}$$

where x and y are the coordinates of the s-th point. The second term in (27.2) is associated with mirror-image forces acting on the surface of the free cylinder.

The quantity T in (27.1), generally speaking, depends not only on the differences $\mathbf{R}_{ss'}$, but also on the position of the point s (on $\mathbf{R}_s$). In order to determine the intensity distribution we must know T over a range of distances $R_{ss'}$ of the order of the mean distance between the closest dislocations, i.e., much smaller than R. Since, for large distances r_{ts} between the point s and the defect, the difference $\mathbf{u}_{ts\delta} - \mathbf{u}_{ts'\delta}$ falls off relatively slowly (as $1/r_{ts}$), the main contribution to the two-dimensional integral (27.1) for T comes not from neighboring but from dislocations (at a distance of about R from the point s under consideration). A simple analytical expression for T is not hard to obtain if we consider the case in which the number of dislocations in the crystal is so large (order of 10^6 to 10^8) that, for the actual range of $R_{ss'}$ values considered, not only the ratio $R/R'_{ss'}$ but also the logarithm of this ratio is much greater than unity, i.e., the condition

$$\varepsilon = \left[\ln\frac{R}{R'_{ss'}}\right]^{-1} \ll 1, \tag{27.3}$$

is satisfied, where $\mathbf{R}'_{ss'}$ is the projection of the vector $\mathbf{R}_{ss'}$ on the XY plane.

Then on neglecting terms of the order of $\sim\varepsilon$, in accordance with [222], we may in general neglect the contribution of the nearest dislocations [corresponding to the range of integration $r_{ts} \lesssim R'_{ss'}$ in (27.1)] and effects due to "image forces" [second term in (27.2)]. In this approximation T depends only on the distance $\mathbf{R}_{ss'}$ and is determined by the expression

$$T = \frac{1}{8\pi} n_g (\mathbf{q}_1\mathbf{b})^2 R'^2_{ss'} \ln\frac{2\pi R}{(\mathbf{q}_1\mathbf{b}) R'_{ss'}}, \tag{27.4}$$

where n_g is the dislocation density (the number of dislocation lines appertaining to unit area of the XY plane).

Putting (27.4) into (27.1) and carrying out a summation (integration) with respect to s and s', it is not difficult to show that, for the system of dislocations in the cylinder considered, the regions of high intensity near the reciprocal-lattice points (up to an accuracy of terms in ε) have the form of discs, while the intensity distribution is Gaussian:

$$I(\mathbf{q}_1) = \frac{8\pi^3 N}{v} f^2 \delta(q_z) \frac{1}{\sigma^2} \exp\left[-\frac{\pi(q_x^2+q_y^2)}{\sigma^2}\right], \tag{27.5}$$

$$\sigma^2 = \frac{1}{2} n_g (\mathbf{q}_1\mathbf{b})^2 \ln \frac{\sqrt{\pi}\sigma R}{\mathbf{q}_1\mathbf{b}} \approx \frac{1}{2} n_g (\mathbf{q}_1\mathbf{b})^2 \ln\left[\sqrt{\frac{\pi n_g}{2}} R \ln\left(\sqrt{\frac{\pi n_g}{2}} R\right)\right]. \tag{27.6}$$

The width of this distribution is proportional to $\sqrt{n_g}$ and q_1.

In deriving formulas (27.5) the logarithmic factor in (27.4) was considered constant. Neglecting terms $\sim\varepsilon$, this is legitimate in the important range of values $q \lesssim \sigma$. For larger q, on the wings of the distribution, the region of very small $R'_{ss'}$ becomes important, and here we must allow for the dependence of the logarithmic factor in (27.4) on $R'_{ss'}$. It may be shown that, in view of this, if $q \gg \sigma$, when the Gaussian distribution of (27.5) gives a vanishingly small intensity, the logarithmic factor in (27.4) leads to relatively slowly falling wings of the distribution (see below).

We may use the same arguments to discuss the scattering of x rays by systems of dislocations in which the Burgers vectors are parallel to several directions (characteristic for the particular lattice) rather than to one only. If, as before, we consider that there is no correlation between the dislocations and that the numbers of dislocations with Burgers vectors **b** and **−b** are the same, then the problem reduces simply to averaging expressions of the (27.4) type over all possible orientations of the dislocations. The corresponding expressions for T and for the scattering intensity (27.1) are quite easy to obtain in the case of high dislocation densities, when we may neglect corrections $\sim\varepsilon$. The dislocations in fact lead to a broadening of the x-ray peaks $I(\mathbf{q}_1/2\pi)$ near each reciprocal-lattice point, forming nonisotropic Gaussian distributions. The widths of these distributions increase on increasing the dislocation density (varying as $\sqrt{n_g}$), and also increase with the order number of the reflection (varying as q_1). The character of the anisotropy of the distributions depends on the type of the dislocation system and differs for different points in the reciprocal lattice.

Explicit expressions for the intensity distributions in reciprocal-lattice space tend to be rather cumbersome [222]. Hence we shall here only give the more simple expressions for the intensity distribution on the Debye photograph, obtained by averaging over the orientations of the crystallites. Clearly such average distributions should also be Gaussian [see (12.9)]. For example, in elastically isotropic crystals with a face-centered cubic lattice, containing screw dislocations in which the Burgers vectors are parallel to directions of the <110> type, the intensity distribution on the Debye photograph has the form

$$I_D = \frac{2\pi^2}{q_1^2} \frac{f^2}{v} \frac{pN}{\sigma_D} \exp\left(-\frac{\pi Q^2}{\sigma_D^2}\right), \tag{27.7}$$

where p is the multiplicity factor and σ_D^2 is given by the formula

$$\sigma_D^2 = \frac{1}{12} n_g b^2 q_1^2 (1 - \Gamma)\, l, \tag{27.8}$$

here

$$l = \ln \frac{\sqrt{\pi}\sigma_D R}{q_1 b} \approx \ln\left[\sqrt{\frac{\pi n_g}{12}} R \ln\left(\sqrt{\frac{\pi n_g}{12}} R\right)\right]$$

and Γ is a factor depending on the Miller indices h_i:

$$\Gamma = (h_1^2 h_2^2 + h_1^2 h_3^2 + h_2^2 h_3^2)(h_1^2 + h_2^2 + h_3^2)^{-2}.$$

For crystals with a body-centered cubic lattice containing screw dislocations with Burgers vectors parallel to the <111> directions, the intensity distribution is determined in an analogous way; in the corresponding formulas we only have to replace $n_g/12$ by $n_g/9$ and $1-\Gamma$ by $1-2\Gamma$.

Expression (27.7) determines the intensity in the central part of the distribution only. For small $R_{ss'}$ the dependence of the logarithmic factor in T on $R_{ss'}$ becomes important, superimposing itself on the main $T \sim R_{ss'}^2$ relationship. This leads to deviations from the Gaussian law on the wings of the distribution for large Q. It is not hard to show that for $Q \gg \sigma$ the intensity I_D falls off as $1/Q^3$:

$$I_D = \frac{\pi}{2q_1^2} \frac{f^2}{v} \frac{pN}{\sigma_D} \frac{1}{l} \frac{\sigma_D^3}{Q^3} \qquad (Q \gg \sigma_D). \tag{27.9}$$

For $Q = \sigma_D/2$, expression (27.9) is $\sim l$ times smaller than (27.7) and the transformation from the relation (27.7) to (27.9) takes place in a part of the distribution where the intensity becomes fairly small (some $l \sim \varepsilon^{-1}$ smaller than at the maximum). The law $I_D \sim 1/Q^3$ representing the fall-off in the scattering intensity due to dislocations in the wings of the distribution was obtained in another form by Wilkens [229].

It is clear that a Fourier transformation of the Gaussian intensity distribution (27.7) will also lead, in accordance with (15.6), to a Gaussian dependence of the Fourier coefficients A_n^u on the number n for $n > (\sigma_D d)^{-1}$. In this case for the (h00) reflections $\ln A_n^u \sim h^2 n^2$.

For very small n $[n \ll (\sigma_D d)^{-1}]$, it follows from (27.4) that the relatively slow fall-off in intensity (27.9) on the wings of the distribution will, strictly speaking, lead to the appearance of an additional logarithmic factor $\ln(R/dq_1bn)$ in $\ln A_n^u$, replacing the constant $\ln(R\sigma_D/q_1b)$ at larger n. This logarithmic factor, however, would only appear in cases in which a very large range of values of Q was subjected to harmonic analysis. In practice, the range is usually taken as only two or three times the line width, without embracing the wings of the distribution. Instead of the logarithmic factor in question (depending on n), the $\ln A_n^u$ for small n will contain the constant $\ln(R\sigma_D/q_1b)$, as in the case of large n, and $\ln A_n^u \sim n^2$ over the whole range of n values.

The integral width of distribution (27.7), i.e., the width of the line on the x-ray diffraction picture, equals σ_D in units of Q, while in angular units, in accordance with (13.15) and (27.8), it equals

$$2\delta\theta = \frac{\lambda\sigma_D}{2\pi} \sec\theta = \sqrt{\frac{n_g}{3}}\, b\sqrt{l}\sqrt{1-\Gamma}\, \tan\theta. \tag{27.10}$$

Thus the x-ray line broadening attributable to dislocations is approximately proportional to $\sqrt{n_g}$. As always for broadening associated with distortions, on increasing the order of reflection the half-width increases in proportion to tan θ.* The presence of the factor $1-\Gamma$ (or $1-2\Gamma$) in the expression for σ_D^2 means that the broadening will depend not only on the length of the reciprocal-lattice vector $\mathbf{K}_n$ (i.e., on $\sum_i h_i^2$), but also on its orientation. In the case of screw dislocations in elastically isotropic crystals, for large values of $\sum_i h_i^2$, the broadening is greater for reflections of the (h00) type than for (hhh) reflections.

Edge dislocations with straight dislocation lines lead to the same type of Gaussian intensity distribution as screw dislocations. Only the character of the orientation dependence of the broadening changes, the (hhh) lines broadening more than the (h00) type. As a result of this, if an elastically isotropic crystal contains the same number of screw and edge dislocations, the corresponding orientation relationship almost entirely compensate each other and the ratio of the widths of lines of the (h00) and (hhh) type with the same $\sum_i h_i^2$ differs little from unity (it equals 1.04 in the case of a body-centered cubic lattice and 1.06 in that of a face-centered cubic lattice [230]). This conclusion (namely, the practical absence of any orientation dependence of line width) agrees with experimental results for tungsten [100, 232] (an elastically isotropic crystal). A sharper orientation dependence may be observed in severely anisotropic crystals [233].

The foregoing results are obtained by neglecting terms of the order

$$\varepsilon \sim \left\{ \ln \left[\sqrt{\frac{\pi n_g}{12}} R \ln \left(\sqrt{\frac{\pi n_g}{12}} R \right) \right] \right\}^{-1}$$

(here we have replaced $R'_{ss'}$ in (27.3) by its value in the most important region). Allowing for these terms would lead to deviations from the Gaussian form of the intensity distribution and to corrections in the formulas given for the line widths. However, in the

*The more complicated angular dependence of line width obtained in [224] $2\delta\theta \sim$ (sec θ + const·tan θ) is associated with the artificial division of the crystals into blocks in these earlier papers.

present cases of crystals containing a large number of dislocations ($\sim 10^6 - 10^8$), $\varepsilon \sim 0.1$, and such corrections to the broadening never exceed 5 to 20%. Corrections no greater than these arise from the fact that, in polycrystalline specimens, the displacements may be caused by dislocations of other grains in addition to the one under consideration. This fact leads to only a slight change in the effective grain size R under the logarithm in (27.8) (and to a slight additional broadening of the fluctuation type in elastically anisotropic crystals; see [222]).

In real crystals the dislocation lines are not, of course, straight, as in the model considered, but bend in a specific manner. It is clear, however, that the presence of a certain bending of the dislocation lines proceeding from one end of a grain to the other will not change the order of magnitude of the line widths or the qualitative conclusions regarding the broadening of the x-ray lines (another picture of the intensity distribution may arise in the case considered in §28, in which the dislocation lines close into loops inside the grain).

More substantial changes in the results presented may occur if the dislocation distribution is not completely chaotic (random), there being some kind of correlation in the arrangement of the dislocations. Such a nonrandom distribution of dislocations with straight lines will lead to line broadening as before.* However, the expressions for the intensity distribution and the value and angular dependence of the line width will alter. For example, if the dislocations of one sign are arranged in groups consisting of m dislocations, then the value of the broadening will increase $\sqrt{m}$ times (for the same n_g). The results also change if the dislocations lie along specific slip planes.

The appearance of characteristic correlation lengths in a nonrandom dislocation distribution should lead to deviations from the earlier-derived relationship between line width and scattering angle $2\delta\theta \sim \tan\theta$. This effect will appear most sharply if the dis-

*In principle it is possible that correlation will lead to the screening of the field of displacements of a given dislocation by other dislocations. However, since in plastically deformed crystals the arrangement of the defect is determined mainly by a kinetic (and not solely a thermodynamic) process, the appearance of this type of very special correlation is not particularly likely.

locations are joined into walls and form block boundaries, i.e., the boundaries of sharply distinguished regions of coherent scattering with fairly large disorientation angles (for this each boundary must contain a large number of dislocations). In agreement with the results given in §13, the line width $2\delta\theta$ on the Debye photograph will in this case be determined not by the dislocation density n_g but by the sizes of the blocks, and will be proportional to $\sec\theta$ [see formula (13.77)].

A more complicated picture will occur if the dislocations do not all participate in the block walls, some of them remaining distributed at random over the crystal. In this case, according to [234], the intensity distribution is not Gaussian, but corresponds to a convolution of the Laue scattering-intensity distribution for undistorted blocks and a Gaussian distribution arising from scattering by large distorted crystals.

The relation between the angular width and the scattering angle lies in an intermediate position between $\tan\theta$ and $\sec\theta$. If, for example, the crystal consists of incoherently scattering blocks of cubic shape, the edges of which are parallel to the cubic axes and have a length Λ, then the angular width is given by the formula

$$2\delta\theta = \frac{\lambda\sec\theta}{2\pi}\sigma_D\left\{\Phi\left(\frac{\sigma_D\Lambda}{2\sqrt{\pi}}\right) - \frac{2}{\Lambda\sigma_D}\left[1-\exp\left(-\frac{\sigma_D^2\Lambda^2}{4\pi}\right)\right]\right\}^{-1}, \quad (27.11)$$

where σ_D is given by a formula of the type (27.8), and

$$\Phi(x) = \frac{2}{\sqrt{\pi}}\int_0^x e^{-t^2}\,dt$$

is the probability integral. If $\sigma_D^2\Lambda^2 \gg 4\pi$, then the expression in curly brackets ≈ 1 and the presence of blocks has no effect on the line widths, proportional to $\tan\theta$. If, however, $\sigma_D^2\Lambda^2 \ll 4\pi$, this expression equals $\sigma_D\Lambda/2\pi$, i.e., $\delta\theta$ is proportional to $\sec\theta$ and is solely determined by the block size. In the range of values $\sigma_D\Lambda \sim 2\sqrt{\pi}$, however, the relation between $\delta\theta$ and θ is more complicated.

It is an important point that the condition $\sigma_D\Lambda \sim 2\sqrt{\pi}$ begins to be satisfied and the randomly distributed dislocations start appreciably affecting the line widths for a relatively low concentration of dislocations. Thus in the present case of grains containing a large number of dislocations ($n_g R^2 \sim 10^6 - 10^8$) the condition $\sigma_D \Lambda = 4\sqrt{\pi}$ is satisfied if $n_g \Lambda^2 h^2 \approx 2$, i.e., for example, in the case of the (400) reflection, if one dislocation (not entering into the boundaries) corresponds to approximately 10 blocks. Obviously, when carrying out an x-ray-diffraction determination of dislocation density by reference to the part of the line broadening proportional to $\tan\theta$, the density of the dislocations forming grain boundaries is not taken into account.

The results presented determine the scattering-intensity distribution near reciprocal-lattice points or lines on the x-ray diffraction photograph, but not in the neighborhood of the zero point (for small scattering angles). In the latter case, when $\mathbf{q}_1 = \mathbf{q}$, the behavior of T at all $R_{ss'} \lesssim R$ is important, rather than simply that corresponding to values of $R_{ss'}$ of the order of the distance between dislocations, so that the approximate expression (27.4) and the formulas for I obtained therefrom cease to be valid. On the other hand, for small scattering angles, the products $\mathbf{q}_1 \delta \mathbf{R}_s$ may be regarded as small quantities, and we may determine the scattering intensity by expanding in powers of these quantities. We shall not discuss the resultant low-angle scattering distribution here, however, as this has been considered in a number of papers [235–240], both for straight dislocation lines and dislocation loops. We simply note that, in discussing the results of low-angle scattering by deformed crystals, one must take due account of the considerable effect of double Bragg reflection (see, for example, [241]).

§28. Scattering of X Rays by Crystals Containing Chaotically Distributed Dislocation Loops

In the preceding section we considered the x-ray-diffraction effects due to dislocations with straight dislocation lines, passing through the whole crystal. Another simple model of dislocation structure is that of chaotically distributed (random) dislocation loops, closed within the crystal, arranged along specific systems of planes (for crystals of given symmetry) and with a given set of possible Burgers-vector directions. Such structures may be formed after the quenching of metals as a result of the condensation of vacancies into flat discs and their subsequent bursting, or on irradiating the crystal with fast neutrons, i.e., the model is not really too idealized but corresponds to distributions of dislocations which may in fact occur in practice. Dislocation loops also arise on plastic deformation; however, in this case their distribution is probably not random but more complex.

At large distances from a dislocation loop (as compared with its radius) the displacements fall off in inverse proportion to the square of the distance and are determined by the following expression [242, 243]:

$$\mathbf{u}_{ts\delta}=\frac{bR_0^2}{r_{ts}^2}\mathbf{U}_\delta \qquad (r_{ts}\gg R_0). \tag{28.1}$$

Here the index δ characterizes the plane in which the loop lies and the direction of its Burgers vector $\mathbf{b}_\delta$, $b = |\mathbf{b}_\delta|$; the effective radius of the loop (generally speaking, the loop does not have to have the form of a circle) R_0 is determined by the relation $\pi R_0^2 = S_0$, where S_0 is the area of the loop; $\mathbf{r}_{ts}$ is the distance from the center of the loop to the s-th cell under consideration; $\mathbf{U}_\delta$ is a vector of length approximately unity, depending on the direction of the normal to the plane of the loop and the directions $\mathbf{r}_{ts}/r_{ts}$ and $\mathbf{b}_\delta/b_\delta$. For the sake of brevity we shall not give the explicit form of this. We shall here assume for simplicity that R_0 is the same for all the loops. At small distances ($r_{ts} \lesssim R_0$), displacements of the order of the Burgers vector ($u_{ts\delta} \sim b$) arise near the dislocation loops.

In accordance with the general results of §14, the character of the x-ray-diffraction effects associated with defects is determined by the law governing the fall-off in the displacements at large distances from the defect. Since the displacements (28.1) around a loop fall off in inverse proportion to the distance squared, we find that, according to the classification given in §14, loops are not defects of the second class, like dislocations with straight dislocation lines, but defects of the first class. Hence the picture of the intensity distribution in a crystal containing dislocation loops [227] may differ qualitatively from the distribution considered in §27.

The fields of displacements (28.1) at large distances from a loop are reminiscent of Coulomb fields of displacements (26.2). Hence the picture of the scattering-intensity distribution in crystals with dislocation loops should also largely resemble the intensity distribution corresponding to the case of Coulomb centers of displacements studied in §§26 and 18 (for severely and slightly distorted crystals). Differences existing between the loops and Coulomb centers are associated with the severe anisotropy of the field of displacements around the loops, with the existence of loops of different types (enumerated by the index δ), and also with the fact that the maximum displacements around the loops do not exceed b in order of magnitude, which makes it difficult to satisfy conditions of the (26.7) and (26.1) types simultaneously.

As in the case of Coulomb centers, the picture of the scattering-intensity distribution differs qualitatively in the case of slightly and severely distorted crystals, for which the conditions $M \ll 1$ and $M \gg 1$ are respectively satisfied. We must therefore consider these two cases separately. In both cases we may consider that the conditions $c_\delta \ll 1$ are satisfied, where c_δ is the concentration of loops of type δ (the ratio of the number of loops to the total number of atoms), and for a random distribution of loops we may use the general formulas of §14, putting $\varphi_{ts} = 0$ in these (as in the case of dislocations with straight lines). We shall consider for the sake of definiteness that the concentrations of the loops of different types are the same.

28.1. Slightly Distorted Crystals. In slightly distorted crystals with $M \ll 1$, in accordance with the general results of §14, x-ray-diffraction effects associated with dislocation loops should reduce to a weakening of the intensity of the lines on the x-ray diffraction picture, to the appearance of diffuse scattering, and to a certain displacement in the lines. The weakening of the intensity may be determined from the general formula (14.13), in which instead of $\mathbf{u}_{ts\delta}$ we must substitute the expression for the displacements around the loop and make an extra summation over the types of loops δ.

A simple analytical expression for M may be obtained for lines with large Miller indices for which $q_1 b \gg 1$. Then in the sum of (14.13) the main contribution comes from the region of large $r_{ts} \gg R_0$, for which the displacements are determined by formula (28.1), and it is easy to integrate over $|\mathbf{r}_{ts}|$ as was done in the derivation of the asymptotic expression (24.11). Remembering that the quantity $C(\mathbf{m})\,\mathbf{e}(\mathbf{m})$ in (7.2) is in the present case equal to $bR_0^2\mathbf{U}_\delta$, we find from (24.11) and (24.12) that M is determined by the expression

$$M = N_l R_0^3 (q_1 b)^{3/2} A(\varkappa);\ A(\varkappa) = \frac{\sqrt{2\pi}}{3\lambda} \sum_{\delta=1}^{\lambda} \int |\varkappa \mathbf{U}_\delta|^{3/2} d\Omega \quad (q_1 b \gg 1). \qquad (28.2)$$

Here $\varkappa = \frac{\mathbf{q}_1}{q_1}$, $N_l = \frac{1}{v} \sum_\delta c_\delta$ is the total number of loops in unit volume, and λ is the number of different systems of loops. The quantity $A(\varkappa)$ depends on the direction but not on the length of the diffraction vector $\mathbf{q}_1$.

Thus, in view of the fact that the local displacements around the loops are relatively large, for large reflection indices M increases in proportion to $(\sum_i h_i^2)^{3/4}$ (and not $\sum_i h_i^2$, as in substitution-type solutions). For smallish q_1 (when $(q_1 b)^2 \sim \sum_i h_i^2 \sim 1$), strictly speaking, formula (28.2) ceases to be valid; however, as before, it gives the correct order of magnitude of M and clearly leads to a small quantitative error.

The quantities $A(\varkappa)$ may be calculated by numerical integration. These quantities, generally speaking, depend on the direction of the vector $\varkappa$; however, in elastically isotropic crystals this dependence is only weak. For example, in crystals with face-centered cubic lattices, for which the dislocation loops lie with equal probability in different {111} planes, while their Burgers vectors are directed along the <110> axes [244], for reflections of the (h00) type with $\sigma = 0.34$ (for Al) $A_{h00} = 0.45$, while for reflections of the (hhh) type $A_{hhh} = 0.39$ [245]. A stronger dependence of M on the direction of the diffraction vector $\mathbf{q}_1$ may be obtained on taking account of elastic anisotropy.

We see from (28.2) that M is proportional to N_l and R_0^3 and may thus vary over a wide range, depending on the concentration and dimensions of the loops. Thus for example, if $N_l = 10^{13}$ cm^{-3} and $R_0 = 10^{-5}$ cm (such parameters of loop distribution were found in [246] for quenched aluminum), then M = 0.12 for the (200) reflection and M = 1.0 for the (800) reflection. For $N_l = 1.4 \cdot 10^{15}$ cm^{-3}, $R_0 = 1.5 \cdot 10^{-6}$ cm (such parameters were found in [247] for copper irradiated in a stream of neutrons), M = 0.5 for the (800) reflection. For loops of large radius (for example, those formed by plastic deformation), M may considerably exceed unity [if $R_0 = 10^{-4}$ cm,

$N_l = 10^{12}$ cm^{-3}, then M = 12 for the (200) reflection]. On the other hand, for loops of small radius, M may be much smaller than unity; thus for $N_l = 3 \cdot 10^{15}$ cm^{-3}, $R_0 = 4 \cdot 10^{-7}$ cm (copper crystals irradiated less intensively by a stream of neutrons [248]), M = 0.02 for the (800) reflection.

We may compare the values of M for loops and for point defects, for example, vacancies. In the latter case it follows from (24.13) $[(1/v)(\partial v/\partial c) \sim 1]$ that

$$2M \sim N_V v \sum_i h_i^2$$

(N_V is the number of vacancies in unit volume), whereas for the loops, according to (28.2) ($A(\varkappa) \sim 1$)

$$2M \sim N_l R_0^3 \left(\sum_i h_i^2\right)^{3/4}.$$

Hence for the same concentration of defects the value of M for loops is $\sim R_0^3/v$ times greater than for vacancies. It also follows from this that, when loops are formed in a crystal supersaturated with vacancies as a result of the coalescence of the latter (one loop arises from $\sim R_0^2/d^2$ vacancies), M increases by $\sim R_0/d$ times, i.e., it may increase sharply.

Diffuse scattering at defects of the first type is determined by the general formula (14.17). For $M \ll 1$ in weakly distorted crystals, this expression may be expanded in powers of concentration, and attention may be restricted to the linear terms in the expansion (since the local distortions around individual defects are, generally speaking, not small, the expansion in powers of the displacements carried out for solutions in §16 is not legitimate here). Remembering that there are λ types of loops, we may use (14.17) and (14.9), together with an expansion of this kind for the diffuse scattering intensity at loops with $\mathbf{q}_1 \neq 2\pi \mathbf{K}_n$ in order to obtain the expression

$$I_1 = N_l \frac{1}{\lambda} \sum_{\delta=1}^{\lambda} |\Phi_{\delta q}(\mathbf{q}_1)|^2, \qquad (28.3)$$

where the scattering amplitude for defects of type δ is determined by the formula

$$\Phi_{\delta q}(q_1) = \sum_s (f + \varphi_{ts\delta}) e^{iqr_{ts}} e^{iq_1 u_{ts\delta}} \approx \frac{1}{v} \int (f + \varphi_{ts\delta}) e^{iqr_{ts}} e^{iq_1 u_{ts\delta}} d\mathbf{r}_{ts}, \qquad (28.4)$$

where in the case of dislocation loops we must put $\varphi_{ts\delta} = 0$ in this formula.

The calculation of the integral of (28.4) is considerably simplified in the most interesting region of small q, in which the diffuse-scattering intensity rises sharply. In this region, with $q \ll R_0^{-1}(q_1 b)^{-1/2}$, the most important interval in the integral is that of large r_{ts} ($r_{ts} \gg R_0\sqrt{q_1 b}$), in which $\mathbf{u}_{ts\delta}$ is determined by the asymptotic formula (28.1), $\mathbf{q}_1\mathbf{u}_{ts\delta} \ll 1$ and $\exp(i\mathbf{q}_1\mathbf{u}_{ts\delta})$ may be replaced by the linear approximation. After integrating (28.4) with respect to the modulus of the vector $\mathbf{r}_{ts}$, expression (28.3) for the diffuse-scattering intensity takes the form

$$I_1 = N_l f^2 \frac{b^2 R_0^4}{v^2} \frac{q_1^2}{q^2} P(\varkappa, \mathbf{n}),$$

$$P(\varkappa, \mathbf{n}) = \frac{1}{\lambda} \sum_{\delta=1}^{\lambda} \left| \int \frac{\varkappa \mathbf{U}_\delta q r_{ts}}{q r_{ts}} d\Omega \right|^2. \qquad (28.5)$$

Here the factor P is determined by the orientation of the loops and their Burgers vectors relative to the crystallographic axes, and depends only on the directions of the vectors $\mathbf{q}_1 = \varkappa q_1$ and $\mathbf{q} = \mathbf{n}q$, but not on their lengths. In the case of the above-mentioned system of loops in elastically isotropic crystals with face-centered cubic lattices and with $\sigma = 1/3$, we find that, for reflections of the (h00) type, $P = 11\pi^2/36$ for $\mathbf{q} \| \mathbf{q}_1$, and $P = 11\pi^2/24$ for $\mathbf{q} \perp \mathbf{q}_1$ [245].

Thus in the neighborhood of the reciprocal lattice points, as in the case of point defects, the diffuse-scattering intensity rises in proportion to $1/q^2$. In view of the fact that loops of several types are participating, the curves of equal diffuse scattering for the resulting intensity distribution pass to one side of the points and have an oval rather than a lemniscate shape [($P(\varkappa, \mathbf{n})$ does not vanish]. Since according to (18.1) the vacancies produce scattering

$$I_1 \sim \frac{N_v f^2 q_1^2}{q^2}$$

(for vacancies $a_q \sim 1$), in the region of small $q \ll R_0^{-1}$ each loop produces diffuse scattering $\sim R_0^4/d^4$ times greater than a vacancy, and when vacancies units into loops the I_1 in this region increases by $\sim R_0^2/d^2$ times.

For $q > R_0^{-1}$ the value of I_1 falls off with increasing q more rapidly than $1/q^2$, i.e., the diffuse-scattering intensity distribution $I_1(\mathbf{q}_1/2\pi)$ is concentrated in regions with dimensions $\sim 1/R_0$ in the neighborhood of the reciprocal-lattice points. These scattering characteristics are reminiscent of the scattering intensity in crystals containing particles of a new phase; however, in the case of loops, the effects associated with distortions appear in pure form, and for small h_i we find that over the whole range $q \lesssim 1/R_0$ the intensity $I_1 \sim q^{-2}$, whereas in the case of separate particles this kind of relationship should appear for much smaller q (see §29).

Experimentally, the formation of regions of intense diffuse scattering near the points of the reciprocal lattice was observed by Elistratov and Madzhitov [249] when studying aluminum and copper single crystals subjected to slight uniaxial strain. After deformation the diffuse-scattering intensity increased sharply over almost plane, drawn-out regions, the length of which near the (111) point in copper was no greater than 0.17/d. In copper these regions made large angles with the reciprocal-lattice vectors and could not therefore be explained by the disorientation of blocks on deformation. Since the regions of high intensity near the (002) and $(\bar{1}11)$ points differed, their formation could not be explained by scattering at microvacancies or cavities in the undistorted crystal (see §13). For this reason, the effects observed in [249] were explained by diffuse scattering at dislocation loops.

From the extent of the scattering region, the diameter of the loops in copper was roughly estimated as about 50 Å. The difference in the character of the orientation dependence of scattering intensity in Cu and Al may naturally be explained by the great difference between these crystals as regards elastic anisotropy. In order to explain the details of the orientation dependence of intensity distribution obtained for Cu, we must calculate $P(\boldsymbol{\varkappa}, \mathbf{n})$ with due allowance for the severe elastic anisotropy of copper, also remembering that for uniaxial deformation the concentrations of loops oriented in different ways may differ considerably.

The change in the diffuse scattering on the Debye photograph after the plastic deformation of copper single crystals was studied by Iveronova and Katsnel'son [250]. It was found that, in samples deformed by grinding, the scattering intensity a long way from the x-ray lines was much greater than in annealed samples. Special analysis led to the conclusion that this rise in intensity was due not to the "tails" of the lines but to diffuse scattering at defects. There was a general nonmonotonic rise in intensity with increasing scattering angle. The results were explained in [250] by assuming that the diffuse scattering was caused by point defects or groups of these (i.e., by the effects considered in §18), or by dislocation loops of small radius such as may arise in the course of plastic deformation.

28.2. Severely Distorted Crystals. For fairly large concentrations and radii of the loops, the value of M (28.2) becomes fairly large, and instead of the criterion $M \ll 1$ the opposite criterion $M \gg 1$ is satisfied. Here the intensity I_0 of the regular reflections (14.16) is exponentially small. The intensity I_1 of the smooth distribution (14.17), however, as in the case of Coulomb centers with isotropic fields of distortions considered in §26, is converted into narrow, bell-shaped distributions, which are interpreted as broadened lines on the x-ray diffraction picture.* It is precisely these distributions which are of special interest in the case of severely distorted crystals.

In the case under consideration, in which there are several types of loops with the same concentrations $c_\delta = N_l v$, we find that, according to formula (14.17) (in which we must put $\varphi_{ts} = 0$, $\mathbf{q}_1 \neq 2\pi\mathbf{K}_n$), the intensity I_1 is determined by expression (27.1), in which $\mathbf{R}_{ss'}$, as in §26, corresponds to a lattice deformed homogeneously by image forces. In order to determine this we must thus know T as a function of the vector $\mathbf{R}_{ss'}$. The calculation carried out in [227] showed that T could be represented in simple analytical form in two cases. For fairly small $R_{ss'}$, for which the criteria

$$b \ll R_{ss'} \ll R_0 (q_1 b)^{-1}, \quad q_1 b \gg 1 \tag{28.6}$$

*Since the local displacements near the loops are relatively small (in order of magnitude these are not greater than b), according to (28.2) the condition $M \gg 1$ and the condition (26.7) (in which, in the case of loops, $r_0 \sim R_0$ and $c \sim N_l v$) can only be satisfy simultaneously for $q_1 b \gg 1$. This particular case will be discussed quantitatively in the following paragraphs.

are satisfied, T may be approximately written in the form

$$T = N_l\,(q_1 b)^2 R_0 R_{ss'}^2 g_{\varkappa}\left(\frac{\mathbf{R}_{ss'}}{R_{ss'}}\right) + iN_l\, q_1 b R_0^2 \mathbf{g}'\mathbf{R}_{ss'}, \tag{28.7}$$

where

$$g_{\varkappa}\left(\frac{\mathbf{R}_{ss'}}{R_{ss'}}\right) = \frac{1}{2\lambda b^2 R_0}\times$$

$$\times \sum_{\delta=1}^{\lambda} \int \left[\left(\frac{\mathbf{R}_{ss'}}{R_{ss'}}\nabla\right)(\mathbf{u}_{ts\delta}\boldsymbol{\varkappa})\right]^2 \cos\left[(\mathbf{R}_{ss'}\nabla)(\mathbf{u}_{ts\delta}\mathbf{q}_1)\right] d\mathbf{r}_{ts}, \tag{28.8}$$

$$\mathbf{g}' = \frac{\pi}{3}\frac{1}{b\lambda}\sum_{\delta=1}^{\lambda}\Big\{\mathbf{v}_\delta(\boldsymbol{\varkappa}\mathbf{b}_\delta) + \mathbf{b}_\delta(\boldsymbol{\varkappa}\mathbf{v}_\delta) - \boldsymbol{\varkappa}(\mathbf{b}_\delta\mathbf{v}_\delta) +$$

$$+\frac{1}{5(1-\sigma)}\left[4\boldsymbol{\varkappa}(\mathbf{b}_\delta\mathbf{v}_\delta) - \mathbf{b}_\delta(\boldsymbol{\varkappa}\mathbf{v}_\delta) - \mathbf{v}_\delta(\boldsymbol{\varkappa}\mathbf{b}_\delta)\right]\Big\} \tag{28.9}$$

($\boldsymbol{\nu}_\delta$ are unit vectors normal to the planes of the loops). The dimensionless quantity $g_{\varkappa}(\mathbf{R}_{ss'}/R_{ss'})$ depends only slightly on $R_{ss'}$, and in the range of $R_{ss'}$ principally required for subsequent analysis is of the order of 0.1. For very small $R_{ss'}$ this quantity contains the logarithmic factor $\ln(R_0/R_{ss'})$. The expression given for the dimensionless vector $\mathbf{g}'$ ($g' \sim 1$) relates to elastically isotropic crystals.

For larger values of $R_{ss'}$, satisfying the criteria

$$(q_1 b)^{3/2} R_0 \gg q_1 b R_{ss'} \gg R_0, \quad q_1 b \gg 1, \tag{28.10}$$

T is approximately equal to

$$T = B_l R_{ss'} \psi_{\varkappa}\left(\frac{\mathbf{R}_{ss'}}{R_{ss'}}\right), \quad B_l = \frac{\pi}{24} N_l b R_0^2 q_1, \tag{28.11}$$

where the dimensionless factor $\psi_{\varkappa}(\mathbf{R}_{ss'}/R_{ss'})$ depends on the directions (but not the lengths) of the vectors $\mathbf{q}_1 = \varkappa q_1$ and $\mathbf{R}_{ss'}$. An explicit expression for this factor is given in [227]. For very large $R_{ss'}$ the quantity T tends to the limiting value 2M; however, in the sum (27.1) over s and s', this region gives an exponentially small contribution and is not important for the following discussion.

For small q, in the region of the maximum of the I_1 distribution, the most important part in the integral

$$I_1 = f^2 \frac{N}{v} \int \exp(i\mathbf{q}'\mathbf{R}_{ss'}) e^{-T} d\mathbf{R}_{ss'} \qquad (28.12)$$

[compare (27.1)] is the range of $R_{ss'}$ for which Re T $\lessapprox$ 1. Remembering that according to (28.2) $M \sim N_l R_0^3 (q_1 b)^{3/2}$, we easily see from (28.7) that Re T ~ 1 for small values of $R_{ss'}$, satisfying the criterion (28.6), if M is very large and the condition

$$M \gg (q_1 b)^{3/2} \gg 1 \qquad (28.13)$$

is satisfied.

Substituting (28.7) for the T in (28.12) and neglecting the slight variation of $g_\varkappa(\mathbf{R}_{ss'}/R_{ss'})$ with $R_{ss'}$, we find that in this case the intensity distribution I_1 is approximately described by an anisotropic Gaussian distribution. The maximum intensity of this lies at the point $\mathbf{q} = 0$, where $\mathbf{q} = \mathbf{q}' + q_1 N_l b R_0^2 \mathbf{g}'$, and corresponds to the changed lattice constant of the defect-containing crystal. The integral intensity of the distribution $I_1(\mathbf{q}_1)$ is approximately equal to $8\pi^3 f^2 N/v$, and the value of the intensity at the maximum I_1^{max} and the integral half-width $2q_i$ introduced on p. 254 are determined by the formulas

$$I_1^{max} = \frac{\sqrt{\pi}}{4} \frac{N}{v} f^2 [N_l R_0 (q_1 b)^2]^{-3/2} I_\varkappa,$$
$$2q_i = 4 \sqrt[3]{3} \sqrt{\pi} I_\varkappa^{-1/2} \sqrt{N_l R_0}\, b q_1, \qquad (28.14)$$

where

$$I_\varkappa = \int \left[g_\varkappa \left(\frac{\mathbf{R}_{ss'}}{R_{ss'}} \right) \right]^{-3/2} d\Omega$$

is a numerical factor. Thus the broadening is proportional to q_1 and the square root of the dislocation density calculated for unit area $\sim N_l R_0$.

Averaging the distribution (28.12), (28.7) over the orientations of the crystals by formula (12.9) and remembering (13.15), we find that the scattering-intensity distribution in the Debye photograph I_{1D} is also Gaussian in the central region

$$I_{1D}=\frac{\pi}{q_1^2}\frac{pNf^2}{v}\sqrt{\frac{\pi}{N_l(q_1b)^2R_0g_\varkappa(\varkappa)}}\exp\left[-\frac{Q^2}{4N_l(q_1b)^2R_0g_\varkappa(\varkappa)}\right]. \quad (28.15)$$

The integral width of this distribution in angular units equals

$$2\delta\theta=4\sqrt{\pi}\,[g_\varkappa(\varkappa)]^{1/2}\sqrt{N_lR_0b^2}\tan\theta, \quad (28.16)$$

i.e., is proportional to tan θ and the square root of the dislocation density $\sim N_lR_0$. If, for example, $N_l = 10^{15}$ cm^{-3}, $R_0 = 10^{-5}$ cm, b = $2\cdot10^{-8}$ cm, tan θ = 3, then considering that $[g_\varkappa(\varkappa)]^{1/2} \sim 0.1$, we obtain in order of magnitude $2\delta\theta \sim 10^{-2}$. In view of the fact that, strictly speaking, $g_\varkappa(\mathbf{R}_{ss'}/R_{ss'})$ is not a constant quantity, but depends logarithmically on $R_{ss'}$, we find that, on the wings of the distribution, with

$$Q \gg q_1b\sqrt{N_lR_0}[g_\varkappa(\varkappa)]^{1/2},$$

as in the case of linear dislocations [see (27.9)], I_{1D} falls off in accordance with a power law rather than in the Gaussian manner, i.e., as $1/Q^3$. It is precisely this distribution of intensity I_{1D} which, on satisfying condition (28.13), will be taken for a broadened line on the Debye photograph.

It is an important point that, in the case of severely distorted crystals, for which criterion (28.13) is satisfied, the shape of the scattering-intensity distribution I_1, the order of width of the distribution for a given dislocation density, and the dependence of the width on the density and scattering angles are the same as in the earlier-considered case of rectilinear dislocations. In particular, the Fourier coefficients of the distribution depend on n in accordance with the law $\ln A_n^u \sim h^2n^2$ (if we neglect the additional logarithmic dependence on n for small n, which only appears on choosing a very large range of integration in the Fourier transformation).

In the case of rather less severely distorted crystals, when instead of (28.13) the condition

$$(q_1b)^{3/2} \gg M \gg 1, \quad (28.17)$$

is satisfied, it follows from (28.2), (28.11), and (28.10) that T $\sim$ 1 for values of $R_{ss'}$ lying in the range (28.10). The intensity distribution I_1 in reciprocal-lattice space is in this case determined by integral (28.12), in which T is replaced by the expression (28.11). The resultant distribution has the same integral intensity $8\pi^3 f^2 N/v$ as above, and the integral half-width is

$$2q_i = \frac{\pi}{12}(3\pi^2)^{1/3}\left\{\int\left[\psi_\varkappa\left(\frac{\mathbf{R}_{ss'}}{R_{ss'}}\right)\right]^{-3} d\Omega\right\}^{-1/3} N_l b R_0^2 q_1. \qquad (28.18)$$

In contrast to the case in which criterion (28.13) is satisfied, $2q_i$ now depends more strongly on the density of the loops and on their radius. It follows from (28.18), (28.1), and (28.17) that

$$q_i \sim \frac{2\pi M}{R_0 (q_1 b)^{1/2}} < q_1 b \frac{2\pi}{R_0}$$

and since $R_0 \gg d$,

$$2q_i \ll \frac{2\pi}{d}.$$

For $q \gg q_i$ the intensity I_1 falls off rapidly, i.e., near each reciprocal-lattice point, I_1 is described by a narrow, bell-shaped distribution. The maximum of the distribution lies at $\mathbf{q}' = 0$ and is displaced through a distance $N_l b R_0^2 q_1 \mathbf{g}'$ (comparable with the width of the distribution) relative to the maximum in the case considered above.

Averaging the expression for I_1 over the orientations of the crystals in this case leads to a Lorentz intensity distribution on the Debye photograph in the neighborhood of the central part of the intensity peak*

$$I_{1D} = \frac{2\pi}{q_1^2}\frac{pNf^2}{v}\frac{B_l \psi_\varkappa(\varkappa)}{Q^2 + [B_l \psi_\varkappa(\varkappa)]^2}. \qquad (28.19)$$

*Distribution (28.18) is the same as in the case considered in §26 (isotropic Coulomb fields of displacements). The case of crystals severely distorted by dislocation loops, $M \gg (q_1 b)^{3/2}$, however, has no analog in the problem considered in §26, since in order to satisfy this criterion it is essential that $N_l R_0^3 \gg 1$, or in the notation of §26, that $cr_0^3/v \gg 1$, and this contradicts condition (26.7). If, for example, the Coulomb centers correspond to particles of a new phase, then the condition $cr_0^3/v \gg 1$ is equivalent to the requirement that the volume concentration of the particles should exceed unity, and this is clearly not satisfied.

The integral width of this curve in units of Q equals $B_l\psi_\varkappa(\varkappa)$, and in angular units

$$2\delta\theta = \frac{\pi}{12} N_l b R_0^2 \psi_\varkappa(\varkappa) \tan\theta. \tag{28.20}$$

The quantity $\psi_\varkappa(\varkappa)$ for the above-considered systems of loops in elastically isotropic crystals with face-centered cubic lattices equals 9.5 for (h00) reflections and $\psi_\varkappa(\varkappa) = 6.5$ for (hhh) reflections, which should lead to a considerable orientation dependence of the line widths, even in elastically isotropic crystals. If, for example, $N_l = 3\cdot10^{17}\ \mathrm{cm}^{-3}$, $R_0 = 0.5\cdot10^{-6}$ cm, $b = 2\cdot10^{-8}$ cm, and $\tan\theta = 6$, then $B_l = 2\cdot10^{-4}q_1$, and for reflections of the (hhh) type $2\delta\theta = 1.5\cdot10^{-2}$.

The dependence of I_{1D} on Q for large Q is determined by the behavior of T in the small $R_{ss'}$ range, for which instead of (28.11) equation (28.7) is used for T. Hence on the wings of the distribution I_{1D} falls off not on a Lorentz law but more rapidly (as $1/Q^3$ for fairly large Q).

The Lorentz intensity distribution (28.19) corresponds to a linear dependence of the logarithm of the Fourier coefficient A_n^u on its serial number:

$$\ln A_n^u = -\psi_\varkappa(\varkappa) B_l d_x |n| = -\frac{\pi}{24}\psi_\varkappa(\varkappa) N_l b R_0^2 d_x q_1 |n| \tag{28.21}$$

[for (h00) reflections]. Deviations from the Lorentz curve on the wings of the distribution [and deviations from the law (28.11) for small $R_{ss'}$] disrupt this relationship at small $n < R_0/d_x q_1 b$ (when $|\ln A_n^u| \ll 1$). In accordance with (28.7), in this region $A_n^u \sim h^2n^2$, and the curve of $\ln A_n^u$ bends away from the linear dependence on n.

The formulas given above were derived for reflections with large Miller indices ($q_1 b \gg 1$). However, the qualitative results, in particular the conclusions regarding the concentration of the I_1 distribution into narrow, bell-shaped peaks, will also be valid for small q_1, although the shape of the distribution may change.

Thus as the concentration of the dislocation loops and the radius increase there will at first be a greater weakening of the intensity of the nonbroadened, δ-like regular reflections, while intense diffuse scattering will appear in the range $q \lesssim 1/R_0$. Thus for $M \gg 1$ the δ-shaped Bragg distributions will cease to be noticeable, and the intensity of the diffuse scattering will concentrate into nar-

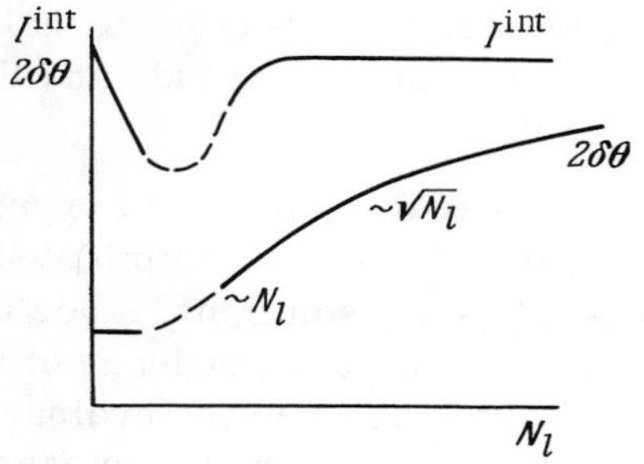

Fig. 19. Schematic relationships for the integral intensity I^{int} and width $2\delta\theta$ of a line on the Debye photograph as functions of the concentration of dislocation loops N_l.

row peaks, interpreted experimentally as broadened x-ray lines with the same intensity as in the undistorted crystal. After this a rise in N_l and R_0 will lead to an increase in line width, the intensities remaining the same. This is shown schematically in Fig. 19.

§29. Scattering of X Rays by Crystals Containing the Nuclei of a New Phase

The method set out in §14 is convenient not only for considering the scattering of x rays by randomly distributed dislocation structures but also for studying the influence of particles (nuclei) of a new phase on scattering. Such particles are a few tens or hundreds of Angstroms in size and differ from the principal (matrix) phase in respect of composition and (or) structure; they develop at a particular stage of the phase transformation during the precipitation of a new phase.

The x-ray-diffraction effects resulting from these particles are associated, first, with the change of structure amplitude in the volumes occupied by the particles, and, secondly, with the static displacements arising around them. The first of these effects was discussed earlier in §13, in which the case of no static distortions was considered. The local displacements around each particle may, however, in some cases be extremely large (this requires the use of the method set out in §14), and the picture of the scattering-intensity distribution changes qualitatively on allowing for the distortions. In view of this, in this section we shall consider the two factors (the change in structure amplitude and the distortions) simultaneously [221, 253].

The study of intensity distribution in crystals containing the nuclei of a new phase is much more complicated than, for example, the case of homogeneous solid solutions, since the structure of the particles, their shapes, the time dependence of their sizes, and other such characteristics cannot in the ordinary way be determined by independent experiments and also cannot be calculated by contemporary theories of phase transformations. In view of this we are compelled to calculate the intensities for certain simplified models of nuclei, so that, by making a qualitative comparison between the calculated intensity distribution and the experimental values, we may select an appropriate model for the precipitating particles and estimate their sizes and properties.

The model of a particle may be characterized by specifying the functions φ_{ts} and $\mathbf{u}_{ts}$, which according to (14.2) and (14.1) determine the changes in the structure amplitudes of the cells and the static displacements of the atoms around the particle ($\mathbf{R}_t$ determines the radius vector of the center of the particle), and also by giving the conditions for coherence between the particle and the matrix phase. Clearly the simplest model of the nucleus of a new phase in an elastically isotropic crystal is a particle homogeneous in structure and composition, filling a sphere of radius r_0 in a solid solution with constant concentration.

If the structures of the phases differ, then for $\mathbf{q}_1 \approx 2\pi\mathbf{K}_n$, where $\mathbf{K}_n$ are points of the reciprocal lattice of the matrix phase, the regions occupied by the particles of the new phase will not give any contribution to the scattering amplitude, and the corresponding structure amplitude for these may be regarded as zero. On the other hand, for $\mathbf{q}_1 \approx 2\pi\mathbf{K}'_n$, where $\mathbf{K}'_n$ are reciprocal-lattice points of the new phase, the structure amplitudes $f_s = f'$ are in practice only different from zero in the regions occupied by this phase. Hence in this case

$$\begin{array}{lll} \varphi_{ts} = -f & \text{for} \quad r_{ts} < r_0, & \\ \varphi_{ts} = 0 & \text{for} \quad r_{ts} > r_0; & (\mathbf{q}_1 \approx 2\pi\mathbf{K}_n) \\ \varphi_{ts} = f' - f & \text{for} \quad r_{ts} < r_0, & \\ \varphi_{ts} = -f & \text{for} \quad r_{ts} > r_0. & (\mathbf{q}_1 \approx 2\pi\mathbf{K}'_n) \end{array} \qquad (29.1)$$

If, however, the two phases have identical structures, related coherently, and in the process of precipitation the number of atoms in the neighborhood of the precipitate may be regarded as unchanged, then $\varphi_{ts} = f' - f$ for $r_{ts} < r_0$ and $\varphi_{ts} = 0$ for $r_{ts} > r_0$.

The displacements $\mathbf{u}_{ts}$ around the particle in the model taken increase linearly for $r_{ts} < r_0$, and then fall off on a Coulomb law [31]:

$$
\begin{aligned}
\mathbf{u}_{ts} &= \frac{C}{r_0^3}\mathbf{r}_{ts} \quad \text{for} \quad r_{ts} < r_0, \\
\mathbf{u}_{ts} &= C\frac{\mathbf{r}_{ts}}{r_{ts}^3} \quad \text{for} \quad r_{ts} > r_0, \\
C &= \frac{1+\sigma}{9(1-\sigma)}\frac{\Delta v}{v}r_0^3,
\end{aligned}
\tag{29.2}
$$

where $\Delta v/v$ is the relative difference in the effective atomic volumes of the new and matrix phases* (equal to the average atomic volume of the phase under consideration, multiplied by the ratio of the number of atoms of this phase to the number of atoms in the same volume of the undeformed matrix phase), and it is remembered that $|\Delta v|/v \ll 1$.

The homogeneous new-phase nuclei in question may arise as a result of allotropic phase transformations taking place without change of composition, and also as a result of transformations involving a change of composition, if the effective diffusion length exceeds the distance between the particles. However, in the early stages of aging in alloys, an impoverished region must necessarily develop in the matrix around the new nucleus. The intensity distributions for models taking account of the formation of this kind of impoverished layer are described by much more cumbersome formulas and will not be considered here (see [221, 253]).

If the atomic volumes of the phases differ, then in elastically anisotropic crystals the new particles which are energetically most

*Owing to the presence of a current of vacancies during the formation of the new-phase particles, together with possible plastic deformation, the number of atoms in the new phase varies in a (generally speaking) unknown manner. For this reason, and also because of possible changes in the lattice constants of small particles resulting from surface-tension forces, the ratio $\Delta v/v$ in (29.2) cannot be determined from independent experimental data, but must be considered as a parameter of the theory.

favorable (on account of the reduction in elastic energy) are not spherical (or cubic) but disc-shaped, oriented in a specific manner with respect to the crystallographic axes [254, 255]. Depending on the orientation, particles of several (λ) types develop in cubic crystals; these types are characterized by giving the functions $\varphi_{ts\delta}$ and $\mathbf{u}_{ts\delta}$ (which transform one into the other by symmetry transformation). The new-phase particles in a cubic matrix must clearly always have a shape drawn out along certain axes if their own lattice symmetry is noncubic. In this case the fields of displacements in the matrix are determined not only by the effective atomic volume of the new phase but also by the effective tensors δu_{lm} (analogous to the tensors $L_{lm}\delta c$ defined by formulas (5.10) or (5.5), different for different orientations δ); they will not have cubic symmetry, but a symmetry of lower order. At large distances (compared with the dimensions of the particles), however, the displacements will as before fall off as $1/r_{ts}^2$.

It is an important point that the conditions for the matching of the phases at the boundaries, i.e., in essence, surface effects, may also lead to an apparent change in the structure of the small precipitating particles in the case of disc-shaped precipitates (for example, to the appearance of a tetragonal structure), even in cases where, in the undistorted state, the new phase would have cubic symmetry. This effect may also be roughly described by assigning "noncubic" tensors L_{lm}^{δ}, although in this case these will depend sharply on the dimensions of the particles.

Let us now study the intensity distribution in crystals containing particles of a new phase, mainly on the model of (29.1) and (29.2). We shall consider that the particles are distributed at random (homogeneous decomposition), that their volume concentration cn is much smaller than unity (c is the ratio of the number of particles to the number of atoms in the crystal, while n is the number of atoms in a particle), and that effects associated with dislocations arising as a result of plastic deformation at a certain stage in the aging process may be neglected.

As in the previous case of dislocation loops, the picture of the intensity distribution differs qualitatively in slightly and severely distorted crystals (depending on the concentration of the particles and the distortions created by these). In slightly distorted crystals, for which the condition $M \ll 1$ is satisfied, the x-ray-diffraction effects associated with new-phase particles reduce to a weakening of the intensity of the regular reflections by a factor exp (−2M) and to the appearance of diffuse scattering (and also to a slight displacement of the lines on the x-ray-diffraction picture).

The average structure amplitude $\bar{f}$ and the value of M in crystals containing new-phase particles may be determined from formulas (14.10) and (14.13). Substituting (29.1) and (29.2) into these formulas instead of φ_{ts} and u_{ts} and summing (integration) over t, we easily see that for spherical new-phase particles with a different structure

$$\bar{f}_3 = f(1 - cn),$$

$$2M = 3cn\left(\alpha_0^2 n^{2/3}\sum_{i=1}^{3} h_i^2\right)^{3/4} f\left(\sqrt{\alpha_0^2 n^{2/3}\sum_{i=1}^{3} h_i^2}\right). \tag{29.3}$$

Here

$$\alpha_0 = \frac{\sqrt[3]{6\pi^2}}{9\mathfrak{h}}\frac{1+\sigma}{1-\sigma}\frac{\Delta v}{v}, \quad f(x) = \int_0^x (t - \sin t)\, t^{-7/2}\, dt,$$

where $\mathfrak{h} = \sqrt[3]{4}$ for a face-centered and $\mathfrak{h} = \sqrt[3]{2}$ for a body-centered cubic lattice of the matrix phase.

In the case of small local distortions and small Miller indices h_i

$$\alpha_0^2 n^{2/3}\sum_{i=1}^{3} h_i^2 \ll 10,$$

we may use the expansion of f (x) in the form

$$2M = cn\alpha_0^2 n^{2/3}\sum_{i=1}^{3} h_i^2\left[1 - \frac{1}{100}\alpha_0^2 n^{2/3}\sum_{i=1}^{3} h_i^2 + \ldots\right]. \tag{29.4}$$

In the opposite case, in which

$$\alpha_0^2 n^{2/3}\sum_{i=1}^{3} h_i^2 \gg 10,$$

M may be determined by means of the asymptotic expression

$$2M = \frac{4\sqrt{2\pi}}{5} cn\left(\alpha_0^2 n^{2/3}\sum_{i=1}^{3} h_i^2\right)^{3/4}. \tag{29.5}$$

We see from (29.4) and (29.5) that, in accordance with the general results presented in §24, for small q_1 and smallish local distortions, M is proportional to q_1^2 (or $\sum_{i=1}^{3} h_i^2$); with increasing q_1, and for $\alpha_0^2 n^{2/3} \sum_{i=1}^{3} h_i^2 \sim 10$, deviations from the linear relationship set in; then for large reflection indices or large local distortions $M \sim q_1^{3/2}$. The graph of 2M/cn against $\alpha_0^2 n^{2/3} \sum_{i=1}^{3} h_i^2$ is shown in Fig. 20, which also gives the approximate curves for small and large $\sum_{i=1}^{3} h_i^2$.

Deviations from linearity appear for small $\sum_{i=1}^{3} h_i^2$, if the $|\Delta v|/v$ are large. For instance, with $\sigma = 0.3$, $n = 10^4$, $\Delta v/v = 0.1$, $\mathfrak{h} = \sqrt[3]{4}$ we have $\alpha_0^2 n^{2/3} = 1.2$, and for high reflection indices the deviations from linearity are considerable. In view of the fact that $M \sim n^{2/3}$ (29.4) or $M \sim n^{1/2}$ (29.5), for large particle dimensions M may be large even for a small concentration cn (if the distortions are not eliminated by plastic deformation). For example, with cn = 0.01, $n = 10^4$, and $\sum_{i=1}^{3} h_i^2 \sim 10$ we have $2M \sim 0.1$.

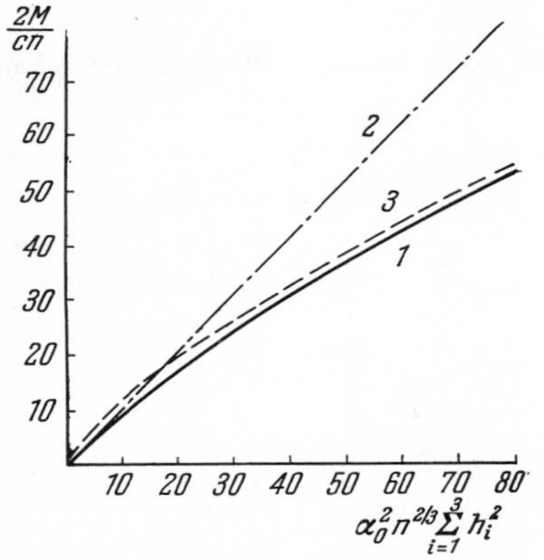

Fig. 20. Ratio 2M/cn as a function of the sum of the squares of the Miller indices. 1) Graph of the function $2M/cn = y = 3x^{3/4} f(\sqrt{x})$; 2) graph of the function $y = x (x \ll 10)$; 3) graph of the function $y = (4\sqrt{2\pi}/5)\, x^{3/4}$ $(x \gg 10)$.

In considering more complicated models, we may also study the influence of the shape of the precipitates, elastic anisotropy, and the presence of an impoverished layer on the magnitude of M [253]. The transition from a spherical to a disc-like or needle-like form of particles leads to a comparatively slight fall in M (by $\lesssim$ 30% on changing the ratio of the axes by a factor of 8). A considerably sharper fall in the value of M in the region for which $M \sim q_1^2$ (by a vector of several times) may be produced by the appearance of an impoverished layer. For large q_1, in the presence of an impoverished layer, M is proportional to $q_1^{3/2}$ or else tends to a constant limit, according to whether the oppositely signed changes in volume in the particle and the impoverished layer are equal in magnitude or not (i.e., whether the distortions penetrate through the impoverished layer into the matrix phase). On allowing for elastic anisotropy and the nonspherical form of the particles, M depends not only on the length of the vector $\mathbf{q}_1$ but also on its direction.

It follows from the general results of §14 that the regular Bragg reflections in slightly distorted crystals containing particles of a new phase are not broadened, providing that no dislocation structure, dividing the crystal into blocks, is formed. This conclusion agrees with experimental data [256, 257]. On the other hand, the presence of new-phase particles should lead to the appearance of intense diffuse scattering in the neighborhood of the reciprocal-lattice points of the matrix and new phase. The intensity distribution in slightly distorted crystals may be determined from formula (28.3) and (28.4) if we replace the N_l in them by the number of precipitating particles per unit volume N_p.

For a spherical form of particles, these are of the same type and the summation over δ in (28.3) drops out. If the displacements are not very large, then (28.4) may be expanded in powers of $\mathbf{u}_{ts}$ and attention confined to linear terms in the expansion. Then, for the above-considered model of homogeneous, spherical particles with differing structure, the diffuse-scattering intensity in the neighborhoods of the reciprocal-lattice points of the matrix phase will, according to (28.3), (28.4), and (29.2), be equal to

$$I_1 = N_p |\Phi_q(\mathbf{q}_1)|^2,$$

$$\Phi_{\mathbf{q}}(\mathbf{q}_1) = 3f\frac{n}{v}\left[\eta(qr_0) - \alpha'\frac{\mathbf{q}\mathbf{q}_1}{q^2}\frac{\sin qr_0}{qr_0}\right], \tag{29.6}$$

$$\eta(x) = \frac{x\cos x - \sin x}{x^3}, \quad \alpha' = \frac{1+\sigma}{9(1-\sigma)}\frac{\Delta v}{v},$$

where ν is the number of atoms per cell (the part played by the higher terms in the expansion in powers of the displacements is discussed in [221]).

In the absence of distortions, when $\alpha' = 0$, formula (29.6) describes a spherically symmetric bell-shaped intensity distribution around each reciprocal-lattice point of the matrix, corresponding to the effects of particle shape considered in §13.

The second term in formula (29.6) for $\Phi_{\mathbf{q}}(\mathbf{q}_1)$ is associated with distortions. If the distortions are large and

$$\alpha' q_1 r_0 \sim \alpha' n^{1/3} \gg 1,$$

they play a considerable part over the whole region of intense diffuse scattering, and allowing for these effects may greatly alter the size of the particles determined from data relating to the width of the intensity distribution. However, even in the case of slightly distorted crystals (α' small), for fairly small q the principal part is played by the second term in formula (29.6) for $\Phi_{\mathbf{q}}(\mathbf{q}_1)$. In view of this, I_1 does not tend to a constant limit on approaching a reciprocal-lattice point, but increases as q^{-2}, i.e., the curve relating I_1 to q should have a hyperbolic shape rather than a bell-shaped one. The curves of equal diffuse scattering in the case of spherical particles accordingly have a shape drawn out in the $\mathbf{q}_1$ direction rather than spherical form.

It is an important point that, on allowing for distortions, the reciprocal-lattice points cease to be centers of symmetry, and in the neighborhoods of different points (different $\mathbf{q}_1$) the intensity distributions differ. These characteristics enable us to distinguish effects associated with distortions. By studying scattering at small angles (for which $\mathbf{q}_1 = \mathbf{q}$) the part played by distortions may be greatly reduced.

Distortions have a much smaller effect on the scattering-intensity distribution near a reciprocal-lattice point of the new phase.

It follows from (28.4), (29.1), and (29.2) that in this case

$$\Phi_{\mathbf{q}}(\mathbf{q}_1) = 3f' \frac{n}{v} \eta(q_p r_0), \tag{29.7}$$

where $\mathbf{q}_p = \mathbf{q}_1 - 2\pi\mathbf{K}_n' + \alpha'\mathbf{q}_1$ and $\mathbf{q}_p/2\pi$ denotes the distance from the reciprocal-lattice point of a uniformly compressed or extended particle of the new phase. If all the precipitates are oriented in the same way, the intensity distribution is the same as in the absence of distortions, but displaced relative to the reciprocal-lattice point [disorientation of the particles leads to diffuseness (spread) of the distribution in a plane perpendicular to $\mathbf{q}_1$].

On allowing for the nonspherical shape of the particles,* in the limit of $\mathbf{q} \to 0$, the I_1 in undistorted crystals tends to infinity as q^{-2}, as before. The elastic anisotropy of the matrix, as indicated in [253], may (in the case of noncubic structure of the precipitating particles) lead to a considerable change in the character of the angular dependence of the intensity distribution (the curves of equal diffuse scattering then no longer pass through a reciprocal-lattice point as $q \to 0$).

As $q \to 0$, the main contribution to the scattering amplitude is determined by the term proportional to the Fourier component of the displacements of the atoms. These Fourier components

$$\mathbf{u}_{\mathbf{q}\delta} = -iv^{-1} \int \mathbf{u}_{ts\delta} \exp(i\mathbf{q}\mathbf{r}_{ts})\, d\mathbf{r}_{ts}$$

may be expressed in terms of the components of a Fourier function of the form

$$s_{\mathbf{q}\delta} = v^{-1} \int s_\delta(\mathbf{r}_{ts}) \exp(i\mathbf{q}\mathbf{r}_{ts})\, d\mathbf{r}_{ts}$$

[$s_\delta(\mathbf{r}_{ts}) = 1$ inside the volume occupied by particles of type δ and $s_\delta(\mathbf{r}_{ts}) = 0$ outside this volume], in much the same way as was done

* The frequently used one-dimensional model of the new-phase particles (set out, for example, in [257]) does not give the relation $I_1 \sim q^{-2}$ for small q, and in accordance with the observations made in §14 may lead to a qualitatively incorrect description of the intensity distribution, even for disc-shaped precipitates.

in §5 for distortions due to concentration inhomogeneities:

$$\mathbf{u}_{q\delta} = \mathbf{A}_{q\delta} s_{q\delta}. \tag{29.8}$$

Here the $\mathbf{A}_{q\delta}$ are determined by equations (5.8) (or the equations of Appendix II) in which L_{lm}^{δ} now denotes δu_{lm}^{δ}, the average deformation produced inside the particles by the change in its structure and composition in the absence of "pressure" on the part of the matrix (but with due allowance for surface forces). Remembering that, for small q, smaller than the inverse dimensions of the particles, $s_{q\delta} = n/\nu$, the intensity I_1 in the small q region, for which the main contribution comes from the term proportional to q^{-2}, may according to (28.3), (28.4), and (29.8) be written

$$I_1 = N_p f^2 \frac{1}{\lambda} \frac{n^2}{\nu^2} \sum_{\delta=1}^{\lambda} (\mathbf{q}_1 \mathbf{A}_{q\delta})^2 = N_p f^2 \frac{n^2}{\lambda \nu^2} \frac{1}{q^2} \sum_{\delta=1}^{\lambda} (\mathbf{q}_1 \mathbf{e}_{q\delta})^2 a_{q\delta}^2. \tag{29.9}$$

For particles of the new phase oriented in different ways, the scalar products $\mathbf{q}_1 \mathbf{A}_{q\delta}$ do not usually vanish at the same time, as a result of which the curves of equal diffuse scattering do not pass through the reciprocal-lattice points, but have the same character as in the case of interstitial atoms capable of occupying positions of several types, discussed in §18. If we know the tensors L_{lm}^{δ}, then formula (29.9) enables us to calculate the angular dependence of the intensity I_1 for small q, with due allowance for elastic anisotropy. The influence of elastic anisotropy on the diffuse-scattering intensity distribution associated with the particles of the new phase was considered in [258].

The existence of an impoverished layer around the particles of the new phase may according to [221, 253] lead to a considerable reduction in the coefficient of q^{-2} in I_1. The value of this coefficient may serve as a measure of the penetration of the distortions through the impoverished layer into the matrix.

The experimental study of diffuse scattering by new-phase particles has been the subject of a large number of papers (see, for example, [257, 259–261]). The authors of these papers, however, have usually just studied the general form of the "regions of anomalous scattering" and have not made a detailed study of the intensity distribution, which is needed in order to compare the theory allowing for distortions with experiment.

Let us now consider the intensity distribution I_1 in severely distorted crystals, for which the condition $M \gg 1$ is satisfied. This distribution was studied in §26 for the case of spherically symmetric strong Coulomb fields of displacements (at considerable distances from defects). According to (29.2) it is precisely these fields which occur for $r_{ts} > r_0$ around spherical particles of the new phase in elastically isotropic crystals. Hence the results of §26 may be directly applied in order to study the intensity distribution in severely distorted crystals containing new-phase particles. It is only essential that, in addition to the condition $M \gg 1$, condition (26.7) should also be satisfied; in the present case the latter reduces to the requirement that the volume concentration of the new phase should be much less than unity (for a nonspherical shape of the particles it is necessary that their maximum dimensions should be much less than the distance between the particles). For this reason it follows, for example, from (26.11) and the definitions (26.5) and (29.2), that the intensity distribution I_1 on the Debye photograph for the particles described in model A has the form

$$I_{1D} \sim \frac{\varphi_1 B}{(\varphi_1 B)^2 + Q^2},$$

$$\varphi_1 \approx 3.2, \quad B = \frac{\pi c\,|C|\,q_1}{2v} = \frac{1}{24}\,\frac{1+\sigma}{1-\sigma}\,\frac{|\Delta v|}{v}\,cnq_1, \quad Q \ll \frac{B}{cn}. \tag{29.10}$$

On allowing for the impoverished layer, the value of $|C|$ falls and formula (29.10) for B ceases to hold. A rather more accurate formula for I_{1D}, taking account of the asymmetry of the line for not-too-large values of M, is given by formula (26.14) (applicable for spherical particles).

The scattering-intensity distribution in reciprocal-lattice space near the reciprocal-lattice points of the matrix phase is given in the case under consideration by the expression (26.6).* If,

*The intensity distributions in the neighborhood of the reciprocal-lattice points of the new phase (if its structure differs from that of the matrix) which have widths $\gg \varphi_1 B$ in slightly distorted crystals broaden very little on passing to severely distorted crystals. If, however, their widths in slightly distorted crystals are $\ll \varphi_1 B$, then, in severely distorted crystals, the same distributions as those found in the neighborhood of the matrix points should develop in the neighborhood of the reciprocal-lattice points of the new phase.

for example, $(1+\sigma)(1-\sigma)^{-1}|\Delta v|v^{-1} = 0.2$, cn = 0.03, then B = $0.25\cdot10^{-3}q_1$ and for $\theta = 60°$, $\delta\theta = 0.004 = 13'$. Thus the distributions I_{1D} form relatively narrow "quasi-lines." The x-ray lines I_{0D} (which according to §26 are displaced with respect to the "quasi-lines" by a distance of the order of the width of the latter) have exp (2M) times lower integral intensity, and for sufficiently large M cannot be observed experimentally. The effect of the new-phase particles in this case essentially reduces to the replacement of the lines by the "quasi-lines," i.e., to the broadening of the lines on the x-ray diffraction picture.

Basing his arguments on the foregoing considerations, Gitgarts [262] explained the broadening of x-ray lines obtained from the matrix phase during the aging of the alloy ÉI 437A (the aging process in effect constitutes the precipitation of cubic particles of the γ' phase, $Ni_3(Al, Ti)$, from the Ni–Cr–Al–Ti solution). In agreement with theory, considerable broadening was observed in cases in which the estimated value of M was greater than 2 to 3 units. The calculated values of x-ray line broadening agreed satisfactorily with the experimental values: $2\delta\theta \sim (1-2)\cdot10^{-2}$.

In comparing theory with experiment, one must remember that in some cases a considerable influence may be exerted on the scattering-intensity distribution by dislocations formed at a particular stage of the decomposition process, which are not considered here. In addition to this, in a number of cases in which the criteria for the applicability of the kinematic theory of scattering are not adequately satisfied, effects associated with a change of extinction may appear during decomposition [263].

In this chapter we have only considered certain types of defects influencing the scattering-intensity distribution in severely distorted crystals. X-ray line broadening may also be associated with other types of defects of the second class, for example, with stacking faults or with antiphase domain boundaries in ordered alloys. The characteristic x-ray-diffraction effects associated with these defects will not be considered here, nor will those associated with the modulated structures formed in a number of cases by decomposing solutions (see, for example, the monographs [67, 71]).

PART II

INELASTIC SCATTERING OF X RAYS AND THERMAL NEUTRONS IN CRYSTALS

Chapter VIII

Scattering of X Rays at Thermal Vibrations of the Atoms in Crystals

§30. Scattering of X Rays at Thermal Vibrations in Ideal Crystals

The scattering of waves is only elastic if the perturbation is static. If, however, as a result of the motion of the atoms in the crystal, the perturbation changes with time, then the scattered wave is modulated by a perturbing potential, its frequency changes as a result of the addition or subtraction of the frequencies of the scattering system, and the scattering is to some extent inelastic. Whereas the study of the elastic scattering of x rays and neutrons considered above provides us with information regarding the imperfections of the crystal, the study of inelastic scattering, largely determined by the character of the atomic motion, enables us to study the dynamics of this motion.

The scattering of x rays and neutrons at the thermal vibrations of crystals has been studied in greatest detail; at the present time this provides the best method of determining the dispersion curves as a function of the distribution of vibration frequencies. The thermal scattering of x rays will be considered in this chapter, while the inelastic scattering of neutrons will be considered in later chapters.

Although the scattering of x-ray quanta at thermal vibrations is in fact inelastic, nevertheless the change of energy in scattering is of the order of the energy of a phonon, i.e., about 10^{-2} to 10^{-1} eV, and is much smaller than not only the actual energy of the scattered photon ($\sim 10^4$ to 10^5 eV) but also the indeterminacy of the latter associated with the natural and instrumental width of the x-ray line. In practice this kind of energy change is not observed experimentally, and in order to determine the vibration frequencies only the angular and not the energy distribution of scattering intensity may be used. On the other hand, the relatively small change in the energy of the photon on scattering enables us to use the general expression (12.3) for studying scattering at thermal vibrations, as in the case of the intensity of elastic scattering at static inhomogeneities. It is only necessary that instead of the static displacements $\delta\mathbf{R}_{s\gamma}$ we should substitute the thermal displacements $\mathbf{u}_{s\gamma}$.

For not too high temperatures, the scattering at thermal vibrations may be considered on the harmonic approximation. The theory of this scattering has been treated in a large number of papers (see, for example, [91–93, 158–161, 172, 264–272] and the reviews [65, 161, 273–276]). We see from (12.3) that the problem of determining the scattering intensity reduces in essence to the calculation of the time average of the expression

$$\langle \exp\left[i\mathbf{q}_1 (\mathbf{u}_{s\gamma} - \mathbf{u}_{s'\gamma'})\right] \rangle$$

or the equivalent (according to the general principles of statistical physics) average value taken over a statistical set. This average may most simply be calculated if we consider that, in the harmonic approximation of the theory of vibrations, the probability of any linear combination of normal coordinates, in particular $\mathbf{q}_1(\mathbf{u}_{s\gamma} - \mathbf{u}_{s'\gamma'})$, is Gaussian (see footnote on p. 221).

Carrying out the averaging process with this probability distribution in the same way as in deriving the formula for the Debye–Waller factor (23.2), we immediately obtain

$$\langle \exp\left[i\mathbf{q}_1 (\mathbf{u}_{s\gamma} - \mathbf{u}_{s'\gamma'})\right] \rangle = \exp\left[-\frac{1}{2} \langle (\mathbf{q}_1\mathbf{u}_{s\gamma} - \mathbf{q}_1\mathbf{u}_{s'\gamma'})^2 \rangle \right].$$

Substituting this expression into (12.3) (with $\delta\mathbf{R}_{s\gamma}$ replaced by $\mathbf{u}_{s\gamma}$) and allowing for (23.2), we may write the intensity I_T of the scattering of x rays at the thermal vibrations of an ideal crystal in the form

$$I_T = \sum_{s,s'=1}^{N} \sum_{\gamma,\gamma'=1}^{\nu} f_\gamma^0 e^{-M_\gamma} f_{\gamma'}^{0*} e^{-M_{\gamma'}} \exp\left[iq_1 (\mathbf{R}_{s\gamma} - \mathbf{R}_{s'\gamma'})\right] e^{M_{s\gamma s'\gamma'}},$$

$$M_{s\gamma s'\gamma'} = \langle (\mathbf{q}_1 \mathbf{u}_{s\gamma}) (\mathbf{q}_1 \mathbf{u}_{s'\gamma'}) \rangle. \tag{30.1}$$

Here it is considered that in an ideal crystal the atomic factors $f_{s\gamma}$ for atoms at the lattice points of any sublattice γ take the same values of f_γ^0.

In order to simplify the formulas, let us confine attention to monatomic crystals. Then $M_\gamma = M$ are determined by expressions (23.5) and $M_{s\gamma s'\gamma'} = M_{ss'}$ may easily be calculated by using the expansion in normal coordinates $q_{\mathbf{k}n}$ (23.4). Remembering that for these normal coordinates

$$\langle q_{\mathbf{k}n} q_{\mathbf{k}'n'} \rangle = \frac{1}{2} \left(n_{\mathbf{k}n} + \frac{1}{2} \right) \delta_{\mathbf{k}\mathbf{k}'} \delta_{nn'},$$

$$\chi_{\mathbf{k}} (\mathbf{R}_s) \chi_{\mathbf{k}} (\mathbf{R}_{s'}) + \chi_{-\mathbf{k}} (\mathbf{R}_s) \chi_{-\mathbf{k}} (\mathbf{R}_{s'}) = \cos \mathbf{k} (\mathbf{R}_s - \mathbf{R}_{s'}),$$

we may write $M_{ss'}$ in the form of a sum over the wave vector $\mathbf{k}$ and the number of the vibration branch n:

$$M_{ss'} = \frac{\hbar}{2Nm} \sum_{\mathbf{k}n} (\mathbf{q}_1 \mathbf{e}_{\mathbf{k}n})^2 \frac{2n_{\mathbf{k}n} + 1}{\omega_{\mathbf{k}n}} \cos \mathbf{k} (\mathbf{R}_s - \mathbf{R}_{s'}). \tag{30.2}$$

The values of M in three-dimensional crystals are finite, but $M_{ss'}$ tends to zero with increasing distance $|\mathbf{R}_s - \mathbf{R}_{s'}|$. Hence thermal vibrations do not lead to broadening of the x-ray lines but only reduce their intensity and lead to the appearance of thermal diffuse scattering. For not-too-high temperatures the value of $M_{ss'}$ is small, and in order to determine the intensity of this scattering (as in the case of the diffuse scattering at static distortions in solutions considered in Chapter V) it is convenient to expand expression (30.1) for I_T in powers of $M_{ss'}$. The zero term of the expansion determines the intensity distribution of the regular reflections at $\mathbf{q}_1 \approx 2\pi\mathbf{K}_n$; these have the same shape as in the absence of vibrations. The thermal motion here only leads to a reduction in the structure amplitudes, since each atomic scattering factor f_γ^0 is multiplied by $\exp(-M_\gamma)$.

The first term I_{1T} of the expansion in (30.1) for monatomic crystals in powers of $M_{ss'}$ is simplified if we consider that the sum $\sum_s \exp[i(\mathbf{q}_1 \pm \mathbf{k})\mathbf{R}_s]$ equals N for $\mathbf{q}_1 \pm \mathbf{k} = 2\pi\mathbf{K}_n$ and zero if $\mathbf{q}_1 \pm \mathbf{k} \neq 2\pi\mathbf{K}_n$ (for simplicity we shall consider that $\mathbf{q}_1$ as well as $\mathbf{k}$ satisfy cyclical conditions). Thus in the sum over $\mathbf{k}$ only terms with $\mathbf{k} = \pm\mathbf{q} = \pm(\mathbf{q}_1 - 2\pi\mathbf{K}_n)$ remain, and

$$I_{1T} = Nf^{02}e^{-2M}\frac{\hbar}{2m}\sum_{n=1}^{3}(\mathbf{q}_1\mathbf{e}_{\mathbf{q}n})^2\frac{2n_{\mathbf{q}n}+1}{\omega_{\mathbf{q}n}}. \qquad (30.3)$$

In particular, for T = 0

$$I_{1T} = Nf^{02}e^{-2M}\frac{\hbar}{2m}\sum_{n=1}^{3}(\mathbf{q}_1\mathbf{e}_{\mathbf{q}n})^2\frac{1}{\omega_{\mathbf{q}n}}, \qquad (30.4)$$

and for $k_B T \gg \hbar\omega_{\mathbf{q}n}$ $\left(\text{when } n_{\mathbf{q}n} + \frac{1}{2} \approx \frac{k_B T}{\hbar\omega_{\mathbf{q}n}}\right)$

$$I_{1T} = Nf^{02}e^{-2M}\frac{k_B T}{m}\sum_{n=1}^{3}(\mathbf{q}_1\mathbf{e}_{\mathbf{q}n})^2\frac{1}{\omega_{\mathbf{q}n}^2}. \qquad (30.5)$$

Expressions (30.3) to (30.5) describe smooth intensity distributions in reciprocal-lattice space, corresponding to diffuse scattering at thermal vibrations. The intensity of this scattering increases sharply for small q, when $(\mathbf{q}_1/2\pi$ falls in the neighborhood of some reciprocal-lattice point. In fact, for small q and acoustic vibrations, $\omega_{\mathbf{q}n} \sim q$, while at high temperatures (above the Debye point θ) (30.5) shows that (as in the case of diffuse scattering at static distortions in solid solutions) I_{1T} increases in proportion to $1/q^2$ over the whole range of small $q \ll k_m \sim 2\pi/d$. According to (30.4), for low temperatures, as q falls, I_{1T} first rises in proportion to 1/q, and then, when $\hbar\omega_{\mathbf{q}n} < k_B T$, I_{1T} rises more rapidly (as $1/q^2$), in accordance with formula (30.5). The region of this sharp rise in I_{1T} at low temperatures embraces values of $q < (T/\theta)k_m$ and is especially narrow in crystals with large θ.

In the region of small q the results given [formulas (30.3) to (30.5)] are valid not only for monatomic but also for polyatomic crystals, for which the main contribution to scattering in this region comes from acoustic vibrations. In the latter case we need only regard f^0 as the structure amplitude for the reciprocal-lattice point under consideration.

The form of the surfaces of equal diffuse scattering for small q is determined by the orientation dependence of the frequencies and polarization vectors of the acoustic vibrations as $q \to 0$, when these vibrations may be considered on the continuum approximation. In elastically anisotropic crystals the form of these surfaces may be extremely complicated [275–276a].

For a given change in the wave vector $\mathbf{q}_1$, the intensity of diffuse scattering I_{1T} is, according to (30.3), determined by the frequencies ω_{qn} and the polarization vectors $\mathbf{e}_{qn}$ of only those phonons which have the given wave vector $\pm\mathbf{q}$. Each term in the sum (30.3) with respect to n may be interpreted as the intensity of radiation diffracted in a corresponding wave of thermal vibrations with wave vector $\pm\mathbf{q}$. Thus only individual waves of oscillations take part in the scattering I_{1T} for a given $\mathbf{q}_1$, and this scattering is called "single-phonon."

The next term I_{2T} in the expansion of expression (30.1) in powers of $M_{ss'}$ determines the intensity of two-phonon scattering associated with two waves of vibrations, in which the wave vectors $\mathbf{k}$ and $\mathbf{k}'$ obey the relation

$$\pm \mathbf{k} \pm \mathbf{k}' = \mathbf{q}_1 + 2\pi \mathbf{K}'_n,$$

where $\mathbf{K}'_n$ is some vector of the reciprocal lattice. This scattering was considered in [277, 278]. The intensity I_{2T} is expressed in the form of a sum (integral) over $\mathbf{k}$, and at high temperatures is proportional to T^2. In the region of small q, the value of I_{2T} does not experience such a sharp rise as I_{1T}, and single-phonon processes give the main contribution to the scattering. However, in those regions of reciprocal-lattice space where I_{1T} reaches a minimum, two-phonon processes may give a substantial contribution to the scattering (up to 60% of I_{1T} in aluminum at room temperature [278]). The contribution of three-phonon and more complicated processes, corresponding to higher terms in the expansion of (30.1) in powers of $M_{ss'}$, is usually very slight at low temperatures (in aluminum, at room temperature, I_{3T} is no more than 6% of I_{1T}, according to the estimate given in [278]).

Expressions (30.3) to (30.5) enable us to determine the thermal-scattering intensity if we know $\omega_{\mathbf{k}n}$ and $\mathbf{e}_{\mathbf{k}n}$. However, it is clearly of greatest interest to consider the reverse problem of determining the vibration spectrum from experimental data relating to thermal scattering. The solution of this problem is made difficult by the fact that data relating to I_{1T} for a given $\mathbf{q}$ have to be used in order to determine three independent frequencies $\omega_{\mathbf{q}n}$ (and polarization vectors $\mathbf{e}_{\mathbf{q}n}$). The situation simplifies considerably, however, in cases in which the vectors $\mathbf{q}$ and $\mathbf{q}_1$ are parallel and lie along directions of high symmetry, for example, directions of the [100], [110], [111] type in cubic crystals. It follows from symmetry considerations that in these cases one of the polarization vectors $\mathbf{e}_{\mathbf{q}n}$ is parallel to $\mathbf{q}$ (and hence also to $\mathbf{q}_1$), while the two others are perpendicular, and the vibration waves are purely longitudinal or purely transverse. The scalar product $\mathbf{q}_1\mathbf{e}_{\mathbf{q}n}$ for the transverse waves equals zero, and hence the sum (30.3) is left with only one term, corresponding to scattering at longitudinal vibrations:

$$I_{1T} = Nf^{02}e^{-2M}\frac{\hbar}{2m}q_1^2\frac{2n_{\mathbf{q}\parallel}+1}{\omega_{\mathbf{q}\parallel}}. \qquad (30.6)$$

This expression contains only one unknown quantity, the frequency of the longitudinal vibrations $\omega_{\mathbf{q}\parallel}$ for directions of high symmetry $\left(n_{\mathbf{q}\parallel} = \left[\exp\frac{\hbar\omega_{\mathbf{q}\parallel}}{k_B T} - 1\right]^{-1}\right)$, and this may be determined from experimental values of I_{1T}.

In order to determine the frequencies of transverse waves, polarized, for example, in the [100] direction, we must study the scattering for such vectors $\mathbf{q}_1$ that the vector $\mathbf{q}$ will be perpendicular to the direction in question, for example, that it will lie along the [001] axis. Then the vectors $\mathbf{e}_{\mathbf{q}n}$ will be parallel to the cubic axes, i.e., parallel or perpendicular to $\mathbf{q}$. If we denote the angle between $\mathbf{q}_1$ and the high-symmetry [100] axis by ψ, then expression (30.3) for I_{1T} will in this case take the form

$$I_{1T} = Nf^{02}e^{-2M}\frac{\hbar}{2m}\left[\frac{2n_{\mathbf{q}\parallel}+1}{\omega_{\mathbf{q}\parallel}}\sin^2\psi + \frac{2n_{\mathbf{q}\perp}+1}{\omega_{\mathbf{q}\perp}}\cos^2\psi\right]. \qquad (30.7)$$

If the frequency of the longitudinal vibrations $\omega_{\mathbf{q}\parallel}$ has already been determined in the manner described above, then formula (30.7) offers the possibility of finding the frequencies of the transverse vibrations $\omega_{\mathbf{q}\perp}$ from the experimental values of I_{1T}.

In order to extract I_{1T} from experimental data relating to diffuse-scattering intensity, we must subtract from the total intensity all terms corresponding to Compton and two-phonon (and also multiphonon) scattering. These contributions are determined by calculation based on approximate formulas, which naturally introduces a certain error into I_{1T}. After this, the method described above is used to determine the dependence of the frequencies of the longitudinal and transverse vibrations on the wave vector for directions of high symmetry. Knowing these frequencies, we may find the force constants for some model of the vibrations in such a way as to make the calculated values of $\omega_{\mathbf{k}n}$ describe the experimental data in the best possible manner, and then, by solving the corresponding secular equations, we may calculate the $\omega_{\mathbf{k}n}$ and $\mathbf{e}_{\mathbf{k}n}$ for any $\mathbf{k}$.

This kind of experimental determination of the vibration spectrum has been carried out in a number of papers (see, for example, [273, 275, 276, 278−280, 438]). Clearly, a failing of the x-ray-diffraction method of determining frequencies is the fact that one only uses information relating to certain lines in reciprocal-lattice space, and only determines the frequencies for these directions from direct experiment* (a considerable error is also introduced by the necessity of including corrections for Compton and two-phonon scattering). In principle, the neutron-diffraction method of determining vibration frequencies is free from these failings, as we shall see in §33.

§31. Scattering of X Rays at Thermal Vibrations in Solid Solutions

It is typical of thermal scattering in ideal crystals that single-phonon scattering involving a specified change in the wave vector of the x rays $\mathbf{q}_1$ is determined by interaction with only one wave of vibrations of the given branch. This is due to the fact that the normal vibrations in an ideal crystal are described by plane waves

*In principle all three frequencies $\omega_{\mathbf{q}n}$ and polarization vectors $\mathbf{e}_{\mathbf{q}n}$ in a monatomic crystal could be determined for any wave vector $\mathbf{q}$ if we measured I_{1T} for six different independent values of $\mathbf{q}_1$ (in six cells of the reciprocal lattice) corresponding to the same $\mathbf{q}$. In practice, however, this method is extremely difficult and clearly not very precise.

with given quasimomenta, and in the course of single-phonon scattering the change in the momentum of the x-ray photon should be equal (apart from the sign) to the momentum of the emitted or absorbed phonon.

The picture becomes much more complicated in the thermal scattering of x rays by solid solutions or other nonideal crystals [281], since in this case the normal vibrations do not correspond to plane waves; they cannot, strictly speaking, be characterized by momentum, and hence in single-phonon scattering all the phonons of the crystal contribute to a given angle. As a result of this, the x-ray-diffraction determination of vibration frequencies in solutions is very difficult, and is in fact only possible in those cases in which the departure from the ideal state is very slight.

Let us consider thermal scattering in the simplest case of disordered solutions with one atom in the cell, in which the atomic factors of the components are similar and the static distortions are insignificant. Then it follows from formula (12.6) (in which $\delta\mathbf{R}_s$ is replaced by $\mathbf{u}_s$ and $f_s \approx f$ may be taken outside the summation sign) that the single-phonon thermal diffuse-scattering intensity is expressed in terms of the Fourier components of the thermal displacements $\mathbf{u}_\mathbf{k}$:

$$I_{1T} = N^2 f^2 \langle |\mathbf{q}_1 \mathbf{u}_\mathbf{q}|^2 \rangle, \quad \mathbf{u}_s = i \sum_\mathbf{k} \mathbf{u}_\mathbf{k} e^{-i\mathbf{k}\mathbf{R}_s}, \quad \mathbf{u}_\mathbf{k} = -\frac{i}{N} \sum_s \mathbf{u}_s e^{i\mathbf{k}\mathbf{R}_s}. \quad (31.1)$$

The problem thus reduces to calculating the average value of $\langle |\mathbf{q}_1 \mathbf{u}_\mathbf{q}|^2 \rangle$. At high temperatures we may use the classical approximation and average over the thermal vibrations by means of the probability factor $(-U/k_BT)$, where U is the potential energy of the atoms.

We shall consider that the force constants for each pair of atoms in the solution $V_{ss'}^{\alpha\alpha'}$ depend only on the sorts of atoms in question, i.e., they may be represented in the form of the square bracket on the left-hand side of (8.4), and that the constants $V''_{ss'}$ are negligibly small (the elastic modulis depend linearly on the composition). In the harmonic approximation U is a quadratic but nondiagonal function of $\mathbf{u}_\mathbf{q}$, which makes it difficult to calculate the averages $\langle |\mathbf{q}_1 \mathbf{u}_\mathbf{q}|^2 \rangle$. This calculation may be carried out quite easily, however, by the method of successive approximations in cases in which the force constants of the pairs of atoms differ little. In such cases (compare [281])

$$I_{1T}=Nf^2k_BT\mathbf{q}_1\Big[Q_\mathbf{q}^{-1}+2\sum_\rho\varepsilon(\rho)\sum_\mathbf{k}Q_\mathbf{q}^{-1}(Q'_\mathbf{q}+Q'_\mathbf{k}-Q'_{\mathbf{q}-\mathbf{k}})\times$$

$$\times Q_\mathbf{k}^{-1}(Q'_\mathbf{q}+Q'_\mathbf{k}-Q'_{\mathbf{q}-\mathbf{k}})Q_\mathbf{q}^{-1}\cos(\mathbf{q}-\mathbf{k})\rho\Big]\mathbf{q}_1, \qquad (31.2)$$

where $Q_\mathbf{k}^{-1}$ is a tensor inverse to the tensor $Q_{\mathbf{k}ij}$, determined from formula (6.4) and based on the average force constants $V_{ss'}$, while the tensor components $Q'_\mathbf{k}$, $Q'_{\mathbf{k}ij}$, are determined by this formula after replacing $V_{ss'}$ by $V'_{ss'}$ [see (8.4)]. For $\rho=0, \varepsilon(0)=c(1-c)$.

If the correlation parameters do not change with temperature (i.e., the order is "frozen"), then, as in ideal crystals, the thermal-scattering intensity (31.2) is proportional to T at high temperatures. The law $I_{1T}\sim q^{-2}$ as $q\to 0$ is also preserved. Passing to the solid solution, however, results in a severe complication of the relation between scattering intensity and force constants, making it much more difficult to determine these from experimental data. In ideal crystals $Q'_\mathbf{q}=0$ and only the first term is left in (31.2). For the vectors **q** lying along directions of high symmetry, the principal axes of the tensors $Q_\mathbf{q}$ are also parallel to these directions. This enables us to determine $Q_\mathbf{q}$ immediately (and of course $Q_\mathbf{q}^{-1}$) for such **q** from experimental data relating to single-phonon scattering. Knowing the $Q_\mathbf{q}$, even if only along certain directions, we can easily find the values of the force constants in any simplified model.*

In solid solutions, however, $Q'_\mathbf{q}\neq 0$ and the second term in (31.2) may be substantial (this term is associated with fluctuational inhomogeneities of the solution), and this makes it difficult to determine the force constants from x-ray data. In practice such a determination is only possible if the term in question is fairly small, i.e., if the force constants of the components of the solution

*In principle we may use the intensity I_{1T} for six independent values of $\mathbf{q}_1$ corresponding to a given **q** in order to determine $Q_\mathbf{q}^{-1}$ (and hence $Q_\mathbf{q}$) in an ideal crystal for any **q** (see note on p. 301). A Fourier transformation of these values of $Q_\mathbf{q}$ in the reciprocal-lattice cell would, in accordance with (6.4), determine all the force constants $V_{ss'ij}$ directly from experimental data, without recourse to any model. In practice, however, this method (which in principle enables us to use information regarding I_{1T} over the whole cell) is rather complicated.

differ little and the condition

$$c(1-c)\left(\frac{\lambda'}{\lambda}\right)^2 \ll 1, \tag{31.3}$$

is satisfied, where λ' is the maximum value of the derivative of the elastic modulus λ with respect to the concentration, and we remember that usually $|\varepsilon(\rho)| \ll \varepsilon(0)$.

Only in the range of small q, for which $I_{1T} \sim q^{-2}$, may the expressions for I_{1T} in ideal crystals and solid solutions, respectively, be written in a single form, as obtained on the macroscopic theory:

$$I_{1T} = Nf^2 \frac{k_B T}{v} (\lambda_{iljm} q_l q_m)_{ij}^{-1} q_{1i} q_{1j}. \tag{31.4}$$

It follows from this formula that in solid solutions, as in ideal crystals, an x-ray-diffraction determination of the elastic moduli is quite possible on the basis of data relating to the intensity I_{1T} at small q.

If both the force constants and the masses of the component atoms are nearly the same, we may consider the differences as small parameters and easily carry out a quantum calculation of the thermal-scattering intensity [281]. As in the case of ideal crystals, I_{1T} will thus be expressed in terms of the frequencies of the normal vibrations of the "average" periodic crystal and the corresponding polarization vectors. It is an important point, however, that in contrast to ideal crystals the I_{1T} in solutions is not simply determined by three frequencies ω_{qn} and vectors $\mathbf{e}_{qn}$, but also depends on the frequencies and polarizations of all the vibrations of the crystal (on account of the fact that the normal vibrations in solutions are not plane waves). Because of this, if there is a considerable difference in the atoms of the solution, it is impossible to determine the vibration frequencies in a solution directly from experimental data relating to x-ray diffraction.

Such a determination becomes possible (to a first approximation) only if the normal vibrations are approximately plane waves. For this, however, we must have not only a small difference between the force constants of pairs of atoms of different sorts, but also a small difference between the masses of the atoms, i.e., in addition to satisfying condition (31.3) (which is sufficient to enable us to determine the force constants at high temperatures), we must also satisfy the condition $(m_A - m_B)^2 \ll m^2$.

In addition to diffuse thermal scattering, solid solutions also give rise to diffuse scattering at the static inhomogeneities considered in Chapter V. It is clear that, for an x-ray-diffraction study of the vibration frequencies or force constants, we must first of all be able to separate these two types of scattering. If the atomic factors f_A and f_B are similar and the scattering at static inhomogeneities is due only to distortions resulting from the difference in the atomic radii, then such a separation may be carried out for scattering in directions of high symmetry in cubic crystals [282] by using the fact that (as indicated by symmetry considerations) according to equations (6.3) to (6.6) $\mathbf{A}_k \parallel \mathbf{k}$ for these directions, i.e., the waves of static distortions are purely longitudinal.

After measuring the diffuse-scattering intensity $I_{1\parallel}$ for $\mathbf{q} \parallel \mathbf{q}_1$, for example, along the [100] direction, we may determine the total effect of scattering at the static distortions and the longitudinal vibrations. Then we have to determine $I_{1\perp}$ for $q \perp 2\pi\mathbf{K}_n$ ($\mathbf{q} \parallel$ [010]) and for the same length of the vector $\mathbf{q}$, and subtract the contribution of $I_{1\parallel} q^2/q_1^2$ due to longitudinal vibrations and static displacements from the experimental value. This separates out that part of the scattering associated simply with transverse thermal vibrations. This method makes it possible to determine the frequencies of the transverse vibrations for directions of high symmetry in solutions with similar masses and force constants, and also the elastic moduli of the solutions. The method was used to study vibrations in a disordered Ni_3Fe alloy in [283].

It is more difficult to separate effects associated with static displacements and longitudinal vibrations. For this purpose, using the results of measurements at a single temperature, we must employ some approximate expressions for the intensity of the scattering at static inhomogeneities [283]. The desired separation of intensities may also be carried out more accurately in the more general case (for any orientation of the vectors $\mathbf{q}$ and for considerably differing f_A and f_B values) if we use the results of measurements at two temperatures and consider that $I_{1T} \sim T$ for $\hbar\omega_{qn} \lessdot k_B T$. We must nevertheless remember that the short- (and long-) range order in the solutions at these two temperatures must be identical (processes involving the establishment of order must be "frozen"), since both the scattering at static inhomogeneities and also thermal scattering [see (31.2)] may depend considerably on $\varepsilon(\rho)$.

Chapter IX

Inelastic Scattering of Neutrons at Vibrations of Ideal Harmonic Crystals

§32. Inelastic Neutron Scattering Cross Section and Correlation Functions

Thermal neutrons have wavelengths of the same order (~1Å) as x rays. From the point of view of studying the dynamics of crystals, however, it is extremely important that, in contrast to x rays, the energies of thermal neutrons ($\sim k_B T \sim 10^{-2}$ eV) have the same order of magnitude as the characteristic energies of the vibrational and other motions of the atoms (or spins) in the crystal. Hence the change of energy on scattering may be comparable with the energy of the incident neutron (or greater than this), so that we may study the energy distribution of inelastically scattered neutrons experimentally and thus determine the characteristic energies of the crystal. The finding of this distribution constitutes the best existing method of studying the dynamics of the atoms and spins in the crystal.*

The inelastic scattering of neutrons is characterized by the doubly differential cross section

$$\sigma(\mathbf{q}_1, E) = \frac{d^2\Sigma}{d\Omega\, dE},$$

*The theory of inelastic neutron scattering has been treated in monographs and reviews [75, 276, 284–286].

calculated for unit solid angle and unit energy. Usually this cross section is considered as a function of the change in the wave vector (momentum) of the neutron on scattering $\mathbf{q}_1 = \mathbf{k}_2 - \mathbf{k}_1$ ($\mathbf{k}_1$ and $\mathbf{k}_2$ are the wave vectors of the incident and scattered neutron waves) and the change in its energy $E = \frac{\hbar^2 k_2^2}{2m_n} - \frac{\hbar^2 k_1^2}{2m_n}$. Describing the interaction between neutrons and nuclei by means of the Fermi quasipotential V ($\mathbf{r}$), the nuclear scattering cross section $\sigma(\mathbf{q}_1, E)$ may be calculated by the ordinary formula of the first approximation in the Born theory of scattering:

$$\sigma(\mathbf{q}_1, E) = \frac{m_n^2}{4\pi^2\hbar^4}\frac{k_2}{k_1}\sum_{m,\, m_0} Z^{-1}\exp\left(-\frac{E_{m_0}}{k_B T}\right)|(m|V_{-\mathbf{q}_1}|m_0)|^2\,\delta(E+E_m-E_{m_0}),$$

$$V_{\mathbf{q}_1} = \int V(\mathbf{r})\exp(i\mathbf{q}_1\mathbf{r})\,d\mathbf{r}. \qquad (32.1)$$

Here we are averaging over the initial states of the scattering system m_0 with a Gibbs statistical weight (Z is the sum of the states) and summing over all possible final states m for which the law of energy conservation in the neutron/scattering system combination is satisfied.

Using the integral representation of the δ function

$$\delta(E+E_m-E_{m_0}) = \frac{1}{2\pi\hbar}\int_{-\infty}^{\infty}\exp(i\omega t)\exp\frac{i(E_m-E_{m_0})t}{\hbar}\,dt \quad \left(\omega = \frac{E}{\hbar}\right), \qquad (32.2)$$

remembering that

$$\sum_m (m_0|V_{\mathbf{q}_1}|m)(m|V^*_{\mathbf{q}_1}|m_0)\exp\frac{i(E_m-E_{m_0})t}{\hbar} =$$

$$= \sum_m (m_0|V_{\mathbf{q}_1}|m)(m|e^{\frac{iHt}{\hbar}}V^*_{\mathbf{q}_1}e^{-\frac{iHt}{\hbar}}|m_0) = (m_0|V_{\mathbf{q}_1}V^*_{\mathbf{q}_1}(t)|m_0) \qquad (32.3)$$

[where we have transformed to the Heisenberg representation of the operators and $V_{\mathbf{q}_1} = V_{\mathbf{q}_1}(0)$], and introducing the notation for the quantum-statistical mean

$$\langle\ldots\rangle=\sum_{m_0} Z^{-1}\exp\left(-\frac{E_{m_0}}{k_B T}\right)(m_0|\ldots|m_0),$$

we may convert expression (32.1) to integral form

$$\sigma(\mathbf{q}_1, E)=\frac{m_n^2}{8\pi^3\hbar^5}\frac{k_2}{k_1}\int_{-\infty}^{\infty}\langle V^*_{\mathbf{q}_1}V_{\mathbf{q}_1}(t)\rangle\exp(i\omega t)\,dt. \tag{32.4}$$

This kind of elimination of the δ function and transformation to integration with respect to time was used for a neutron-scattering problem by Akhiezer and Pomeranchuk [287], and the transformation to the Heisenberg operator was carried out by Wick [288], Van Hove [289], and Glauber [290].

The expression for the scattering cross section associated with the nuclei of the crystal may be put in a more specific form if instead of V ($\mathbf{r}$) we substitute the sum (12.11), integrate over the neutron coordinate $\mathbf{r}$, and also average over the spin states of the nuclei and over the isotopes, as was done on p. 120. Then, remembering the notation of (12.14), we may write $\sigma(\mathbf{q}_1, E)$ in the form

$$\sigma(\mathbf{q}_1, E)=\frac{1}{8\pi^2\hbar}\frac{k_2}{k_1}\sum_{s\gamma s'\gamma'}\left[\sqrt{\sigma_{cs\gamma}}\sqrt{\sigma_{cs'\gamma'}}+\delta_{ss'}\delta_{\gamma\gamma'}\sigma_{is\gamma}\right]\times$$

$$\times\exp[i\mathbf{q}_1(\mathbf{R}_{s\gamma}-\mathbf{R}_{s'\gamma'})]\exp[i\mathbf{q}_1(\delta\mathbf{R}^S_{s\gamma}-\delta\mathbf{R}^S_{s'\gamma'})]\times$$

$$\times\int_{-\infty}^{\infty}\langle e^{i\mathbf{q}_1\mathbf{u}_{s\gamma}(t)}\times e^{-i\mathbf{q}_1\mathbf{u}_{s'\gamma'}}\rangle e^{-i\omega t}\,dt, \tag{32.5}$$

where we have replaced t by $-t$, $\delta\mathbf{R}_{s\gamma}$ is divided into static and thermal displacements as in (25.2) (in this section we shall denote the latter by $\mathbf{u}_{s\gamma}$, omitting the index "T"), and $\sigma_{cs\gamma}$ and $\sigma_{is\gamma}$ are the cross sections of coherent and incoherent scattering for the nucleus of the element lying at the point $s\gamma$. In ideal crystals $\sigma_{cs\gamma}=\sigma_{c\gamma}$ are the same for all nuclei of the γ sublattice, $\delta\mathbf{R}^S_{s\gamma}=0$, and $\sigma(\mathbf{q}_1, E)$ falls naturally into two terms:

$$\sigma(\mathbf{q}_1, E)=\sigma_c(\mathbf{q}_1, E)+\sigma_i(\mathbf{q}_1, E), \tag{32.6}$$

$$\sigma_c(\mathbf{q}_1, E) = \frac{1}{8\pi^2\hbar}\frac{k_2}{k_1}\sum_{s\gamma s'\gamma'}\sqrt{\sigma_{c\gamma}\sigma_{c\gamma'}}\, e^{i\mathbf{q}_1(\mathbf{R}_{s\gamma}-\mathbf{R}_{s'\gamma'})} \times$$
$$\times \int_{-\infty}^{\infty} \langle e^{i\mathbf{q}_1\mathbf{u}_{s\gamma}(t)} e^{-i\mathbf{q}_1\mathbf{u}_{s'\gamma'}}\rangle\, e^{-i\omega t}\, dt, \qquad (32.7)$$

$$\sigma_i(\mathbf{q}_1, E) = \frac{1}{8\pi^2\hbar}\frac{k_2}{k_1} N \sum_{\gamma} \sigma_{i\gamma} \int_{-\infty}^{\infty} \langle e^{i\mathbf{q}_1\mathbf{u}_{s\gamma}(t)} e^{-i\mathbf{q}_1\mathbf{u}_{s\gamma}}\rangle\, e^{-i\omega t}\, dt. \qquad (32.8)$$

The cross section $\sigma_i(\mathbf{q}_1, E)$ is associated with the scattering of neutrons accompanied by a possible change in the spin state of the nuclei and with scattering at a completely random distribution of isotopes. The intensity of this scattering is composed additively of the intensities of the scattering created by the individual nuclei; the waves scattered by different nuclei do not interfere at all and there is no coherence (no phase relationship) between the incident and scattered waves. For this reason $\sigma_i(\mathbf{q}_1, E)$ is called the incoherent neutron-scattering cross section. On the other hand, in the cross section $\sigma_c(\mathbf{q}_1, E)$ associated with scattering at "average" (with respect to the isotopes) nuclei, a considerable part is played by the interference of waves scattered by different nuclei, and specific phase relationships are preserved between these waves. The cross section of this scattering, $\sigma_c(\mathbf{q}_1, E)$, is usually called the coherent-scattering cross section.

If the energy of the incident neutron is fairly large, greatly exceeding the change in energy on scattering, then the factor k_2/k_1 in (32.7) and (32.8) is close to unity. In this case it is easy to integrate the cross sections $\sigma_c(\mathbf{q}_1, E)$ and $\sigma_i(\mathbf{q}_1, E)$ with respect to energies, remembering that

$$\frac{1}{2\pi\hbar}\int_{-\infty}^{\infty} dE \exp\left(-\frac{iEt}{\hbar}\right) = \delta(t). \qquad (32.9)$$

The appearance of the δ function $\delta(t)$ enables us immediately to calculate the integrals with respect to t, which reduce to the mean

$$\langle \exp(i\mathbf{q}_1\mathbf{u}_{s\gamma}) \exp(-i\mathbf{q}_1\mathbf{u}_{s'\gamma'})\rangle$$

of the (low commuting) operators taken at the same moments of time.

Remembering (12.14), we may at once confirm that the resultant expression for the integral (with respect to energies) scattering cross section

$$\sigma(\mathbf{q}_1) = \int \sigma(\mathbf{q}_1, E)\, dE$$

coincides with expression (12.13), derived on the static approximation for the case in which the nuclei may be regarded as immobile. For this approximation to be valid, we thus require that $k_2 \approx k_1$, and the latter condition is satisfied if the energy of the incident neutron greatly exceeds the characteristic energies of the thermal motions of the atoms in the crystal (energies of the phonons), and also if the masses of the atoms greatly exceed the energy of the neutron (so that we may neglect recoil energy). For x rays this static approximation (used in Part I) is clearly always satisfied to great accuracy.

Expressions (32.7) and (32.8) describe both the elastic and the inelastic scattering of neutrons. It is not difficult to separate out the part of the cross section proportional to the δ function $\delta(\omega)$ and that corresponding to angular scattering if we remember that, in the integration of (32.7) and (32.8) with respect to t, only the part of the integral corresponding to limitingly large time intervals plays a part in the δ function. On the other hand, for fairly long time intervals, considerably exceeding the relaxation time in the system, correlation between the displacements of the atoms $\mathbf{u}_{s\gamma}(t)$ and $\mathbf{u}_{s'\gamma'}(0)$ vanishes and the means of the products of the operators in (32.7) and (32.8) may be replaced by the products of the means.

Remembering that, according to (23.2)

$$\langle \exp[i\mathbf{q}_1\mathbf{u}_{s\gamma}(t)]\rangle = \exp(-M_\gamma),$$

i.e., that such means reduce to Debye–Waller factors, we may divide the means of the product

$$\langle e^{i\mathbf{q}_1\mathbf{u}_{s\gamma}(t)} e^{-i\mathbf{q}_1\mathbf{u}_{s'\gamma'}}\rangle = e^{-(M_\gamma + M_{\gamma'})} + [\langle e^{i\mathbf{q}_1\mathbf{u}_{s\gamma}(t)} e^{-i\mathbf{q}_1\mathbf{u}_{s'\gamma'}}\rangle - e^{-(M_\gamma + M_{\gamma'})}] \quad (32.10)$$

into two components, one of which tends to zero as $t \to \infty$. Only the first, constant term in (32.10) gives a contribution to the elastic scattering cross section

$$\sigma_c^y(\mathbf{q}_1, E) = \delta(\omega)\frac{1}{4\pi\hbar}\left|\sum_{s\gamma}\sqrt{\sigma_{c\gamma}}\,e^{-M_\gamma}e^{i\mathbf{q}_1\mathbf{R}_{s\gamma}}\right|^2,$$

$$\sigma_i^y(\mathbf{q}_1, E) = \delta(\omega)\frac{1}{4\pi\hbar}N\sum_{\gamma}\sigma_{i\gamma}e^{-2M_\gamma}, \qquad (32.11)$$

which in ideal crystals reduces to the Bragg regular reflections (the intensity of which is weakened by the Debye–Waller factor) and to the angle-independent incoherent diffuse scattering σ_i^y. The second term in (32.10), tending to zero as $t \to \infty$, after substitution in (32.7) and (32.8), gives a smooth function of energy, describing the inelastic scattering.

We see from (32.5) to (32.8) that the energy distribution of the inelastic scattering of neutrons is determined by the Fourier components of the time correlation functions

$$\langle \exp[i\mathbf{q}_1\mathbf{u}_{s\gamma}(t)]\exp[-i\mathbf{q}_1\mathbf{u}_{s'\gamma'}]\rangle.$$

The cross section may also be expressed in terms of a four-dimensional Fourier component of the correlation function in space and time, which was derived in the classical treatment of Van Hove [289] on neutron scattering and constitutes the natural generalization of the space-correlation function [of the type of $\varepsilon(\boldsymbol{\rho})$ in Chapter I].

For this purpose let us consider, for example, a system (not necessarily a crystal) consisting of atoms of one type, and let us enumerate the atoms by means of an index s. Instead of $\mathbf{R}_s + \mathbf{u}_s$ we introduce the radius vector of the s-th atom $\mathbf{r}_s$. Then the coherent-scattering cross section (32.7) may be written in the form

$$\sigma_c(\mathbf{q}_1, E) = \frac{1}{8\pi^2\hbar}N\frac{k_2}{k_1}\sigma_c\int g(\mathbf{r}, t)\,e^{i(\mathbf{q}_1\mathbf{r}-\omega t)}\,d\mathbf{r}\,dt, \qquad (32.12)$$

where

$$g(\mathbf{r}, t) = \frac{1}{8\pi^3N}\sum_{s,s'=1}^{N}\int\langle e^{i\mathbf{k}\mathbf{r}_s(t)}e^{-i\mathbf{k}\mathbf{r}_{s'}}\rangle\,e^{-i\mathbf{k}\mathbf{r}}\,d\mathbf{k} =$$

$$= \frac{1}{N}\left\langle\sum_{s,s'=1}^{N}\int d\mathbf{r}'\,\delta(\mathbf{r}-\mathbf{r}_s(t)-\mathbf{r}')\,\delta(\mathbf{r}'+\mathbf{r}_{s'}(0))\right\rangle =$$

$$= \frac{1}{N} < \int d\mathbf{r}' \rho(\mathbf{r}-\mathbf{r}', t) \rho(-\mathbf{r}', 0) >. \qquad (32.13)$$

In the last-but-one transformation we have used the convolution formula for the Fourier transformation of the ordered product of operators, and in the last transformation we have introduced the operator

$$\rho(\mathbf{r}, t) = \sum_{s=1}^{N} \delta(\mathbf{r}-\mathbf{r}_s)$$

of the density atoms.

For t = 0 the operators $\mathbf{r}_s$ and $\mathbf{r}_{s'}$ commute and the function

$$g(\mathbf{r}, 0) = \frac{1}{N} \left\langle \sum_{s, s'=1}^{N} \delta(\mathbf{r}+\mathbf{r}_{s'}-\mathbf{r}_s) \right\rangle = \delta(\mathbf{r}) + \frac{1}{N} \left\langle \sum_{\substack{s, s'=1 \\ (s \neq s')}}^{N} \delta(\mathbf{r}+\mathbf{r}_{s'}-\mathbf{r}_s) \right\rangle \qquad (32.14)$$

reduces to the sum of a δ function and the ordinary space-correlation function. The function $g(\mathbf{r}, t)$ also has a simple physical sense in the classical approximation, in which we may also neglect the noncommutativity of the operators $\mathbf{r}_s(t)$ and $\mathbf{r}_{s'}(0)$. In this approximation, after integrating with respect to $\mathbf{r}'$ in (32.13)

$$g(\mathbf{r}, t) = \frac{1}{N} \left\langle \sum_{s, s'=1}^{N} \delta(\mathbf{r}+\mathbf{r}_{s'}(0)-\mathbf{r}_s(t)) \right\rangle. \qquad (32.15)$$

This function determines the density of particles at the point $\mathbf{r}$ at the instant of time t, on condition that at t = 0 one of the atoms lay at the origin of coordinates. On allowing for quantum effects the function $g(\mathbf{r}, t)$ becomes complex and its physical interpretation is more complicated [289, 291].

In the same way, the incoherent-scattering cross section (32.8) for the system under consideration may be written in the form

$$\sigma_i(\mathbf{q}_1, E) = \frac{1}{8\pi^2\hbar} N \frac{k_2}{k_1} \sigma_i \int g_s(\mathbf{r}, t) e^{i(\mathbf{q}_1\mathbf{r}-\omega t)} d\mathbf{r}\, dt, \qquad (32.16)$$

where

$$g_s(\mathbf{r}, t) = \frac{1}{8\pi^3} \int \langle e^{i\mathbf{k}\mathbf{r}_s(t)} e^{-i\mathbf{k}\mathbf{r}_s} \rangle e^{-i\mathbf{k}\mathbf{r}} d\mathbf{k} =$$

$$= \left\langle \int dr' \delta(\mathbf{r} - \mathbf{r}' - \mathbf{r}_s(t)) \, \delta(\mathbf{r}' + \mathbf{r}_s(0)) \right\rangle. \qquad (32.17)$$

The function $g_s(\mathbf{r}, t)$ is called the autocorrelation function and characterizes the correlation between the positions of the same particle at different instants of time.

The use of the correlation functions is very convenient for a qualitative study of the character of the distribution of neutrons scattered by complex systems such as liquids in which no explicit expressions can be obtained for scattering cross sections. The general character of the behavior of the correlation functions $g(\mathbf{r}, t)$ and $g_s(\mathbf{r}, t)$ at different times t in such complex systems may usually be predicted on the basis of general considerations founded on the introduction of characteristic relaxation times in the system and characteristic lengths [289]. The general picture of the relation between the cross sections and the limiting energy and momentum is formulated in this way.

It should be noted, however, that for specific calculations of the cross sections $\sigma(\mathbf{q}_1, E)$ it is more convenient not to calculate the space-time correlation functions $g(\mathbf{r}, t)$ but to make a direct determination of the four-dimensional Fourier component (with respect to $\mathbf{r}$ and t), which is directly related to the scattering cross sections.* The calculation of this Fourier component is considerably simpler (as in the case of spatial correlation considered in Part I).

§33. Single-Phonon Coherent Scattering of Neutrons and Determination of the Dispersion of the Oscillation Frequencies of the Atoms in the Crystal

If the thermal displacements of the atoms in a crystal and the change in the momentum of a neutron on scattering are not too large, the inelastic neutron-scattering cross section for thermal oscillations (vibrations) may naturally be determined by expanding

*Many papers have been written on space-time correlation functions in different systems; see, for example, [292–295].

the expressions (32.7) and (32.8) in series with respect to the displacements, i.e., $\mathbf{q}_1\mathbf{u}_{s\gamma}(t)$ and $\mathbf{q}_1\mathbf{u}_{s'\gamma'}$. The zero term of the expansion and also terms of the type

$$\{\mathbf{q}_1\mathbf{u}_{s\gamma}(t)\}^{2n}\{\mathbf{q}_1\mathbf{u}_{s'\gamma'}\}^0 \text{ and } \{\mathbf{q}_1\mathbf{u}_{s\gamma}(t)\}^0\{\mathbf{q}_1\mathbf{u}_{s'\gamma'}\}^{2n}$$

(terms of the $\{\mathbf{q}_1\mathbf{u}_{s\gamma}(t)\}^0\,\mathbf{q}_1\mathbf{u}_{s'\gamma'}$ type vanish on averaging) are plainly proportional to the δ function $\delta(\omega)$ and correspond to elastic scattering.

The first term in the expansion of the $[\mathbf{q}_1\mathbf{u}_{s\gamma}(t)]\,(\mathbf{q}_1\mathbf{u}_{s'\gamma'})$ type corresponds to the linear term in the expansion of the scattering amplitude in powers of the displacements, and for small $\mathbf{q}_1\mathbf{u}_{s\gamma}$ gives the main contribution to the single-phonon scattering cross section, in which the scattering of the neutrons is accompanied by the emission or absorption of one of the phonons. The term of the $\{\mathbf{q}_1\mathbf{u}_{s\gamma}(t)\}^2\,\{\mathbf{q}_1\mathbf{u}_{s'\gamma'}\}^2$ type determined two-phonon scattering, the elementary act of which involves two phonons, and so on (here we are only concerned with the principal contributions to the corresponding cross sections, since the higher terms of the expansions also give a certain contribution, for example, to the single-phonon scattering cross section).

From the point of view of studying the dynamics of the vibrations of the atoms in the crystal, single-phonon scattering is of principal interest, and this has been discussed in a number of papers; see, for example, [76, 287, 296–301]. The coherent part of this scattering, as we shall see later, may be experimentally separated in a quite natural way from the total scattering cross section; only one wave of vibrations takes part in the corresponding scattering process, and a study of this scattering enables us directly to determine the frequencies and polarizations of the phonons. Confining ourselves to the case of small thermal displacements, in determining the single-phonon coherent-scattering cross section of an ideal crystal $\sigma_c^{(1)}(\mathbf{q}_1, E)$, we may limit consideration to terms of the $[\mathbf{q}_1\mathbf{u}_{s\gamma}(t)]\,(\mathbf{q}_1\mathbf{u}_{s'\gamma'})$ type only in the expansion

$$\sigma_c^{(1)}(\mathbf{q}_1, E) = \frac{1}{8\pi^2\hbar}\frac{k_2}{k_1}\sum_{s\gamma s'\gamma'}\sqrt{\sigma_{c\gamma}\sigma_{c\gamma'}}\,e^{i\mathbf{q}_1(\mathbf{R}_{s\gamma}-\mathbf{R}_{s'\gamma'})}\times$$

$$\times\int_{-\infty}^{\infty}\langle(\mathbf{q}_1\mathbf{u}_{s\gamma}(t))\,(\mathbf{q}_1\mathbf{u}_{s'\gamma'})\rangle\,e^{-i\omega t}\,dt. \qquad (33.1)$$

In the harmonic approximation, expression (33.1) may easily be calculated by transforming from the thermal vibrations $\mathbf{u}_{s\gamma}$ to normal coordinates. In an ideal crystal the normal coordinates may be derived in the form of traveling plane waves (these differ slightly from the real normal coordinates used in §23). According to [162–164], the expansion in such normal coordinates may be written in the form

$$\mathbf{u}_{s\gamma}=\sum_{\mathbf{k}n}\left(\frac{\hbar}{2Nm\omega_{\mathbf{k}n}}\right)^{1/2}\mathbf{e}_{\mathbf{k}n\gamma}e^{i\mathbf{k}\mathbf{R}_{s\gamma}}(a_{\mathbf{k}n}-a^{+}_{-\mathbf{k}n}),\quad \mathbf{e}^{*}_{-\mathbf{k}n\gamma}=-\mathbf{e}_{\mathbf{k}n\gamma}. \tag{33.2}$$

Here $a^{+}_{\mathbf{k}n}$ and $a_{\mathbf{k}n}$ are the operators of the generation and annihilation of a phonon of the n-th branch with wave vector $\mathbf{k}$, the values of $\mathbf{k}/2\pi$ lie within the reciprocal-lattice cell, $\mathbf{e}_{\mathbf{k}n\gamma}$ are the polarization vectors, satisfying the normalization condition

$$\sum_{s\gamma}\mathbf{e}_{\mathbf{k}n\gamma}\mathbf{e}^{*}_{\mathbf{k}'n'\gamma}m_{\gamma}\exp\left[i(\mathbf{k}-\mathbf{k}')\mathbf{R}_{s\gamma}\right]=mN\delta_{\mathbf{k}\mathbf{k}'}\delta_{\gamma\gamma'},$$

m_γ is the mass of the atom at lattice point γ, and m is the mass of the cell.

In the harmonic approximation, the operators a and a^+ have a very simple time dependence:

$$a_{\mathbf{k}n}(t)=a_{\mathbf{k}n}\exp(-i\omega_{\mathbf{k}n}t),\qquad a^{+}_{\mathbf{k}n}(t)=a^{+}_{\mathbf{k}n}\exp(i\omega_{\mathbf{k}n}t).$$

The means of the products of these operators in this approximation only differ from zero for identical indices:

$$\langle a_{\mathbf{k}n}a^{+}_{\mathbf{k}'n'}\rangle=(n_{\mathbf{k}n}+1)\,\delta_{\mathbf{k}\mathbf{k}'}\delta_{nn'},\qquad \langle a^{+}_{\mathbf{k}n}a_{\mathbf{k}'n'}\rangle=n_{\mathbf{k}n}\delta_{\mathbf{k}\mathbf{k}'}\delta_{nn'},$$

$$n_{\mathbf{k}n}=\left(\exp\frac{\hbar\omega_{\mathbf{k}n}}{k_BT}-1\right)^{-1}$$

(the means $\langle a_{\mathbf{k}n}a_{\mathbf{k}'n'}\rangle$ and $\langle a^{+}_{\mathbf{k}n}a^{+}_{\mathbf{k}'n'}\rangle$ are always equal to zero). Substituting expansion (33.2) into (33.1) and remembering these simplifications, we may sum over s and s' (it should be remembered that for any vector $\mathbf{K}_n$ of the reciprocal lattice $\exp(2\pi i\mathbf{K}_n\mathbf{R}_s) = 1$ and that the sum $\sum_s \exp i(\mathbf{q}-\mathbf{k})\mathbf{R}_s$ equals N for $\mathbf{q}=\mathbf{k}$ and equals 0 for $\mathbf{q}\neq\mathbf{k}$; compare p. 298), integrate over t, and put the single-phonon coherent-scattering cross section in the form of the sum of a smallish number of terms (with respect to the vibration branches):

$$\sigma_c^{(1)}(\mathbf{q}_1,E)=N\frac{k_2}{k_1}\sum_{n=1}^{3\nu}\frac{|Q_{\mathbf{q}_1 n}|^2}{\omega_{\mathbf{q}n}}\times$$

$$\times\left[n_{\mathbf{q}n}\delta(\omega-\omega_{\mathbf{q}n})+(n_{-\mathbf{q}n}+1)\delta(\omega_{-\mathbf{q}n}+\omega)\right], \qquad (33.3)$$

where $\mathbf{q}=\mathbf{q}_1-2\pi\mathbf{K}_n$ lies in the first cell of the reciprocal lattice, $\omega_{-\mathbf{q}n}=\omega_{\mathbf{q}n}$ (and $n_{-\mathbf{q}n}=n_{\mathbf{q}n}$),

$$Q_{\mathbf{q}_1 n}=\frac{1}{\sqrt{8\pi m}}\sum_{\gamma=1}^{\nu}\sqrt{\sigma_{c\gamma}}\,\mathbf{q}_1\mathbf{e}_{\mathbf{q}n\gamma}\exp(2\pi i\mathbf{K}_n\mathbf{R}_\gamma). \qquad (33.4)$$

More detailed consideration, allowing for the higher terms of the expansion, leads to the appearance of the Debye–Waller factors $\exp(-M_\gamma)$ along with $\sqrt{\sigma_{c\gamma}}$ in formula (33.4).

The first term in (33.3) describes processes in which the scattering of the neutrons is accompanied by the absorption of phonons and the second term describes processes with the emission of phonons. We see from (33.3) that, as a result of interference effects in single-phonon coherent scattering, only one phonon of each branch of vibrations (corresponding to the Bragg condition for scattering at a structure modulated by the vibration in question) takes part in the scattering of neutrons with a given change of momentum $\hbar\mathbf{q}_1=\hbar(\mathbf{k}_2-\mathbf{k}_1)$. If we ascribe the momentum $\hbar(\mathbf{q}+2\pi\mathbf{K}_n)$ to the phonon absorbed on scattering, then the interference condition may be considered as the law of conservation of momentum

$$\mathbf{k}_2-\mathbf{k}_1=\mathbf{q}_1=\mathbf{q}+2\pi\mathbf{K}_n, \qquad (33.5)$$

in accordance with which the change in the momentum of the neutron on scattering equals the momentum of the absorbed phonon. In the case of the emission of a phonon we simply replace $\mathbf{q}$ by $-\mathbf{q}$ in this equation.

The presence of the δ functions in (33.3) is associated with the fact that the increase in energy during single-phonon scattering must (on the harmonic approximation) be exactly equal to the energy of the absorbed phonon, i.e., the law of energy conservation must be obeyed:

$$\hbar\omega = \frac{\hbar^2 k_2^2}{2m_n} - \frac{\hbar^2 k_1^2}{2m_n} = \hbar\omega_{qn}. \qquad (33.6)$$

In the case of the emission of a phonon in this equation we simply change the sign of $\hbar\omega_{qn}$.

The satisfaction of the two laws of the conservation of energy and momentum during single-phonon coherent scattering offers the possibility of separating this from other forms of scattering experimentally. In principle this may be done most simply if we study the relation between the scattering cross section $\sigma(\mathbf{q}_1, E)$ and the energy for a given value of $\mathbf{q}$.* Then, according to (33.3), 3ν δ-shaped peaks (for positive and negative E) should be observed in the energy distribution, corresponding to single-phonon coherent scattering. In the harmonic approximation, for ideal crystals, these sharp peaks have zero width (neglecting instrumental broadening) and may be separated experimentally from the smooth energy distributions corresponding to multiphonon and incoherent scattering.

Usually, however, the experimental study of the energy distribution of scattered neutrons is carried out by another method, in which the wave vector of the incident monochromatic neutrons $\mathbf{k}_1$, the orientation of the crystal, and the scattering angle (direction of $\mathbf{k}_2$) are given, while the value of $|\mathbf{k}_2|$ changes together with the energy. The single-phonon scattering cross section was studied in detail in this case by Placzek and Van Hove [299] for an arbitrary law of phonon dispersion.

The simplest picture arises in the case of very slow ("cold") incident neutrons, when their energy is negligibly small compared

* The changes in the energy and momentum of the neutron on scattering are (generally speaking) related. Hence in order that the change in E should not involve a change in $\mathbf{q}$ (for a given wave vector of the incident monochromatic neutrons $\mathbf{k}_1$) when studying the energy distribution of the scattered neutrons by the crystal-spectrometer method, on passing to a new energy value we must at the same time change the scattering angle and crystal orientation in such a way that $\mathbf{q}$ may remain unaltered [302].

with the energy of a phonon. Then putting $\mathbf{k}_1 = 0$ and remembering that the frequency of the vibrations $\omega_{\mathbf{q}n}$ may be regarded as a periodic function of $\mathbf{q}$ with the periods of the reciprocal lattice, the conservation laws (33.5) and (33.6) may be rewritten in the form

$$\frac{\hbar^2 k_2^2}{2m_n} = \hbar\omega_{\mathbf{k}_2 n}. \tag{33.7}$$

Formula (33.7) may be considered as an equation determining the value of the momentum (and energy) of a scattered neutron for a given scattering direction and at the same time the energy of a phonon with wave vector $\mathbf{k}_2$. For any scattering direction and for each branch n, equation (33.7) has a solution, i.e., in any direction peaks of single-phonon coherent scattering arise in the energy distribution of the scattered neutrons.

Actually for fairly large k_2 the difference

$$\frac{\hbar^2 k_2^2}{2m_n} - \hbar\omega_{\mathbf{k}_2 n}$$

is positive, since $\omega_{\mathbf{k}_2 n}$ cannot exceed the maximum frequency of the vibrations of the crystal ω_m. On the other hand, for small k_2 this difference is negative, since as $k_2 \rightarrow 0$ the frequency $\omega_{\mathbf{k}_2 n}$ tends to a constant limit (for the optical branches of the vibrations), or (for the acoustic branches) tends linearly (more slowly than k_2^2) to zero. Hence for every n and $\mathbf{k}_2/k_2$ the difference in question passes at any rate once through zero, i.e., equation (33.7) has a solution.

The set of solutions of this equation forms a surface S_n in $\mathbf{k}$ space, and all the 3ν surfaces associated with different n may be considered as a single (generally speaking, mutually intersecting) "surface of scattering" S. We see from (33.7) that the surface S lies inside a sphere of radius

$$k_m = (2m_n\omega_m\hbar^{-1})^{1/2}.$$

Generally speaking, this is multiply connected. Considering the difference $\frac{\hbar^2 k_2^2}{2m_n} - \hbar\omega_{\mathbf{k}_2 n}$ as before, it is easy to confirm that the surface S passes through every region of $\mathbf{k}$ space containing reciprocal-lattice point $2\pi\mathbf{K}_n$ and the point at which $\omega_{\mathbf{k}n}$ reaches a maximum value of ω_m (in particular, S passes through each cell of the reciprocal lattice situated in a sphere of radius k_m). Thus a ray drawn from the origin of coordinates in any direction of **k** space intersects the surface S at least 3ν times (if it falls on no self-intersection points), but, generally speaking, the number of intersections may be greater.

By studying the peaks in question in the energy distribution for various scattering directions, we may establish the surface S and thus determine the vibration frequencies $\omega_{\mathbf{k}n}$ for certain values of k. In order to determine these frequencies for all **k**, we must use neutrons with a nonzero wave vector $\mathbf{k}_1$. The conservation laws (33.5) and (33.6) may in this case be written in the form of a single relation

$$\frac{\hbar^2 k_2^2}{2m_n} = \frac{\hbar^2 k_1^2}{2m_n} + \hbar\omega_{\mathbf{k}_2 - \mathbf{k}_1 n}, \tag{33.8}$$

which also gives the S surface in **k** space, in this case lying between spheres with radii

$$k_1 \text{ and } (k_1^2 + 2m_n\omega_m\hbar^{-1})^{1/2}.$$

The study of these surfaces (i.e., of the peaks in the energy distribution) for various $\mathbf{k}_1$ offers the possibility of determining the phonon frequencies $\omega_{\mathbf{k}n}$ for all values of **k**.

In addition to the peaks in the energy distribution lying at positive values of the energy E given to the neutron and corresponding to scattering processes involving the absorption of phonons, (33.3) shows that there may also be peaks at negative values of $E = -\hbar\omega_{\mathbf{q}n}$, corresponding to the emission of phonons. However, in contrast to the case of phonon absorption, processes involving phonon emission with small energies of the incident neutrons are not admitted by the law of energy conservation [for this case we must reverse the sign of $\hbar\omega_{\mathbf{k}_2-\mathbf{k}_1 n}$ in (33.8)]. Only if k_1 exceeds a certain minimum value are such processes possible for certain scattering directions, and then, beginning from some energy E_1 of the incident neutrons (smaller than $\hbar\omega_m$), for all directions. In other words, we may say that the emission of phonons becomes possible if the velocity of the neutron is large enough to satisfy the condition of the Čerenkov radiation of phonons (this point of view was employed by Kaganov in discussing neutron scattering [303]).

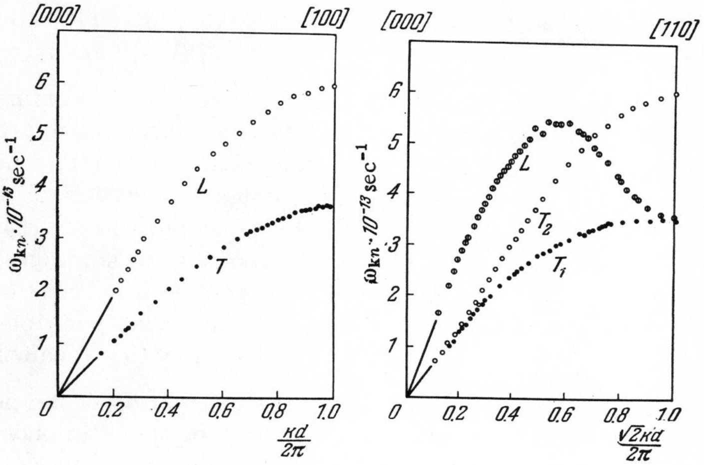

Fig. 21. Vibration frequencies as functions of wave vector for the [100] and [110] directions in Al at 300°C, as given in [308].

This neutron-diffraction method of determining the vibration frequencies has an advantage over the x-ray-diffraction method in this respect, that, first, it offers the possibility of determining the frequencies ω_{kn} for any **k** from direct experiment, and secondly that the frequencies are determined not from the values of single-phonon scattering intensity (which in the case of x rays is not determined very accurately owing to the impossibility of introducing corrections for multiphonon and Compton scattering) but from the positions of the peaks in the energy distribution, which may usually be distinguished much more accurately.*

The vibration frequencies have been determined for a large number of crystals by this method (for example, in Al [38, 304, 306–308], Cu [309–312], Pb [313], Ni [314], Fe [315], Nb [316], Zn [317], Ge [318, 319], NaI [320, 321], NaF [440], KBr [321], MgO [322], GaAs [323], and so on; see also [324]). By way of example

*Here the error may be due to the fact that these peaks are not infinitely narrow, but are always diffuse as a result of instrumental broadening (associated in particular with a certain angular and energy spread of the incident neutrons) and also as a result of physical broadening due to anharmonicity and the nonideal state of the crystal (see Chap. X).

Fig. 21 shows $\omega_{\mathbf{k}n}$ as functions of **k** for the [100] and [110] directions, as determined to an accuracy of 1 or 2% in [308].

The study of single-phonon coherent neutron scattering also (in principle) offers the possibility of determining the polarization vectors $\mathbf{e}_{\mathbf{k}n\gamma}$ as well as the vibration frequencies. For this purpose we must measure the intensities of the coherent-scattering peaks, which according to (33.3) and (33.4) depend on the vectors $\mathbf{e}_{\mathbf{k}n\gamma}$, for a number of different values of $\mathbf{q}_1$ corresponding to some given $\mathbf{q}$. In practice, however, it is much more complicated to measure the intensities of these peaks than it is to determine the positions of their maxima, which are used in finding the vibration frequencies.

We note that according to (33.1) the intensities of the peaks corresponding to the emission or absorption of acoustic phonons tend to infinity as $\omega_{\mathbf{q}n}^{-2} \sim q^{-2}$ for small q (in this case $\bar{n}_{\mathbf{q}n} \approx k_B T/\hbar\omega_{\mathbf{q}n}$).

§34. Single-Phonon Incoherent Scattering of Neutrons and Determination of the Distribution Function of the Oscillation Frequencies

The study of the energy distribution of single-phonon incoherent neutron scattering is also of considerable interest, as it offers the possibility of directly determining the vibration (oscillation) frequency-distribution function of the crystal, and this completely determines many important characteristics, in particular the whole thermodynamics of an ideal crystal in the harmonic approximation.

As in the previous case of coherent scattering, for small amplitudes of the thermal vibrations we may expand the incoherent scattering cross section (32.8) in series in powers of $\mathbf{u}_{S\gamma}(t)$ and $\mathbf{u}_{S\gamma}$, the main contribution to the single-phonon scattering cross section $\sigma_i^{(1)}(\mathbf{q}_1, E)$ for small $\mathbf{u}_{S\gamma}$ coming from terms in the expansion of the $(\mathbf{q}_1\mathbf{u}_{S\gamma}(t)) \times (\mathbf{q}_1\mathbf{u}_{S\gamma})$ type:

$$\sigma_i^{(1)}(\mathbf{q}_1, E) = \frac{1}{8\pi^2\hbar}\frac{k_2}{k_1} N \sum_{\gamma} \sigma_{i\gamma} \int_{-\infty}^{\infty} \langle (\mathbf{q}_1\mathbf{u}_{s\gamma}(t))\,(\mathbf{q}_1\mathbf{u}_{s\gamma}(0))\rangle\, e^{-i\omega t}\, dt. \quad (34.1)$$

Substituting for $\mathbf{u}_{S\gamma}$ the expansion in normal coordinates (33.2), averaging in the manner of §33, passing from the sum over **k** to an integral, and integrating with respect to t, we may write the expression for $\sigma_i^{(1)}(\mathbf{q}_1, E)$ in the form

$$\sigma_i^{(1)}(\mathbf{q}_1, E) = \frac{1}{8\pi m}\frac{k_2}{k_1}\frac{v}{8\pi^3}\times$$

$$\times \sum_\gamma \sigma_{i\gamma} \sum_n \int d\mathbf{k} \frac{|\mathbf{q}_1 \mathbf{e}_{\mathbf{k}n\gamma}|^2}{\omega_{\mathbf{k}n}} [n_{\mathbf{k}n}\delta(\omega_{\mathbf{k}n}-\omega)+(n_{\mathbf{k}n}+1)\,\delta(\omega_{\mathbf{k}n}+\omega)]. \quad (34.2)$$

Whereas, in the case of single-phonon coherent scattering, the interference conditions require the satisfaction of the law of conservation of momentum, and only one phonon of each branch makes a contribution to the scattering cross section (33.3), in incoherent scattering only one nucleus participates, there is no interference, and the change in the momentum of the neutron is transferred not to a single phonon but to the crystal as a whole. The law of momentum conservation is not satisfied, and in incoherent scattering a phonon with any momentum may be either emitted or absorbed. However, the law of energy conservation (33.6) (with $\mathbf{q}$ replaced by $\mathbf{k}$), requiring that the change in the energy of the neutron should equal the energy of the absorbed phonon, must also be satisfied in the case of incoherent single-phonon scattering [it appears in the presence of the δ functions in (34.2)].

The expression for the cross section $\sigma_i^{(1)}(\mathbf{q}_1, E)$ is greatly simplified in the case of cubic crystals with one atom per cell. In crystals with a Bravais lattice the summation over γ vanishes, and $\mathbf{e}_{\mathbf{k}n\gamma} = \mathbf{e}_{\mathbf{k}n}$ are the same for all atoms in the crystal. For each polarization vector $\mathbf{e}_{\mathbf{k}n}$ in a cubic crystal we may set up two other vectors $\mathbf{e}_{\mathbf{k}'n}$ and $\mathbf{e}_{\mathbf{k}''n}$ in such a way that they are mutually perpendicular and transform one into the other by certain transformations of cubic symmetry (i.e., they correspond to the same frequencies $\omega_{\mathbf{k}n}$). Since the sum of the terms $(\mathbf{q}_1 \mathbf{e}_{\mathbf{k}n})^2$ for every such triad of wave vectors $\mathbf{k}$, $\mathbf{k}'$, $\mathbf{k}''$ equals q_1^2, while the remaining factors in (34.2) for these terms are the same, we may replace $(\mathbf{q}_1 \mathbf{e}_{\mathbf{k}n})^2$ by $1/3\, q_1^2$ under the sign of the summation with respect to $\mathbf{k}$. Then for cubic crystals with a Bravais lattice

$$\sigma_i^{(1)}(\mathbf{q}_1, E) = \frac{1}{24\pi m}\frac{v}{8\pi^3}\frac{k_2}{k_1}\sigma_i q_1^2\times$$

$$\times \sum_n \int d\mathbf{k} \frac{1}{\omega_{\mathbf{k}n}} [n_{\mathbf{k}n}\delta(\omega_{\mathbf{k}n}-\omega)+(n_{\mathbf{k}n}+1)\,\delta(\omega_{\mathbf{k}n}+\omega)]. \quad (34.3)$$

By means of the vibration frequency-distribution function $g(\omega)$, defined by the formula

$$g(\omega)=\frac{1}{d\omega}\frac{1}{N}\sum_{\substack{\mathbf{k}n \\ (\omega<\omega_{\mathbf{k}n}\leqslant\omega+d\omega)}} 1 = \frac{v}{8\pi^3}\frac{1}{d\omega}\sum_{n}\int_{(\omega<\omega_{\mathbf{k}n}\leqslant\omega+d\omega)} d\mathbf{k} =$$

$$=\frac{v}{8\pi^3}\sum_{n}\int_{S_n(\omega)}\frac{dS_n}{|\nabla_{\mathbf{k}}\omega_{\mathbf{k}n}|}=\frac{v}{8\pi^3}\sum_{n}\int d\mathbf{k}\,\delta(\omega-\omega_{\mathbf{k}n}) \tag{34.4}$$

and characterizing the number of vibrations with frequencies falling in the range ω, $\omega+d\omega$ (dS_n is an element of area of the surface $S_n(\omega)$ on which $\omega_{\mathbf{k}n}=\omega$), expression (34.3) may be put in the form

$$\sigma_i^{(1)}(\mathbf{q}_1, E)=\frac{N}{24\pi m}\frac{k_2}{k_1}\sigma_i q_1^2\frac{g(|\omega|)}{|\omega|}\begin{cases} n(\omega), & \omega>0, \\ n(|\omega|)+1, & \omega<0. \end{cases} \tag{34.5}$$

Thus the energy distribution of the cross section $\sigma_i^{(1)}(\mathbf{q}_1, E)$ is determined by the behavior of the function $g(\omega)$. In the Debye approximation $\omega_{\mathbf{k}n}\sim k$, $\nabla_{\mathbf{k}}\omega_{\mathbf{k}n}$ is a constant, and the surface $S_n(\omega)$ is a sphere. Hence according to (34.4) $g(\omega)\sim k^2$, i.e., $g(\omega)$ is proportional to ω^2 and in lattices with one atom per cell may be written in the form

$$g(\omega)=9\frac{\omega^2}{\omega_m^3}\quad(\omega<\omega_m), \tag{34.6}$$

where it is considered that in accordance with (34.4) $g(\omega)$ is normalized in such a way that its integral equals 3ν. For $\omega>\omega_m$ in this approximation $g(\omega)$ vanishes sharply.

In real crystals $g(\omega)$ is only proportional to ω^2 for small ω, for which the continuum approximation is valid. This function differs considerably from (34.6) and usually has several peaks (especially in the presence of optical branches of the vibrations). The function $g(\omega)$ is continuous, but it has radical singularities associated with the extremal points $\mathbf{k}_0$ (minima, maxima, or saddle points) at which $\nabla_k \omega_{kn} \mid_{k=k_0} = 0$ and which must necessarily exist in the vibration spectrum as a result of the translational symmetry of the crystal [325, 326].

Such extremal points are associated, in particular, with the maximum frequencies of each branch of vibrations and with the minimum frequencies of the optical branch. If the frequency of the phonon reaches a critical value $\omega_{cr} = \omega_{k_0 n}$, then some hollows on the $S(\omega)$ surface vanish or new ones appear, and the equation of the surface near the extremum point has a simple form. For example, near a minimum point, after reducing to the principal axes, this equation may be written in the form

$$\omega_{kn} = \omega_{cr} + \sum_{i=1}^{3} \omega_i k_i^2 \tag{34.7}$$

(all $\omega_i > 0$), and for $\omega > \omega_{cr}$ new ellipsoids appear on the surface $S_n(\omega)$, vanishing for $\omega < \omega_{cr}$. Near a maximum point (all $\omega_i < 0$), new ellipsoids appear for $\omega < \omega_{cr}$. Passage through a saddle point (ω_i have different signs) leads to a transformation from a hyperboloid to a two-hollow paraboloid and also changes the number of hollows. The change in the number of hollows on the surface $S(\omega)$ leads to the radical singularities of the function $g(\omega)$ mentioned before. Actually, integration over the surface of a supplementary ellipsoid, for example, near a minimum point, leads, according to (34.4), to the appearance of an extra term $\sim \sqrt{\omega - \omega_{cr}}$ for ($\nabla_k \omega_{kn} \sim k$, $\int dS_n \sim k^2$ and $\delta g(\omega) \sim k \sim \sqrt{\omega - \omega_{cr}}$), which is absent for $\omega < \omega_{cr}$. Thus

$$g(\omega) = g(\omega_{cr}) + \begin{cases} T\,|\omega - \omega_{cr}|^{1/2} + O(\omega - \omega_{cr}), & \omega > \omega_{cr}, \\ O(\omega - \omega_{cr}), & \omega < \omega_{cr}. \end{cases} \tag{34.8}$$

The same radical terms appear near other extremal points for frequencies lying on the same side of the critical frequency as that for which new hollows develop on the surface $S(\omega)$. In particular, near the maximum frequency ω_m, the function $g(\omega)$ tends to zero as $\sqrt{\omega_m - \omega}$.

It follows from (34.5) that the dependence of the single-phonon incoherent-scattering cross section on the transferred energy

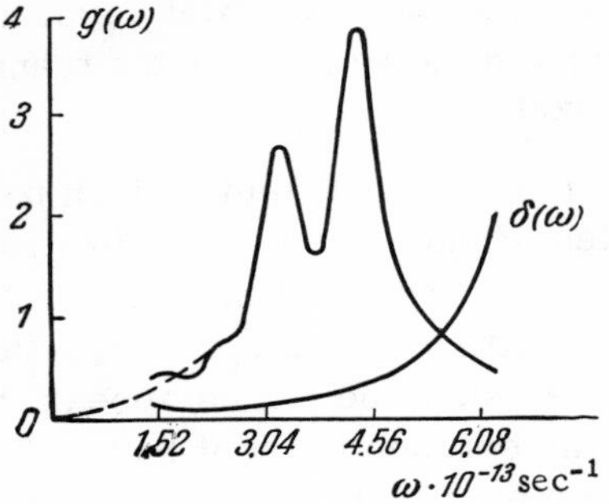

Fig. 22. Frequency-distribution function of the vibrations $g(\omega)$ in vanadium from data presented in [328]. The broken curve for the low-frequency part of the spectrum was calculated on the Debye approximation for $\theta = 338°K$. The curve $\delta(\omega)$ determines the error with which the function $g(\omega)$ is restored.

$\hbar\omega$ is described by a smooth distribution (with radical singularities) lying in the range $\omega_m < \omega < \omega_m$ and, in cubic crystals, not depending on the scattering direction. All the quantities entering into (34.5), apart from $g(\omega)$, may be regarded as known. Hence a study of the single-phonon incoherent scattering of neutrons offers the possibility of directly determining the frequency-distribution function of the vibrations $g(\omega)$ in monatomic cubic crystals.

In this way $g(\omega)$ has been determined for a number of crystals (for example in V [327–331], Ni [331, 332], and Ti [331]). For illustration Fig. 22 presents the $g(\omega)$ for V as given in [328].

The determination of $g(\omega)$ is also possible in monatomic noncubic crystals [333–336] if one studies the cross sections $\sigma_i^{(1)}(\mathbf{q}_1, E)$ for three positions of a single crystal distinguished by cyclic permutation of the coordinates q_i. The problem of determining $g(\omega)$ is considerably complicated in the case of polyatomic crystals, for which one has to make measurements with crystals of different isotopic compositions [336].

In order to determine $g(\omega)$ by the method discussed, we must be able to separate the single-phonon incoherent scattering from the coherent and multiphonon scattering. It is clear that a study of incoherent scattering is easier to carry out in crystals in which the cross section σ_i is large compared with σ_c. In particular, in the presence of isotopes with negative scattering amplitudes, we may choose isotopic composition such that the cross section σ_c becomes equal to zero and the coherent scattering vanishes [337]. Other methods of eliminating the coherent scattering have also been proposed [336, 338]. As shown in [287, 288, 290, 339–342], multiphonon coherent and incoherent scattering play a relatively small part in the scattering of relatively slow neutrons consisting of heavy atoms at lowish temperatures. Corrections for this scattering may be introduced by way of an iteration process [341, 342].

Chapter X

Energy Distribution of the Single-Phonon Scattering of Neutrons and Determination of the Relaxation Characteristics of the Phonons

§35. Single-Phonon Scattering of Neutrons by Solid Solutions

The most characteristic feature of the scattering of neutrons at the thermal vibrations of an ideal harmonic crystal considered in the preceding chapter was the appearance of peaks in the energy spectrum described by δ functions of energy. These δ functions correspond to the satisfaction of the laws of conservation of energy and momentum in the course of single-phonon coherent scattering, and their appearance is due to singularities of the normal vibrations in an ideal crystal and to the fact that these vibrations are described by infinite monochromatic waves.

In a nonideal crystal, for example, in a solid solution (and also on taking account of anharmonicity in an ideal crystal), the character of the normal vibrations changes qualitatively. Strictly speaking, these vibrations cannot be characterized by giving the wave vector; their variation in space becomes extremely complicated, and only over small regions (with dimensions of the order of the mean free path of a phonon) may they be considered as plane waves. As a result of this the interference conditions leading to the development of peaks in the energy distribution of coherent scattering, strictly speaking, cease to be valid (single-phonon scattering with a given momentum transfer may now arise from interaction with different phonons possessing different energies).

However, even in a nonideal or anharmonic crystal it is usually convenient to introduce approximate normal coordinates, corresponding to infinite plane waves of vibrations. In contrast to ideal harmonic crystals, such normal vibrations are now not independent and do not correspond to stationary states of vibrations of the crystals. The presence of inhomogeneities in the crystal or the interaction of phonons with each other and with other elementary excitations produces scattering and attenuation of the waves. The appearance of a finite "lifetime" of the waves leads to a certain departure from monochromatic properties and to indeterminacy of their frequency (energy). Hence, although, in this form of the problem, the coherent scattering of neutrons may be associated with the excitation or absorption of one of the "zero-approximation" phonons, the indeterminacy in the energy leads to diffuseness of the corresponding δ-shaped distribution in the energy spectrum of the scattered neutrons.

In real crystals, this kind of diffuseness of the energy distribution, associated with the scattering of phonons at static inhomogeneities (in particular that due to differences in the masses of isotopes) and at each other, must always take place. In view of the fact that the vibration spectrum may only be determined in cases for which the distribution is fairly narrow, it is important to make a theoretical study of its shape and width. No less important is the fact that a study of the broadening may give valuable new information regarding the interaction of phonons with inhomogeneities in the crystal and with each other, regarding their relaxation times, regarding the order in the arrangement of atoms in the solution, and so on.

These questions concerning the influence of static inhomogeneities and anharmonicity on the energy distribution of single-phonon coherent neutron scattering (and also certain new effects in the energy and angular distribution of incoherent scattering associated with the departure of the crystal from the ideal state and with anharmonicity) will be considered in this chapter. First of all, in this section and in the one following, we shall consider what is evidently the simplest case of coherent-scattering peak spreading in solid solutions, on the general lines of [344].

The scattering cross section for binary A – B solutions may be determined from the general formula (32.5). The coherent and incoherent scattering cross sections for individual nuclei $\sigma_{cs\gamma}$ and $\sigma_{is\gamma}$ in this formula take the values σ_{cA}, σ_{cB} and σ_{iA}, σ_{iB}, depending on the type of atom lying at the point $s\gamma$. By means of the numbers $c_{s\gamma}$ defined by formula (1.1), we may, for example, write $\sqrt{\sigma_{cs\gamma}}$ in the form

$$\sqrt{\sigma_{cs\gamma}} = c_{s\gamma}\sqrt{\sigma_{cA}} + (1 - c_{s\gamma})\sqrt{\sigma_{cB}}.$$

For not-very-high temperatures, low neutron energies, and large masses of the atoms in the crystal, the products $\mathbf{q}_1\mathbf{u}_{s\gamma}$ are smallish, and in the expansion of exp $(i\mathbf{q}_1\mathbf{u}_{s\gamma})$ we need only retain the linear terms. In ideal crystals, these describe the most interesting processes of the single-phonon scattering of neutrons. The cross section of this kind of scattering may in the absence of static distortions be written in the form

$$\sigma^{(1)}(\mathbf{q}_1, E) = \frac{1}{8\pi^2\hbar}\frac{k_2}{k_1}\sum_{s\gamma s'\gamma'}\Big\{\sqrt{\sigma_{c\gamma}}\sqrt{\sigma_{c\gamma'}} + (\sqrt{\sigma_{cA}} - \sqrt{\sigma_{cB}})\left[\sqrt{\sigma_{c\gamma}}(c_{s'\gamma'} - c_{\gamma'}) + \sqrt{\sigma_{c\gamma'}}(c_{s\gamma} - c_{\gamma})\right] + (\sqrt{\sigma_{cA}} - \sqrt{\sigma_{cB}})^2 (c_{s\gamma} - c_{\gamma})(c_{s'\gamma'} - c_{\gamma'}) + \delta_{ss'}\delta_{\gamma\gamma'}\left[\sigma_{i\gamma} + (\sigma_{iA} - \sigma_{iB})(c_{s\gamma} - c_{\gamma})\right]\Big\} \times \exp\left[i\mathbf{q}_1(\mathbf{R}_{s\gamma} - \mathbf{R}_{s'\gamma'})\right]\int_{-\infty}^{\infty}\langle(\mathbf{q}_1\mathbf{u}_{s\gamma}(t))(\mathbf{q}_1\mathbf{u}_{s'\gamma'})\rangle e^{-i\omega t}\,dt, \tag{35.1}$$

where

$$\sqrt{\sigma_{c\gamma}} = c_\gamma\sqrt{\sigma_{cA}} + (1 - c_\gamma)\sqrt{\sigma_{cB}}; \quad \sigma_{i\gamma} = c_\gamma\sigma_{iA} + (1 - c_\gamma)\sigma_{iB}. \tag{35.2}$$

As in the ideal crystal, the thermal displacements may be put in the form of an expansion in plane waves (33.2) (although not corresponding to the exact normal coordinates). Using expansion (1.7) for $c_{s\gamma} - c_\gamma$ as well, we may put the cross section $\sigma^{(1)}(\mathbf{q}_1, E)$ in the form

$$\sigma^{(1)}(\mathbf{q}_1, E) = \sigma_1(\mathbf{q}_1, E) + \sigma_2(\mathbf{q}_1, E) + \sigma_3(\mathbf{q}_1, E), \tag{35.3}$$

$$\sigma_1(\mathbf{q}_1, E) = N\frac{k_2}{k_1}\sum_{nn'}\frac{Q_{\mathbf{q}_1 n}Q^*_{\mathbf{q}_1 n'}}{\sqrt{\omega_{\mathbf{q}n}\omega_{\mathbf{q}n'}}}\varphi_{\mathbf{q}n\mathbf{q}n'}(\omega), \tag{35.4}$$

$$\sigma_2(\mathbf{q}_1, E) = N\frac{k_2}{k_1}\sum_{nn'}\Big\{-2\,\mathrm{Re}\sum_{\mathbf{k}}\frac{Q_{\mathbf{q}_1 n}S^*_{\mathbf{q}_1 n'}(\mathbf{k})}{\sqrt{\omega_{\mathbf{q}n}\omega_{\mathbf{k}n'}}}[\varphi_{\mathbf{q}n-\mathbf{k}n'}(\omega) - \chi_{\mathbf{q}n-\mathbf{k}n'}(\omega)] + \sum_{\mathbf{k}\mathbf{k}'}\frac{S_{\mathbf{q}_1 n}(\mathbf{k})\,S^*_{\mathbf{q}_1 n'}(\mathbf{k}')}{\sqrt{\omega_{\mathbf{k}n}\omega_{\mathbf{k}n'}}}[\varphi_{\mathbf{k}n\mathbf{k}'n'}(\omega) - \chi_{\mathbf{k}n\mathbf{k}'n'}(\omega)]\Big\}, \tag{35.5}$$

$$\sigma_3(\mathbf{q}_1, E) = \frac{k_2}{k_1}\sum_{nn'}\Big\{\sum_{\mathbf{k}}\frac{b_{nn'}(\mathbf{k})}{\sqrt{\omega_{\mathbf{k}n}\omega_{\mathbf{k}n'}}}\varphi_{\mathbf{k}n\mathbf{k}n'}(\omega) + \sum_{\mathbf{k}\mathbf{k}'}\sum_{\gamma}\frac{b'_{nn'\gamma}(\mathbf{k}, \mathbf{k}')}{\sqrt{\omega_{\mathbf{k}n}\omega_{\mathbf{k}'n'}}}c_{\mathbf{k}-\mathbf{k}'\gamma}[\varphi_{\mathbf{k}n\mathbf{k}'n'}(\omega) - \chi_{\mathbf{k}n\mathbf{k}'n'}(\omega)]\Big\}. \tag{35.6}$$

Here $Q_{\mathbf{q}_1 n}$ is given by formula (33.4),

$$S_{\mathbf{q}_1 n}(\mathbf{k}) = \frac{1}{\sqrt{8\pi m}}\sum_{\gamma}\left[\left(\sqrt{\sigma_{cA}} - \sqrt{\sigma_{cB}}\right)c_{\mathbf{q}+\mathbf{k}\gamma} - \sqrt{\sigma_{c\gamma}}\,\mathbf{q}_1\mathbf{R}_{\mathbf{q}+\mathbf{k}\gamma}\right] \times \mathbf{q}_1\mathbf{e}_{\mathbf{k}n\gamma}\exp(2\pi i\mathbf{K}_n\mathbf{R}_\gamma), \tag{35.7}$$

$$b_{nn'}(\mathbf{k}) = \frac{1}{8\pi m}\sum_{\gamma}\sigma_{i\gamma}(\mathbf{q}_1\mathbf{e}_{\mathbf{k}n\gamma})(\mathbf{q}_1\mathbf{e}^*_{\mathbf{k}n'\gamma}),$$

$$b'_{nn'\gamma}(\mathbf{k}, \mathbf{k}') = \frac{1}{8\pi m}(\sigma_{iA} - \sigma_{iB})(\mathbf{q}_1\mathbf{e}_{\mathbf{k}n\gamma})(\mathbf{q}_1\mathbf{e}^*_{\mathbf{k}'n'\gamma}),$$

while $\varphi(\omega)$ and $\chi(\omega)$ are given by the Fourier components of the time correlation functions for the operators of the generation and annihilation of phonons*

$$\varphi_{\mathbf{k}n\mathbf{k}'n'}(\omega) = \varphi'_{\mathbf{k}n\mathbf{k}'n'}(\omega) + \varphi''_{\mathbf{k}n\mathbf{k}'n'}(\omega), \tag{35.8a}$$

$$\varphi'_{\mathbf{k}n\mathbf{k}'n'}(\omega) = \frac{1}{2\pi}\int_{-\infty}^{\infty} dt\, e^{-i\omega t}\langle a_{\mathbf{k}n}(t)\,a^+_{\mathbf{k}'n'}(0)\rangle, \tag{35.8b}$$

$$\varphi''_{\mathbf{k}n\mathbf{k}'n'}(\omega) = \frac{1}{2\pi}\int_{-\infty}^{\infty} dt\, e^{-i\omega t}\langle a^+_{\mathbf{k}n}(t)\,a_{\mathbf{k}'n'}(0)\rangle, \tag{35.8c}$$

*Remembering (36.5) we may show that $\chi_{\mathbf{k}n-\mathbf{k}n'}(\omega) = 0$.

$$\chi_{\mathbf{k}n\mathbf{k}'n'}(\omega)=\frac{1}{2\pi}\int_{-\infty}^{\infty}dt\,e^{-i\omega t}\left[\langle a_{\mathbf{k}n}^{+}(t)\,a_{\mathbf{k}'n'}^{+}(0)\rangle+\langle a_{-\mathbf{k}n}(t)\,a_{-\mathbf{k}'n'}(0)\rangle\right]. \quad (35.8\text{d})$$

Formulas (35.3) to (35.8) relate to a somewhat more general case than (35.1), for which static displacements occur in the solution [these displacements are accounted for by the last term in the square bracket of formula (35.7) for $S_{q_1n}(\mathbf{k})$], but $\delta\mathbf{R}_{s\gamma}$ and $\sqrt{\sigma_{cA}}-\sqrt{\sigma_{cB}}$ may be considered as small quantities and we need only consider terms quadratic in these.

For the limiting transformation to an ideal harmonic crystal $\varphi''_{\mathbf{k}n\mathbf{k}n}(\omega)=n_{\mathbf{k}n}\,\delta(\omega-\omega_{\mathbf{k}n})$ reduces to a δ function, while the remaining functions $\varphi''_{\mathbf{k}n\mathbf{k}'n'}(\omega)$ vanish. Thus the expression (35.4) for σ_1 transforms into formula (33.3) for the coherent-scattering cross section, while expressions (35.5) and (35.6) for σ_2 and σ_3 transform into the formula for incoherent scattering by ideal crystals. Let us continue, even in the present case of nonideal crystals, to call the scattering σ_1 (somewhat arbitrarily) coherent scattering and the scattering corresponding to the sum $\sigma_2+\sigma_3$ incoherent (actually the interference of the scattered waves appears in the latter form of scattering).

We see from the formulas presented that the problem of determining the energy distribution of the scattered neutrons reduces to calculating the spectral representations of the single-phonon correlation functions. These may be most simply determined by the method of temperature (thermal) Green's functions, using the simple relation connecting the spectral representations of the double-time lagging and leading Green's functions $g(\omega)$ and the spectral representations of the correlation functions [345, 346]:

$$\varphi''_{\mathbf{k}'n'\mathbf{k}n}(\omega)=i\left(\exp\frac{\hbar\omega}{k_BT}-1\right)^{-1}\lim_{\delta\to+0}\left[g_{\mathbf{k}n\mathbf{k}'n'}(\omega+i\delta)-g_{\mathbf{k}n\mathbf{k}'n'}(\omega-i\delta)\right], \quad (35.9)$$

$$\varphi''_{\mathbf{k}n\mathbf{k}'n'}(\omega)=\exp\left(-\frac{\hbar\omega}{k_BT}\right)\varphi'_{\mathbf{k}n\mathbf{k}'n'}(-\omega). \quad (35.10)$$

In order to determine the phonon Green's functions $g_{\mathbf{k}n\mathbf{k}'n'}$ we must give the explicit form of the Hamiltonian. If we use the expansion of the displacements in plane waves (33.2), then, in the harmonic approximation, the Hamiltonian of the vibrations of a nonideal crystal is described by a quadratic but nondiagonal form of the operators of the generation and annihilation of phonons, a and a^+. The Hamiltonian may be put in the form [155]

$$H = \sum_{\mathbf{k}n} \hbar\omega_{\mathbf{k}n} a^+_{\mathbf{k}n} a_{\mathbf{k}n} + \sum_{\mathbf{k}n\mathbf{k}'n'} V_{\mathbf{k}n\mathbf{k}'n'} a^+_{\mathbf{k}n} a_{\mathbf{k}'n'} -$$

$$-\frac{1}{2} \sum_{\mathbf{k}n\mathbf{k}'n'} (V'_{\mathbf{k}n\mathbf{k}'n'} a^+_{\mathbf{k}n} a^+_{\mathbf{k}'n'} + V'^*_{\mathbf{k}n\mathbf{k}'n'} a_{\mathbf{k}n} a_{\mathbf{k}'n'}). \qquad (35.11)$$

The quantities V and V' characterizing the probability of the scattering of phonons at static inhomogeneities are determined by the differences between the masses of the atoms and the force constants [see (36.5) to (36.7)]. It is an important point that $V_{\mathbf{k}n\mathbf{k}n'} = 0$ and $V'_{\mathbf{k}n-\mathbf{k}n'} = 0$.

The calculation of the Green's functions and phonon correlation functions for the Hamiltonian (35.11) is presented in Appendix III. In the case of small differences between the atoms in the solution (small V and V'), the correlation functions may be presented in the form

$$\varphi''_{\mathbf{k}n\mathbf{k}n}(\omega) = \varphi'_{\mathbf{k}n\mathbf{k}n}(-\omega) \exp\left(-\frac{\hbar\omega}{k_B T}\right) = \frac{1}{\pi} \frac{\Gamma_{\mathbf{k}n}(\omega)\, n(\omega)}{[\omega - \omega_{\mathbf{k}n} - P_{\mathbf{k}n}(\omega)]^2 + \Gamma^2_{\mathbf{k}n}(\omega)}, \qquad (35.12)$$

$$\varphi''_{\mathbf{k}n'\mathbf{k}n}(\omega) = \frac{P_{\mathbf{k}nn'}(\omega)\, \varphi''_{\mathbf{k}n'\mathbf{k}n'}(\omega)}{\omega - \omega_{\mathbf{k}n}} + \frac{1}{\pi} \frac{\Gamma_{\mathbf{k}nn'}(\omega)\, n(\omega)}{\omega - \omega_{\mathbf{k}n}} \times$$

$$\times \frac{\omega - \omega_{\mathbf{k}n'} - P_{\mathbf{k}n'}(\omega)}{[\omega - \omega_{\mathbf{k}n'} - P_{\mathbf{k}n'}(\omega)]^2 + \Gamma^2_{\mathbf{k}n'}(\omega)} \quad (\omega \approx \omega_{\mathbf{k}n'},\ n \neq n'), \qquad (35.13)$$

$$\varphi''_{\mathbf{k}'n'\mathbf{k}n}(\omega) = \frac{1}{\hbar} \frac{V_{\mathbf{k}n\mathbf{k}'n'}}{\omega - \omega_{\mathbf{k}n}} \varphi''_{\mathbf{k}'n'\mathbf{k}'n'}(\omega) \ \text{for} \ \mathbf{k} \neq \mathbf{k}',\ n \neq n',\ \omega \neq \omega_{\mathbf{k}n}). \qquad (35.14)$$

Here

$$P_{\mathbf{k}n} \equiv P_{\mathbf{k}nn}, \quad \Gamma_{\mathbf{k}n} \equiv \Gamma_{\mathbf{k}nn},$$

$$P_{\mathbf{k}nn'}(\omega) = \frac{1}{\hbar^2} P \sum_{\mathbf{k}''n''} \left[\frac{V_{\mathbf{k}n\mathbf{k}''n''} V_{\mathbf{k}''n''\mathbf{k}n'}}{\omega - \omega_{\mathbf{k}''n''}} - \frac{V'_{\mathbf{k}n\mathbf{k}''n''} V'^*_{\mathbf{k}''n''\mathbf{k}n'}}{\omega + \omega_{\mathbf{k}''n''}} \right], \qquad (35.15)$$

$$\Gamma_{\mathbf{k}nn'}(\omega)=\frac{\pi}{\hbar^2}\sum_{\mathbf{k}''n''}[V_{\mathbf{k}n\mathbf{k}''n''}V_{\mathbf{k}''n''\mathbf{k}n'}\delta(\omega-\omega_{\mathbf{k}''n''})-V'_{\mathbf{k}n\mathbf{k}''n''}V'^{*}_{\mathbf{k}''n''\mathbf{k}n'}\delta(\omega+\omega_{\mathbf{k}''n''})]. \tag{35.16}$$

According to (35.12) the quantity $P_{\mathbf{k}n}$ in the second approximation of the theory of perturbations determines the displacement of the vibration frequency **kn** associated with the departure of the crystal from the ideal state, while $\Gamma_{\mathbf{k}n}$ determines the damping of the phonon.

We see from (35.4) that the energy distribution of single-phonon coherent scattering is determined by the spectral representation of the correlation time function (autocorrelation), which does not vanish as V and V' → 0, and also that of the functions $\varphi_{\mathbf{k}n\mathbf{k}n'}$, corresponding to a single **k** and different n. This distribution will be considered in the following section.

§36. Energy Distribution of the Single-Phonon Coherent Scattering of Neutrons by Nonideal Crystals

We see from (35.4), (35.12), and (35.13) that, in the present case of solutions with atoms of similar masses and force constants, the main contribution to coherent scattering a long way from the points at which the vibration branches come together arises from the diagonal terms σ_{1nn} in the sum of (35.4), which correspond to the absorption of a phonon

$$\sigma'_{1nn}(\mathbf{q}_1, E)=N\frac{k_2}{k_1}\frac{|Q_{\mathbf{q}_1n}|^2}{\pi\omega_{\mathbf{q}n}}\frac{\Gamma_{\mathbf{q}n}(\omega)\,n(\omega)}{[\omega-\omega_{\mathbf{q}n}-P_{\mathbf{q}n}(\omega)]^2+\Gamma^2_{\mathbf{q}n}(\omega)} \tag{36.1}$$

or its emission

$$\sigma''_{1nn}(\mathbf{q}_1, -E)=N\frac{k_2}{k_1}\frac{|Q_{\mathbf{q}_1n}|^2}{\pi\omega_{\mathbf{q}n}}\frac{\Gamma_{\mathbf{q}n}(\omega)\,[n(\omega)+1]}{[\omega-\omega_{\mathbf{q}n}-P_{\mathbf{q}n}(\omega)]^2+\Gamma^2_{\mathbf{q}n}(\omega)}\,. \tag{36.2}$$

As in the case of an ideal crystal [see (33.3)], these terms determine the intensity of a series of peaks in the energy distribution of the scattered neutrons for each $\mathbf{q}_1$, the maxima lying at

$$\pm\,\omega=\omega_{\mathbf{q}n}+P_{\mathbf{q}n}(\omega_{\mathbf{q}n})$$

and corresponding to the renormalized frequencies of different branches of vibrations. In nonideal crystals, however, these peaks are broadened and have finite widths $\Gamma_{\mathbf{q}n}$.* The quantity $\Gamma_{\mathbf{q}n}$, as indicated by (35.16), is determined by the probability $w_{\mathbf{q}n}$ of the scattering of a phonon $\mathbf{q}n$ at static inhomogeneities or by the corresponding lifetime of the phonon $\tau_{\mathbf{q}n} = w_{\mathbf{q}n}^{-1}$:

$$\Gamma_{\mathbf{q}n} = \tau_{\mathbf{q}n}^{-1} \tag{36.3}$$

and in the harmonic approximation considered does not depend on the temperature.

If the peaks are fairly narrow and $\Gamma_{\mathbf{q}n}(\omega)$ does not depend very much on frequency, so that

$$\frac{d\Gamma_{\mathbf{q}n}(\omega)}{d\omega} \ll 1, \tag{36.4}$$

then the form of each peak is described by a symmetric Lorentz curve. In general the shape of the curve is more complicated owing to the dependence of $\Gamma_{\mathbf{q}n}$ on ω.

Relation (36.3), linking the width of the experimental peak and the lifetime of the phonon, is not only applicable in the case of small static inhomogeneities but is also extremely general and holds, for example, in the case of scattering at impurity atoms with greatly differing masses [when formula (35.16) for Γ has ceased to be valid] or in the case of scattering due to anharmonicity (see §37). This relation offers the possibility of determining the relaxation characteristics of phonons from experimental data relating to the broadening of coherent-scattering peaks.

The nondiagonal terms in (35.4) ($n \neq n'$) correspond to more complex scattering processes in which phonons belonging to two branches of vibrations take part (this scattering only appears for $\Gamma \neq 0$ in nonideal or anharmonic crystals). It follows from (35.13) that these are also most substantial at

$$\pm\,\omega = \omega_{\mathbf{q}n'} + P_{\mathbf{q}n'}.$$

* The scattering of phonons by static inhomogeneities also leads to an analogous effect of the broadening of the spectral distribution of infrared light absorption by optical vibrations [348a].

These terms lead to a slight change in the intensity of the peaks [as a result of the first term in (35.13)] and to the appearance of asymmetry in the distribution [associated with the second term in (35.13)]. The degree of asymmetry has the order of magnitude $\Gamma_{\mathbf{q}nn'}(\omega_{\mathbf{q}n'} - \omega_{\mathbf{q}n})^{-1}$ (if all the $Q_{\mathbf{q}_1 n}$ have the same order) and increase sharply as the frequencies of the vibrations of different branches approach one another.

For fairly small values of $|\omega_{\mathbf{q}n} - \omega_{\mathbf{q}n'}|$ expression (35.13) ceases to be applicable and the functions $\varphi_{\mathbf{q}n\mathbf{q}n'}(\omega)$ are determined by the more accurate expressions for the Green's functions (III.11), (III.12). The widths and maxima of the peaks are determined not only by $P_{\mathbf{q}n}$, $\Gamma_{\mathbf{q}n}$, but also by $P_{\mathbf{q}nn'}$, $\Gamma_{\mathbf{q}nn'}$ and depend considerably on the frequency difference $\omega_{\mathbf{q}n} - \omega_{\mathbf{q}n'}$, while the shape of the resultant distribution becomes extremely complicated (as the branches of vibrations come closer they begin interacting strongly).

Let us now consider the extent of the damping or attenuation $\Gamma_{\mathbf{q}n}$. For this we must know the explicit expressions for $V_{\mathbf{k}n\mathbf{k}'n'}$. We shall consider that such quantities as the density of the crystal and the elastic moduli depend linearly on the concentrations c_γ. Then $V_{\mathbf{k}n\mathbf{k}'n'}$ will depend linearly on the Fourier components of the fluctuations of these concentrations. Let us confine ourselves to solutions in which only one sub-lattice may have atoms of two sorts lying at its lattice points, while identical atoms lie in other sub-lattices (for example, crystals with one lattice point in the cell, crystals of the (NaK)Cl type, and so on). In this case the quantity $c_{\mathbf{k}'-\mathbf{k}\gamma} = c_{\mathbf{k}'-\mathbf{k}}$ is only nonzero for one γ (the index γ may thus be omitted) and

$$V_{\mathbf{k}n\mathbf{k}'n'} = h_{\mathbf{k}n\mathbf{k}'n'} c_{\mathbf{k}'-\mathbf{k}}, \qquad V'_{\mathbf{k}n\mathbf{k}'n'} = h_{\mathbf{k}n\mathbf{k}'n'} c_{\mathbf{k}'+\mathbf{k}}. \tag{36.5}$$

Here, for example, the quantities $h_{\mathbf{k}n\mathbf{k}'n'}$, for the long-wave acoustic vibrations in crystals with one atom in the cell are determined on the approximation of an isotropic elastic continuum by the formula

$$h_{\mathbf{k}n\mathbf{k}'n'} = \frac{\hbar}{2\rho\sqrt{\omega_{\mathbf{k}n}\omega_{\mathbf{k}'n'}}} \Big\{ (\mathbf{e}_{\mathbf{k}n}\mathbf{e}_{\mathbf{k}'n'})\, \omega_{\mathbf{k}n}\omega_{\mathbf{k}'n'}\rho' +$$

$$+ (\mathbf{e}_{\mathbf{k}n}\mathbf{k})(\mathbf{e}_{\mathbf{k}'n'}\mathbf{k}') \left(K' - \frac{2}{3}\mu'\right) + [(\mathbf{e}_{\mathbf{k}n}\mathbf{e}_{\mathbf{k}'n'})(\mathbf{k}\mathbf{k}') + (\mathbf{k}\mathbf{e}_{\mathbf{k}'n'})(\mathbf{k}'\mathbf{e}_{\mathbf{k}n})]\, \mu' \Big\}, \tag{36.6a}$$

$$\omega_{\mathbf{k}1}=\sqrt{\frac{K+4\mu/3}{\rho}}\,k,\quad \omega_{\mathbf{k}2}=\sqrt{\frac{\mu}{\rho}}\,k, \tag{36.6b}$$

where n = 1 corresponds to longitudinal vibrations ($\mathbf{e}_{\mathbf{k}1} \parallel \mathbf{k}$), n = 2 or 3 to transverse ($\mathbf{e}_{\mathbf{k}n} \perp \mathbf{k}$), ρ is the density, K and μ are the bulk and shear moduli, and ρ', K', μ' are the derivatives of the corresponding quantities with respect to the concentration c.

In the frequently occurring case in which the relative difference in the masses of the atoms is much greater than the relative difference in the force constants, we find that for all branches of vibrations and all values of **k** and **k'** the quantity $h_{\mathbf{k}n\mathbf{k}'n'}$ is determined by the simple expression

$$h_{\mathbf{k}n\mathbf{k}'n'}=\frac{1}{2}\hbar\sqrt{\omega_{\mathbf{k}n}\omega_{\mathbf{k}'n'}}\,\mathbf{e}_{\mathbf{k}n\gamma}\mathbf{e}_{\mathbf{k}'n'\gamma}\varepsilon,\quad \varepsilon=\frac{m_A-m_B}{m}=\frac{\rho'}{\rho}, \tag{36.7}$$

where $\mathbf{e}_{\mathbf{k}n\gamma}$ is the polarization vector for the sub-lattice γ under consideration (in which the atoms are arranged in a disordered manner).

Substituting (36.5) into formula (35.16) for $\Gamma_{\mathbf{k}nn'}(\omega)$, discarding the second term in this formula (only important a long way from resonance for negative ω, when the scattering in question is very small), and passing from the sum to a surface integral over the surfaces $S_{n'}(\omega)$ on which $\omega_{\mathbf{k}n'}=\omega$, we write $\Gamma_{\mathbf{q}n}(\omega)$ in the form

$$\Gamma_{\mathbf{q}n}(\omega)=\frac{vN}{8\pi^2\hbar^2}\sum_{n'}\int\limits_{S_{n'}(\omega)}\frac{dS_{n'}}{|\nabla_{\mathbf{k}}\omega_{\mathbf{k}n'}|}h^2_{\mathbf{q}n\mathbf{k}n'}\overline{|c_{\mathbf{k}-\mathbf{q}'}|^2}. \tag{36.8}$$

The average values of $\overline{|c_{\mathbf{k}-\mathbf{q}}|^2}$, and hence $\Gamma_{\mathbf{q}n}$, depend greatly on the order and correlation in the solution. The simplest results are obtained in ideal solutions, where $\overline{|c_{\mathbf{k}}|^2}$ is determined by formula (1.14) and does not depend on **k**. Integral (36.8) is not hard to calculate in explicit form on the approximation of an isotropic continuum [when $S_{n'}(\omega)$ is a sphere] for the long-wave acoustic or optical vibrations in the solid solution.

In the first case, substituting expression (1.14) for $\overline{|c_{\mathbf{k}-\mathbf{q}}|^2}$ into (36.8) and (36.6) for $h_{\mathbf{q}n\mathbf{k}n'}$, we find that for longitudinal and transverse acoustic vibrations

$$\Gamma_{q1} = \frac{vw_1 q^4}{24\pi}\left(\frac{\omega}{\omega_{q1}}\right)^2\left[(1+2\chi^3)\left(\frac{\rho'}{\rho}\right)^2 + \frac{45K'^2 + 8(2+3\chi^5)\mu'^2}{15\chi^4\mu^2}\right]c(1-c) \sim$$

$$\sim 10\left(\frac{q}{k_m}\right)^3 \omega\varepsilon_1^2 c(1-c), \qquad (36.9)$$

$$\Gamma_{q2} = \frac{vw_2 q^4}{12\pi}\left(\frac{\omega}{\omega_{q2}}\right)^3\left[\frac{1+2\chi^3}{2\chi^3}\left(\frac{\rho'}{\rho}\right)^2 + \frac{2+3\chi^5}{5\chi^5}\left(\frac{\mu'}{\mu}\right)^2\right]c(1-c) \sim$$

$$\sim \left(\frac{q}{k_m}\right)^3 \omega\varepsilon_1^2 c(1-c). \qquad (36.10)$$

Here w_n is the velocity of longitudinal or transverse sound, $\chi = w_1/w_2$, in the resonance region $\omega \approx \omega_{qn}$, k_m is the maximum value of the wave vector of the phonon, and ε_1 is the largest quantity among ρ'/ρ, K'/K, μ'/μ. The last equations in (36.9) and (36.10) determine the order of the quantity Γ_q. For frequencies of longitudinal vibrations greater than the maximum frequency of transverse vibrations $\omega_{\perp m}$, scattering processes corresponding to the annihilation of a longitudinal phonon and the generation of a transverse phonon are excluded, and in (36.9) we must replace the square bracket by the expression

$$\left(\frac{\rho'}{\rho}\right)^2 + (45K'^2 + 16\mu'^2)(15\chi^4\mu^2)^{-1}$$

[we must also omit the factor of 10 in the estimate of (36.9)].

It is plain that, with the exception of singular points in the vibration spectrum (see below) formulas (36.9) and (36.10) give the correct order of magnitude of Γ_{qn} in ideal solutions. As we see from these formulas, for large q ($q \sim k_m$), components differing substantially in their properties ($\varepsilon_1 \sim 1$), and a high concentration ($c \sim 1/2$), Γ_{qn} has the same order as ω_{qn}, i.e., the peak in the energy distribution spreads itself out (although the theory of perturbations is inapplicable in this case, all the formulas derived on the basis of this theory give a correct estimate of Γ_{qn}).

In solutions of isotopes (except for very light elements), we usually have $\varepsilon_1 < 0.1$, and the broadening of the peaks associated with the presence of isotopes is small ($\Gamma_q < 10^{-2}\omega_q$) and usually smaller than the broadening due to anharmonicity.* Since for low frequencies $\Gamma_q \sim q^4$ in all cases (including the case of $\varepsilon_1 \sim 1$), on scattering at low-frequency vibrations we should observe sharply-defined peaks (the explicit form of the expression for Γ_q at $\varepsilon_1 \sim 1$ will nevertheless be different).

A different dependence of Γ_{qn} on $\mathbf{q}$ is obtained in the case of long-wave optical vibrations. Let us consider, for example, the simplest case in which the static inhomogeneities are only associated with the difference in the masses of the atoms, while the point $\mathbf{k} = 0$ is occupied by an analytical minimum or maximum $\omega_n(\mathbf{k})$, the other branches not having vibrations at this frequency. Then for cubic crystals

$$\omega_n(\mathbf{k}) = \omega_0 + \frac{1}{2}\omega_2 k^2$$

(we neglect the effects of retardation in ionic crystals as these are only important for small k), and, as indicated by (36.8), (1.14), and (36.7), the $\Gamma_{q\parallel}$ and $\Gamma_{q\perp}$ for longitudinal and transverse optical vibrations are equal to

$$\Gamma_{q\parallel}(\omega) = \frac{v\omega_{q\parallel}\omega q(\omega)}{24\pi\,|\omega_2|}\,|\mathbf{e}_{qn\parallel}|^4\varepsilon^2 c(1-c) \sim \frac{\omega_0}{\Delta\omega}\frac{q}{k_m}\,\omega\varepsilon^2 c(1-c),$$

$$\Gamma_{q\perp}(\omega) = \frac{v\omega_{q\perp}\omega q(\omega)}{12\pi\,|\omega_2|}\,|\mathbf{e}_{qn\perp}|^4\,\varepsilon^2 c(1-c), \qquad (36.11)$$

where $q(\omega)$ is the wave vector corresponding to the frequency $\omega_{qn} = \omega$ (in the resonance region $\omega \approx \omega_q$, $q(\omega) \approx q$), and

$$\Delta\omega \sim \frac{1}{2}|\omega_2|\,k_m^2$$

is the width of the zone of frequencies under consideration.

We see from (36.11) that, as q diminishes, the value of Γ_{qn} now falls off as q rather than q^4, i.e., the broadening may be considerable even for small q. For a given ε the broadening is es-

*Formulas (32.5), (35.3)–(35.6), which were derived for the case of a negligibly small difference in the vibrations of the isotopes of a given element, are also applicable to binary solution of isotopes if the isotopes in question are considered as single-isotope atoms of different sorts.

pecially large for narrow bands, for example, for optical vibrations in molecular crystals.

A similar type of formula holds for $\Gamma_{qn}(\omega)$ (in order of magnitude) near other minima and maxima of the $\omega_n(\mathbf{k})$ relationships (including the maximum frequency of the acoustic vibrations) if only the branch of vibrations under consideration lies in the neighborhood of the frequency ω. The q in (36.11) denotes the distance to the extremal point in **k** space. If the vibrations of other branches have the same frequency, then at small q the main part in Γ_{qn} is played by the term corresponding to these branches, the order of magnitude of which is given by formulas (36.9) and (36.10).

According to (36.11), near the minimum or maximum point in question ($\mathbf{k} = 0$):

$$\Gamma_{qn} \sim \sqrt{|\omega - \omega_{cr}|}.$$

It follows from (36.8) that the same type of radical singularity applies to the damping of Γ_{qn} at all analytic extremal points of the spectrum at which $\nabla_k \omega_{kn'} = 0$. for one of the branches. As in the case of the frequency-distribution function of the vibrations (see §34), the term proportional to $|\omega - \omega_{cr}|^{1/2}$ only appears on the side of the critical frequency ω_{cr} for which new hollows appear on the surface $\omega_{n'}(\mathbf{k}) = \omega$ (on the other side of the point ω_{cr} the value of Γ_{qn}, does not, generally speaking, vanish, in contrast to the example considered earlier). It should be noted that this type of radical singularity of Γ_{qn} only appears in the second approximation of the theory of perturbations, and in subsequent approximations it is spread out over a frequency range of $\sim \Gamma$ [348], in analogy with the manner in which the singularities of the frequency-distribution function of the vibrations are spread out (see §38).

A simple expression for Γ_{qn}, valid not only for long-wave vibrations but also for any **q**, is obtained in the case of ideal solutions with a cubic lattice of the Bravais type, in which we may neglect the difference in the force constants, and only the difference between the masses of the atoms in the solution is important. In this case we may at once express the damping in terms of the frequency-distribution function of the vibrations $g(\omega)$. In fact, by substituting (1.14) and (36.7) into formula (35.16) for $\Gamma_{knn}(\omega)$ and (on the basis of the considerations discussed on p. 323) replacing the $(\mathbf{e}_{\mathbf{k}n}\mathbf{e}_{\mathbf{k}'n'})^2$ under the summation sign by $(1/3)\, e_{\mathbf{k}n}^2 = 1/3$, and also remembering the definition of (34.4) for $g(\omega)$, we immediately obtain

$$\Gamma_{\mathbf{q}n}(\omega) = \frac{\pi}{12}\, \omega_{\mathbf{q}n}\omega\varepsilon^2 g(|\omega|)\, c(1-c). \tag{36.12}$$

Thus in order to calculate $\Gamma_{\mathbf{q}n}(\omega)$ in this case we only have to know the frequency-distribution function $g(\omega)$. Together with $g(\omega_{\mathbf{q}n})$ the damping $\Gamma_{\mathbf{q}n}(\omega_{\mathbf{q}n})$ expressed as a function of $\omega_{\mathbf{q}n}$ has characteristic peaks.

It follows from (35.15), (1.14), (36.7), and (34.4) that the displacement of the frequencies $P_{\mathbf{q}n}(\omega)$ in the case under consideration may be written in the form

$$P_{\mathbf{q}n}(\omega) = \frac{1}{6}\, \omega_{\mathbf{q}n}\varepsilon^2 c(1-c)\, P\int_0^{\omega_m} d\omega_1 \frac{\omega_1^2}{\omega^2-\omega_1^2}\, g(\omega_1), \tag{36.13}$$

i.e., the displacement is also unambiguously determined by the function $g(\omega_1)$.

In the more general case of ideal cubic solutions with several atoms in the cell, in which also only the differences in the masses of the atoms are important and the impurity atoms only lie in the sublattice γ, the damping and displacement may analogously be written in the form

$$\Gamma_{\mathbf{q}n}(\omega) = \frac{\pi}{12}\, \omega_{\mathbf{q}n}\omega\varepsilon^2 e_{\mathbf{q}n\gamma}^2 \sum_n \overline{e_{\mathbf{k}n\gamma}^2}\, g_n(|\omega|)\, c(1-c), \tag{36.14}$$

$$P_{\mathbf{q}n}(\omega) = \frac{1}{6}\, \omega_{\mathbf{q}n} e_{\mathbf{q}n\gamma}^2 \varepsilon^2 c(1-c)\, P\int_0^{\omega_m} d\omega_1 \frac{\omega_1^2}{\omega^2-\omega_1^2} \sum_n \overline{e_{\mathbf{k}n\gamma}^2}\, g_n(\omega_1). \tag{36.15}$$

Here $\overline{e_{\mathbf{k}n\gamma}^2}$ is the mean square of the length of the polarization vector $e_{\mathbf{k}n\gamma}^2$ on the isofrequency surface of the n-th branch of vibrations $\omega_{\mathbf{k}n} = |\omega|$, while $g_n(\omega)$ is the frequency-distribution function of the vibrations of the n-th branch.

In nonideal solutions correlation is important, and generally speaking, $\overline{|c_{\mathbf{k}}|^2}$ depends on **k** in a complicated manner. In view of this, the calculation of $\Gamma_{\mathbf{q}n}$ from formula (36.8) is extremely complex. Simple expressions for $\Gamma_{\mathbf{q}n}$ in nonideal solutions are only obtained in the case of long-wave acoustic vibrations, or near the maximum or minimum frequency of some branch, when the other branches have no vibrations at this frequency. In this case the $|\mathbf{k}-\mathbf{q}|$ in (36.8) are small and $\overline{|c_{\mathbf{k}-\mathbf{q}}|^2}$ may be determined from formula (2.10) [if long-range elastic forces do not intrude; otherwise one must employ expression (9.4)]. Hence, fairly close to the minimum points, for which

$$\beta\,|\mathbf{k}-\mathbf{q}|^2 \ll \varphi_{cc},$$

formulas (36.9) to (36.11) may also be used for nonideal solutions, if (in the absence of distortions) we make the substitution

$$c\,(1-c) \to \frac{k_B T}{v\varphi_{cc}} \tag{36.16}$$

in these.

It follows from this that, as a rule, the establishment of short-range order in the solution should lead to an increase in $\Gamma_{\mathbf{q}n}$ for long-wave vibrations in decomposing solutions, and to a corresponding fall in ordering solutions. A still sharper fall in $\Gamma_{\mathbf{q}n}$ should occur on the establishment of long-range order in the solution. For example, in the case of almost completely ordered solutions with two types of lattice points, in formulas (36.9) to (36.11) we must replace $c\,(1-c)$ by $c\,(1-c)-\nu\,(1-\nu)\,\eta^2$, and for $c \approx \nu$ and values of the long-range-order parameter η close to unity the value of $\Gamma_{\mathbf{q}n}$ will become very small.

A sharp increase in $\Gamma_{\mathbf{q}n}$ should take place near the critical point on the decomposition curve. In order to estimate this effect, let us consider undistorted solutions, in which the influence of long-range forces on the fluctuations is not important, and let us use expressions (2.49) and (2.48) for $\overline{|c_{\mathbf{k}}|^2}$.

For long-wave acoustic or optical vibrations, at very small values of q, for which

$$\beta q^2 \ll \varphi_{cc} \quad \text{or} \quad q \ll h\,(T-T_k)^{\frac{5}{4(2-\psi)}}$$

(see p. 38), $\Gamma_{\mathbf{q}n}$ are determined by formulas (36.9) to (36.11), in which we have substituted (36.16), and vary in proportion to q^4 (in the case of acoustic vibrations) or q (in the case of optical vibrations). However, since φ_{cc} is very small near the critical point, the proportionality factor in these relationships rises sharply on approaching the critical point. If, moreover, φ_{cc} becomes so small that the condition

$$\beta q^2 \gg \varphi_{cc} \quad \text{or} \quad q \gg h\,(T-T_k)^{\frac{5}{4(2-\psi)}}$$

(in a solution of critical composition) is satisfied, it then follows from (36.8), (36.6), (2.48), and (2.49) that, for acoustic vibrations, in order of magnitude*

$$\Gamma_{qn} \sim \frac{1}{\psi}\left(\frac{q}{k_m}\right)^{1+\psi}\omega\varepsilon^2 \quad \left(k_m \gg q \gg h\,(T-T_k)^{\frac{5}{4(2-\psi)}}\right), \tag{36.17}$$

while for optical vibrations

$$\Gamma_{qn} \sim \frac{1}{\psi}\frac{\omega_0}{\Delta\omega}\left(\frac{q}{k_m}\right)^{-(1-\psi)}\omega\varepsilon^2. \tag{36.18}$$

In this range of q values, in the neighborhood of the critical point, Γ_{qn} also rises rapidly and the relation between Γ_{qn} and q changes sharply. For acoustic vibrations it is close to the law $\Gamma_{qn} \sim q^2$ [according to (2.46) $\psi \ll 1$], while for optical vibrations near the critical point, as indicated by (36.11), (36.16), and (36.18), as q increases the value of Γ_{qn} first rises, passes through a maximum, and then falls off in accordance with the law $q^{-(1-\psi)}$. A rise in Γ_{qn} on approaching the critical point should also take place for all other analytical extremal frequencies (at which $\nabla_{\mathbf{k}}\,\omega_{\mathbf{k}n} = 0$).

A sharp rise in Γ_{qn} may also take place during phase transformations of the second kind. According to [344], near an ordinary phase-transformation point, this increase in damping should only take place for certain values of $\mathbf{q}$ in two cases: if the vector $\mathbf{q}/2\pi$ lies near the surface of the new Brillouin zone which appears on ordering, or if the optical and acoustic branches of the vibrations which are obtained on referring the vibrational spectrum to

*If we suppose, as in [344], that $\psi = 0$, then in formulas (36.17) and (36.18) $(1/\psi)(q/k_m)^{\psi}$ is replaced by $(\varphi_{cc}/\beta q^2)$. For small ψ [see formula (2.46)] this has no great effect on the relationship between Γ_{qn} and q.

the reciprocal-lattice cell of the ordered solution intersect, and **q** lies near the surface of intersection of these branches. The damping of the long-wave vibrations may increase sharply in the ordered phase near the critical point on the curve of phase transformations of the second kind. The damping of phonons in the region of the order/disorder phase transformation of the second kind in β brass was studied experimentally in [419].

In the foregoing discussion we have considered the effect of a departure of the crystal from the ideal state on the damping and frequency shift of the vibrations in the case of solutions of arbitrary composition in which, however, the differences between the masses and force constants of the component atoms were small. Closed expressions for the damping and shift (displacement) may also be obtained in the case of impurity atoms with arbitrary masses and force constants if the impurity concentration is not too great. The theory of neutron scattering in such solutions has been developed by Elliot and Maradudin [420].

§37. Influence of the Anharmonicity of the Vibrations on the Energy Distribution of Single-Phonon Coherent Scattering

In ideal crystals the main reason for the spreading of the peaks in the coherent-scattering energy distribution is usually the anharmonicity of the vibrations. On allowing for the cubic and higher terms in the expansion of the potential energy of the crystal in terms of the displacements, the Hamiltonian of the vibrations does not decompose into independent terms corresponding to individual oscillators, as in the harmonic approximation. Anharmonicity leads to interaction of the phonons and hence to the possibility of their decomposition (into other phonons) and scattering at one another. Plane waves of vibrations now only describe approximate stationary single-particle states in a many-body problem, their lifetimes become finite, and the corresponding indeterminacy in the energy of a phonon leads to the spreading of the single-phonon peaks of coherent neutron scattering. Many papers have been devoted to the influence of anharmonicity on the damping and frequency of phonons and the scattering of neutrons in recent years [349–360] (in the case of $T = 0$ these effects were studied in [362–364]).

If we confine attention to terms quadratic in q_1 ("single-phonon" scattering),* the coherent-scattering cross section is given by formula (35.4). As in the previously considered case of nonideal crystals, the problem of determining the energy distribution of the scattered neutrons reduces to calculating the spectral representations of the correlation functions $\varphi_{qnqn'}(\omega)$. The latter are essentially determined by the dynamic properties of the system, i.e., its Hamiltonian H, for which we must now take the Hamiltonian of an ideal anharmonic crystal.

Retaining only the cubic terms in the expansion of potential energy in powers of the displacements and certain fourth-order terms of subsequent importance, this Hamiltonian may be written in the form

$$H=\sum_{\mathbf{k}n}\hbar\omega_{\mathbf{k}n}a^{+}_{\mathbf{k}n}a_{\mathbf{k}n}+$$
$$+\frac{1}{6}\sum_{\mathbf{k}n\mathbf{k}'n'\mathbf{k}''n''}V_{\mathbf{k}n\mathbf{k}'n'\mathbf{k}''n''}(a_{\mathbf{k}n}+a^{+}_{-\mathbf{k}n})(a_{\mathbf{k}'n'}+a^{+}_{-\mathbf{k}'n'})(a_{\mathbf{k}''n''}+a^{+}_{-\mathbf{k}''n''})+$$
$$+\frac{1}{2}\sum_{\mathbf{k}n\mathbf{k}'n'}V_{-\mathbf{k}n\mathbf{k}n-\mathbf{k}'n'\mathbf{k}'n'}\left(a^{+}_{\mathbf{k}n}a_{\mathbf{k}n}+\frac{1}{2}\right)\left(a^{+}_{\mathbf{k}'n'}a_{\mathbf{k}'n'}+\frac{1}{2}\right). \quad (37.1)$$

Here, for example,

$$V_{\mathbf{k}n\mathbf{k}'n'\mathbf{k}''n''}=\left(\frac{\hbar}{2mN}\right)^{3/2}(\omega_{\mathbf{k}n}\omega_{\mathbf{k}'n'}\omega_{\mathbf{k}''n''})^{-1/2}V^{ii'i''}_{s\gamma s'\gamma's''\gamma''}\times$$
$$\times e_{\mathbf{k}n\gamma i}e_{\mathbf{k}'n'\gamma'i'}e_{\mathbf{k}''n''\gamma''i''}\exp\left[i\left(\mathbf{k}\mathbf{R}_{s\gamma}+\mathbf{k}'\mathbf{R}_{s'\gamma'}+\mathbf{k}''\mathbf{R}_{s''\gamma''}\right)\right], \quad (37.2)$$

where i = 1, 2, 3 enumerate Cartesian coordinates, summation is carried out over twice-repeated indices s, γ, i, and $V^{ii'i''}_{s\gamma s'\gamma's''\gamma''}$ are the coefficients in the third-order terms of the expansion of potential

*Strictly speaking, the cross section (35.4) corresponds to single-phonon scattering only in the harmonic approximation; on allowing for anharmonicity it also includes many-phonon processes. Nevertheless, we shall call (35.4) the single-phonon scattering cross section for anharmonic crystals also, remembering that on reducing the anharmonicity constant the corresponding sharp peaks contract into δ-like distributions representing single-phonon coherent scattering by a harmonic crystal.

energy in powers of the displacements:

$$U=\frac{1}{6}V^{ii'i''}_{s\gamma s'\gamma' s''\gamma''}u_{s\gamma i}u_{s'\gamma' i'}u_{s''\gamma'' i''}$$

(see, for example, [163]). It is clear that the quantities $V_{\mathbf{k}n\mathbf{k}'n'\mathbf{k}''n''}$ only differ from zero for

$$\mathbf{k}+\mathbf{k}'+\mathbf{k}''=2\pi\mathbf{K}_n,$$

that they are symmetric with respect to the pairs of indices **kn**, and that they satisfy the relations

$$V^*_{-\mathbf{k}n-\mathbf{k}'n'-\mathbf{k}''n''}=V_{\mathbf{k}n\mathbf{k}'n'\mathbf{k}''n''}.$$

As in the study of nonideal crystals, the calculation of the phonon correlation functions φ' and φ'' may conveniently be carried out by means of thermal Green's functions. As a rule, the anharmonicity constants are not large, and in calculating the polarization operator (inverse Green's function) we may use perturbation theory. It is usually sufficient, in the expressions for the damping and displacement of the phonon, to confine attention to terms quadratic in the third-order anharmonicity constants and linear in the fourth-order constants (these terms make comparable contributions to the frequency shift). This is equivalent to allowing for the processes of mutual phonon interaction represented in Fig. 23.

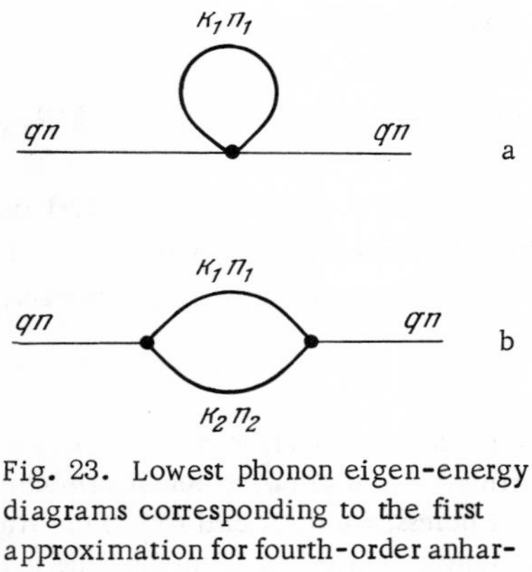

Fig. 23. Lowest phonon eigen-energy diagrams corresponding to the first approximation for fourth-order anharmonicity (a) and to the second approximation for third-order anharmonicity (b).

A calculation carried out on this approximation [349] led to the same expressions (35.12) and (35.13) for the correlation functions as in the case of nonideal crystals, i.e., the energy distribution of the peaks of single-phonon coherent scattering had the same character as in the case considered in §36. The quantities $\Gamma_{\mathbf{k}nn'}$ and $P_{\mathbf{k}nn'}$ entering into these formulas are determined by the anharmonicity constants:

$$\Gamma_{\mathbf{k}nn'}(\omega)=\frac{\pi}{2\hbar^2}\sum_{\mathbf{k}_1n_1\mathbf{k}_2n_2} V_{-\mathbf{k}n\mathbf{k}_1n_1\mathbf{k}_2n_2}V^*_{-\mathbf{k}n'\mathbf{k}_1n_1\mathbf{k}_2n_2}\{(1+n_{\mathbf{k}_1n_1}+n_{\mathbf{k}_2n_2})\times$$
$$\times[\delta(\omega-\omega_{\mathbf{k}_1n_1}-\omega_{\mathbf{k}_2n_2})-\delta(\omega+\omega_{\mathbf{k}_1n_1}+\omega_{\mathbf{k}_2n_2})]+2(n_{\mathbf{k}_1n_1}-n_{\mathbf{k}_2n_2})\times$$
$$\times\delta(\omega+\omega_{\mathbf{k}_1n_1}-\omega_{\mathbf{k}_2n_2})\}, \qquad (37.3)$$

$$P_{\mathbf{k}nn'}(\omega)=\frac{1}{2\hbar^2}P\sum_{\mathbf{k}_1n_1\mathbf{k}_2n_2} V_{-\mathbf{k}n\mathbf{k}_1n_1\mathbf{k}_2n_2}V^*_{-\mathbf{k}n'\mathbf{k}_1n_1\mathbf{k}_2n_2}\left(\frac{1+n_{\mathbf{k}_1n_1}+n_{\mathbf{k}_2n_2}}{\omega-\omega_{\mathbf{k}_1n_1}-\omega_{\mathbf{k}_2n_2}}-\right.$$
$$\left.-\frac{1+n_{\mathbf{k}_1n_1}+n_{\mathbf{k}_2n_2}}{\omega+\omega_{\mathbf{k}_1n_1}+\omega_{\mathbf{k}_2n_2}}+2\frac{n_{\mathbf{k}_1n_1}-n_{\mathbf{k}_2n_2}}{\omega+\omega_{\mathbf{k}_1n_1}-\omega_{\mathbf{k}_2n_2}}\right)+$$
$$+\frac{1}{\hbar}\sum_{\mathbf{k}_1n_1}V_{-\mathbf{k}n\mathbf{k}n-\mathbf{k}_1n_1\mathbf{k}_1n_1}\left(n_{\mathbf{k}_1n_1}+\frac{1}{2}\right). \qquad (37.4)$$

It is clear that here $P_{\mathbf{k}n}\equiv P_{\mathbf{k}nn}$ has the sense of the frequency shift in the vibrations of the phonon **k**n due to anharmonicity, while $\Gamma_{\mathbf{k}n}\equiv\Gamma_{\mathbf{k}nn}$ represents the corresponding damping. From the form of the arguments of the δ functions describing the laws of conservation in the elementary processes of interaction, it follows that the first term in the curly brackets of (37.3) accounts for processes involving the decomposition of the phonon under consideration into two others, and the second term accounts for scattering processes.

Expressions (37.3) and (37.4), obtained on the basis of perturbation theory, are clearly only valid if the interaction between the phonons is fairly small. For these formulas to be applicable it is not only necessary that the conditions

$$\Gamma_{\mathbf{q}n},\ |P_{\mathbf{q}n}|\ll\omega_{\mathbf{q}n}$$

should be satisfied (these conditions, as indicated by the foregoing estimates, as usually adequately satisfied, except possibly at very high temperatures), but also that ω_{qn} should greatly exceed the damping of the phonons taking part in scattering or decomposition processes, especially thermal phonons excited at the given temperature [otherwise the δ functions in (37.3) will be replaced by diffuse δ-like functions, which will greatly alter the results]. The latter condition means that, for acoustic phonons, these results will cease to be applicable in the region of long phonon wavelengths λ_Φ (as compared with the free range of thermal phonons l_Φ), for which the condition $\lambda_\Phi \ll l_\Phi$ is no longer valid.

Such long-wave phonons, however, are not usually studied by neutron diffraction.

The damping and the displacement, generally speaking, depend in a complicated way on the wave vector of the phonon and the temperature [at high temperatures only, it follows at once from the general form of formulas (37.3) and (37.4) that $\Gamma_{qnn'}$ and $P_{qnn'}$ are proportional to T]. These relationships, however, are greatly simplified and may be put in a simple form in the case of long-wave vibrations. For small quasimomenta $V_{-\mathbf{k}n\mathbf{k}_1n_1\mathbf{k}_2n_2}$ may be put in the form

$$V_{-\mathbf{k}n\mathbf{k}_1n_1\mathbf{k}_2n_2} = \frac{kk_1k_2}{\sqrt{\omega_{\mathbf{k}n}\omega_{\mathbf{k}_1n_1}\omega_{\mathbf{k}_2n_2}}} V^{-1/2} A_{-\mathbf{k}n\mathbf{k}_1n_1\mathbf{k}_2n_2} \Delta(\mathbf{k}_1 + \mathbf{k}_2 - \mathbf{k}), \quad (37.5)$$

where

$$\Delta(\mathbf{q}) = 1 \text{ for } \mathbf{q} = 0, \quad 2\pi\mathbf{K}_n,$$
$$\Delta(\mathbf{q}) = 0 \text{ for } \mathbf{q} \neq 0, \quad 2\pi\mathbf{K}_n,$$

and for small quasimomenta the quantity $A_{-\mathbf{k}n\mathbf{k}_1n_1\mathbf{k}_2n_2}$ does not depend on the length of the vectors $\mathbf{k}$, $\mathbf{k}_1$, $\mathbf{k}_2$ (but depends on their direction). Then expression (37.3) for $\Gamma_{qn}(\omega)$ takes the form

$$\Gamma_{qn}(\omega) = \frac{\pi}{2\hbar^2 V} \frac{q^2}{\omega_{qn}} \sum_{\mathbf{k}_1n_1\mathbf{k}_2n_2} \frac{k_1^2k_2^2}{\omega_{\mathbf{k}_1n_1}\omega_{\mathbf{k}_2n_2}} |A_{-\mathbf{q}n\mathbf{k}_1n_1\mathbf{k}_2n_2}|^2 \Delta(\mathbf{k}_1 + \mathbf{k}_2 - \mathbf{q}) \times$$
$$\times \{(1 + n_{\mathbf{k}_1n_1} + n_{\mathbf{k}_2n_2})[\delta(\omega - \omega_{\mathbf{k}_1n_1} - \omega_{\mathbf{k}_2n_2}) - \delta(\omega + \omega_{\mathbf{k}_1n_1} + \omega_{\mathbf{k}_2n_2})] +$$
$$+ 2(n_{\mathbf{k}_1n_1} - n_{\mathbf{k}_2n_2})\delta(\omega + \omega_{\mathbf{k}_1n_1} - \omega_{\mathbf{k}_2n_2})\}. \quad (37.6)$$

For T = 0, only the first term, corresponding to the decomposition or decay of a phonon, remains in the curly brackets of (37.6). For the branch of acoustic vibrations with the greatest frequency (in the approximation of the isotropic continuum, for the longitudinal phonons) decomposition of this kind is possible for the smallest quasimomenta $\hbar q$. Carrying out the summation in (37.6), we easily see that for $\omega = \omega_{q1}$

$$\Gamma_{q1}(\omega_{q1}) = B_1 \left(\frac{q}{k_m}\right)^5 \omega_m \quad (q \ll k_m), \tag{37.7}$$

where B_1 is a constant, and ω_m is the maximum frequency of acoustic vibrations, i.e.,

$$\Gamma_{qn} \sim q^5.$$

In the case of transverse phonons, for fairly small q, the decomposition of one phonon into two others is impossible. Hence in this case at T = 0 the broadening associated with anharmonism is absent, and only the slight broadening due to isotopic disorder (discussed in §37) remains. Only after reaching a certain threshold quasimomentum does the decomposition of a transverse phonon become possible, leading to the corresponding broadening.

For nonzero temperatures and all values of quasimomentum, a nonzero broadening associated with the scattering of the transverse phonon at the longitudinal phonon appears. For very low temperatures, for which

$$\hbar\omega_{q2} \gg k_B T,$$

this broadening depends exponentially on temperature and in the approximation of the isotropic continuum equals

$$\Gamma_{q2}(\omega_{q2}) = B_2 \left(\frac{q}{k_m}\right)^4 \frac{k_B T}{\hbar\omega_m} \exp\left[-\frac{\hbar(w_1 - w_2)q}{2k_B T}\right]\omega_m \quad (k_B T \ll \hbar\omega_{q2}, \quad q \ll k_m). \tag{37.8}$$

At higher temperatures, for which

$$\hbar\omega_{q2} \gg k_B T, \text{ but } k_B T \ll \hbar\omega_m,$$

we have

$$\Gamma_{\mathbf{q}2}(\omega_{\mathbf{q}2}) = B_2' \frac{q}{k_m} \left(\frac{k_B T}{\hbar\omega_m} \right)^4 \omega_m \quad (\hbar\omega_{\mathbf{q}2} \ll k_B T \ll \hbar\omega_m) \tag{37.9}$$

in agreement with the expression of [365] for the range of a phonon. Finally, at high temperatures (greater than the Debye value)

$$\Gamma_{\mathbf{q}2}(\omega_{\mathbf{q}2}) = B_2'' \frac{q}{k_m} \frac{k_B T}{\hbar\omega_m} \omega_m \quad (k_B T \gg \hbar\omega_m,\ q \ll k_m). \tag{37.10}$$

For longitudinal phonons in elastically anisotropic crystals at nonzero temperatures, according to [366], a considerable part is played by collision processes between longitudinal and short-wave transverse phonons; in these, a transverse phonon of another branch with almost the same frequency is generated (such pairs of transverse phonons with similar frequencies and wave vectors always occur when branches of transverse vibrations intersect; this should take place in cubic crystals, for example, in directions of the [100] type). The corresponding contribution to the damping in cubic anisotropic crystals at low temperatures and low frequencies equals

$$\Gamma_{\mathbf{q}1}(\omega_{\mathbf{q}1}) = B_1' \left(\frac{q}{k_m} \right)^2 \left(\frac{k_B T}{\hbar\omega_m} \right)^3 \omega_m \quad (\hbar\omega_{\mathbf{q}1} \ll k_B T \ll \hbar\omega_m), \tag{37.11}$$

and at high temperatures

$$\Gamma_{\mathbf{q}1}(\omega_{\mathbf{q}1}) = B_1'' \left(\frac{q}{k_m} \right)^2 \frac{k_B T}{\hbar\omega_m} \omega_m \quad (k_B T \gg \hbar\omega_m;\ q \ll k_m). \tag{37.12}$$

Since, for acoustic vibrations, $d^2\omega_{\mathbf{q}}/dq^2 < 0$, the laws of energy and momentum conservation, operating in the second approximation of perturbation theory in accordance with (37.6), make processes involving the scattering of longitudinal phonons at longitudinal phonons impossible. This possibility reappears for long-wave longitudinal phonons, however, if we take account of the indeterminacy in the energy of the short-wave phonons, which causes the δ function in (37.6) to be replaced by a δ-like function with a finite width (see [367, 368] and especially [369]). The corresponding processes may give a substantial contribution to the damping $\Gamma_{\mathbf{q}1}$, greater than the contribution given by formulas (37.11) and (37.12).

The functions $\Gamma_{qn}(\omega)$ should have characteristic singularities near the threshold points, beginning from which the decomposition of a given phonon into two others becomes possible. For example, in the isotropic case, for optical phonons with a dispersion law

$$\omega_{k0} = \omega_0 + \frac{1}{2}\omega_2 k^2 \quad (\omega_2 > 0)$$

a decomposition of this kind, accompanied by the emission of an acoustic phonon with frequency $\omega_k = wk$ (Čerenkov radiation of an acoustic phonon), only becomes possible after reaching the threshold values of wave vector and frequency

$$k_t = \frac{w}{\omega_2}, \quad \omega_t = \omega_0 + \frac{1}{2}\omega_2 k_t^2 .$$

It follows from (37.6) that at T = 0, in accordance with [363], this threshold point has the effect that, for $q > k_t$, a cubic term of the order of $(q-k_t)^3$ appears in the damping $\Gamma_{q0}(\omega_{q0})$ vanishing for $q < k_t$. At nonzero temperatures, formula (37.6) of the second approximation of perturbation theory leads to a "singularity" term in $\Gamma_{q0}(\omega_{q0})$, proportional to $T(q-k_t)^2$, having different signs for $q > k_t$ and $q < k_t$ [349]. Allowing for the finite lifetime of the phonons at $T \neq 0$, however, causes this singularity to be "spread" over a finite frequency range [348].

The temperature dependence of the vibration frequencies is determined by the first and second terms in formula (37.4) for the displacement of the frequency $P_{qn}(\omega_{qn})$, respectively due to anharmonicity of the third and fourth orders, and also by the temperature dependence of the frequencies ω_{qn} of the zero-approximation Hamiltonian resulting from the thermal expansion of the crystal (and also determined by the anharmonicity of the vibrations). All these three causes lead (at high temperatures) to a linear dependence of the renormalized frequency $\omega_{qn} + P_{qn}(\omega_{qn})$ on temperature; at low temperatures, however, the dependence of this frequency on T is given by the term proportional to T^4.

It follows from (37.4) and (37.5) for acoustic vibrations at small q that $P_{qn}(\omega_{qn})$, like ω_{qn}, depends linearly on q. It follows from (35.4) and (35.12) that the maximum of the peak in the coherent-scattering energy distribution determines the renormalized vibration frequency $\omega_{qn} + P_{qn}$. This fact must be borne in mind when determining the force constants in different harmonic models of the vibrations from neutron-diffraction data (the harmonic frequency ω^0_{qn} may be determined by linear extrapolation of the high-temperature experimental values of $\omega_{qn} + P_{qn}$ to T = 0).

In order to determine the value of the damping, we must know the constants B in formulas (37.7) to (37.12). A simple but very coarse estimate of these constants may be obtained by comparing the sums entering into the formula for Γ_{qn} and the formulas for other quantities associated with anharmonicity. Thus, for example, for the constant B_1 in (37.7) we obtained [349] the estimate $B_1 \sim \beta$, where β determines the correction to the part of the high-temperature specific heat associated with anharmonicity of the third order, $C'_V = 3k_B N\beta T/\theta$, and usually $\beta \sim 0.1$. The other constants B in the above formulas for Γ_{qn} have the same order.

It follows from this, in particular, that in the case of short-wave vibrations, and also for optical phonons if the law of energy conservation allows their decomposition into two acoustic phonons, $\Gamma_{qn} \sim (0.01$—$0.1)\,\omega_m$ at low and $\Gamma_{qn} \sim 0.1\,k_B T/\hbar$ at high temperatures. The relatively high value of the damping indicates, in particular, that the shape of the intensity distributions of the peaks may deviate considerably from the Lorentz form (the derivative $\partial\Gamma_{qn}/\partial\omega$ several times exceeds the ratio Γ_{qn}/ω_{qn}). Finally, the frequency shift P_{qn} at $q \sim k_m$, as indicated by (37.4) and (37.3), has the same order of magnitude as the damping of the short-wave phonons.

In order to make a specific calculation of the damping and frequency shift, we must set up some model of the forces of interatomic interaction, determine the anharmonicity constants in this model from independent experimental data (for example, from thermal expansion), and then calculate Γ_{qn} and P_{qn} from formulas (37.3) and (37.4) by numerical integration. Detailed calculations of this kind were made by Maradudin and Fein [352] for crystals with face-centered cubic lattices on the nearest-neighbor approximation of the central-interaction model. For values of the parameters corresponding to lead it was found, for example, that for $q = 2\pi/d$ ($\mathbf{q} \parallel \mathbf{k}_x$) at T = 425°K the damping $\Gamma_q = 0.06\omega_m$ for longitudinal vibrations, while for $q = \pi/d$ the damping $\Gamma_q = 3\cdot10^{-3}\omega_m$. The term linear with respect to T in the frequency $\delta\omega_{qn}$ (allowing for the temperature dependence of ω_{qn}) for $q = \pi/d$ in this case equals $-0.008\,(T/\theta)\,\omega_m$ (an order smaller than the estimate given above).

An analogous calculation carried out by Cowley [370] for alkali halide crystals (considering anharmonicity on the model of rigid ions for nearest neighbors) led to the following values of $\Gamma_{q\|}$, $\Gamma_{q\perp}$, $\delta\omega_{q\|}$, $\delta\omega_{q\perp}$ for longitudinal and transverse optical vibrations:

in KBr at 290°K

$$\Gamma_{q\perp} = 0.013\omega_{q\perp}, \qquad \delta\omega_{q\perp} = -0.10\omega_{q\perp},$$
$$\Gamma_{q\|} = 0.027\omega_{q\|}, \qquad \delta\omega_{q\|} = -0.07\omega_{q\|};$$

in KBr at 5°K

$$\Gamma_{q\perp} = 0.002\omega_{q\perp}, \qquad \delta\omega_{q\perp} = -0.023\omega_{q\perp},$$
$$\Gamma_{q\|} = 0.013\omega_{q\|}, \qquad \delta\omega_{q\|} = -0.006\omega_{q\|};$$

in NaI at 90°K

$$\Gamma_{q\perp} = 0.012\omega_{q\perp}, \qquad \delta\omega_{q\perp} = -0.031\omega_{q\perp},$$
$$\Gamma_{q\|} = 0.049\omega_{q\|}, \qquad \delta\omega_{q\|} = -0.025\omega_{q\|}.$$

The relative large value of the damping in this case leads to a considerable deviation of the shape of the coherent-scattering peaks from the Lorentz form (see Fig. 24, which gives the single-phonon scattering cross section for longitudinal vibrations in NaI

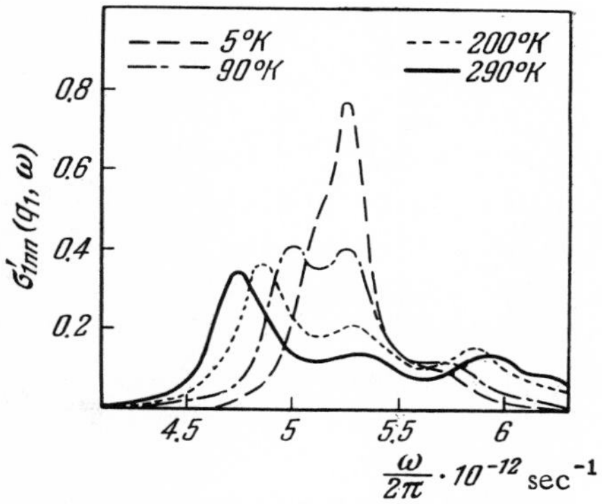

Fig. 24. Single-phonon coherent neutron-scattering cross section for longitudinal optical vibrations in NaI (q = 0) as a function of the transferred energy, as calculated in [370].

as calculated in [370]). Calculations of the width and shape of the broadened peaks in the scattered-neutron energy distribution were carried out by Cowley [421] for a model of the strontium titanate crystal also; in these calculations allowance was made for the effect of "interaction" between neighboring branches of vibrations, as discussed on pp. 335 and 336.

A few papers have been written on the experimental study of the temperature dependence of the coherent-scattering peak maxima and peak broadening. For aluminum the vibration frequencies were determined over a wide temperature range from 290 to 930°K [306]. We see from Fig. 25 that, in agreement with theory, $\omega_{qn} + P_{qn}$ depends linearly on T. The relative frequency reduction $\delta\omega_{qn}/\omega_{qn} = 0.12$ (for $\omega_q = 4\cdot10^{13}$ sec^{-1}) on changing the temperature from 300 to 800°K also agrees with the theoretical estimate.

The damping of longitudinal (with $\omega_q = 3\cdot10^{13}$ sec^{-1}) and transverse (with $\omega_q = 2.4\cdot10^{13}$ sec^{-1}) vibrations at 800 to 900°K was

$$\Gamma_q \sim (4-5)\cdot10^{12}\ \text{sec}^{-1} \sim 0.15\,\omega_q.$$

For vibrations with $\omega \sim \omega_m$ in lead we also have $\Gamma_q \sim 0.1\omega_q$ [371]. These values of Γ_q agree with theoretical estimates. Peak broadening was also observed in alkali halid crystals in [320].

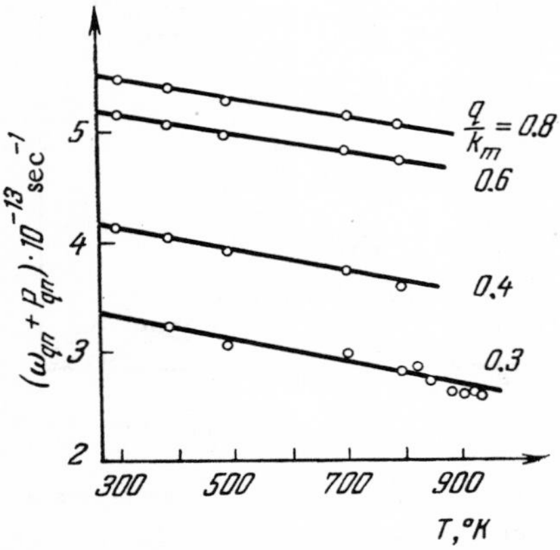

Fig. 25. Temperature dependence of the renormalized vibration frequencies in aluminum according to [306].

General formulas for the single-phonon scattering cross section may also be obtained without using perturbation theory and expanding in powers of the displacements [351]. In practice, single-phonon scattering peaks may only be separated in those cases in which the damping is fairly small (although the frequency shift need not in general be so). Allowing for the higher terms in the expansion of the cross section in powers of the displacements leads to terms describing interference effects between single-phonon and many-phonon scattering [358, 359], and also to a displacement and asymmetry of the coherent-scattering peaks. Estimates of these terms made in [358] showed, however, that for smallish q_1 the corresponding effects were slight, and even at high temperatures led to corrections no greater than a few percent.

The damping associated with anharmonicity of the fourth order [372–375] (for example, that resulting from the decomposition of a phonon into three others) may be considerable in the case of high-frequency phonons, for which the law of energy conservation makes decomposition into two phonons impossible. If, however, the latter processes are allowed, then the damping associated with fourth-order anharmonicity is relatively small, although at high temperatures (for which it varies as T^2) the part played by this effect may increase.

The nonideal state of the crystal, together with the effects considered in §36 due to the scattering of phonons at static inhomogeneities, also leads to certain special features in the decomposition and scattering of phonons due to anharmonicity. These features are associated with the fact that, in nonideal crystals (in contrast to ideal crystals), the law of quasimomentum conservation does not have to be satisfied in the elementary scattering acts (the momentum may be transferred to the defect, i.e., to the crystal as a whole). The influence of these effects on the damping of phonons in solid solutions was discussed in [376].

The damping of phonons may be due not only to their interaction with one another but also to interaction with other quasiparticles, for example, with spin waves in ferromagnetic [377] or antiferromagnetic [378] crystals, and with conduction electrons in conductors [379–382]. According to various calculations, in typical metals the interaction with conduction electrons for $q \ll k_m$ leads to a small contribution toward the damping, $\Gamma_{qn} \sim 10^{-3}\omega_{qn}$, relatively larger at low frequencies, and to characteristic singularities of the frequency for values of q equal to twice the Fermi wave vector [383, 384, 428, 429]. A considerable degree of damping and frequency shift may arise from electron-phonon interaction in semiconductors with a considerable concentration of conduction electrons [381].

In addition to the broadening of the single-phonon coherent-scattering peaks, electron-phonon interaction also leads to a specific nuclear (nonmagnetic) scattering of neutrons at conduction electrons [381]. For example, if the electrons in ionic crystals are in a polaron state [385], then this kind of scattering results from the perturbation created by the displacements of the ions in the polaron potential well, and according to the estimates of [381] may be considerable in the presence of a fairly high concentration of polarons.

There should also be characteristic singularities in the damping of phonons in crystals containing fine electron impurity centers. In this case the electron-phonon interaction leads to a sharp resonance increase in the damping of the phonon when its frequency approaches some Bohr frequency of the electron center. As a result of this, there should be a considerable broadening of the peak of the single-phonon coherent neutron scattering, and the peak may deviate considerably from the Lorentz shape [386].

Sharp peaks in the energy distribution of scattered neutrons may be associated with the absorption or emission of not only phonons but also other elementary Bose excitations, for example, spin waves in magnetics (see reviews [77, 286, 387]). The interaction of spin waves with each other, with phonons, with electrons, and with static inhomogeneities should also lead to the broadening of such peaks [377, 388–390].

The interaction of elementary excitations leads to a broadening of the peaks in the energy distribution of scattered neutrons not only in crystals but also in quantum fluids. These effects were studied in the case of the scattering of neutrons by the Bose fluid He^4 [363, 391–393] and the Fermi fluid He^3 [394, 395].

§38. Influence of Static Inhomogeneities and Interaction between Elementary Excitations on the Single-Phonon Incoherent Scattering of Neutrons

Static inhomogeneities and anharmonicity of the vibrations lead not only to the broadening and displacement of the peaks of coherent neutron scattering but also to characteristic features in single-phonon incoherent scattering. The cross section of this scattering in solid solutions $\sigma_2 + \sigma_3$ is determined by expressions (35.5) and (35.6), containing terms of the zero, first, and second orders of smallness relative to the constants V of interaction with static inhomogeneities. In order to discover the effects of present interest, it is sufficient to confine attention to the principle terms of zero order. Then, as indicated by (35.12) to (35.14), we need only retain terms containing the functions $\varphi_{\mathbf{k}n\mathbf{k}'n'}$ with $\mathbf{k} = \mathbf{k}'$, $n = n'$, in the sums of (35.5) and (35.6), and the expressions for σ_2 and σ_3 in a disordered solution with one atom in the cell simplify considerably:

$$\sigma_2(\mathbf{q}_1, E) = N\frac{k_2}{k_1}\frac{1}{8\pi m}\sum_{\mathbf{k}n}\frac{1}{\omega_{\mathbf{k}n}}\left[\sqrt{\sigma_{cA}} - \sqrt{\sigma_{cB}} - \sqrt{\sigma_c}\,\mathbf{q}_1\mathbf{A}_{\mathbf{k}+\mathbf{q}}\right]^2 \times$$

$$\times (\mathbf{q}_1\mathbf{e}_{\mathbf{k}n})^2\overline{|c_{\mathbf{k}+\mathbf{q}}|^2}\varphi_{\mathbf{k}n\mathbf{k}n}(\omega), \qquad (38.1)$$

$$\sigma_3(\mathbf{q}_1, E) = \frac{k_2}{k_1}\frac{1}{8\pi m}\sigma_i\sum_{\mathbf{k}n}\frac{1}{\omega_{\mathbf{k}n}}(\mathbf{q}_1\mathbf{e}_{\mathbf{k}n})^2\varphi_{\mathbf{k}n\mathbf{k}n}(\omega). \qquad (38.2)$$

Here it is taken into consideration that $S^*_{\mathbf{q}_1 n}(\mathbf{q}) = 0$ and the relation (5.2) between $\mathbf{R}_\mathbf{k}$ and $c_\mathbf{k}$; is employed: $\sigma_c = c\sigma_{cA} + (1-c)\sigma_{cB}$. In ideal crystals $\sigma_2 = 0$ and the incoherent single-phonon scattering cross section equals $\sigma_3(\mathbf{q}_1, E)$.

A departure of the crystal from ideal structure leads to two new features in the incoherent scattering as compared with the case of scattering by ideal harmonic crystals considered in §34 [344]. Firstly, a departure of the solution from ideal form leads to the appearance of a characteristic sharp dependence of σ_2 on $\mathbf{q}$. Secondly, the broadening of the levels leads to spreading of the singularities in the frequency-distribution function of the vibrations and the energy distribution of the cross section $\sigma_2 + \sigma_3$ discussed in §34 (the latter effect is also produced by anharmonicity).

Let us first consider the effect in ideal solutions, for which $\overline{|c_{\mathbf{k}}|^2}$ is determined by formula (1.14). For fairly small $\Gamma_{\mathbf{k}n}$ the functions φ' and φ'' may according to (35.12) be replaced by δ functions (except for the neighborhoods of the singular points of the frequency-distribution function discussed below). Let us confine ourselves for simplicity to considering a cubic crystal in the approximation of an isotropic continuum, for which $\mathbf{A}_{\mathbf{k}}$ is determined by formula (5.14), while $\omega_{\mathbf{k}n}$ does not depend on the direction of $\mathbf{k}$. Let us denote by $g_n(\omega)$ the frequency-distribution function of the vibrations of the n-th branch (normalized to unity) and by $q_{\omega n}$ the length of the wave vector of the n-th branch corresponding to the frequency $\omega_{qn} = \omega$.

The expression for σ_2 simplifies in two limiting cases, for which

$$k_m \gg q \gg q_{\omega n} \quad \text{or} \quad q \ll q_{\omega n} \ll k_m.$$

Moreover in the case of processes in which a phonon is absorbed

$$\sigma_2(\mathbf{q}_1, E) = \frac{1}{3} N \frac{k_2}{k_1} \frac{1}{8\pi m} \frac{n(\omega)}{\omega} q_1^2 c(1-c) \times$$
$$\times \sum_n g_n(\omega) \left[\sqrt{\sigma_{cA}} - \sqrt{\sigma_{cB}} - \sqrt{\sigma_c}\, a^0 \frac{\mathbf{q}_1 \mathbf{q}}{q^2} \right]^2 \quad (q \gg q_{\omega n}), \qquad (38.3)$$

$$\sigma_2(\mathbf{q}_1, E) = \frac{1}{3} N \frac{k_2}{k_1} \frac{1}{8\pi m} \frac{n(\omega)}{\omega} q_1^2 c(1-c) \times$$
$$\times \sum_n g_n(\omega) \left[\left(\sqrt{\sigma_{cA}} - \sqrt{\sigma_{cB}}\right)^2 + \chi_n \sigma_c a^{02} \frac{q_1^2}{q_{\omega n}^2} \right] \quad (q \ll q_{\omega n}), \qquad (38.4)$$

where $\chi_n = 3/5$ for longitudinal vibrations and $\chi_n = 2/5$ for transverse vibrations. The expression for σ_3 has the form

$$\sigma_3(\mathbf{q}_1, E) = \frac{1}{3} N \frac{k_2}{k_1} \frac{1}{8\pi m} \frac{n(\omega)}{\omega} q_1^2 g(\omega) \sigma_i, \qquad (38.5)$$

analogous to (34.5). In the case of processes of neutron scattering in which a phonon is emitted, we must replace $n(\omega)$ by $n(|\omega|)+1$, ω by $|\omega|$, and $g_n(\omega)$ by $g_n(|\omega|)$ in (38.4) and (38.5).

Thus allowing for distortions has the result that σ_2 depends not only on E but also on $\mathbf{q}$ (in addition to the ordinary relationship $\sigma_2 \sim q_1^2$). Effects associated with distortions are particularly large if the change in neutron energy $E = \hbar\omega$ during scattering is small or close to the energy of the long-wave optical vibrations, while the end of the vector $\mathbf{q}_1/2\pi$ lies close to a reciprocal-lattice point. If q and $q_{\omega n}$ are small enough, the terms in (38.3) and (38.4) due to distortions become dominant, and as q, $q_{\omega n} \to 0$ the value of σ_2 tends to infinity as q^{-2} or $q_{\omega n}^{-2}$ (in the general case of crystals with several atoms in the cell, not considered here, q^{-2} and $q_{\omega n}^{-2}$ acquire an additional factor $\frac{1}{3v}\overline{(\sum_\gamma e_{\mathbf{k}n\gamma})^2}$, where the averaging is carried out over the directions $\mathbf{k}$ as $k \to 0$). The resultant characteristic dependence of σ_2 on $\mathbf{q}$ and E may be used for experimentally determining the limiting frequencies of the long-wave optical vibrations. We see from (38.5) that σ_3 does not depend on the distortions.

For small q and $q_{\omega n}$ formulas (38.3) and (38.4) may also be applied to nonideal solutions if we replace $c(1-c)$ in them by $k_BT/v\varphi_{cc}(\mathbf{q})$ $(q \gg q_{\omega n})$. Thus in this range of q and $q_{\omega n}$ values the value of σ_2 changes when short-range order is established in the solution, usually increasing in decomposing solutions and falling in ordering solutions. A specially sharp rise in σ_2 should take place in this region on approaching the critical point on the decomposition curve, when φ_{cc} becomes very small.

Let us now consider the spreading of the singularities of the frequency-distribution function of the vibrations $g(\omega)$ and the energy distribution of single-phonon incoherent scattering. As in the ideal crystal, the function $g(\omega)$ in the nonideal crystal may be represented quite strictly in the form of a sum of the spectral representations of the correlation functions of the phonons:

$$g(\omega) = \sum_{\mathbf{k}n} \varphi_{\mathbf{k}n\mathbf{k}n}(\omega). \tag{38.6}$$

If we replace $\varphi_{\mathbf{k}n\mathbf{k}n}(\omega)$ by δ functions, then at frequencies ω_{cr} corresponding to analytical extremal points at which $\nabla_{\mathbf{k}}\,\omega_{\mathbf{k}n'}=0$, the functions $g(\omega)$ will, in accordance with the arguments of §34, have radical singularities (34.8). The transformation from δ functions to smooth functions (35.12) will clearly lead to the spreading or blurring of these singularities.

Let us, for example, consider that, in addition to the branch n', containing the minimum point $\omega_{kn'}$, under consideration, other branches of vibrations also lie at the frequency ω_{cr}, and that the value of $\Gamma_{kn'}(\omega) = \Gamma$ near the extremal point is constant. Then, substituting (35.12) into (38.6) and integrating over **k**, we find that, on allowing for damping, the term $T(\omega-\omega_{cr})^{1/2}$ describing the singularity in question should be replaced near the minimum point by

$$T(\omega-\omega_{cr})^{1/2} \rightarrow \frac{T}{\sqrt{2}}\{[(\omega-\omega_{cr})^2+\Gamma^2]^{1/2}+(\omega-\omega_{cr})\}^{1/2}. \qquad (38.7)$$

Here ω_{cr} is the frequency of the extremal point considered, allowing for its displacement by $P(\omega_{cr})$, and terms of the $P(\omega_{cr})/\omega_{cr}$ type are disregarded in comparison with unity.

For $\omega-\omega_{cr} \gg \Gamma$ expression (38.7) passes into $T(\omega-\omega_{cr})^{1/2}$, i.e., the damping plays no part. For $\omega-\omega_{cr} = 0$, however, the right-hand side equals $T\sqrt{\Gamma/2}$ and no longer falls to zero. For negative $\omega-\omega_{cr}$, at which $|\omega-\omega_{cr}| \gg \Gamma$, the right-hand side of (38.7) equals $T\Gamma/2\sqrt{\omega_{cr}-\omega}$, i.e., it falls off as $(\omega_{cr}-\omega)^{-1/2}$. Thus the singularity $g(\omega)$ is spread out over a frequency range $\sim\Gamma$.

On the basis of equation (38.7), singularities in the energy distribution of incoherent neutron scattering also spread out in a similar way. This result remains qualitatively valid if the damping $\Gamma_{k'n'}(\omega)$ depends on the direction of the vector **k'**. Then we simply have an additional averaging over the directions:

$$T(\omega-\omega_{cr})^{1/2} \rightarrow \frac{T}{4\pi\sqrt{2}}\int d\Omega_{k'}\{[(\omega-\omega_{cr})^2+\Gamma^2_{k'n'}(\omega)]^{1/2}+ \\ +(\omega-\omega_{cr})\}^{1/2} \qquad (38.8)$$

(the integration is carried out over a solid angle with vertex at the minimum point), and this introduces no qualitative change into the frequency dependence of the diffuse singularity. It is clear that this spreading of the singularities $g(\omega)$ will take place in ideal crystals as a result of anharmonicity (especially at high temperatures) and as a result of the interaction of phonons with other quasiparticles.*

If the masses or force constants of the atoms of the solution differ substantially, the expressions given for the incoherent-scattering cross section cease to be valid. For greatly differing impurity atoms, the scattering cross section may be studied for a low impurity concentration. An investigation of this kind was carried out by Kagan and Iosilevskii [396] in the case of an arbitrary difference in the masses of the atoms but the same force constants (and in the absence of static displacements). It is an important point that, in this case, the single-phonon incoherent-scattering cross section for impurity atoms is expressed in terms of the frequency-distribution function of the vibrations of an ideal impurity-free crystal $g_0(\omega)$. Hence by choosing impurity nuclei with a large scattering cross section and studying the energy distribution of the impurity incoherent scattering we may in principle determine the function $g_0(\omega)$. Clearly this method may prove particularly useful in the case of a matrix with a small incoherent-scattering cross section. In the classical approximation the theory of neutron scattering by impurity atoms with arbitrary masses and force constants was developed by Waller [397].

§39. Scattering of Neutrons at Local Vibrations

In discussing the singularities of neutron scattering by solid solutions in the preceding sections, we mainly considered the case in which the atoms of the solution had similar masses and force constants. New effects arise in the case of greatly differing masses or force constants, when the character of the normal vibrations near impurity atoms changes qualitatively. Near light impurity atoms (or atoms with very rigid bonds), in particular, local vibrations develop; the frequencies of these lie in the region of the forbidden frequencies of the ideal crystal, while the amplitudes fall off rapidly (exponentially) on moving away from the defect. The existence of such local vibrations was first predicted by Lifshits [217, 218, 348a, 398], who developed the theory of these vibrations

*If other branches have no vibrations at the minimum or maximum frequency ω_{cr}, the singularity $g(\omega)$ spreads out in accordance with a different, exponential law [218].

and laid the foundations of the systematic study of vibrations in nonideal crystals.* One of the methods for studying local vibrations is based on investigating the inelastic scattering of neutrons accompanied by the excitation or absorption of quanta of these vibrations [344, 396, 401, 402]. Let us consider the cross section of this scattering in the case of small concentrations of impurity atoms.

For the sake of being definite, let us suppose that an impurity atom lies at the origin of coordinates. The thermal displacements of the atoms in the case under consideration may most conveniently be expanded not by reference to plane waves but by reference to the exact (and real) normal coordinates of the harmonic Hamiltonian of the vibrations. This expansion may be written in the form

$$\mathbf{u}_{s\gamma} = \sum_{\varkappa} \mathbf{u}_{s\gamma\varkappa} (a_{\varkappa} + a_{\varkappa}^{+}) + \sum_{k} \mathbf{u}_{s\gamma k} (a_k + a_k^{+}). \qquad (39.1)$$

Here $\varkappa$ enumerates the local vibrations with frequencies $\omega_{\varkappa}$ and k the vibrations of the continuous spectrum, not constituting plane waves in the defect-containing crystal (the index k combines the wave vector **k** and the serial number of the n branch of these vibrations). The quantities $\mathbf{u}_{s\gamma\varkappa}$ fall off rapidly with distance from the center.

The single-phonon scattering cross section for local vibrations (for smallish q_1 and smallish amplitudes of the vibrations) may be determined from formula (32.5) by expanding in powers of $\mathbf{u}_{s\gamma}$ and retaining only terms of the $(\mathbf{q}_1\mathbf{u}_{s\gamma}(t))(\mathbf{q}_1\mathbf{u}_{s'\gamma'})$ type. By replacing $\mathbf{u}_{s\gamma}$ with the sum of (39.1) and separating out from the sum just one principal term corresponding to the excitation or absorption of a quantum of the local vibration under consideration $\varkappa$, we may put the cross section of this single-phonon scattering in the form [344]

$$\sigma_{\varkappa}(\mathbf{q}_1, E) = \frac{1}{4\pi\hbar} N_g \frac{k_2}{k_1} \Big\{ \sum_{s\gamma} \Big| \sqrt{\sigma_{cs\gamma}}\, \mathbf{q}_1 \mathbf{u}_{s\gamma\varkappa} \exp(i\mathbf{q}\mathbf{R}_{s\gamma}) \exp(i\mathbf{q}_1 \delta \mathbf{R}_{s\gamma}^{c}) \Big|^2 +$$

$$+ \sum_{s\gamma} \sigma_{is\gamma} (\mathbf{q}_1 \mathbf{u}_{s\gamma\varkappa})^2 \Big\} \varphi_{\varkappa\varkappa}(\omega). \qquad (39.2)$$

*At the present time there are a number of excellent reviews on the theory of vibrations of nonideal crystals [218, 276, 398–400].

Here N_g is the number of defects in the crystal, $\sigma_{cs\gamma}$ and $\sigma_{is\gamma}$ are respectively determined by the coherent and incoherent scattering cross sections of the nuclei (impurity atoms or atoms of the matrix) lying at points $s\gamma$, the summation with respect to $s\gamma$ is carried out in the region around the center under consideration (for a small concentration of centers these regions do not overlap), and the correlation function $\varphi_{\varkappa\varkappa}(\omega)$ is given by formula (35.8) (in which $a_{\mathbf{k}n}$ must be replaced by $a_{\varkappa}$). In (39.2) we have omitted small terms containing $\varphi_{\varkappa\varkappa'}(\omega)$ with $\varkappa \neq \varkappa'$, which only become important in the case of close frequencies of the local vibrations (this case is not considered here).

In the harmonic approximation, the Hamiltonian becomes diagonalized in variables $a_{\varkappa}$, $a_{\varkappa}^{+}$, and $\varphi_{\varkappa\varkappa}(\omega)$ reduces to the δ functions

$$\varphi_{\varkappa\varkappa}(\omega) = n_{\varkappa}\delta(\omega - \omega_{\varkappa}) + (n_{\varkappa} + 1)\,\delta(\omega + \omega_{\varkappa}). \qquad (39.3)$$

Hence the cross section $\sigma_{\varkappa}(\mathbf{q}_1, E)$ corresponds to two sharp peaks in the energy distribution, lying at energies of

$$E = \pm\hbar\omega_{\varkappa}.$$

These peaks may be separated from the single-phonon coherent-scattering peaks discussed above, because they only appear in the forbidden range of frequencies on introducing defects into the crystal. In addition to this, the position of these peaks should remain unchanged on varying the scattering angles or crystal orientation, while the coherent-scattering peaks are then displaced.

The expression for the incoherent-scattering intensity corresponding to local vibrations $\sigma_{c\varkappa}$ [the first term in (39.2)] simplifies if the defect in a crystal with a Bravais lattice contains only one impurity atom and static distortions may be neglected. Then

$$\sigma_{c\varkappa}(\mathbf{q}_1, E) = \frac{1}{4\pi\hbar} N_g \frac{k_2}{k_1} \times$$

$$\times \left| \sqrt{\sigma_c} \sum_{s} \mathbf{q}_1\mathbf{u}_{s\varkappa} e^{i\mathbf{q}_1\mathbf{R}_s} + \left(\sqrt{\sigma_c'} - \sqrt{\sigma_c}\right) \mathbf{q}_1\mathbf{u}_0 \right|^2 \varphi_{\varkappa\varkappa}(\omega), \qquad (39.4)$$

where σ_c and σ_c' are the cross sections for scattering by a matrix atom and the impurity atom, while $\mathbf{u}_0 = \mathbf{u}_s|_{\mathbf{R}_s=0}$. The cross section

$\sigma_{c\varkappa}(\mathbf{q}_1, E)$ is here connected with the Fourier component of the quantities $\mathbf{u}_{s\varkappa}$ characterizing the amplitudes of the different atoms taking part in the local vibration $\varkappa$. It was emphasized by Elliot and Maradudin [402] that, by studying the cross section of this scattering for various scattering angles and crystal orientations, i.e., for different $\mathbf{q}_1$, and for a given $E \approx \hbar\omega_{\varkappa}$, one may determine the distribution of the quantities $\mathbf{u}_{s\varkappa}$ around the defect [the incoherent part of the cross section, according to (39.2), depends in a trivial way on $\mathbf{q}_1$].

In order to obtain an explicit determination of the cross section $\sigma_{\varkappa}$ and to estimate this numerically we must know the values of $\mathbf{u}_{\varkappa}$ and determine the expression in the curly brackets of (39.2) or (39.3). This calculation was performed by Kagan and Iosilevskii [396] and Elliot and Maradudin [402, 420] for the case of a single impurity atom in a cubic crystal, only distinguished by mass from the atoms of the matrix. It was also found possible to express the cross section $\sigma_{c\varkappa}(\mathbf{q}_1, E)$ in terms of the characteristics (frequencies and polarizations) of the vibrations of the ideal crystal

$$\sigma_{c\varkappa}(\mathbf{q}_1, E) = N_g \frac{k_2}{k_1} \frac{1}{8\pi m} \omega_{\varkappa} \left\{ \frac{1}{3N} \sum_{\mathbf{k}n} \frac{\omega_{\mathbf{k}n}^2}{(\omega_{\varkappa}^2 - \omega_{\mathbf{k}n}^2)^2} \right\}^{-1} \times$$

$$\times \sum_n (\mathbf{q}_1 \mathbf{e}_{\mathbf{q}n})^2 \left\{ \frac{\sqrt{\sigma_c}}{\omega_{\varkappa}^2 - \omega_{\mathbf{q}n}^2} + \left(1 - \frac{m'}{m}\right)^{-1} \frac{\sqrt{\sigma_c'} - \sqrt{\sigma_c}}{\omega_{\varkappa}^2} \right\}^2 \varphi_{\varkappa\varkappa}(\omega) \qquad (39.5)$$

(m' and m are the masses of the impurity atom and the matrix atom).

Estimates based on this formula showed [396] that the integral intensity of the peaks representing scattering at local vibrations might be considerable, even for small impurity concentrations, and these peaks might be distinguished above the background of multi-phonon scattering. It should be noted that, in addition to single-phonon scattering at local vibrations, there should also be multi-phonon scattering with peaks at $\omega = \pm 2\omega_{\varkappa}, \pm 3\omega_{\varkappa}$ and so on [396]; this, however, should be very weak. A relatively weak peak associated with scattering at local vibrations should be observed in the scattered-neutron spectrum (as in the Mössbauer spectrum) in the region of very small $|\omega| \lesssim \Gamma_{\varkappa}$ as well [403, 404, 422].

The scattering of neutrons at local vibrations was observed experimentally by Mozer et al. [405] in a palladium-base alloy containing a small concentration of nickel impurity atoms. In accordance with the predictions of the theory of local vibrations, in this case $\omega_\varkappa$ only slightly (10%) exceeds the maximum frequency of the crystal vibrations. A considerably greater change in the energy of the neutrons occurred in the case of scattering by local vibrations around light hydrogen atoms dissolved in vanadium [406]. The inelastic scattering of neutrons at local vibrations was also studied in the case of local vibrations at impurity atoms of beryllium in vanadium [441] and nickel [442].

As a result of anharmonicity, the normal vibrations interact with each other, as a result of which the spectral distribution of $\varphi_{\varkappa\varkappa}(\omega)$ no longer reduces to δ functions, but is broadened. This broadening may be associated, in particular, with the finite lifetime of the local vibration due to its decomposition into crystal vibrations. In this case of smallish $\omega_\varkappa(\omega_\varkappa < 2\omega_m)$, such processes are determined mainly by the Hamiltonian of third-order anharmonicity, which may be written in the form

$$H_3 = \sum_{\varkappa k_1 k_2} \left(\frac{1}{2} V_{\varkappa k_1 k_2} a_\varkappa a_{k_1}^+ a_{k_2}^+ + V_{k_1 \varkappa k_2} a_\varkappa^+ a_{k_1} a_{k_2}^+ + \right.$$

$$\left. + \frac{1}{2} V'_{\varkappa k_1 k_2} a_\varkappa a_{k_1} a_{k_2} + \text{c.c.} \right), \qquad (39.6)$$

where V and V' are some constants of the third-order anharmonicity.

Calculation of the correlation function of $\varphi_{\varkappa\varkappa}(\omega)$ by the method of thermal Green's functions, allowing for second-order terms in V and V', leads to an expression of the Lorentz type (35.12), in which **kn** is replaced by $\varkappa$, and the damping and shift are determined by the expressions

$$\Gamma'_\varkappa(\omega) = \frac{\pi}{2\hbar^2} \sum_{k_1 k_2} [|V_{\varkappa k_1 k_2}|^2 (1 + n_{k_1} + n_{k_2})\, \delta(\omega - \omega_{k_1} - \omega_{k_2}) +$$

$$+ 2|V_{k_1 \varkappa k_2}|^2 (n_{k_2} - n_{k_1})\, \delta(\omega - \omega_{k_1} + \omega_{k_2})], \qquad (39.7)$$

$$P'_\varkappa(\omega) = \frac{1}{2\hbar^2} P \sum_{k_1 k_2} \Big[|V_{\varkappa k_1 k_2}|^2 \frac{1 + n_{k_1} + n_{k_2}}{\omega - \omega_{k_1} - \omega_{k_2}} +$$

$$+ 2|V_{k_1 \varkappa k_2}|^2 \frac{n_{k_2} - n_{k_1}}{\omega - \omega_{k_1} + \omega_{k_2}} - |V'_{\varkappa k_1 k_2}|^2 \frac{1 + n_{k_1} + n_{k_2}}{\omega + \omega_{k_1} + \omega_{k_2}} +$$

$$+V_{\varkappa\varkappa k_2}V_{k_1k_1k_2}(1+2n_{k_1})\left(\frac{1}{\omega-\omega_\varkappa-\omega_{k_2}}-\frac{1}{\omega-\omega_\varkappa+\omega_{k_2}}\right)+$$

$$+\frac{1}{\hbar}\sum_k V_{\varkappa\varkappa kk}\left(n_k+\frac{1}{2}\right)\Bigg]. \qquad (39.8)$$

The first term in (39.7) corresponds to processes involving the decomposition of the local vibration into two phonons and the second to processes in which the vanishing of the local-vibration quantum is accompanied by the annihilation of one phonon and the generation of another of higher frequency (these processes are clearly only possible if the local frequency lies on the forbidden band of frequencies between two permitted bands). The last term in (39.8) is due to the main contribution of the fourth-order anharmonicity.

We see from (39.7) that the broadening considered is proportional to T at high temperatures, while as $T \rightarrow 0$ it tends to a nonzero limit. The shift (39.8) is also proportional to T at high temperatures and contains a term of the order of T^4 at low temperatures.

Specific calculations of $\Gamma'_\varkappa(\omega)$ and $P'_\varkappa(\omega)$ are extremely laborious, since it is necessary to consider both the complicated law of the spatial variation in the amplitudes of the local vibrations near the center and also the distortion of the vibrations of the continuous spectrum by the impurity center. In view of this, it has only proved possible to make such calculations with the help of very simplified models [399, 407–409]. Maradudin [408] made such a calculation for a defect in a linear lattice on the nearest-neighbor approximation for values of the anharmonism parameters corresponding to lead. For a ratio $\omega_\varkappa/\omega_m \approx 1.2-1.4$ it was found that for $T > \theta$

$$\Gamma'_\varkappa(\omega_\varkappa) \approx 0.14\,(T/\theta)\,\omega_m$$

(θ is the Debye temperature). This value somewhat exceeds the value of $\Gamma'_\varkappa$ obtained on the three-dimensional model, which, however, did not consider the distortion of the continuous-spectrum vibrations [399, 407]. For $T=0$, according to Maradudin's estimate, $\Gamma_\varkappa$ falls by an order of magnitude as compared with the case $T \sim \theta$.

Interaction between vibrations leads not only to a finite lifetime of the local excitations and to a corresponding broadening of the spectral distribution of local phonons, but also to a specific modulation broadening of the distribution of scattered neutrons; this is determined by the modulation of the frequency of a given local vibration as a result of its interaction with other vibrations, and is related to the low-frequency fluctuations of the corresponding interaction potential (it is not determined directly by the lifetime of the excitation under consideration). Although such modulation broadening is due to fourth-order anharmonicity (and third-order anharmonicity in higher approximations), in a number of cases it plays no less important a part than the decomposition broadening considered above.

Thus, for example [410], the interaction of local vibrations of the type $V_{\varkappa\varkappa'}N_{\varkappa}N_{\varkappa'}$ ($N_{\varkappa} = a^{+}_{\varkappa}a_{\varkappa}$) with one another, and also terms in the Hamiltonian of the fourth order relative to the coordinate of the local vibration $V_{\varkappa\varkappa}N^{2}_{\varkappa}$ under consideration in the "quasiharmonic" approximation, with an infinite lifetime of the excitations, lead to a slight difference between the energies of the quantum transitions of the given vibration $\varkappa$ for different $N_{\varkappa}$ and $N_{\varkappa'}$ ($\varkappa' \neq \varkappa$), and to the splitting of the line at frequency $\omega_{\varkappa}$ into a series of lines separated by intervals of $\sim V_{\varkappa\varkappa'}$.

This result changes qualitatively, however, if we consider the finite lifetime of the local excitations. As this time decreases, the lines of the split multiplet (for example, in the scattering spectrum) first broaden and then start overlapping and merge into a single wide distribution. It is an important factor here that the existence of transitions between the local states leads to the partial averaging of the fluctuation effects corresponding to different occupation numbers, as a result of which there is a contraction of the spectral distibution, the more so the more frequently quantum transitions take place. As a result of this, the extent of the corresponding broadening is inversely proportional to the probability of a transition between the local levels, i.e., to the square of the third-order anharmonicity constant (and proportional to $V^{2}_{\varkappa\varkappa'}$). Owing to the fact that the small anharmonicity constant occurs in the denominator of the expression for this type of modulation broadening, it may be comparable in magnitude with the broadening due to the finite lifetime.

For example, in the case in which there is only one local vibration, the damping and frequency shift $\Gamma_{\varkappa}$ and $P_{\varkappa}$ in a spectral distribution of the (35.12) type are given by the expressions [410]

$$\Gamma_{\varkappa}(\omega) = \Gamma'_{\varkappa}(\omega) + 2n_{\varkappa}(n_{\varkappa}+1)V^2_{\varkappa\varkappa}\frac{3\Gamma'_{\varkappa}(\omega)}{(\omega-\omega'_{\varkappa})^2+9\Gamma'^2_{\varkappa}(\omega)}, \qquad (39.9)$$

$$P_{\varkappa}(\omega) = P'_{\varkappa}(\omega) + n_{\varkappa}V_{\varkappa\varkappa} + 2n_{\varkappa}(n_{\varkappa}+1)V^2_{\varkappa\varkappa}\frac{\omega-\omega'_{\varkappa}}{(\omega-\omega'_{\varkappa})^2+9\Gamma'^2_{\varkappa}(\omega)}, \qquad (39.10)$$

where $\omega'_{\varkappa}$ and $V_{\varkappa\varkappa}$ are constants renormalized in some manner, $\Gamma'_{\varkappa}$ and $P'_{\varkappa}$ are determined by formulas (39.7) and (39.8), and the second terms are associated with modulation effects.

We see from (39.9) that modulation broadening may be comparable with that resulting from decomposition [formulas (39.9) and (39.10) are derived for the case in which $V_{\varkappa\varkappa} < \Gamma'_{\varkappa}$] at high temperatures (it is in fact proportional to T) and tends to zero exponentially as $T \to 0$. The quantities $\Gamma_{\varkappa}(\omega)$ and $P_{\varkappa}(\omega)$ in this case depend strongly on ω, as a result of which the energy distribution no longer has a Lorentz shape (at large $V_{\varkappa\varkappa}$ fine structure of this distribution should appear [410]).

A specially important part is played by modulation effects in the case of high-frequency local vibrations, when, as a result of the law of energy conservation, processes involving the decomposition of a local excitation into two crystal excitations are forbidden, the damping (39.7) vanishes, and the damping due to processes involving decomposition into a larger number of phonons, associated with anharmonicities of higher order, is also small. At low temperatures, for which $n_{\varkappa} \ll 1$ in the case of local vibrations, so that interaction between local vibrations does not lead to any appreciable broadening, modulation broadening associated with the interaction of a local vibration with crystal vibrations and determined by terms of the

$$\sum_{\varkappa k_1 k_2} V_{\varkappa\varkappa k_1 k_2}(N_{\varkappa} - n_{\varkappa})\, a^+_{k_1} a_{k_2}$$

type in the Hamiltonian may be important. The corresponding broadening [410, 411] equals

$$\Gamma''_{\varkappa}(\omega_{\varkappa}) = \frac{\pi}{\hbar^2}\sum_{k_1 k_2}|V_{\varkappa\varkappa k_1 k_2}|^2 (n_{k_1}+1)\, n_{k_2}\,\delta(\omega_{k_1}-\omega_{k_2}) \qquad (39.11)$$

and at high temperatures is proportional to T^2. It is an important point that, as shown by the analysis presented in [412], the high-temperature law $\Gamma_{\varkappa} \sim T^2$ in this case may be "extended" to extremely low temperatures, sometimes an order below the Debye temperature (as $T \to 0$ is proportional to T^7). In certain cases (H^- centers in alkali halide crystals and in CaF_2) it may be shown that such modulation broadening plays the principal part [412, 413].

In particular, by starting from modulation-broadening principles, we may give a perfectly natural explanation to the fact that the broadening is greater for local vibrations near H^- centers than near D^- centers (in the decomposition mechanism the higher-frequency local vibrations at the H^- centers should have a smaller width). This is associated with the fact that the ratio of the modulation widths $\Gamma''_{\varkappa 1}$ and $\Gamma''_{\varkappa 2}$ for the two isotopes equals the inverse ratio of their masses [412]:

$$\frac{\Gamma''_{\kappa 1}}{\Gamma''_{\kappa 2}} = \frac{m_2}{m_1}. \qquad (39.12)$$

The broadening of the spectral distribution of local vibrations may also be associated with their interaction with other nonlocalized excitations in the crystals, for example, with conductivity electrons. This damping may play a relatively large part in metals in the case of high-frequency local vibrations, for which the law of energy conservation forbids the decomposition of the local vibration into two crystal excitations. Owing to the large width of the conduction band (as compared with $\omega_{\varkappa}$), processes in which a quantum of local vibration vanishes (or is generated) and a conduction electron passes from a filled to an unfilled state are always forbidden by the conservation law.

Damping due to the interaction of local vibrations with conduction electrons may be expressed to a certain approximation in terms of constants in the Hamiltonian of electron–phonon interaction for an ideal crystal

$$H_i = \sum_{\mathbf{q}_1 n_1 \mathbf{q}_2 n_2 \mathbf{k} j} V_{\mathbf{q}_1 n_1 \mathbf{q}_2 n_2 \mathbf{k} j} \left(b^+_{\mathbf{q}_1 n_1} b_{\mathbf{q}_2 n_2} a_{\mathbf{k} j} + \text{c.c.}\right) \qquad (39.13)$$

where $b^+_{\mathbf{q}n}$ and $b_{\mathbf{q}n}$ are the operators of the generation and annihilation of electrons of the n-th band with wave vector $\mathbf{q}$, and $\mathbf{k}$ and j are the wave vector and serial number of the branch of the phonon. For example, in the simplest case in which a local vibration develops near an impurity atom differing only in mass from the atoms of the matrix, the electron wave functions and the constants of electron–phonon interaction varying only slightly near the defect, the value of the electron–phonon damping of the local vibrations $\Gamma_{\varkappa l}(\omega)$ is, according to [443], determined by the formula

$$\Gamma_{K l}(\omega) = \frac{m}{N}\left(1 - \frac{m'}{m}\right)^2 \omega_K^3 \sum_{\mathbf{k}jj'} A_{\mathbf{k}j}^K A_{\mathbf{k}j}^K{}' \,\Gamma_{\mathbf{k}jj'}(\omega),$$

$$\Gamma_{\mathbf{k}jj}{}' = 2\pi \sum_{\mathbf{q}_1\mathbf{q}_2 n_1 n_2} V_{\mathbf{q}_1 n_1 \mathbf{q}_2 n_2 \mathbf{k}j} V^+_{\mathbf{q}_1 n_1 \mathbf{q}_2 n_2 \mathbf{k}j'}$$

$$[n(E_{\mathbf{q}_2 n_2}) - n(E_{\mathbf{q}_1 n_1})]\,\delta(\omega + E_{\mathbf{q}_2 n_2} - E_{\mathbf{q}_1 n_1}),$$

$$A_{\mathbf{k}j}^K = \frac{\omega_{\mathbf{k}j}^{1/2}(\mathbf{u}_K\, l_{\mathbf{k}j})^2}{\omega_K^2 - \omega_{\mathbf{k}j}^2}, \; \mathbf{u}_K^2 = \frac{1}{m}\left[\left(1 - \frac{m'}{m}\right)^2 \omega_K^4 (3N)^{-1} \sum_{\mathbf{k}j} (\omega_{\mathbf{k}j}^2 - \omega_K^2) - \left(1 - \frac{m'}{m}\right)\right]^{-1} \qquad (39.14)$$

Here $\omega_{\mathbf{k}j}$, $l_{\mathbf{k}j}$, and $E_{\mathbf{q}n}$ are the frequency and polarization vector of the vibration $\mathbf{k}j$ and the energy of the electron in the ideal crystal, respectively.

If we use the Fröhlich model in order to estimate the electron–phonon interaction, then for high-frequency local vibrations in typical metals (one electron per atom, Fermi energy of the order of 3 eV, velocity of sound about $5 \cdot 10^5$ cm/sec, effective mass of the order of the mass of a free electron, dimensionless Fröhlich interaction constant F ~ 0.5) formula (39.14) leads to the estimate

$$\Gamma_{K l}(\omega_K) \sim 2 \cdot 10^{10} \frac{m}{m'} \sec^{-1}. \qquad (39.15)$$

It follows from this that for m/m' ~ 100 and $\omega_\varkappa \sim 4 \cdot 10^{14}$ sec^{-1} the ratio $\Gamma_\varkappa/\omega_\varkappa \sim 5 \cdot 10^{-3}$, while for m/m' ~ 10 and $\omega_\varkappa \sim 1.5 \cdot 10^{14}$ sec^{-1} $\Gamma_\varkappa/\omega_\varkappa \sim 2 \cdot 10^{-3}$.

In the case of high-frequency vibrations ($\omega_\varkappa > 2\omega_m$), the $\Gamma_{\varkappa l}$ in metals may be comparable with the previously considered damping due to anharmonicity, or may even exceed the latter. In contrast to the damping caused by anharmonicity, the electron–phonon damping does not depend on temperature (for $\xi_l \gg T$), and its role is relatively great at low temperatures. A study of the temperature of the overall damping may be important in order to separate out the damping $\Gamma_{\varkappa l}$.

As indicated by (39.14), for a given value of the constant of electron–phonon interaction, $\Gamma_{\varkappa l}$ is proportional to the square of the density of electron states on the Fermi surface, i.e., it should be greater in metals with a high density of states, for example, in transition metals. In these cases we may expect that the value of $\Gamma_{\varkappa l}$ will be considerably greater than in the estimates given above. It is not impossible that this mechanism will, for example, make a considerable contribution to the damping of the local vibrations at Be impurity atoms in Ni [442].

A considerable influence may also be exerted on the spectral distribution of the local vibrations by their interaction with electrons localized at fine impurity centers in nonmetallic crystals. This type of interaction will lead to a displacement of the frequencies $\omega_{\varkappa}$. These displacements are different for different electron states, as a result of which the spectral distribution of local vibrations will have a multiplet structure (for an electron-energy difference $\lesssim k_B T$) if the lifetimes of the electronic and vibrational states are fairly long. As the lifetime falls, the shape of the distribution changes considerably; the multiplet structure becomes blurred and gradually vanishes. Effects such as these (the splitting and broadening of the spectral distribution as a result of electron–phonon interaction), largely analogous to the modulation effects considered earlier, were discussed in [443, 444].

Analogous effects of the decomposition and modulation broadening of the spectral distribution should occur not only for local vibrations but also for the localized spin excitations which arise near defects in ferromagnetics [445, 446]. Estimates of the corresponding damping factors associated with spin–spin and spin–phonon interaction are presented in [447].

In addition to the decomposition and modulation broadening of the spectral distribution of local vibrations, for high concentrations of impurity centers, concentration broadening should play a considerable part. This is associated with the interaction of local vibrations at different centers, leading to the blurring of the local level in the impurity band of vibration frequencies [218, 448].

The vibration spectrum changes substantially not only in the case of light but also in that of heavy impurity atoms. In this case a characteristic peak appears in the frequency-distribution function of the vibrations in the low-frequency region; this may be interpreted as being due to quasistationary, relatively long-lived "quasilocal" vibrations near heavy impurity atoms [414–416]. In the incoherent, inelastic scattering of neutrons, accompanied by the generation or annihilation of such quasilocal excitations, the energy distribution should acquire sharp maxima [396, 417] reminiscent of the peaks corresponding to scattering at local vibrations, but lying in a range of much lower E.

In addition to this, the resonance interaction of phonons with quasilocal excitations should lead to a sharp increase in the damping of the phonons in the region of the quasilocal frequencies, and to the appearance of characteristic features in the energy distribution of the scattered neutrons [399, 418, 420], to a certain extent analogous to the effects arising on introducing fine electronic impurity centers into the crystal (see §37).

The scattering of neutrons at quasilocal vibrations has been observed experimentally in a dilute solution of W in Cr [423] and in a solution of Pb in Mg [449].

Appendix

I. Calculation of the Mean Squares of the Fourier Components $\overline{|c_{\mathbf{k}}|^2}$ on the Microscopic Theory

Following [23], let us calculate the mean values $\overline{c_{\mathbf{k}\gamma}c^*_{\mathbf{k}\gamma'}}$ for the kind of splitting of the crystal into sublattices described in §3. Let us consider the Fourier components of the fluctuations corresponding to a specific vector **k**. Let us enumerate the atomic planes perpendicular to this vector by the index δ. If **k** is not perpendicular to any system of atomic planes, then the crystal may be divided into "infinitely-thin" layers perpendicular to **k**, the serial number of which we may also denote by the index δ. The numbers of nodes (lattice points) belonging to one of the sublattices are the same for different parallel planes containing the points of this sublattice. Let us denote this number by n_0.

On summing over the points lying in this plane (layer), the exponential factor in (3.2) remains constant. Hence in the sum (3.2) over s we may replace $c_{s\gamma}$ by the average concentration c^{δ}_{γ} of the A atoms at the points of sublattice γ in the plane δ_{γ}. If we then direct the Z axis parallel to the vector **k**, expression (3.2) for $c_{\mathbf{k}\gamma}$ takes the following form

$$c_{\mathbf{k}\gamma} = \frac{n_0}{N^0} \sum_{\delta_{\gamma}=1}^{N^0/n_0} (c^{\delta}_{\gamma} - c_{\gamma})\, e^{ikZ_{\delta\gamma}}, \tag{I.1}$$

where Z_{δ_γ} is the interval cut off on the Z axis by the plane δ_γ, reckoned from the origin of coordinates.

We see from (I.1) and (3.2) that the fluctuations c_k are determined by the deviations of the concentrations c_γ^δ in various planes from the average concentrations c_γ. The probability of some fluctuational variation in the quantities c_γ^δ may be determined from the general formula (2.1) of the thermodynamic theory of fluctuations. The minimum work required to create such a fluctuation reversibly may be written in the form of an expansion of the thermodynamic potential of the whole crystal Φ in powers of $c_\gamma^\delta - c_\gamma$:

$$R = \frac{1}{2}\sum_\gamma \sum_\delta \frac{\partial^2\Phi}{\partial c_\gamma^{\delta 2}}(c_\gamma^\delta - c_\gamma)^2 + \sum_{\substack{\gamma,\gamma' \\ (\gamma<\gamma')}} \sum_{\delta_{\gamma'}\delta'_{\gamma'}} \frac{\partial^2\Phi}{\partial c_\gamma^\delta \partial c_{\gamma'}^{\delta'}}(c_\gamma^\delta - c_\gamma)(c_{\gamma'}^{\delta'} - c_{\gamma'}) +$$

$$+ \sum_\gamma \sum_{\substack{\delta_\gamma, \delta'_\gamma \\ (\delta_\gamma < \delta'_\gamma)}} \frac{\partial^2\Phi}{\partial c_\gamma^\delta \partial c_\gamma^{\delta'}} (c_\gamma^\delta - c_\gamma)(c_\gamma^{\delta'} - c_\gamma). \qquad \text{(I.2)}$$

If we choose a fairly large ν', then for $\delta \neq \delta'$ the planes with identical γ are situated a long way from each other, the derivatives $\partial^2\Phi/\partial c_\gamma^\delta \partial c_\gamma^{\delta'}$ are small, and the last term in (I.2) may be discarded (in some cases these derivatives may also be discarded for small ν'). The derivatives of Φ with respect to the concentrations in the atomic planes entering into the first two terms are related to the derivatives with respect to the ordinary concentrations, referred to the whole crystal, by the obvious equations

$$\frac{\partial^2\Phi}{\partial c_\gamma^{\delta\,2}} = \frac{n_0}{N^0}\frac{\partial^2\Phi}{\partial c_\gamma^2}, \qquad \frac{\partial^2\Phi}{\partial c_\gamma^\delta \partial c_{\gamma'}^{\delta'}} = \frac{n_0}{N^0}\frac{z''}{z'}\frac{\partial^2\Phi}{\partial c_\gamma \partial c_{\gamma'}}, \qquad \text{(I.3)}$$

where z' is the total number of points of the sublattice γ' closest to a given point of the sublattice γ, while z" is the number of points of the sublattice γ' lying in the plane δ' and constituting neighbors of a point in the sublattice γ lying in the plane δ (if such neighboring γ' points do not exist in the plane δ', then the corresponding derivative $\partial^2\Phi/\partial c_\gamma^\delta \partial c_{\gamma'}^{\delta'}$ equals zero).

Let us determine the value of R in the case of an undulating variation in the quantities c_{γ}^{δ}:

$$c_{\gamma}^{\delta} - c_{\gamma} = c_{\mathbf{k}\gamma} e^{-ikZ_{\gamma\delta}} + c_{\mathbf{k}\gamma}^{*} e^{ikZ_{\gamma\delta}}. \tag{I.4}$$

Putting (I.4) and (I.3) into (I.2) and considering that

$$k\,(Z_{\gamma'\delta'} - Z_{\gamma\delta}) = \mathbf{k}\boldsymbol{\rho}_{\pi\gamma\gamma'},$$

where the vector $\mathbf{k}$ is directed along the Z axis, while $\boldsymbol{\rho}_{\pi\gamma\gamma'}$ is a vector drawn from a point of the sublattice γ situated in the plane δ to one of the points (numbered π) of the sublattice γ' in the plane δ', we find that the probability distribution of the fluctuations of some $\mathbf{k}$-th Fourier component $c_{\mathbf{k}}$ may be written in the form

$$w \sim \exp\left(-\frac{R_{\mathbf{k}}}{k_B T}\right) = \exp\left[-\frac{1}{2}\sum_{\gamma,\,\gamma'=1}^{\nu} a_{\gamma\gamma'}\,(c_{\mathbf{k}\gamma} c_{\mathbf{k}\gamma'}^{*} + c_{\mathbf{k}\gamma}^{*} c_{\mathbf{k}\gamma'})\right], \tag{I.5}$$

where

$$a_{\gamma\gamma} = \frac{1}{k_B T}\frac{\partial^2 \Phi}{\partial c_{\gamma}^2}, \qquad a_{\gamma\gamma'} = \frac{1}{z' k_B T}\frac{\partial^2 \Phi}{\partial c_{\gamma}\partial c_{\gamma'}} \sum_{\pi=1}^{z'} \cos \mathbf{k}\boldsymbol{\rho}_{\pi\gamma\gamma'}. \quad (\gamma \neq \gamma'). \tag{I.6}$$

We may use (I.5) in the usual manner (as in §2) to determine the average values of the squares and products of the Fourier components:

$$\frac{1}{2}\,\overline{(c_{\mathbf{k}\gamma} c_{\mathbf{k}\gamma'}^{*} + c_{\mathbf{k}\gamma}^{*} c_{\mathbf{k}\gamma'})} = b_{\gamma\gamma'}. \tag{I.7}$$

Here $b_{\gamma\gamma'}$ form a matrix reciprocal to the matrix $\|a_{\gamma\gamma'}\|$, which is given by formula (I.6). It follows from (3.2) and (I.7) that the average value $\overline{|c_{\mathbf{k}}|^2}$ equals

$$\overline{|c_{\mathbf{k}}|^2} = \frac{1}{\nu'^2} \sum_{\gamma,\,\gamma'=1}^{\nu'} b_{\gamma\gamma'}. \tag{I.8}$$

Thus in order to determine the mean-square of the Fourier components of the fluctuations of concentration we must know the thermodynamic potential of the solution as a function of the variables c_{γ}, calculate the matrix $\|a_{\gamma\gamma'}\|$ from formulas (I.6), and then determine the sum of all the matrix elements of the reciprocal matrix $\|b_{\gamma\gamma'}\|$.

If ν' is large, then the inversion of the matrix $\|a_{\gamma\gamma'}\|$ is, generally speaking, a complicated problem. However, in a number of cases we may calculate the sum of all the matrix elements of the reciprocal matrix $\|b_{\gamma\gamma'}\|$ directly, without having to invert the matrix $\|a_{\gamma\gamma'}\|$. This becomes possible if the sum A of the matrix elements of each row of the matrix $\|a_{\gamma\gamma'}\|$ does not depend on the number of the row. Then we may easily see that

$$\overline{|c_{\mathbf{k}}|^2} = \frac{1}{\nu'^2} \sum_{\gamma,\, \gamma'=1}^{\nu'} b_{\gamma\gamma'} = \frac{1}{\nu' A}, \tag{I.9}$$

where

$$A = \frac{1}{k_{\mathrm{B}}T} \frac{\partial^2 \Phi}{\partial c_\gamma^2} + \frac{1}{z' k_{\mathrm{B}} T} \sum_{\substack{\gamma'=1 \\ (\gamma' \neq \gamma)}}^{\nu'} \frac{\partial^2 \Phi}{\partial c_\gamma \partial c_{\gamma'}} \sum_{\pi=1}^{z'} \cos \mathbf{k} \boldsymbol{\rho}_{\pi\gamma\gamma'}. \tag{I.10}$$

In fact, by summing the equations

$$\sum_{\gamma''=1}^{\nu'} b_{\gamma'\gamma''} a_{\gamma''\gamma} = \delta_{\gamma\gamma'},$$

(which relate the matrix elements of the direct and reciprocal matrix) over all γ and γ', we obtain

$$\sum_{\gamma,\, \gamma',\, \gamma''=1}^{\nu'} b_{\gamma'\gamma''} a_{\gamma''\gamma} = \nu'.$$

Carrying out the summation with respect to γ in this equation and remembering that $\sum_{\gamma=1}^{\nu'} a_{\gamma''\gamma} = A$, we obtain

$$\sum_{\gamma,\, \gamma'=1}^{\nu'} b_{\gamma\gamma'} = \frac{\nu'}{A},$$

i.e., (I.9).

II. Equations for the Quantities $A_{\mathbf{k}}$ in Crystals of Different Symmetries

In crystals of hexagonal symmetry, equations (5.8), after allowing for (5.10), take the form

$$(c_{11}n_\perp^2 + c_{44}n_{||}^2)A_{k\perp} + (c_{13}+c_{44})\, n_\perp n_{||} A_{k||} =$$

$$= \frac{1}{k}\left[(c_{11}+c_{12})\frac{1}{d_\perp}\frac{\partial d_\perp}{\partial c} + c_{13}\frac{1}{d_{||}}\frac{\partial d_{||}}{\partial c}\right] n_\perp, \qquad \text{(II.1a)}$$

$$(c_{13}+c_{44})\, n_\perp n_{||} A_{k\perp} + (c_{44}n_\perp^2 + c_{33}n_{||}^2)\, A_{k||} =$$

$$= \frac{1}{k}\left[2c_{13}\frac{1}{d_\perp}\frac{\partial d_\perp}{\partial c} + c_{33}\frac{1}{d_{||}}\frac{\partial d_{||}}{\partial c}\right] n_{||}, \qquad \text{(II.1b)}$$

$$\mathbf{A}_{k\perp} \parallel \mathbf{n}_\perp,$$

where $n_{||}$, $\mathbf{n}_\perp$, $A_{k||}$, $\mathbf{A}_{k\perp}$ are the projections of the vectors $\mathbf{n}$ and $\mathbf{A}_k$ on the hexagonal axis and on the perpendicular plane, while $d_{||}$ and $d_\perp$ are the lengths of the sections directed parallel and perpendicular to this axis. We see from (II.1) that in hexagonal crystals the modulus of $\mathbf{A}_k$ only depends on the angle between $\mathbf{k}$ and the hexagonal axis Z, without changing when $\mathbf{k}$ is rotated around this axis. Moreover $\mathbf{A}_k$ lies in a plane passing through Z and $\mathbf{n}$, but is in general not parallel to $\mathbf{n}$. Only if $\mathbf{n}$ is perpendicular or parallel to the Z axis do we have $\mathbf{A}_k \parallel \mathbf{n}$, i.e., the displacements in the fluctuation wave are directed along the vector $\mathbf{k}$. In the first case

$$a_k = \frac{1}{c_{11}}\left[(c_{11}+c_{12})\frac{1}{d_\perp}\frac{\partial d_\perp}{\partial c} + c_{13}\frac{1}{d_{||}}\frac{\partial d_{||}}{\partial c}\right], \qquad \text{(II.2)}$$

and in the second

$$a_k = \frac{1}{c_{33}}\left[2c_{13}\frac{1}{d_\perp}\frac{\partial d_\perp}{\partial c} + c_{33}\frac{1}{d_{||}}\frac{\partial d_{||}}{\partial c}\right]. \qquad \text{(II.3)}$$

For crystals of rhombic symmetry, (5.8) and (5.10) yield the following system of equations for determining $\mathbf{A}_k$:

$$(c_{11}n_x^2 + c_{66}n_y^2 + c_{55}n_z^2)\, A_{kx} + (c_{12}+c_{66})\, n_x n_y A_{ky} + (c_{13}+c_{55}) n_x n_z A_{kz} =$$

$$= \frac{1}{k}\left(c_{11}\frac{1}{d_x}\frac{\partial d_x}{\partial c} + c_{12}\frac{1}{d_y}\frac{\partial d_y}{\partial c} + c_{13}\frac{1}{d_z}\frac{\partial d_z}{\partial c}\right) n_x. \qquad \text{(II.4)}$$

Two other equations are obtained from (II.4) by cyclic substitution. In this case $\mathbf{A}_k \parallel \mathbf{n}$ for the directions [100], [010], and [001]. For example, for the [100] direction

$$a_{\mathrm{k}}=\frac{1}{c_{11}}\left(c_{11}\frac{1}{d_x}\frac{\partial d_x}{\partial c}+c_{12}\frac{1}{d_y}\frac{\partial d_y}{\partial c}+c_{13}\frac{1}{d_z}\frac{\partial d_z}{\partial c}\right). \tag{II.5}$$

In crystals of tetragonal symmetry (tetragonal axis directed along the Z axis) the equations for determining $\mathbf{A}_{\mathrm{k}}$ may be obtained from (II.4) if we remember that

$$c_{22}=c_{11}, \quad c_{23}=c_{13}, \quad c_{55}=c_{44} \text{ and } \frac{1}{d_y}\frac{\partial d_y}{\partial c}=\frac{1}{d_x}\frac{\partial d_x}{\partial c}.$$

In the case of cubic crystals the equations for $\mathbf{A}_{\mathrm{k}}$ simplify, since in these crystals there are only three independent elastic moduli, and on varying the composition the crystal expands or contracts isotropically, so that the diagonal components of the tensor (5.5) are identical and equal to

$$L_{xx}=\frac{1}{3}\cdot\frac{1}{v}\frac{\partial v}{\partial c}.$$

Taking account of this, we may use (II.4) to obtain the following set of equations for determining the $A_{\mathrm{k}i}$:

$$Q_{\mathrm{k}ij}A_{\mathrm{k}j}=P_{\mathrm{k}i},$$

$$Q_{\mathrm{k}11}=c_{44}+(c_{11}-c_{44})\,n_x^2, \quad Q_{\mathrm{k}12}=(c_{12}+c_{44})\,n_x n_y,$$

$$P_{\mathrm{k}1}=\frac{1}{3}(c_{11}+2c_{12})\frac{1}{v}\frac{\partial v}{\partial c}\frac{n_x}{k}. \tag{II.6}$$

The solution of this system of equations may be written in the form of (5.11) and (5.12).

In interstitial solutions such as tetragonal martensite, if we neglect the concentration dependence of the elastic moduli, the expressions for $Q_{\mathrm{k}ij}$, as in the case of cubic crystals, will be determined by formula (II.6), but the formulas for the $P_{\mathrm{k}i}$ must allow for the considerable difference of the components of the tensor L_{ij} resulting from the tetragonal symmetry of the interstices:

$$\frac{P_{\mathrm{k}1}}{n_x}=\frac{P_{\mathrm{k}2}}{n_y}=\frac{1}{k}\left[(c_{11}+c_{12})\frac{1}{d_1}\frac{\partial d_1}{\partial c}+c_{12}\frac{1}{d_3}\frac{\partial d_3}{\partial c}\right],$$

$$P_{\mathbf{k}3} = \frac{n_z}{k}\left[2c_{12}\frac{1}{d_1}\frac{\partial d_1}{\partial c} + c_{11}\frac{1}{d_3}\frac{\partial d_3}{\partial c}\right]. \tag{II.7}$$

III. The Phonon Green's Function and the Correlation Function of the Phonon in a Nonideal Crystal

The double-time lagging Green's functions for the operators

$$a_{\mathbf{k}n},\ a^{+}_{\mathbf{k}'n'} \quad \text{or} \quad a_{\mathbf{k}n},\ a_{\mathbf{k}'n'}$$

are given by the expressions (see, for example, [346])

$$\begin{aligned} g_{\mathbf{k}n\mathbf{k}'n'}(t) &= -i\Theta(t)\langle[a_{\mathbf{k}n}(t),\ a^{+}_{\mathbf{k}'n'}(0)]\rangle, \\ F_{\mathbf{k}n\mathbf{k}'n'}(t) &= -i\Theta(t)\langle[a^{+}_{\mathbf{k}n}(t),\ a^{+}_{\mathbf{k}'n'}(0)]\rangle, \end{aligned} \tag{III.1}$$

where the step function

$$\Theta(t) = 1 \ \text{ for } t > 0 \ \text{ and } \ \Theta(t) = 0 \ \text{ for } t < 0.$$

The leading Green's function is obtained on replacing t by −t in $\Theta(t)$ and changing the sign of the expression. If the Hamiltonian is given by formula (35.11), the equations of motion for these Green's functions have the form

$$i\frac{dg_{\mathbf{k}n\mathbf{k}'n'}}{dt} = \delta(t)\,\delta_{\mathbf{k}\mathbf{k}'}\delta_{nn'} + \omega_{\mathbf{k}n}g_{\mathbf{k}n\mathbf{k}'n'} + \frac{1}{\hbar}\sum_{\mathbf{k}''n''}\left(V_{\mathbf{k}n\mathbf{k}''n''}\,g_{\mathbf{k}''n''\mathbf{k}'n'} - V'_{\mathbf{k}n\mathbf{k}''n''}F_{\mathbf{k}''n''\mathbf{k}'n'}\right), \tag{III.2}$$

$$i\frac{dF_{\mathbf{k}n\mathbf{k}'n'}}{dt} = -\omega_{\mathbf{k}n}F_{\mathbf{k}n\mathbf{k}'n'} - \frac{1}{\hbar}\sum_{\mathbf{k}''n''}\left(V_{\mathbf{k}''n''\mathbf{k}n}F_{\mathbf{k}''n''\mathbf{k}'n'} - V'^{*}_{\mathbf{k}n\mathbf{k}''n''}\,g_{\mathbf{k}''n''\mathbf{k}'n'}\right). \tag{III.3}$$

Transforming from the Green's functions g(t) and F(t) to their Fourier components

$$g(t) = \int_{-\infty}^{\infty} g(\omega)\exp(-i\omega t)\,d\omega, \quad F(t) = \int_{-\infty}^{\infty} F(\omega)\exp(-i\omega t)\,d\omega, \tag{III.4}$$

we may rewrite equations (III.2) and (III.3) in the form

$$(\omega-\omega_{\mathbf{k}n})\, g_{\mathbf{k}n\mathbf{k}'n'}(\omega)-\frac{1}{\hbar}\sum_{\mathbf{k}''n''}[V_{\mathbf{k}n\mathbf{k}''n''}g_{\mathbf{k}''n''\mathbf{k}'n'}(\omega)-$$

$$-V'_{\mathbf{k}n\mathbf{k}''n''}F_{\mathbf{k}''n''\mathbf{k}'n'}(\omega)]=\frac{1}{2\pi}\delta_{\mathbf{k}\mathbf{k}'}\delta_{nn'}, \qquad \text{(III.5)}$$

$$(\omega+\omega_{\mathbf{k}n})\, F_{\mathbf{k}n\mathbf{k}'n'}(\omega)+\frac{1}{\hbar}\sum_{\mathbf{k}''n''}[V_{\mathbf{k}''n''\mathbf{k}n}F_{\mathbf{k}''n''\mathbf{k}'n'}(\omega)-$$

$$-V'^{*}_{\mathbf{k}n\mathbf{k}''n''}g_{\mathbf{k}''n''\mathbf{k}'n'}(\omega)]=0. \qquad \text{(III.6)}$$

Essentially the sums over **k**" are here integrals, i.e., the equations for the Green's functions in the case under consideration are integral equations. It is an important point that, in contrast to the majority of other nontrivial many-body problems, the exact equations for the Green's functions are closed in this case and include no Green's functions of higher order. This makes the problem far more "transparent" and enables us to solve it by the methods of integral-equation theory. The solution may easily be obtained in two cases: when the quantities V and V' are small and the equations may be solved by the method of iterations [344], or when the concentration of impurity atoms is low and the problem may be solved exactly by the theory of local perturbations [347].

Let us here consider the first case and solve the problem by the method of successive approximations. In the zero approximation (V = V' = 0), only the Green's functions

$$g_{\mathbf{k}n\mathbf{k}n}=\frac{1}{2\pi}\frac{1}{\omega-\omega_{\mathbf{k}n}}.$$

differ from zero. Substituting these expressions in the equations for $g_{\mathbf{k}n\mathbf{k}'n'}$ with $\mathbf{k}\neq\mathbf{k}'$, $n\neq n'$ and in the equation for $F_{\mathbf{k}n\mathbf{k}'n'}$, we find that in the first approximation

$$g_{\mathbf{k}n\mathbf{k}'n'}(\omega)=\frac{V_{\mathbf{k}n\mathbf{k}'n'}}{\hbar(\omega-\omega_{\mathbf{k}n})}g_{\mathbf{k}'n'\mathbf{k}'n'}(\omega)\quad(\mathbf{k}\neq\mathbf{k}',\quad n\neq n'),$$

$$\text{(III.7)}$$

$$F_{\mathbf{k}n\mathbf{k}'n'}(\omega)=\frac{V'^{*}_{\mathbf{k}n\mathbf{k}'n'}}{\hbar(\omega+\omega_{\mathbf{k}n})}g_{\mathbf{k}'n'\mathbf{k}'n'}(\omega).$$

Substituting these expressions into equation (III.5) for $\mathbf{k}'=\mathbf{k}$, $n'=n$, we obtain in the next approximation

$$g_{\mathbf{k}n\mathbf{k}n}(\omega)=\frac{1}{2\pi}\frac{1}{\omega-\omega_{\mathbf{k}n}-R_{\mathbf{k}n}(\omega)}, \tag{III.8}$$

where $R_{\mathbf{k}n}(\omega)\equiv R_{\mathbf{k}nn}(\omega)$, and

$$R_{\mathbf{k}nn'}(\omega)=\frac{1}{\hbar^2}\sum_{\mathbf{k}''n''}\left[\frac{V_{\mathbf{k}n\mathbf{k}''n''}V_{\mathbf{k}''n''\mathbf{k}n'}}{\omega-\omega_{\mathbf{k}''n''}}-\frac{V'_{\mathbf{k}n\mathbf{k}''n''}V'^{*}_{\mathbf{k}''n''\mathbf{k}n'}}{\omega+\omega_{\mathbf{k}''n''}}\right]. \tag{III.9}$$

If, however, we substitute expression (III.7) into equation (III.5) with $\mathbf{k}'=\mathbf{k}$ but $n'\neq n$, then in the range of frequencies $\omega\approx\omega_{\mathbf{k}n'}$

$$g_{\mathbf{k}n\mathbf{k}'n'}(\omega)=\frac{R_{\mathbf{k}nn'}(\omega)}{\omega-\omega_{\mathbf{k}n}}\,g_{\mathbf{k}n'\mathbf{k}n'}(\omega)\qquad(n'\neq n,\quad\omega\approx\omega_{\mathbf{k}n'}). \tag{III.10}$$

If we continue the iteration procedure, then expression (III.8) for $g_{\mathbf{k}n\mathbf{k}n}(\omega)$ retains the same form; only in the polarization operator $R_{\mathbf{k}n}(\omega)$ do we find extra correction terms of higher order in V and V' (see [348]). Thus the method of successive approximations employed essentially constitutes an expansion of the inverse Green's function (or the polarization operator, i.e., the damping and frequency shift) in powers of a small parameter. In the most interesting resonance range of frequencies $\omega\approx\omega_{\mathbf{k}n}$ this expansion clearly gives a better approximation than the expansion of the actual Green's function.

Using the well-known relationship

$$\frac{1}{x+i\delta}=P\frac{1}{x}-i\pi\delta(x)$$

(P denotes the principal value, $\delta=+0$), writing $R(\omega+i\delta)$ in the form

$$R(\omega+i\delta)=P(\omega)-i\Gamma(\omega)$$

and substituting expressions (III.7), (III.8), and (III.10) into relation (35.9), we may easily obtain formulas (35.12) to (35.16) for the phonon correlation functions.

If $\omega_{\mathbf{k}n}$ and $\omega_{\mathbf{k}n'}$ $(n\neq n')$ are similar for different branches of vibrations, we see from (III.10) that the function $g_{\mathbf{k}n\mathbf{k}n'}(\omega)$ rises rapidly in the region of $\omega \approx \omega_{\mathbf{k}n'}$, becoming comparable with $g_{\mathbf{k}n'\mathbf{k}n'}(\omega)$, and the theory of perturbations ceases to be applicable. The convergence may be improved in the same general way as in the case of ordinary perturbation theory in the presence of two neighboring levels if we consider not only $g_{\mathbf{k}n\mathbf{k}n}(\omega)$, but also $g_{\mathbf{k}n\mathbf{k}n'}(\omega) \equiv g_{\mathbf{k}nn'}(\omega)$ $(n \neq n')$ as quantities of the zeroth order of smallness. Then according to [344]

$$g_{\mathbf{k}n\mathbf{k}n}(\omega) = \frac{1}{2\pi} \frac{\omega - \omega_{\mathbf{k}n'} - R_{\mathbf{k}n'}}{(\omega - \omega_{\mathbf{k}n} - R_{\mathbf{k}n})(\omega - \omega_{\mathbf{k}n'} - R_{\mathbf{k}n'}) - R_{\mathbf{k}nn'} R_{\mathbf{k}n'n}}, \tag{III.11}$$

$$g_{\mathbf{k}nn'}(\omega) = \frac{R_{\mathbf{k}nn'}}{\omega - \omega_{\mathbf{k}n} - R_{\mathbf{k}n}} g_{\mathbf{k}n'\mathbf{k}n'}(\omega). \tag{III.12}$$

The Green's functions have an analogous form in the case of neighboring branches of vibrations if the perturbation is associated not with static inhomogeneities but with anharmonicity [305].

These Green's functions have poles lying in the complex plane at the points

$$\omega_{1,2} = \frac{1}{2} [\omega_{\mathbf{k}n} + \omega_{\mathbf{k}n'} + R_{\mathbf{k}n} + R_{\mathbf{k}n'} \pm \pm \sqrt{(\omega_{\mathbf{k}n} - \omega_{\mathbf{k}n'} + R_{\mathbf{k}n} - R_{\mathbf{k}n'})^2 + 2R_{\mathbf{k}nn'} R_{\mathbf{k}n'n}}]. \tag{III.13}$$

Thus in the example considered in [305], for which $\omega_{\mathbf{k}n} + R_{\mathbf{k}n} = \omega_{\mathbf{k}n'} + R_{\mathbf{k}n'}$ and $R_{\mathbf{k}nn'} = R_{\mathbf{k}n'n}$:

$$\omega_1 = \omega_{\mathbf{k}n} + R_{\mathbf{k}n} + R_{\mathbf{k}nn'}, \quad \omega_2 = \omega_{\mathbf{k}n} + R_{\mathbf{k}n} - R_{\mathbf{k}nn'} \tag{III.14}$$

and the spectral distribution for the correlation function $\varphi_{\mathbf{k}n\mathbf{k}n}(\omega)$ will according to (III.11) consist of two overlapping peaks with maxima at the points

$$\omega_{\mathbf{k}n} + P_{\mathbf{k}n} \pm P_{\mathbf{k}nn'}$$

and with different widths

$$\Gamma_{\mathbf{k}n} + \Gamma_{\mathbf{k}nn'} \quad \text{and} \quad |\Gamma_{\mathbf{k}n} - \Gamma_{\mathbf{k}nn'}|.$$

Literature Cited

1. L. D. Landau and E. M. Lifshits, Statistical Physics, Izd. "Nauka," 1964.
2. A. Einstein, Ann. Phys., 33:1275 (1910).
3. L. D. Landau, Zh. Éksperim. i Teor. Fiz., 7:1232 (1937).
4. I. E. Dzyaloshinskii, Zh. Éksperim. i Teor. Fiz., 46:1420 (1964).
5. M. A. Krivoglaz and S. A. Rybak, Zh. Éksperim. i Teor. Fiz., 33:139 (1957).
6. M. A. Krivoglaz, Zh. Éksperim. i Teor. Fiz., 31:625 (1956).
7. M. A. Krivoglaz, Dokl. Akad. Nauk SSSR 117:213 (1957); Zh. Fiz. Khim., 31:1930 (1957).
8. L. Ornstein and F. Zernicke, Proc. Amst. Akad. Sci., 17:793 (1914); 18:1520 (1916); 19:1321 (1917); Phys. Z., 19:134 (1918); 27:761 (1926).
9. M. J. Klein and L. Tisza, Phys. Rev., 76:1861 (1949).
10. A. Münster, Collection "Fluctuation Phenomena in Solids," Ed. R. E. Burgess, Academic Press, New York, 1965, p. 180.
11. L. D. Landau, Zh. Éksperim. i Teor. Fiz., 7:19 (1937).
12. L. Onsager, Phys. Rev., 65:117 (1944); B. Kaufman and L. Onsager, Phys. Rev., 76:1244 (1949); Yu. B. Rumer, Usp. Fiz. Nauk, 53:245 (1954); A. M. Dykhne and Yu. B. Rumer, Usp. Fiz. Nauk, 75:101 (1961).
13. C. Domb, Advances in Physics, 9:149 (1960); C. Domb and M. F. Sykes, J. Math. Phys., 2:63 (1961); M. E. Fischer, J. Math. Phys., 4:278 (1963).

14. G. A. Baker, J. L. Gammel, and J. G. Wiles, J. Math. Anal. Appl., 2:405 (1961); G. A. Baker, Phys. Rev., 124:768 (1961); J. W. Essam and M. E. Fischer, J. Chem. Phys., 38:802 (1963); G. A. Baker, Jr. and D. S. Gaunt, Phys. Rev., 155:545 (1967).
15. L. Onsager, Nuovo Cimento, Suppl., 6:261 (1949); C. N. Yang, Phys. Rev., 85:808 (1952); E. W. Montroll, R. B. Potts, and J. C. Ward, J. Math. Phys., 4:308 (1963).
16. M. I. Bagatskii, A. V. Voronel', and V. G. Gusak, Zh. Éksperim. i Teor. Fiz., 43:728 (1962); G. A. Baker, Phys. Rev., 129:99 (1963); M. E. Fisher, Phys. Rev., 136:1599 (1964); A. V. Voronel', V. G. Snegirev, and Yu. R. Chashkin, Zh. Éksperim. i Teor. Fiz., 48:981 (1965).
17. C. Domb and M. E. Sykes, Phys. Rev., 128:168 (1963); W. Marshall, J. Gammel, and L. Morgan, Proc. Roy. Soc., A275:257 (1963).
18. M. E. Fischer, J. Math. Phys., 5:944 (1964); Physica, 28:172 (1962).
19. R. H. Fowler and E. A. Guggenheim, Statistical Thermodynamics, Cambridge, 1939.
20. M. A. Krivoglaz and A. A. Smirnov, Theory of Ordering Alloys, Fizmatgiz, 1958.
21. T. Muto and Y. Takagi, Theory of Ordering Phenomena in Alloys [Russian translation], IL, 1959.
22. M. A. Krivoglaz, Zh. Éksperim. i Teor. Fiz., 34:355 (1958).
23. M. A. Krivoglaz, Zh. Éksperim. i Teor. Fiz., 32:1368 (1957).
24. T. S. Chang, J. Chem. Phys., 9:169 (1941).
25. J. G. Kirkwood, J. Chem. Phys., 6:70 (1938).
26. R. E. Elliot and W. Marshall, Rev. Modern Phys., 30:75 (1958).
27. M. A. Krivoglaz, Fiz. Metal. i Metalloved., 8:648 (1959).
28. Ya. I. Frenkel', Zh. Éksperim. i Teor. Fiz., 9:952 (1939).
29. Ya. I. Frenkel', Kinetic Theory of Liquids. Selected Works, Vol. III, Izd. Akad. Nauk SSSR, 1959.
30. M. A. Krivoglaz, Zh. Éksperim. i Teor. Fiz., 34:204 (1958).
31. L. D. Landau and E. M. Lifshits, Mechanism of Continuous Media, Gostekhizdat, 1953.
32. M. A. Krivoglaz and E. A. Tikhonova, Ukr. Fiz. Zhurn., 3:297 (1958).
33. K. Zener, Elasticity and Anelasticity of Metals [Russian translation], IL, 1954.

34. G. V. Kurdyumov, Collection of Scientific Papers of the Metal-Science and Heat-Treatment Section, VNITO Vses. Nauchn. Inzh. Tekhn. Obshch., "Metallurg," 1940.
35. M. A. Krivoglaz and E. A. Tikhonova, Ukr. Fiz. Zhurn., 5:174 (1960).
36. G. H. Begbie and M. Born, Proc. Roy. Soc., A188:179 (1947).
37. M. A. Krivoglaz and E. A. Tikhonova, Ukr. Fiz. Zhurn., 5:158 (1960).
38. B. N. Brockhouse and A. T. Stewart, Rev. Modern Phys., 30:236 (1958).
39. A. G. Khachaturyan, Fiz. Tverd. Tela, 4:2840 (1962).
40. H. Kanzaki, J. Phys. Chem. Solids, 2:24 (1957).
41. H. Kanzaki, J. Phys. Chem. Solids, 2:107 (1957).
42. M. A. Krivoglaz, Fiz. Metal. i Metalloved., 10:169 (1960).
43. I. M. Lifshits and L. N. Rozentsveig, Zh. Éksperim. i Teor. Fiz., 17:783 (1947).
44. P. A. Flinn and A. A. Maradudin, Ann. Phys., 18:81 (1962).
45. J. Eshelby, Continuum Theory of Dislocations [Russian translation], IL, 1963, p. 11.
46. J. D. Eshelby, Acta Met., 3:487 (1955).
47. J. R. Hardy, J. Phys. Chem. Solids, 15:39 (1960).
48. L. Tewordt, Phys. Rev., 109:61 (1958); K. H. Bennemann and L. Tewordt, Z. Naturforsch., 15a:772 (1960).
49. A. Seeger, P. Schiller, and H. Kranmüller, Phil. Mag., 5:853 (1960); A. Seeger and E. Mann, J. Phys. Chem. Solids, 12:326 (1960); A. Seeger, E. Mann, and R. V. Jan, J. Phys. Chem. Solids, 23:639 (1962).
50. J. B. Gibson, A. N. Goland, M. Milgram, and G. H. Vineyard, Phys. Rev., 120:1229 (1960).
51. I. M. Lifshits, Izv. Akad. Nauk SSSR, Ser. Fiz., 12:79 (1948).
52. J. D. Eshelby, J. Appl. Phys., 25:255 (1954).
53. M. A. Krivoglaz, Fiz. Tverd. Tela, 3:3682 (1961).
54. M. A. Krivoglaz, Ukr. Fiz. Zhurn., 8:162 (1963).
55. M. A. Krivoglaz, Fiz. Tverd. Tela, 5:3439 (1963).
56. J. W. Cahn, Acta Met., 10:907 (1962).
57. J. W. Cahn, Acta Met., 9:795 (1961).
58. J. W. Cahn, Acta Met., 10:179 (1962).
59. V. L. Bonch-Bruevich and Sh. M. Kogan, Fiz. Tverd. Tela, 1:1221 (1959).
60. G. S. Zhdanov, Fundaments of X-Ray Structural Analysis, Moscow, 1940.

61. G. S. Zhdanov and Ya. S. Umanskii, X-Ray Diffraction of Metals, Metallurgizdat, 1941.
62. W. H. Zachariasen, Theory of the Diffraction of X-Rays by Crystals, New Jersey, 1945.
63. M. Laue, Röntgenstrahlinterferenzen, Leipzig, 1948.
64. A. I. Kitaigorodskii, X-Ray Structural Analysis, Gostekhizdat, 1950.
65. R. W. James, Optical Principles of X-Ray Diffraction [Russian translation], IL, 1950.
66. G. B. Bokii and M. A. Porai-Koshits, Practical Course of X-Ray Structural Analysis, Moscow, 1951.
67. A. J. C. Wilson, X-Ray Optics, Wiley, New York, 1949.
68. A. I. Kitaigorodskii, X-Ray Structural Analysis of Fine-Crystalline and Amorphous Materials, Moscow, 1952.
69. B. Ya. Pines, Lectures of Structural Analysis, Izd. Khar'kov Gos. Univ., Khar'kov, 1957.
70. A. I. Kitaigoroskii, Theory of Structural Analysis, Izd. Akad. Nauk SSSR, 1957.
71. A. Guinier, X-Ray Diffraction of Crystals [Russian translation], Fizmatgiz, 1961.
72. M. A. Krivoglaz, Fiz. Metal. i Metalloved., 12:465 (1961).
73. E. Fermi, Ricerca Sci., 7:13 (1936).
74. G. C. Summerfield, Ann. Phys., 26:72 (1964).
75. A. Akhiezer and I. Pomeranchuk, Some Questions in the Theory of the Nucleus, Gostekhizdat, 1948.
76. I. Pomeranchuk, Zh. Éksperim. i Teor. Fiz., 8:894 (1938).
77. G. E. Bacon, Neutron Diffraction [Russian translation], IL, 1957.
78. P. P. Ewald, Proc. Phys. Soc., 52:167 (1940).
79. M. Laue, Ann. Phys., 26:55 (1936).
80. A. L. Patterson, Phys. Rev., 56:972 (1939).
81. A. M. Elistratov, Kristallografiya, 7:199 (1962).
82. M. Laue, Z. Krist., 64:115 (1926).
83. A. R. Stokes and A. J. C. Wilson, Proc. Cambridge Phil. Soc., 38:313 (1942).
84. G. V. Kurdyumov, V. K. Kritskaya, V. A. Il'ina, and L. I. Lysak, Izv. Akad. Nauk SSSR, Ser. Fiz., 17:297 (1953); V. M. Golubkov, V. A. Il'ina, V. K. Kritskaya, G. V. Kurdyumov, and M. D. Perkas, Probl. Metalloved. i Fiz. Metal., 5:433 (1958).
85. L. I. Lysak, Collection "Physical Bases of the Strength and Ductility of Metals," Metallurgizdat, 1963.

86. A. M. Elistratov, Dokl. Akad. Nauk SSSR, 87:581 (1952).
87. Yu. A. Bagaryatskii, Kristallografiya, 3:578 (1958).
88. I. M. Lifshits, Jubilee Collection Dedicated to the Thirtieth Anniversary of the Great October Socialist Revolution [in Ukrainian], published Akad. Nauk URSR, 1947, p. 87.
89. I. M. Lifshits, Zh. Éksperim. i Teor. Fiz., 8:959 (1938).
90. Yu. A. Bagaryatskii, Dokl. Akad. Nauk SSSR, 77:45 (1951); 92:1157 (1953).
91. E. Schrödinger, Phys. Z., 15:79, 497 (1914).
92. P. Debye, Verh. Deutsch. Phys. Ges., 15:678, 738, 859 (1913); Ann. Phys., 43:49 (1914).
93. P. Debye, Phys. Z., 28:135 (1927).
94. B. E. Warren and B. L. Averbach, J. Appl. Phys., 21:595 (1950); 23:497, 1059 (1952).
95. B. Ya. Pines, Sharp-Focus Tubes and Applied X-Ray Structural Analysis, Gostekhizdat, 1955.
96. B. E. Warren, Progr. Metal. Phys., 8:147 (1959).
97. D. M. Vasil'ev and B. I. Smirnov, Usp. Fiz. Nauk, 73:503 (1961).
98. M. F. Bertaut, Compt. Rend., 228:492 (1949).
99. B. E. Warren and B. L. Averbach, J. Appl. Phys., 23:497 (1952).
100. M. McKeehan and B. E. Warren, J. Appl. Phys., 24:52 (1953).
101. A. R. Stokes, Proc. Phys. Soc., 61:382 (1948).
102. K. Huang, Proc. Roy. Soc., A190:102 (1947).
103. P. H. Miller, Jr. and B. R. Russell, J. Appl. Phys., 24:1248 (1953).
104. J. D. Eshelby, J. Appl. Phys., 24:1249 (1953).
105. J. Van Duijn and J. Van Galen, Physica, 23:622 (1957).
106. R. Feder and A. S. Nowick, Phys. Rev., 109:1959 (1958); F. H. d'Heurle, R. Feder, and A. S. Nowick, J. Phys. Soc. Japan, 18:184 (1963).
107. R. O. Simmons and R. W. Balluffi, Phys. Rev., 117:52 (1960); 119:600 (1960); 125:862 (1962); 129:1533 (1963); 134:A532 (1964).
108. M. Laue, Ann. Phys., 78:167 (1925).
109. Yu. N. Obraztsov, Zh. Éksperim. i Teor. Fiz., 8:593 (1938).
110. I. M. Lifshits, Zh. Éksperim. i Teor. Fiz., 9:481 (1939).
111. A. A. Smirnov and S. V. Vonsovskii, J. Phys. USSR, 5:263 (1941).
112. Z. W. Wilchinsky, J. Appl. Phys., 15:806 (1944).

113. J. M. Cowley, J. Appl. Phys., 21:24 (1950).
114. P. A. Flinn, B. L. Averbach and P. S. Rudman, Acta Cryst., 7:153 (1954).
115. V. M. Danilenko, M. A. Krivoglaz, Z. A. Matysina, and A. A. Smirnov, Fiz. Metal. i Metalloved., 4:28 (1957).
116. B. E. Warren, B. L. Averbach, and B. W. Roberts, J. Appl. Phys., 22:1493 (1951).
117. W. Cochran, Acta Cryst., 9:259 (1956).
118. W. Cochran and G. Kartha, Acta Cryst., 9:941, 944 (1956).
119. B. Borie, Acta Cryst., 10:89 (1957).
120. B. Borie, Acta Cryst., 12:280 (1959); 14:472 (1961).
121. A. A. Smirnov and E. A. Tikhonova, Fiz. Tverd. Tela, 1:1398 (1959); Ukr. Fiz. Zhurn., 4:322 (1959).
122. A. A. Smirnov and E. A. Tikhonova, Fiz. Tverd. Tela, 3:1238 (1961); A. A. Smirnov, E. A. Tikhonova, and A. V. Chalyi, Fiz. Tverd. Tela, 4:77 (1962).
123. M. A. Krivoglaz, Zh. Éksperim. i Teor. Fiz., 34:405 (1958).
124. M. A. Krivoglaz, Kristallografiya, 5:24 (1960).
125. N. Norman and B. E. Warren, J. Appl. Phys., 22:483 (1951).
126. V. I. Iveronova and A. A. Katsnel'son, Kristallografiya, 5:71 (1960); A. A. Katsnel'son, Vestn. Mosk. Gos. Univ., Ser. Fiz., No. 4, p. 131 (1959).
127. A. S. Lashko, Questions on the Physics of Metals and Metal Science, Izd. Akad. Nauk UkrSSR, No. 15, p. 80, 1962.
128. B. E. Warren and B. L. Averbach, Collection "Modern Physical Methods of Research in Metal Science" [Russian translation], Metallurgizdat, 1958, p. 109.
129. S. C. Moss, J. Appl. Phys., 35:3547 (1964).
130. M. A. Krivoglaz, Fiz. Metal. i Metalloved., 8:514 (1959).
131. V. I. Iveronova and A. A. Katsnel'son, Fiz. Metal. i Metalloved., 11:40 (1961); A. A. Katsnel'son, Kristallografiya, 10: 330 (1965).
132. A. Münster, Z. Phys. Chem., Neue Folge, 22:115 (1959).
133. D. S. Gaunt, M. E. Fischer, M. F. Sykes, and J. W. Essam, Phys. Rev. Letters, 13:713 (1964).
134. L. D. Landau, Phys. Z. Sowjetunion, 8:113 (1935).
135. C. B. Walker and D. T. Keating, Phys. Rev., 130:1726 (1963).
136. J. L. Amoros, Presented to the Fifth International Crystallographic Conference in 1960, see Acta Cryst., 13:1070 (1960).
137. M. L. Canut and J. Mendiola, Phys. Stat. Sol., 5:313 (1964).
138. I. Shibuya, J. Phys. Soc. Japan, 16:490 (1961).

139. S. Tanisaki, J. Phys. Soc. Japan, 16:579 (1961); 18:1181 (1963).
140. M. Canut and R. Hosemann, Acta Cryst., 17:973 (1964).
141. Y. Jamada, I. Shibuya, and S. Hoshino, J. Phys. Soc. Japan, 18:1594 (1963).
142. K. Hamano, J. Phys. Soc. Japan, 19:945 (1964).
143. I. Shibuya and T. Mitsui, J. Phys. Soc. Japan, 16:479 (1961).
144. A. Münster and K. Sagel, Mol. Phys., 1:23 (1958).
145. H. Corsepius and A. Münster, Z. Phys. Chem., Neue Folge, 22:1 (1959).
146. G. W. Brady and J. I. Petz, J. Chem. Phys., 34:332 (1961).
147. G. W. Brady and H. L. Frisch, J. Chem. Phys., 35:2234 (1961).
148. J. E. Thomas and P. W. Schmidt, J. Chem. Phys., 39:2506 (1963).
149. Y. Rocard, J. Phys. Radium, 4:165 (1933).
150. P. Debye, J. Chem. Phys., 31:680 (1959).
151. H. L. Frisch and G. W. Brady, J. Chem. Phys., 37:1514 (1962).
152. V. L. Ginzburg, Dokl. Akad. Nauk SSSR, 105:240 (1955).
153. V. L. Ginzburg and A. P. Levanyuk, Collection in Memory of G. S. Landsberg, p. 104, Izd. Akad. Nauk SSSR, 1959; Zh. Éksperim. i Teor. Fiz., 39:192 (1960).
154. V. L. Ginzburg, Usp. Fiz. Nauk, 77:621 (1962).
155. M. A. Krivoglaz, Fiz. Tverd. Tela, 2:1200 (1960).
156. M. A. Krivoglaz and S. A. Rybak, Zh. Tekhn. Fiz., 28:940 (1958).
157. H. Cramer, Mathematical Methods of Statistics, Princeton, 1948.
158. H. Faxen, Ann. Phys., 54:615 (1918).
159. I. Waller, Z. Phys., 17:398 (1923); 51:213 (1928).
160. H. Ott, Ann. Phys., 23:169 (1938).
161. M. Born, Rep. Progr. Phys., 9:294 (1942-1943).
162. Max Born and Kun Huang, Dynamic Theory of Crystal Lattices, Oxford Univ. Press, 1954.
163. R. Peierls, Quantum Theory of Solids, Oxford Univ. Press, 1955.
164. H. Leibfried, Microscopical Theory of the Mechanical and Thermal Properties of Crystals [Russian translation], Fizmatgiz, 1963.
165. G. L. Squires, Phys. Rev., 103:304 (1956).

166. A. S. Kagan and Ya. S. Umanskii, Fiz. Tverd. Tela, 3:2683 (1961).
167. R. E. De Wames, T. Wolfram, and G. W. Lehman, Phys. Rev., 131:528 (1963).
168. P. A. Flinn and G. M. McManus, Phys. Rev., 132:2458 (1963).
169. P. A. Flinn, G. M. McManus, and J. A. Rayne, Phys. Rev., 123:809 (1961).
170. R. E. De Wames, T. Wolfram, and G. W. Lehman, Phys. Rev., 131:529 (1963); R. E. De Wames and G. W. Lehman, Phys. Rev., 135:A170 (1964).
171. M. A. Leontovich, Phys. Z. Sowjetunion, 3:35 (1933).
172. S. G. Kalashnikov and M. A. Leontovich, Zh. Éksperim. i Teor. Fiz., 10:749 (1940).
172a. M. A. Leontovich, Statistical Physics, Gostekhizdat, 1941.
173. M. A. Krivoglaz, Questions of the Physics of Metals and Metal Science, Izd. Akad. Nauk UkrSSR, No. 13, p. 35 (1961).
174. G. Huntington, Usp. Fiz. Nauk, 74:303, 461 (1961).
175. J. R. Neighbours and G. A. Alers, Phys. Rev., 111:707 (1958).
176. F. H. Herbstein, Adv. Phys., 10:313 (1961).
177. G. A. Alers and J. R. Neighbours, Rev. Modern Phys., 31:675 (1959).
178. V. A. Il'ina and V. K. Kritskaya, Dokl. Akad. Nauk SSSR, 110: 765 (1956).
179. J. Shreadborough and J. W. Christian, Proc. Phys. Soc., 74: 609 (1959).
180. F. H. Herbstein, Acta Cryst., 13:1112 (1961).
181. E. A. Owen and R. W. Williams, Proc. Roy. Soc., A188:509 (1947).
182. D. R. Chipman, J. Appl. Phys., 31:2012 (1960).
183. D. R. Chipman and A. Paskin, J. Appl. Phys., 30:1992 (1959).
184. N. N. Zhuravlev and A. A. Katsnel'son, Kristallografiya, 3: 936 (1959).
185. M. Simerska, Chekhosl. Fiz. Zhurn., 12:858 (1962).
186. R. D. Vengrinovich, E. I. Geshko, G. P. Kushta, and V. P. Mikhal'chenko, Ukr. Fiz. Zhurn., 10:393 (1965).
187. L. Cartz, Proc. Phys. Soc., B68:951 (1958).
188. A. P. Zvyagina and V. I. Iveronova, Fiz. Tverd. Tela, 2:118 (1960).
189. A. M. Ratner, Usp. Fiz. Tela, 7:200 (1962).
190. Yu. Kagan, Zh. Éksperim. i Teor. Fiz., 41:659 (1961).
191. Yu. Kagan and V. A. Maslov, Zh. Éksperim. i Teor. Fiz., 41: 1296 (1961).

192. H. Hahn and W. Ludwig, Z. Phys., 161:404 (1961).
193. M. A. Krivoglaz and E. A. Tikhonova, Kristallografiya, 6: 496 (1961).
194. A. A. Maradudin and P. A. Flinn, Phys. Rev., 129:2529 (1963).
195. A. Paskin, Acta Cryst., 10:667 (1957).
196. A. G. Kagan and Ya. S. Umanskii, Izv. Vuzov, Fiz., No. 5, p. 143 (1959).
197. I. P. Mikhailyuk, V. P. Mikhal'chenko, and G. P. Kushta, Ukr. Fiz. Zhurn., 7:1246 (1962).
198. V. I. Iveronova, Z. I. Kuz'mina, S. I. Futengendler, and E. I. Detlaf, Izv. Akad. Nauk SSSR, Ser. Fiz., 15:44 (1951).
199. G. V. Kurdyumov, V. A. Il'ina, V. J. Kritskaya, and L. I. Lysak, Probl. Metallov. i Fiz. Metallov., 4:339 (1955).
200. V. I. Iveronova and A. P. Zvyagina, Izv. Akad. Nauk SSSR, Ser. Fiz., 20:729 (1956).
201. F. H. Herbstein, B. S. Borie, and B. L. Averbach, Acta Cryst., 9:466 (1956); C. R. Houska and B. L. Averbach, J. Appl. Phys., 30:1525 (1959).
202. V. I. Iveronova, A. P. Zvyagina, and A. A. Katsnel'son, Kristallografiya, 2:414 (1957).
203. W. W. Webb, J. Appl. Phys., 33:3546 (1962).
204. M. A. Krivoglaz, Fiz. Metal. i Metalloved., 7:650 (1959).
205. M. Born and R. D. Misra, Proc. Cambridge Phil. Soc., 36: 466 (1940).
206. I. M. Lifshits, Zh. Éksperim. i Teor. Fiz., 9:500 (1939).
207. V. K. Kritskaya, G. V. Kurdyumov, and N. M. Nodia, Zh. Tekhn. Fiz., 25:177 (1955).
208. A. Kochanovska, Czech. Phys. J., 4:463 (1954).
209. M. A. Krivoglaz, Kristallografiya, 4:813 (1959).
210. V. A. Il'ina, V. K. Kritskaya, G. V. Kurdyumov, Yu. A. Osip'yan, and G. I. Stelletskaya, Prob. Metallov. i Fiz. Metal., 5: 462 (1960).
211. V. I. Iveronova and A. P. Zvyagina, Izv. Vuzov, Fiz., No. 6, p. 105 (1960).
212. I. P. Mikhailyuk, Fiz. Metal. i Metalloved., 20:824 (1965).
213. V. I. Iveronova and A. A. Katsnel'son, Kristallografiya, 4:25 (1959).
214. D. B. Bowen, Acta Met., 2:373 (1954).
215. S. A. Nemnonov and L. D. Finkel'shtein, Fiz. Metal. i Metalloved., 7:944 (1959); S. A. Nemnonov, L. D. Finkel'shtein, and K. M. Kolobova, Fiz. Metal. i Metalloved., 9:243 (1960).

216. A. S. Kagan and Ya. S. Umanskii, Dokl. Akad. Nauk SSSR., 132:326 (1960).
217. I. M. Lifshits, Zh. Éksperim. i Teor. Fiz., 17:1017, 1076 (1947).
218. I. M. Lifshits, Usp. Fiz. Nauk, 83:617 (1964).
219. M. A. Krivoglaz and E. A. Tikhonova, Fiz. Metal. i Metalloved., 12:801 (1961).
220. A. N. Men' and A. N. Orlov, Dokl. Akad. Nauk SSSR., 90:753 (1953); Fiz. Metal. i Metalloved., 7:335 (1959); 8:154 (1959).
221. M. A. Krivoglaz, Fiz. Metal. i Metalloved., 9:641 (1960).
222. M. A. Krivoglaz and K. P. Ryaboshapka, Fiz. Metal. i Metalloved., 15:18 (1963).
223. A. J. C. Wilson, Research (London), 2:541 (1949); 3:387 (1950).
224. A. J. C. Wilson, Acta Cryst., 5:318 (1952); Nuovo Cimento, 1:277 (1955).
225. T. Suzuki and B. T. M. Willis, Nature, 177:712 (1956).
226. L. F. Vassamillet, Nuovo Cimento, 13:1133 (1959).
227. M. A. Krivoglaz and K. P. Ryaboshapka, Fiz. Metal. i Metalloved., 16:641 (1963).
228. J. D. Eshelby, J. Appl. Phys., 24:176 (1953).
229. M. Wilkens, Phys. Stat. Sol., 3:1718 (1963).
230. K. P. Ryaboshapka, Questions of the Physics of Metals and Metal Science, Izd. Akad. Nauk Ukr.SSR, No. 19, p. 19 (1964).
231. K. P. Ryaboshapka and L. V. Tikhonov, Fiz. Metal. i Metalloved., 11:489 (1961).
232. O. N. Shivrin and B. M. Mimukhin, Izv. Vuzov, Fiz., No. 3, p. 135 (1958).
233. K. P. Ryaboshapka, Collection "Metal Physics. Imperfections of Crystal Structure," Izd. Akad. Nauk Ukr.SSR, p. 3, 1965.
234. M. A. Krivoglaz and K. P. Ryaboshapka, Questions of the Physics of Metals and Metal Science, Izd. Akad. Nauk Ukr.SSR No. 17, p. 25 (1963).
235. D. L. Dexter, Phys. Rev., 90:1007 (1953).
236. J. Blin, Acta Met., 5:528 (1957).
237. H. H. Atkinson and P. B. Hirsch, Phil. Mag., 3:213, 862 (1958).
238. A. Seeger, Acta Met., 5:24 (1957); J. Appl. Phys., 30:629 (1959).
239. A. Seeger and E. Kröner, Z. Naturforsch., 14a:74 (1959).
240. A. Seeger and M. Rühle, Ann. Phys., 11:216 (1963).

241. Yu. S. Terminasov and L. V. Tuzov, Usp. Fiz. Nauk, 83:223 (1964).
242. J. M. Burgers, Proc. Konikl. Nederl. Acad. (Amst.), 42:293 (1939).
243. J. D. Eshelby, Proc. Roy. Soc., A241:376 (1957); F. Kroupa, Czech. Phys, J., 12B,3:191 (1962).
244. P. B. Hirsch, J. Silcox, R. E. Smallman, and K. H. Westmacott, Phil. Mag., 3:897 (1958).
245. K. P. Ryaboshapka, Questions of the Physics of Metals and Metal Science, Izd. Akad. Nauk Ukr.SSR, No. 19, p. 3 (1964).
246. S. Yoshida, Y. Shimomura, and M. Kiritani, J. Phys. Soc. Japan, 17:1196 (1962).
247. J. Silcox and P. B. Hirsch, Phil. Mag., 4:1356 (1959).
248. J. Silcox and M. J. Whelan, Phil. Mag., 5:1 (1960).
249. A. M. Elistratov and A. A. Madzhitov, Fiz. Metal. i Metalloved., 19:349 (1965).
250. V. I. Iveronova and A. A. Katsnel'son, Fiz. Metal. i Metalloved., 19:105 (1965).
251. A. J. C. Wilson, Proc. Phys. Soc., 80:286 (1962).
252. A. J. C. Wilson, Proc. Phys. Soc., 81:41 (1963); 85:807 (1965).
253. M. A. Krivoglaz, Questions of the Physics of Metals and Metal Science, Izd. Akad Nauk Ukr.SSR, No. 13, p. 17 (1961).
254. N. F. Mott and F. R. N. Nabarro, Proc. Phys. Soc., 52:86 (1940).
255. F. R. N. Nabarro, Proc. Phys. Soc., 52:90 (1940); Proc. Roy. Soc., A175:519 (1940).
256. F. Sebilleau, Publications ONERA, No. 87, Paris, 1957.
257. A. Guinier, Inhomogeneous Metallic Solid Solutions [Russian translation], IL, 1962.
258. A. G. Khachaturyan, Kristallografiya, 10:459 (1965).
259. A. M. Elistratov, Author's Abstract of Dissertation, Inst. Kristallogr., Moscow, 1965.
260. Yu. A. Bagaryatskii and Yu. D. Tyapkin, Kristallografiya, 5:882 (1960).
261. A. Kelly and R. B. Nicholson, Prog. Mater. Sci., 10:149 (1963).
262. M. I. Gitgarts, Fiz. Metal. i Metalloved., 19:380 (1965).
263. K. Toman, Czech. Phys. J., 9:367 (1959).
264. J. Laval, Compt. Rend., 207:169 (1938); 208:1512 (1939); Bull. Soc. Franc. Mineral., 64:1 (1941).
265. W. H. Zachariasen, Phys. Rev., 57:597 (1940).
266. M. Born and K. Sarginson, Proc. Roy. Soc., A179:69 (1941).

267. M. Born, Proc. Roy. Soc., A180:397 (1942).
268. G. H. Begbie and M. Born, Proc. Roy. Soc., A188:179, 189 (1947).
269. W. Hoppe, Z. Krist., 197:406 (1956).
270. J. L. Amoros and M. L. Canut, Bol. R. Soc. Esp. Hist. Nat. (g), 56:305 (1958); 57:43 (1960).
271. J. L. Amoros, M. L. Canut, and A. de Actha, Z. Krist, 114:39 (1960).
272. M. L. Canut and J. L. Amoros, Proc. Phys. Soc., 77:712 (1961).
273. K. Lonsdale, Repts. Prog. in Phys., 9:256 (1942); Rev. Modern Phys., 30:168 (1958).
274. J. Laval, Rev. Modern Phys., 30:222 (1958).
275. C. Wooster, Diffuse X-Ray Reflections from Crystals, Oxford Univ. Press, 1962.
276. A. A. Maradudin, E. W. Montroll, and G. H. Weiss, Solid State Physics, Suppl., V. 3, Academic Press, 1963, Ch. VII.
276a. H. A. Jahn, Proc. Roy. Soc., A178:320 (1942); A180:476 (1942); J. Weigle, Helv. Phys. Acta, 14:595 (1941).
277. P. Olmer, Bull. Soc. Franc. Mineral., 71:145 (1948); Acta Cryst., 1:57 (1948).
278. C. B. Walker, Phys. Rev., 103:547 (1956).
279. S. Annaka and J. L. Amoros, Z. Krist., 114:423 (1960).
280. S. V. Semenovskaya, Ya. S. Umanskii, I. M. Puzei, and E. B. Granovskii, Fiz. Tverd. Tela, 6:1100 (1964).
281. M. A. Krivoglaz, Fiz. Metal. i Metalloved., 13:481 (1962).
282. S. V. Semenovskaya and Ya. S. Umanskii, Fiz. Tverd. Tela, 4:1455 (1962).
283. S. V. Semenovskaya and Ya. S. Umanskii, Dokl. Akad. Nauk SSSR, 157:1103 (1964).
284. V. F. Turchin, Slow Neutrons, Gosatomizdat, 1963.
285. L. S. Kothari and K. S. Singwi, Solid State Physics, 8:110 (1959).
286. Yu. A. Izyumov, Usp. Fiz. Nauk, 80:41 (1963).
287. A. I. Akhiezer and I. Ya. Pomeranchuk, Zh. Éksperim. i Teor. Fiz., 17:769 (1947).
288. G. C. Wick, Phys. Rev., 94:1228 (1954).
289. L. Van Hove, Phys. Rev., 95:249 (1954).
290. R. J. Glauber, Phys. Rev., 98:1692 (1955).
291. L. Van Hove, Physica, 24:404 (1958).
292. G. H. Vineyard, Phys. Rev., 110:999 (1958).

293. K. S. Singwi and A. Sjölander, Phys. Rev., 119:863 (1960); 120:1093 (1960).
294. M. I. Podgoretskii and A. V. Stepanov, Zh. Éksperim. i Teor. Fiz., 40:561 (1961).
295. M. A. Krivoglaz, Zh. Éksperim. i Teor. Fiz., 40:1812 (1961).
296. G. C. Wick, Phys. Z., 38:403, 689 (1937).
297. R. Weinstock, Phys. Rev., 65:1 (1944).
298. I. Waller and P. O. Fröman, Arkiv Fysik, 4:183 (1951); P. O. Fröman, Arkiv Fysik, 4:191 (1951); 5:53 (1952).
299. G. Placzek and L. Van Hove, Phys. Rev., 93:1207 (1954).
300. G. L. Squires, Proc. Roy. Soc., A212:192 (1953); Phys. Rev., 103:304 (1956).
301. M. V. Kazarnovskii, Zh. Éksperim. i Teor. Fiz., 31:696 (1956).
302. B. N. Brockhouse, Inelastic Scattering of Neutrons in Solids and Liquids, Proc. Symp. Vienna 1960, Intern. Atomic Energy Agency, Vienna, 1961, p. 113.
303. M. I. Kaganov, Zh. Éksperim. i Teor. Fiz., 43:153 (1962).
304. R. S. Carter, D. J. Hughes, and H. Palevsky, Phys. Rev., 106: 1168 (1957).
305. Yu. Kagan and A. P. Zhernov, Zh. Éksperim. i Teor. Fiz., 48:971 (1965).
306. K. E. Larsson, U. Dahlborg, and S. Holmryd, Arkiv Fysik, 17:369 (1960).
307. M. M. Bredov, B. A. Kotov, N. M. Okuneva, and A. L. Shakh-Budagov, Fiz. Tverd. Tela, 7:1413 (1965).
308. J. L. Yarnell, J. L. Warren, and S. H. Koenig, Lattice Dynamics, Proc. Intern. Conf. Copenhagen, J. Phys. Chem. Solids, 1:57 (1965).
309. D. Cribier, B. Jacrot, and D. Saint-James, Inelastic Scattering of Neutrons in Solids and Liquids, Intern. Atomic Energy Agency, Vienna, 1961, p. 549.
310. J. Sosnowski and J. Kozubowski, J. Phys. Chem. Solids, 23: 1021 (1962).
311. E. Z. Vintaikin, V. V. Gorbachev, and P. L. Gruzin, Atomnaya Énergiya, 18:507 (1965).
312. S. K. Sinha and G. L. Squires, Lattice Dynamics, Proc. Intern. Conf., Copenhagen, J. Phys. Chem. Solids, 1:53 (1965).
313. A. D. B. Woods, W. Cochran, and B. N. Brockhouse, Phys. Rev., 119:980 (1960).

314. E. Z. Vintaikin and V. V. Gorbachev, Fiz. Tverd. Tela, 7: 1910 (1965).
315. G. G. E. Low, Proc. Phys. Soc., 79:479 (1962).
316. Y. Nakagawa and A. D. B. Woods, Lattice Dynamics, Proc. Intern. Conf., Copenhagen, J. Phys. Chem. Solids, Suppl. 1, p. 39 (1965).
317. E. Maliszewski, J. Rosolowski, D. Sledziewska, and A. Czachor, Lattice Dynamics, Proc. Intern. Conf., Copenhagen, J. Phys. Chem. Solids, Suppl. 1, p. 33 (1965).
318. B. N. Brockhouse and P. K. Iyengar, Phys. Rev., 111:747 (1957); B. N. Brockhouse, Phys. Rev. Letters, 2:256 (1959).
319. A. Ghose, H. Palevsky, D. J. Hughes, I. Pelah, and C. M. Eisenhauer, Phys. Rev., 113:49 (1959).
320. A. D. B. Woods, W. Cochran, and B. N. Brockhouse, Phys. Rev., 119:980 (1960).
321. A. D. B. Woods, B. N. Brockhouse, and R. A. Cowley, Phys. Rev., 131:1025 (1963).
322. G. Peckham, Lattice Dynamics, Proc. Intern. Conf., Copenhagen, J. Phys. Chem. Solids, Suppl. 1, p. 49 (1965).
323. G. Dolling and J. L. T Waugh, Lattice Dynamics, Proc. Intern. Conf., Copenhagen, J. Phys. Chem. Solids, Suppl. 1, p. 19 (1965).
324. Inelastic Scattering of Neutrons in Solids and Liquids, V. 1, 2, Intern. Atomic Energy Agency, Vienna, 1963; Inelastic Scattering of Neutrons, Intern. Atomic Energy Agency, Vienna, 1965.
325. L. Van Hove, Phys. Rev., 89:1189 (1953).
326. J. C. Phillips, Phys. Rev., 104:1263 (1956).
327. C. M. Eisenhauer, I. Pelah, D. J. Hughes, and H. Palevsky, Phys. Rev., 109:1046 (1958).
328. N. A. Chernoplekov, M. G. Zemlaynov, and A. G. Chicherin, Zh. Éksperim. i Teor. Fiz., 43:2080 (1962).
329. K. C. Turberfield and P. A. Egelstaff, Phys. Rev., 127:1017 (1962).
330. N. A. Chernoplekov, Inelastic Scattering of Neutrons in Solids and Liquids, V. 2, p. 17; Intern. Atomic Energy Agency, Vienna, 1963.
331. B. Mozer, K. Otnes, and H. Palevsky, Lattice Dynamics, Proc. Intern. Conf., Copenhagen, J. Phys. Chem. Solids, Suppl. 1, p. 63 (1965).

332. N. A. Chernoplekov, M. G. Zemlyanov, A. G. Chicherin, and B. G. Lyashchenko, Zh. Éksperim. i Teor. Fiz., 44:858 (1963).
333. V. S. Oskotskii, Fiz. Tverd. Tela, 2:701 (1960).
334. L. V. Tarasov, Fiz. Tverd. Tela, 3:1431 (1961).
335. Yu. Kagan, Zh. Éksperim. i Teor. Fiz., 40:312 (1961).
336. Yu. Kagan, Zh. Éksperim. i Teor. Fiz., 42:1375 (1962).
337. A. T. Stewart and B. N. Brockhouse, Rev. Modern Phys., 30: 250 (1958).
338. V. S. Oskotskii, Zh. Éksperim. i Teor. Fiz., 44:657 (1963).
339. G. Placzek, Phys. Rev., 86:377 (1952); 93:895 (1954); 105: 1240 (1957).
340. V. F. Turchin, Zh. Éksperim. i Teor. Fiz., 33:124 (1957).
341. A. Sjölander, Arkiv Fysik, 14:315 (1958).
342. M. S. Nelkin and D. E. Parks, Phys. Rev., 119:1060 (1960).
343. P. A. Egelstaff, Inelastic Scattering of Neutrons in Solids and Liquids, V. 1, p. 65, Intern. Atomic Energy Agency, Vienna, 1963.
344. M. A. Krivoglaz, Zh. Éksperim. i Teor. Fiz., 40:567 (1961).
345. N. N. Bogolyubov and S. V. Tyablikov, Dokl. Akad. Nauk SSSR, 126:53 (1959).
346. D. N. Zubarev, Usp. Fiz. Nauk, 71:71 (1960).
347. R. J. Elliot and D. W. Taylor, Proc. Phys. Soc., 83:189 (1964).
348. M. A. Krivoglaz, Fiz. Tverd. Tela, 3:3678 (1961); Questions of the Physics of Metals and Metal Science, Izd. Akad. Nauk Ukr.SSR, No. 15. p. 100 (1962).
348a. I. M. Lifshits, Zh. Éksperim. i Teor. Fiz., 12:117, 137, 156 (1942).
349. V. N. Kashcheev and M. A. Krivoglaz, Fiz. Tverd. Tela, 3: 1528 (1961).
350. G. Baym, Phys. Rev., 121:741 (1961).
351. J. J. J. Kokkedee, Physica, 28:374 (1962); Inelastic Scattering of Neutrons in Solids and Liquids, V. I, p. 15, Intern. Atomic Energy Agency, Vienna, 1963.
352. A. A. Maradudin and A. E. Fein, Phys. Rev., 128:2589 (1962).
353. A. A. Maradudin, A. E. Fein, and G. H. Vineyard, Phys. Stat. Solidi, 2:1479 (1962).
354. A. A. Maradudin, Phys. Stat. Solidi, 2:1493 (1962).
355. B. A. Thompson, Phys. Rev., 131:1420 (1963).
356. H. Hahn, Inelastic Scattering of Neutrons in Solids and Liquids, V. I, p. 37, Intern. Atomic Energy Agency, Vienna, 1963.

357. M. Lax, J. Phys. Chem. Solids, 25:487 (1964).
358. V. Ambegaokar and A. A. Maradudin, Westinghouse Research Laboratories Report No. 64-929-100-P2, 1964.
359. V. Ambegaokar, J. M. Conway, and G. Baym, Lattice Dynamics, Proc. Intern. Conf., Copenhagen, J. Phys. Chem. Solids, Suppl. 1, p. 261 (1965).
360. P. A. Egelstaff, Lattice Dynamics, Proc. Intern. Conf. Copenhagen, J. Phys. Chem. Solids, Suppl. 1, p. 699 (1965).
361. A. A. Maradudin, Rep. Prog. in Phys., 28:331 (1965).
362. L. Van Hove, Technical Report No. 11, Solid State and Molecular Theory Group, Massachusetts Inst. of Technology, 1959; L. Van Hove, N. M. Hugenholtz, and L. P. Howland, Quantum Theory of Many-Particle Systems, W. A. Benjamin, New York, 1961.
363. L. P. Pitaevskii, Zh. Éksperim. i Teor. Fiz., 36:1168 (1959).
364. V. L. Pokrovskii and A. M. Dykhne, Zh. Éksperim. i Teor. Fiz., 39:720 (1960).
365. L. D. Landau and Yu. B. Rumer, Phys. Z. Sowjetunion, 11:18 (1937).
366. C. Herring, Phys. Rev., 95:954 (1954).
367. H. Bross, Phys. Stat. Solidi, 2:481 (1962); K. Kawasaki and H. Mori, Progress Theor. Phys., 28:784 (1962).
368. S. Simons, Proc. Phys. Soc., 82:401 (1963).
369. A. J. Leggett and D. ter Haar, Clarendon Laboratory Report, No. 150/64, 1964; Phys. Rev., 139:A779 (1965).
370. R. A. Cowley, Lattice Dynamics, Proc. Intern. Conf., Copenhagen, J. Phys. Chem. Solids, 1:295 (1965).
371. B. N. Brockhouse, T. Arase, G. Caglioti, M. Sakamoto, R. N. Sinclair, and A. D. B. Woods, Inelastic Scattering of Neutrons in Solids and Liquids, Intern. Atomic Energy Agency, Vienna, 1961, p. 531; A. D. B. Woods, ibid, 1963, V. II, p. 3.
372. V. N. Kashcheev, Izv. Akad. Nauk LatvSSR, No. 5, p. 67 (1962).
373. D. W. Jepsen and R. F. Wallis, Phys. Rev., 125:1496 (1962).
374. L. É. Gurevich and I. P. Ipatova, Zh. Éksperim. i Teor. Fiz., 45:231 (1963).
375. I. P. Ipatova, A. A. Maradudin, and R. F. Wallis, Fiz. Tverd. Tela, 8:1064 (1966).
376. M. A. Ivanov and M. A. Krivoglaz, Fiz. Tverd. Tela, 6:200 (1964); Questions of the Physics of Metals and Metal Science, Izd. Akad. Nauk Ukr.SSR, No. 19, p. 28 (1964).

377. V. N. Kashcheev and M. A. Krivoglaz, Fiz. Tverd. Tela, 3: 1541 (1961).
378. V. N. Kashcheev, Fiz. Tverd. Tela, 4:1432 (1962).
379. A. B. Migdal, Zh. Éksperim. i Teor. Fiz., 34:1438 (1958).
380. V. L. Bonch-Bruevich, Fiz. Tverd. Tela, 2:1857 (1960).
381. M. A. Krivoglaz, Fiz. Tverd. Tela, 3:2761 (1961).
382. J. J. J. Kokkedee, Physica, 28:893 (1962).
383. W. Kohn, Phys. Rev. Letters, 3:393 (1959); E. J. Woll and W. Kohn, Phys. Rev., 126:1693 (1962).
384. A. M. Afanas'ev and Yu. Kagan, Zh. Éksperim. i Teor. Fiz., 43:1456 (1962).
385. S. I. Pekar, Electron Theory of Crystals, Gostekhizdat, 1951.
386. M. A. Krivoglaz and P. I. Shaldervan, Fiz. Tverd. Tela, 6: 3272 (1964); Ukr. Fiz. Zhurn., 9:1331 (1964).
386a. V. N. Kashcheev and M. A. Krivoglaz, Fiz. Tverd. Tela, 3: 3167 (1961).
387. S. V. Tyablikov, Methods of the Quantum Theory of Magnetism, Izd. "Nauka," 1965.
388. S. V. Vonsovskii and Yu. A. Izyumov, Fiz. Metal. i Metalloved., 10:321 (1960); Yu. A. Izyumov, Fiz. Metal. i Metalloved., 12:480 (1961).
389. V. N. Kashcheev, Fiz. Tverd. Tela, 4:759, 2037 (1962); 5:909 (1963).
390. M. A. Ivanov, Fiz. Tverd. Tela, 6:3092 (1964).
391. A. Akhiezer and I. Pomeranchuk, Zh. Éksperim. i Teor. Fiz., 16:391 (1946).
392. I. M. Khalatnikov and V. N. Zharkov, Dokl. Akad. Nauk SSSR, 93:799 (1953).
393. M. Cohen and R. P. Feynman, Phys. Rev., 107:13 (1957).
394. A. I. Akhiezer, I. A. Akhiezer, and I. Ya. Pomeranchuk, Zh. Éksperim. i Teor. Fiz., 41:478 (1961).
395. A. A. Abrikosov and I. M. Khalatnikov, Zh. Éksperim. i Teor. Fiz., 34:198 (1958); 41:544 (1961).
396. Yu. Kagan and Ya. Iosilevskii, Zh. Éksperim. i Teor. Fiz., 44:1375 (1963).
397. I. Waller, Lattice Dynamics, Proc. Intern. Conf., Copenhagen, J. Phys. Chem. Solids, Suppl. 1, p. 517 (1965).
398. I. M. Lifshits, Nuovo Cimento 3, Suppl. 4, p. 716 (1956).
399. A. A. Maradudin, Astrophysics and Many Body Problems, V. 2, Brandeis Summer Institute, 1962, New York, W. A. Benjamin, 1963.

400. A. A. Maradudin, Theoretical and Experimental Aspects of the Effect of Point Defects and Disorder on the Vibrations of Crystals, Westinghouse Research Laboratories Scientific Papers 15235, 1965.
401. I. Waller, Crystallography and Crystal Perfection, Academic Press, London, 1963, p. 189.
402. R. J. Elliot and A. A. Maradudin, Westinghouse Research Laboratories Scientific Paper 64-929-100-P3, 1964.
403. M. A. Krivoglaz, Zh. Éksperim. i Teor. Fiz., 46:637 (1964).
404. M. Lax and I. Waller, Phys. Rev., 138:A523 (1965).
405. B. Mozer, K. Otnes, and V. W. Myers, Phys. Rev. Letters, 8:278 (1962).
406. R. Rubin, J. Peretti, G. Verdan, and W. Kley, Phys. Letters, 14:100 (1965).
407. P. G. Klemens, Phys. Rev., 122:443 (1961).
408. A. A. Maradudin, Ann. Phys., 30:371 (1964).
409. W. M. Visscher, Phys. Rev., A134:965 (1964).
410. M. A. Ivanov, L. B. Kvashnina, and M. A. Krivoglaz, Fiz. Tverd. Tela, 7:2047 (1965).
411. E. Hanamura and T. Inui, J. Phys. Soc. Japan, 18:690 (1963).
412. M. A. Ivanov, M. A. Krivoglaz, D. N. Mirlin, and I. I. Reshina, Fiz. Tverd. Tela, 8:192 (1966).
413. R. J. Elliot, Lattice Dynamics, Proc. Intern. Conf., Copenhagen, J. Phys. Chem. Solids, Suppl. 1, p. 459 (1965); W. Hayes, G. D. Jones, R. J. Elliot, and C. T. Sennett, ibid, Suppl. 1, p. 475 (1965).
414. Yu. Kagan and Ya. A. Iosilevskii, Zh. Éksperim. i Teor. Fiz., 42:259 (1962).
415. R. Brout and W. M. Visscher, Phys. Rev. Letters, 9:54 (1962).
416. S. Takeno, Progr. Theor. Phys., 29:191 (1963).
417. I. P. Dzyub, Fiz. Tverd. Tela, 6:1866 (1964).
418. I. P. Dzyub, Fiz. Tverd. Tela, 6:3691 (1964).
419. G. Dolling and G. Gilat, Inelastic Scattering of Neutrons, Intern. Atomic Energy Agency, Vienna, 1965, p. 343; Phys. Rev., 138:A1053 (1965).
420. R. J. Elliot and A. A. Maradudin, Inelastic Scattering of Neutrons, Intern. Atomic Energy Agency, Vienna, 1965, p. 231.
421. R. A. Cowley, Inelastic Scattering of Neutrons, Intern. Atomic Energy Agency, Vienna, 1965, p. 297.

422. I. Waller, Inelastic Scattering of Neutrons, Intern. Atomic Energy Agency, Vienna, 1965, p. 225.
423. H. B. Moller and A. R. Mackintosh, Phys. Rev. Letters, 15: 623 (1965).
424. V. G. Vaks, A. I. Larkin, and S. A. Pikin, Zh. Éksperim. i Teor. Fiz., 51:361 (1966).
425. M. E. Fisher and R. J. Burford, Phys. Rev., 156:583 (1967).
426. M. A. Krivoglaz and T'u Hao, Collection "Defects and Properties of the Crystal Lattice," Izd. "Naukova dumka," Kiev, 1968.
427. J. M. Ziman, Principles of the Theory of Solids, Cambridge Univ. Press, 1964.
428. P. L. Taylor, Phys. Rev., 131:1995 (1963).
429. L. M. Roth, H. J. Zeiger, and T. A. Kaplan, Phys. Rev., 149: 519 (1966).
430. M. A. Krivoglaz and T'u Hao, Fiz. Metal. i Metalloved., 21: 817 (1966).
431. M. A. Krivoglaz and T'u Hao, Collection "Defects and Properties of the Crystal Lattice," Izd. "Naukova dumka," Kiev, 1968.
432. R. A. Johnson, G. J. Dienes, and A. C. Damask, Acta Met., 12:1215 (1964).
433. D. T. Keating and A. N. Goland, Acta Met., 15:1805 (1967).
434. P. C. Clapp and S. C. Moss, Phys. Rev., 142:418 (1966).
435. J. Als-Nielsen and O. Dietrich, Phys. Rev., 153:706, 717 (1967); O. Dietrich and J. Als-Nielsen, Phys. Rev., 153:711 (1967).
436. R. M. Nicklow and R. A. Young, Phys. Rev., 152:591 (1966).
437. S. C. Moss, Acta Met., 15:1815 (1967).
438. W. Y. L. Buyers and T. Smith, Phys. Rev., 150:758 (1966).
439. E. C. Swensson, B. N. Brockhouse, and Y. M. Rowe, Phys. Rev., 155:619 (1967).
440. W. Y. L. Buyers, Phys. Rev., 153:923 (1967).
441. B. Mozer, K. Otnes, and C. Thaper, Phys. Rev., 152:535 (1966).
442. M. G. Zemlyanov, V. A. Somenkov, and N. A. Chernoplekov, Zh. Éksperim. i Teor. Fiz., 52:665 (1967).
443. M. A. Ivanov, M. A. Krivoglaz, and V. F. Los', Fiz. Tverd. Tela, 8:28, 67 (1966).
444. M. A. Ivanov, Fiz. Tverd. Tela, 8:3299 (1966).
445. T. Wolfram and J. Callaway, Phys. Rev., 130:2207 (1963).

446. Yu. A. Izyumov, Adv. Phys., 14:569 (1965).
447. M. A. Ivanov, M. A. Krivoglaz, and A. M. Masyukevich, Fiz. Metal. i Metalloved., 20:161 (1965).
448. P. G. Dawber and R. J. Elliot, Proc. Phys. Soc., 81:453 (1963).
449. N. A. Chernoplekov and M. G. Zemlyanov, Zh. Éksperim. i Teor. Fiz., 49:449 (1965).

Index

1-MONTH